Study and Review

When preparing for homework or exams, features like these will help you study and practice effectively.

Numerous, carefully written examples illustrate the concepts and skills as they are introduced, providing step-by-step directions for solving similar problems.

EXAMPLE 12 Solving Problems about Percent Increase or Decrease

(a) An electronics store marked up a laptop computer from their cost of $1200 to a selling price of $1464. What was the percent markup?

(b) The enrollment in a community college declined from 12,750 during one school year to 11,350 the following year. Find the percent decrease to the nearest tenth.

SOLUTION

(a) "Markup" is a name for an increase. Let x = the percent increase (as a decimal).

Subtract to find the amount of increase.

$$x = \frac{1464 - 1200}{1200} \quad \text{Substitute the given values.}$$

Use the original cost.

$$x = \frac{264}{1200}$$

$$x = 0.22 \quad \text{Use a calculator.}$$

The computer was marked up 22%.

(b) Let x = the percent decrease (as a decimal).

$$\text{percent decrease} = \frac{\text{amount of decrease}}{\text{original amount}}$$

Subtract to find the amount of decrease.

$$x = \frac{12,750 - 11,350}{12,750} \quad \text{Substitute the given values.}$$

Use the original enrollment.

$$x = \frac{1400}{12,750}$$

$$x \approx 0.11 \quad \text{Use a calculator.}$$

The college enrollment decreased by about 11%.

Annotations clarify these examples and help you prepare for the exercises that follow.

NEW! Pointers are annotations in the examples that provide on-the-spot reminders and warnings to help you avoid common pitfalls.

Varied exercise sets include drill, conceptual, and applied problems. Many exercises have been updated with new applications and real-life data.

6.5 EXERCISES

Decide whether each statement is true *or* false.

1. 300% of 12 is 36.

2. 25% of a quantity is the same as $\frac{1}{4}$ of that quantity.

3. When 759.367 is rounded to the nearest hundredth, the result is 759.40.

4. When 759.367 is rounded to the nearest hundred, the result is 759.37.

5. To find 50% of a quantity, we may simply divide the quantity by 2.

6. A soccer team that has won 12 games and lost 8 games has a winning percentage of 60%.

7. If 70% is the lowest passing grade on a quiz that has 50 items of equal value, then answering at least 35 items correctly will assure you of a passing grade.

8. 30 is more than 40% of 120.

9. .99¢ = 99 cents

10. If an item usually costs $70.00 and it is discounted 10%, then the discount price is $7.00.

Calculate each of the following using either a calculator or paper-and-pencil methods, as directed by your instructor.

11. 8.53 + 2.785   12. 9.358 + 7.2137

13. 8.74 − 12.955   14. 2.41 − 3.997

21. About how much was spent on Social Security?

22. About how much did the U.S. government spend on education and social services in 2005?

Postage Stamp Pricing Refer to *For Further Thought* on decimal point abuse. At one time, the United States Postal Service sold rolls of 33-cent stamps that featured fruit berries. One such stamp is shown on the left. On the right is a photo of the pricing information found on the cellophane wrapper of such a roll.

100 STAMPS PSA
.33¢ ea. TOTAL $33.00
FRUIT BERRIES
ITEM 7757
BCA

23. Look at the second line of the pricing information. According to the price listed *per stamp*, how many stamps should you be able to purchase for one cent?

24. The total price listed is the amount the Postal Service actually charges. If you were to multiply the listed price *per stamp* by the number of stamps, what should the total price be?

Collaborative Investigations at the end of each chapter provide an opportunity for cooperative learning through exercises that can be done in small groups or with the whole class.

COLLABORATIVE INVESTIGATION

Budgeting to Buy a Car

You are shopping for a sports car and have put aside a certain amount of money each month for a car payment. Your instructor will assign this amount to you. After looking through a variety of resources, you have narrowed your choices to the cars listed in the table.

Year/Make/ Model	Retail Price	Fuel Tank Size (in gallons)	Miles per Gallon (city)	Miles per Gallon (highway)
2010 Ford Mustang	$31,395	16.0	16	24
2010 Ford Taurus SEL	$29,220	19.0	17	25
2010 Toyota Camry Hybrid	$26,150	17.2	33	34
2010 Mazda MX-5 Miata	$26,250	12.7	21	28
2010 Honda CR-V EX-L	$26,495	15.3	21	28
2010 Chevrolet Malibu Hybrid	$25,555	16.0	26	34

Source: www.edmunds.com

As a group, work through the following steps to determine which car you can afford to buy.

A. Decide which cars you think are within your budget.

B. Select one of the cars you identified in part A. Have each member of the group calculate the monthly payment for this car using a different financing option. Use

the formula given below, where P is principal, r is interest rate, and m is the number of monthly payments, along with the financing options table.

Financing Options

Time (in years)	Interest Rate
4	2.0%
5	3.5%
6	5.0%

$$\text{Monthly Payment} = \frac{\frac{Pr}{12}}{1 - \left(\frac{12}{12 + r}\right)^m}$$

C. Have each group member determine the amount of money paid in interest over the duration of the loan for his or her financing option.

D. Consider fuel expenses.

1. Assume you will travel an average of 75 miles in the city and 400 miles on the highway each week. How many gallons of gas will you need to buy each month?

2. Using typical prices for gas in your area at this time, how much money will you need to have available for buying gas?

E. Repeat parts B–D as necessary until your group can reach a consensus on the car you will buy and the financing option you will use. Write a paragraph to explain your choices.

---

81. *Population of Alabama* The 2000 U.S. census showed that the population of Alabama was 4,447,000, with 26.0% represented by African Americans. What is the best estimate of the African American population in Alabama? (*Source:* U.S. Census Bureau.)

  A. 500,000   **B.** 1,500,000
  C. 1,100,000   **D.** 750,000

82. *Population of Hawaii* The 2000 U.S. census showed that the population of Hawaii was 1,212,000, with 21.4% of the population being of two or more races. What is the best estimate of this population of Hawaii? (*Source:* U.S. Census Bureau.)

  A. 240,000   **B.** 300,000
  C. 21,400   **D.** 24,000

Gasoline Prices The line graph shows the average price, adjusted for inflation, that Americans have paid for a gallon of gasoline for selected years between 1958 and 2008. Use this information in Exercises 83 and 84.

AVERAGE GASOLINE PRICES

Source: www.inflationdata.com

(c) Researchers recommend that a person reach approximately 85% of their MET when exercising. Calculate 85% of the ideal MET from part (b). Then refer to the following table. What activity can the woman do that is approximately this value?

Activity	METs	Activity	METs
Golf (with cart)	2.5	Skiing (water or downhill)	6.8
Walking (3 mph)	3.3	Swimming	7.0
Mowing lawn (power mower)	4.5	Walking (5 mph)	8.0
Ballroom or square dancing	5.5	Jogging	10.2
Cycling	5.7	Rope skipping	12.0

Source: Harvard School of Public Health.

86. Repeat parts (a)–(c) of **Exercise 85** for a 55-year-old man.

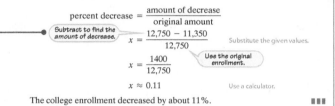

D1314702

Charles D. Miller • Vern E. Heeren • John Hornsby

Mathematical Ideas

Custom Edition for George Mason University

Taken from:
Mathematical Ideas, Twelfth Edition
by Charles D. Miller, Vern E. Heeren, and John Hornsby

Taken from:

Mathematical Ideas, Twelfth Edition
by Charles D. Miller, Vern E. Heeren, and John Hornsby
Copyright © 2012, 2008, 2004 by Pearson Education
Published by Addison-Wesley
Boston, Massachusetts 02116

This special edition published in cooperation with Pearson Learning Solutions.

All trademarks, service marks, registered trademarks, and registered service marks are the property of
their respective owners and are used herein for identification purposes only.

Pearson Learning Solutions, 501 Boylston Street, Suite 900, Boston, MA 02116
A Pearson Education Company
www.pearsoned.com

Printed in the United States of America

13 V092 15

000200010271648846

DE

ISBN 10: 1-256-71962-5
ISBN 13: 978-1-256-71962-5

To my special son, Christopher Michael Hornsby—DAD

To my beloved wife, Carole, my inspiration—VERN

CONTENTS

PREFACE

After eleven editions and over four decades, *Mathematical Ideas* continues to be one of the most popular textbooks in liberal arts mathematics education. We are proud to present the twelfth edition of a text that offers non-physical science students a practical coverage that connects mathematics to the world around them. It is a flexible book that has evolved alongside changing trends but remains steadfast to its original objectives.

This edition continues to feature a theme that was introduced in the previous edition. Movies and television have become entrenched in our society and appeal to a broad range of interests. Every chapter opener contains reference to a popular movie, television show, or event, including discussion of a scene that deals with the mathematics covered in the chapter. The margin notes, long a popular hallmark of the book, include similar references. These references are indicated with a clapboard icon 🎬. Many of the chapter openers and margin notes have been revised for this edition. We hope that users will enjoy visiting Hollywood while learning mathematics.

Mathematical Ideas is written with a variety of students in mind. It is well suited for several courses, including those geared toward the aforementioned liberal arts audience and survey courses in mathematics, finite mathematics, and mathematics for prospective and in-service elementary and middle-school teachers. Ample topics are included for a two-term course, yet the variety of topics and flexibility of sequence makes the text suitable for shorter courses as well. Our main objectives continue to be comprehensive coverage, appropriate organization, clear exposition, an abundance of examples, and well-planned exercise sets with numerous applications.

NEW TO THIS EDITION

- Movie and television references have been updated throughout the book.

- Pointers have been added to Examples. They guide students and provide on-the-spot reminders and warnings to avoid common pitfalls.

- Every chapter now includes an Extension, a mini-section that delves deeper into a related topic.

- Enhancing the already well-respected exercise sets, over 1000 exercises are new or modified.

- Graphing calculator screens have been redesigned and now show the output in Math-Print format (available on some TI-84 calculators).

- Figure and table references within the text are set using the same typeface as the figure or table, making it easier for students to identify and connect them.

- The text has been streamlined to make it easier for students to recognize key content.

- A completely new set of videos has been developed to support student learning outside the classroom. They are useful for online or hybrid courses, as well as student self-study, and are available on DVD and in MyMathLab.

OVERVIEW OF CHAPTERS

- **Chapter 1 (The Art of Problem Solving)** introduces the student to inductive reasoning, pattern recognition, and problem-solving techniques. We continue to provide exercises based on the monthly Calendar from *Mathematics Teacher* and have added new ones throughout this edition, beginning in Section 1.4. At the request of reviewers, Section 1.2 now includes coverage of arithmetic and geometric sequences.

- **Chapter 2 (The Basic Concepts of Set Theory)** includes updated exercises on surveys and a revised discussion of the work of Georg Cantor. (*Note:* Instructors should feel free to cover Chapter 3 before Chapter 2 if they desire.)

- **Chapter 3 (Introduction to Logic)** introduces the fundamental concepts of inductive and deductive logic. There is a new chapter opener from *Shrek the Third*. We have included additional exercises from the work of Raymond Smullyan and expanded the coverage of logical fallacies. The logic problems and Sudoku puzzles from the previous edition have been replaced with new ones.

- **Chapter 6 (The Real Numbers and Their Representations)** introduces some of the basic concepts of real numbers, their various forms of representation, and operations of arithmetic with them. The chapter opener is new. Most of the exercises involving real-life data have been updated, and several new ones have been included.

- **Chapter 7 (The Basic Concepts of Algebra)** can be used to present the basics of algebra (linear and quadratic equations, applications, exponents, polynomials, and factoring) to students for the first time, or as a review of previous courses. There is a new chapter opener, and applications have been updated in this chapter as well.

- **Chapter 10 (Counting Methods)** focuses on elementary counting techniques, in preparation for the chapter to follow. We have included a completely new chapter opener on the coin toss in Super Bowl XLIV, added problems from *Mathematics Teacher*, and included a discussion of "unwanted ordering." The Extension on Magic Squares, formerly in Chapter 5, is now part of this chapter.

- **Chapter 11 (Probability)** covers the basics of probability, odds, and expected value. In this edition, we include problems from *Mathematics Teacher* for the first time.

- **Chapter 12 (Statistics)** is an introduction to statistics that focuses on the measures of central tendency, dispersion, and position and discusses the normal distribution, regression, and correlation. The new chapter opener provides a real life example of Simpson's paradox, and examples and exercises include updated data.

- **Chapter 13 (Personal Financial Management)** provides the student with the basics of the mathematics of finance as applied to inflation, consumer debt, and house buying. We include a section on investing, with emphasis on stocks, bonds, and mutual funds. Examples and exercises have been updated to reflect current interest rates and investment returns. A new Extension, *Ponzi Schemes and Other Investment Frauds*, has been added to this edition.

COURSE OUTLINE CONSIDERATIONS

Chapters in the text are, in most cases, independent and may be covered in the order chosen by the instructor. The few exceptions are as follows:

- Chapter 6 contains some material dependent on the ideas found in Chapter 5.

- Chapter 6 should be covered before Chapter 7 if student background so dictates.

- Chapters 7 and 8 form an algebraic "package" and should be covered in sequential order.

- A thorough coverage of Chapter 11 depends on knowledge of Chapter 10 material, although probability can be covered without teaching extensive counting methods by avoiding the more difficult exercises.

- The latter part of Chapter 12, on inferential statistics, depends on an understanding of probability (Chapter 11).

FEATURES OF THE TWELFTH EDITION

ENHANCED **Chapter Openers** In keeping with the Hollywood theme, chapter openers address a scene or situation from a popular movie or a television series or event. Many are new to this edition. Some openers illustrate the correct use of mathematics, while others address how mathematics is misused. In the latter case, we subscribe to the premise that we can all learn from the mistakes of others. Some openers include a problem statement that the reader is asked to solve. We hope that you enjoy reading these chapter openers as much as we have enjoyed preparing them.

ENHANCED **Varied Exercise Sets** We continue to present a variety of exercises that integrate drill, conceptual, and applied problems and have included over 1000 new or modified exercises to this edition. The text contains a wealth of exercises to provide students with opportunities to practice, apply, connect, and extend the mathematical skills they are learning. We have updated the exercises that focus on real-life data and have retained their titles for easy identification. Several chapters are enriched with new applications, particularly Chapters 6, 7, 8, 11, 12, and 13. We continue to use graphs, tables, and charts when appropriate. Many of the graphs use a style similar to that seen by students in today's print and electronic media.

ENHANCED **Margin Notes** This popular feature is a hallmark of this text and has been retained and updated where appropriate. These notes are interspersed throughout the text and deal with various subjects such as lives of mathematicians, historical vignettes, philatelic and numismatic reproductions, anecdotes on mathematics textbooks of the past, newspaper and magazine articles, and current research in mathematics. Several new Hollywood-related margin notes have also been added.

ENHANCED **Extensions** These mini-sections delve deeper into related topics and include their own exercise sets. New Extensions have been written for chapters that previously did not have this feature.

Collaborative Investigations The importance of cooperative learning is addressed in this end-of-chapter feature.

Problem-Solving Hints Special paragraphs labeled "Problem-Solving Hint" relate the discussion of problem-solving strategies to techniques that have been presented earlier.

ENHANCED **Optional Graphing Technology** We continue to provide sample graphing calculator screens to show how technology can be used to support results found analytically. These screens have been re-designed and now show the output in MathPrint format. It is not essential, however, that a student have a graphing calculator to study from this text. *The technology component is optional.*

Art Program The text continues to feature a full-color design. Color is used for instructional emphasis in text discussions, examples, graphs, and figures. Many new photos have been incorporated to provide visual appeal.

For Further Thought These entries encourage students to share amongst themselves their reasoning processes to gain a deeper understanding of key mathematical concepts.

Example Titles The numerous, carefully selected examples that illustrate concepts and skills are titled so that students can see at a glance the topic under consideration.

UPDATED **Emphasis on Real Data in the Form of Graphs, Charts, and Tables** We continue to use up-to-date information from magazines, newspapers, and the Internet to create real applications that are relevant and meaningful.

Chapter Tests Each chapter concludes with a chapter test so that students can check their mastery of the material.

SUPPLEMENTS

STUDENT SUPPLEMENTS

Student's Solutions Manual
ISBN-10: 0-321-69384-1; ISBN-13: 978-0-321-69384-6

- This manual by Carrie Green provides solutions to the odd-numbered exercises in the exercise sets, the Extensions, and the Appendix exercises, as well as solutions for all the Chapter Test exercises.

Video Resources on DVD with Optional Captioning
ISBN-10: 0-321-71649-3; ISBN-13: 978-0-321-71649-1

- This completely new set of videos was developed by Sue Glascoe of Mesa Community College. Making use of newer teaching technologies, the videos clearly cover important definitions, procedures, and concepts by working through examples and exercises from the textbook. They are ideal for online and hybrid courses, as well as supplemental instruction for traditional courses. Optional subtitles are available.

INSTRUCTOR SUPPLEMENTS

Annotated Instructor's Edition
ISBN-10: 0-321-69406-6; ISBN-13: 978-0-321-69406-5

- This special edition of the text provides answers next to the text exercises for quick reference, when space is available. Longer answers, indicated by an icon ⊡ after the exercise, can be found in the back of the book.

Instructor's Solutions Manual
ISBN-10: 0-321-69405-8; ISBN-13: 978-0-321-69405-8

- This manual by Carrie Green contains solutions to all end-of-section exercises, Extension, Chapter Test, and Appendix exercises.

ENHANCED **Insider's Guide with Math Goes to Hollywood Teaching Notes**
ISBN-10: 0-321-71643-4; ISBN-13: 978-0-321-71643-9

- This updated guide now includes detailed *Math Goes to Hollywood* teaching notes to help instructors integrate the movies from the text into their courses. The new movie notes include the name of the movie, clip segment times, related mathematical topics, correlation to the text, summary of mathematical content, and discussion questions.
- The *Insider's Guide* includes resources to help faculty with course preparation and classroom management. It provides helpful teaching tips correlated to each section of the text, as well as general teaching advice.

Instructor's Testing Manual (online only)
- This manual contains four tests for each chapter of the text. Answer keys are included.

TestGen® (online only)
- TestGen enables instructors to build, edit, print, and administer tests using a computerized bank of questions developed to cover all text objectives.

PowerPoint Lecture Presentation (online only)
- These fully editable lecture slides include definitions, key concepts, and examples for use in a lecture setting and are available for each section of the text.

Online supplements can be found in MyMathLab or downloaded from www.pearsonhighered.com/irc.

MEDIA SUPPLEMENTS

MyMathLab® Online Course

MyMathLab® is a text-specific, easily customizable online course that integrates interactive multimedia instruction with textbook content. MyMathLab gives instructors the tools they need to deliver all or a portion of their course online, whether their students are in a lab setting or working from home.

- **Interactive homework exercises**, correlated to the textbook at the objective level, are algorithmically generated for unlimited practice and mastery. Most exercises are free-response and provide guided solutions, sample problems, and tutorial learning aids for extra help.

- **Personalized Study Plan,** generated when students complete a test or quiz, indicates which topics have been mastered and links to tutorial exercises for topics students have not mastered. The Study Plan can be customized so that the topics available match course contents or so that students' homework results determine mastery.

- **Multimedia learning aids**, such as video lectures and podcasts, animations, and a complete multimedia textbook, help students independently improve their understanding and performance. Instructors can assign these multimedia learning aids as homework to help students grasp the concepts.

- **Homework and Test Manager** allows instructors to assign homework, quizzes, and tests that are automatically graded. They can select just the right mix of questions from the MyMathLab exercise bank, instructor-created custom exercises, and/or Test-Gen® test items.

- **Gradebook,** designed specifically for mathematics and statistics, automatically tracks students' results, lets instructors stay on top of student performance, and gives them control over how to calculate final grades. They can also add offline (paper-and-pencil) grades to the gradebook.

- **MathXL Exercise Builder** allows instructors to create static and algorithmic exercises for their online assignments. They can use the library of sample exercises as an easy starting point, or they can edit any course-related exercise.

- **Pearson Tutor Center** (www.pearsontutorservices.com) access is automatically included with MyMathLab. The Tutor Center is staffed by qualified math instructors who provide textbook-specific tutoring for students via toll-free phone, fax, email, and interactive Web sessions.

- **Specific features for *Mathematical Ideas*** include
  - Completely new concept review videos
  - Interactive mathematics and societal timeline

Students using MyMathLab® do their assignments in the Flash®-based MathXL Player, which is compatible with almost any browser (Firefox®, Safari™, or Internet Explorer®) on almost any platform (Macintosh® or Windows®). MyMathLab is powered by CourseCompass™, Pearson Education's online teaching and learning environment, and by MathXL®, our online homework, tutorial, and assessment system. MyMathLab is available to qualified adopters. For more information, visit www.mymathlab.com or contact your Pearson representative.

MathXL® Online Course

MathXL® is an online homework, tutorial, and assessment system that accompanies Pearson's textbooks in mathematics or statistics.

- **Interactive homework exercises**, correlated to the textbook at the objective level, are algorithmically generated for unlimited practice and mastery. Most exercises are free-response and provide guided solutions, sample problems, and learning aids for extra help.

- **Personalized Study Plan,** generated when students complete a test or quiz or homework, indicates which topics have been mastered and links to tutorial exercises for topics students have not mastered. Instructors can customize the available topics in the study plan to match their course concepts.

- **Multimedia learning aids,** such as video lectures and animations, help students independently improve their understanding and performance. These are assignable as homework, to further encourage their use.

- **Gradebook,** designed specifically for mathematics and statistics, automatically tracks students' results, lets instructors stay informed of student performance, and gives them control over how to calculate final grades.

- **MathXL Exercise Builder** allows instructors to create static and algorithmic exercises for their online assignments. They can use the library of sample exercises as an easy starting point or the Exercise Builder to edit any of the course-related exercises.

- **Homework and Test Manager** lets instructors create online homework, quizzes, and tests that are automatically graded. They can select just the right mix of questions from the MathXL exercise bank, instructor-created custom exercises, and/or TestGen test items.

The new, Flash®-based MathXL Player is compatible with almost any browser (Firefox®, Safari™, or Internet Explorer®) on almost any platform (Macintosh® or Windows®). MathXL is available to qualified adopters. For more information, visit our website at www.mathxl.com, or contact your Pearson representative.

ACKNOWLEDGMENTS

We wish to thank the following reviewers for their helpful comments and suggestions for this and previous editions of the text. (Reviewers of the twelfth edition are noted with an asterisk.)

H. Achepohl, *College of DuPage*
Shahrokh Ahmadi, *Northern Virginia Community College*
Richard Andrews, *Florida A&M University*
Cindy Anfinson, *Palomar College*
*Erika Asano, *University of South Florida, St. Petersburg*
Elaine Barber, *Germanna Community College*
Anna Baumgartner, *Carthage College*
James E. Beamer, *Northeastern State University*
Elliot Benjamin, *Unity College*
Jaime Bestard, *Barry University*
Joyce Blair, *Belmont University*
Gus Brar, *Delaware County Community College*
Roger L. Brown, *Davenport College*
Douglas Burke, *Malcolm X College*
John Busovicki, *Indiana University of Pennsylvania*
Ann Cascarelle, *St. Petersburg Junior College*
Kenneth Chapman, *St. Petersburg Junior College*
Gordon M. Clarke, *University of the Incarnate Word*
M. Marsha Cupitt, *Durham Technical Community College*
James Curry, *American River College*
Rosemary Danaher, *Sacred Heart University*
Ken Davis, *Mesa State College*
Nancy Davis, *Brunswick Community College*
George DeRise, *Thomas Nelson Community College*
Catherine Dermott, *Hudson Valley Community College*
Greg Dietrich, *Florida Community College at Jacksonville*
*Vincent Dimiceli, *Oral Roberts University*
Diana C. Dwan, *Yavapai College*
Laura Dyer, *Belleville Area College*
Jan Eardley, *Barat College*
Joe Eitel, *Folsom College*
Azin Enshai, *American River College*
Gayle Farmer, *Northeastern State University*
Michael Farndale, *Waldorf College*
Gordon Feathers, *Passaic County Community College*
Thomas Flohr, *New River Community College*
Bill Fulton, *Black Hawk College—East*
Anne Gardner, *Wenatchee Valley College*
*Justin M. Gash, *Franklin College*
Donald Goral, *Northern Virginia Community College*
Glen Granzow, *Idaho State University*

Larry Green, *Lake Tahoe Community College*
Arthur D. Grissinger, *Lock Haven University*
Don Hancock, *Pepperdine University*
Denis Hanson, *University of Regina*
Marilyn Hasty, *Southern Illinois University*
Shelby L. Hawthorne, *Thomas Nelson Community College*
Jeff Heiking, *St. Petersburg Junior College*
Laura Hillerbrand, *Broward Community College*
*Corinne Irwin, *University of Texas at Austin*
Jacqueline Jensen, *Sam Houston State University*
Emanuel Jinich, *Endicott College*
Frank Juric, *Brevard Community College-Palm Bay*
Karla Karstens, *University of Vermont*
*Najam Khaja, *Centennial College*
Hilary Kight, *Wesleyan College*
Barbara J. Kniepkamp, *Southern Illinois University at Edwardsville*
Suda Kunyosying, *Shepherd College*
Yu-Ju Kuo, *Indiana University of Pennsylvania*
*Stephane Lafortune, *College of Charleston*
Pam Lamb, *J. Sargeant Reynolds Community College*
John Lattanzio, *Indiana University of Pennsylvania*
John W. Legge, *Pikeville College*
*Dawn Locklear, *Crown College*
*Bin Lu, *California State University, Sacramento*
Leo Lusk, *Gulf Coast Community College*
Sherrie Lutsch, *Northwest Indian College*
Rhonda Macleod, *Florida State University*
Andrew Markoe, *Rider University*
Darlene Marnich, *Point Park College*
Victoria Martinez, *Okaloosa Walton Community College*
Chris Mason, *Community College of Vermont*
Mark Maxwell, *Maryville University*
Carol McCarron, *Harrisburg Area Community College*
Delois McCormick, *Germanna Community College*
Daisy McCoy, *Lyndon State College*
Cynthia McGinnis, *Okaloosa Walton Community College*
Vena McGrath, *Davenport College*
Robert Moyer, *Fort Valley State University*
Shai Neumann, *Brevard Community College*
Barbara Nienstedt, *Gloucester County College*

Chaitanya Nigam, *Gateway Community-Technical College*

Vladimir Nikiforov, *University of Memphis*

*Vicky Ohlson, *Trenholm State Technical College*

Jean Okumura, *Windward Community College*

*Stan Perrine, *Charleston Southern University*

Bob Phillips, *Mesabi Range Community College*

Kathy Pinchback, *University of Memphis*

Priscilla Putman, *New Jersey City University*

Scott C. Radtke, *Davenport College*

*Doraiswamy Ramachandran, *California State University, Sacramento*

John Reily, *Montclair State University*

Beth Reynolds, *Mater Dei College*

Shirley I. Robertson, *High Point University*

Andrew M. Rockett, *CW Post Campus of Long Island University*

Kathleen Rodak, *St. Mary's College of Ave Maria University*

*Cynthia Roemer, *Union County College*

*Lisa Rombes, *Washtenaw Community College*

Abby Roscum, *Marshalltown Community College*

D. Schraeder, *McLennan Community College*

Wilfred Schulte, *Cosumnes River College*

Melinda Schulteis, *Concordia University*

Gary D. Shaffer, *Allegany College of Maryland*

Doug Shaw, *University of North Iowa*

Jane Sinibaldi, *York College of Pennsylvania*

*Nancy Skocik, *California University of Pennsylvania*

Larry Smith, *Peninsula College*

Marguerite Smith, *Merced College*

Charlene D. Snow, *Lower Columbia College*

H. Jeannette Stephens, *Whatcom Community College*

Suzanne J. Stock, *Oakton Community College*

*Dawn M. Strickland, *Winthrop University*

Dian Thom, *McKendree College*

Claude C. Thompson, *Hollins University*

Mark Tom, *College of the Sequoias*

Ida Umphers, *University of Arkansas at Little Rock*

Karen Villarreal, *University of New Orleans*

*Dr. Karen Walters, *Northern Virginia Community College*

Wayne Wanamaker, *Central Florida Community College*

David Wasilewski, *Luzerne County Community College*

William Watkins, *California State University, Northridge*

*Alice Williamson, *Sussex County Community College*

Susan Williford, *Columbia State Community College*

Tom Witten, *Southwest Virginia Community College*

Fred Worth, *Henderson State University*

Rob Wylie, *Carl Albert State College*

Henry Wyzinski, *Indiana University Northwest*

A project of this magnitude cannot be accomplished without the help of many other dedicated individuals. Marnie Greenhut served as acquisitions editor for this edition. Carol Merrigan provided excellent production supervision. Anne Kelly, Greg Tobin, Tracy Patruno, Roxanne McCarley, Elle Driska, and Christine O'Brien of Pearson Addison-Wesley gave us their unwavering support.

Beth Anderson continued to provide outstanding photo research. Terry McGinnis gave her usual excellent behind-the-scenes guidance. Thanks go to Dr. Margaret L. Morrow of Plattsburgh State University and Dr. Jill Van Newenhizen of Lake Forest College, who wrote the material on graph theory and voting/apportionment, respectively. Chris Heeren and Paul Lorczak did an outstanding job of accuracy- and answer-checking. Mike McCraith of Cuyahoga Community College joined the cast with the addition of new movie cards. And finally, we thank our loyal users over these many editions for making this book one of the most successful in its market.

Vern E. Heeren
John Hornsby

THE ART OF PROBLEM SOLVING

T he 1995 movie *Die Hard: With a Vengeance* stars Bruce Willis as New York Detective John McClane. In this film, McClane is tormented by villain Simon Gruber (Jeremy Irons), who plants bombs around the city and poses riddles and puzzles for disarming them. In one situation, Simon gives McClane and store owner Zeus Carver (Samuel L. Jackson) the following riddle by telephone to solve in 5 minutes.

On the fountain there should be two jugs. Do you see them? A 5-gallon and a 3-gallon. Fill one of the jugs with exactly 4 gallons of water, and place it on the scale, and the timer will stop. You must be precise. One ounce more or less will result in detonation.

McClane and Carver were able to solve the riddle and defuse the bomb. Can you solve it? The answer is on page 2.

▮▮▮▮▮▮▮ **1.1 SOLVING PROBLEMS BY INDUCTIVE REASONING**

Characteristics of Inductive and Deductive Reasoning • Pitfalls of Inductive Reasoning

Characteristics of Inductive and Deductive Reasoning

The development of mathematics can be traced to the Egyptian and Babylonian cultures (3000 B.C.–A.D. 260) as a necessity for problem solving. To solve a problem or perform an operation, a cookbook-like recipe was given, and it was performed repeatedly to solve similar problems.

By observing that a specific method worked for a certain type of problem, the Babylonians and the Egyptians concluded that the same method would work for any similar type of problem. Such a conclusion is called a *conjecture*. A **conjecture** is an educated guess based on repeated observations of a particular process or pattern. The method of reasoning we have just described is called *inductive reasoning*.

Solution to the Chapter Opener Problem This is one way to do it: With both jugs empty, fill the 3-gallon jug and pour its contents into the 5-gallon jug. Then fill the 3-gallon jug again, and pour it into the 5-gallon jug until the latter is filled. There is now $(3 + 3) - 5 = 1$ gallon in the 3-gallon jug. Empty the 5-gallon jug, and pour the 1 gallon of water from the 3-gallon jug into the 5-gallon jug. Finally, fill the 3-gallon jug and pour all of it into the 5-gallon jug, resulting in $1 + 3 = 4$ gallons in the 5-gallon jug.

(*Note:* There is another way to solve this problem. See if you can discover the alternative solution.)

> **Inductive Reasoning**
>
> **Inductive reasoning** is characterized by drawing a general conclusion (making a conjecture) from repeated observations of specific examples. The conjecture may or may not be true.

In testing a conjecture obtained by inductive reasoning, it takes only one example that does not work to prove the conjecture false. Such an example is called a **counterexample.**

Inductive reasoning provides a powerful method of drawing conclusions, but there is no assurance that the observed conjecture will always be true. For this reason, mathematicians are reluctant to accept a conjecture as an absolute truth until it is formally proved using methods of *deductive reasoning*. Deductive reasoning characterized the development and approach of Greek mathematics, as seen in the works of Euclid, Pythagoras, Archimedes, and others. During the classical Greek period (600 B.C.–A.D. 450), general concepts were applied to specific problems, resulting in a structured, logical development of mathematics.

> **Deductive Reasoning**
>
> **Deductive reasoning** is characterized by applying general principles to specific examples.

We now look at examples of these two types of reasoning. In this chapter, we often refer to the **natural,** or **counting, numbers:**

$$1, 2, 3, \ldots \quad \text{Natural (counting) numbers}$$

↑

Ellipsis points

The three dots (*ellipsis points*) indicate that the numbers continue indefinitely in the pattern that has been established. The most probable rule for continuing this pattern is "add 1 to the previous number," and this is indeed the rule that we follow.

Now consider the following list of natural numbers:

$$2, 9, 16, 23, 30.$$

What is the next number of this list? What is the pattern? After studying the numbers, we might see that $2 + 7 = 9$, and $9 + 7 = 16$. Do we add 16 and 7 to get 23?

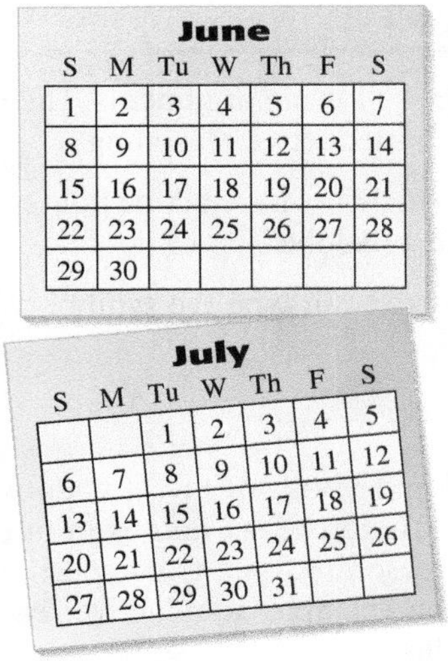

June

S	M	Tu	W	Th	F	S
1	2	3	4	5	6	7
8	9	10	11	12	13	14
15	16	17	18	19	20	21
22	23	24	25	26	27	28
29	30					

July

S	M	Tu	W	Th	F	S
		1	2	3	4	5
6	7	8	9	10	11	12
13	14	15	16	17	18	19
20	21	22	23	24	25	26
27	28	29	30	31		

Figure 1

Do we add 23 and 7 to get 30? Yes. It seems that any number in the given list can be found by adding 7 to the preceding number, so the next number in the list would be $30 + 7 = 37$.

We set out to find the "next number" by reasoning from observation of the numbers in the list. We may have jumped from these observations to the general statement that any number in the list is 7 more than the preceding number. This is an example of *inductive reasoning*.

By using inductive reasoning, we concluded that 37 was the next number. Suppose the person making up the list has another answer in mind. The list of numbers

$$2, 9, 16, 23, 30$$

actually gives the dates of Mondays in June if June 1 falls on a Sunday. The next Monday after June 30 is July 7. With this pattern, the list continues as

$$2, 9, 16, 23, 30, 7, 14, 21, 28, \ldots.$$

See the calendar in **Figure 1**. The correct answer would then be 7. The process used to obtain the rule "add 7" in the preceding list reveals a main flaw of inductive reasoning. *We can never be sure that what is true in a specific case will be true in general. Inductive reasoning does not guarantee a true result, but it does provide a means of making a conjecture.*

We now review some basic notation. Throughout this book, we use *exponents* to represent repeated multiplication.

$$\text{Base} \rightarrow 4^3 = 4 \cdot 4 \cdot 4 = 64 \quad \text{4 is used as a factor 3 times.}$$
$$\uparrow$$
$$\text{Exponent}$$

Exponential Expression

If a is a number and n is a counting number $(1, 2, 3, \ldots)$, then the exponential expression a^n is defined as follows.

$$a^n = \underbrace{a \cdot a \cdot a \cdot \ldots \cdot a}_{n \text{ factors of } a}$$

The number a is the **base** and n is the **exponent.**

With deductive reasoning, we use general statements and apply them to specific situations. For example, consider the **Pythagorean theorem:**

In any right triangle, the sum of the squares of the legs (shorter sides) is equal to the square of the hypotenuse (longest side).

Thus, if we know that the lengths of the shorter sides are 3 inches and 4 inches, we can find the length of the longest side. Let h represent the length of the longest side.

$$3^2 + 4^2 = h^2 \quad \text{Pythagorean theorem}$$
$$9 + 16 = h^2 \quad 3^2 = 3 \cdot 3 = 9; 4^2 = 4 \cdot 4 = 16$$
$$25 = h^2 \quad \text{Add.}$$
$$5 = h \quad \text{The positive square root of 25 is 5.}$$

Thus, the longest side measures 5 inches. We used the general rule (the Pythagorean theorem) and applied it to the specific situation.

Reasoning through a problem usually requires certain *premises*. A **premise** can be an assumption, law, rule, widely held idea, or observation. Then reason inductively or deductively from the premises to obtain a **conclusion.** The premises and conclusion make up a **logical argument.**

■■ **EXAMPLE 1** Identifying Premises and Conclusions

Identify each premise and the conclusion in each of the following arguments. Then tell whether each argument is an example of inductive or deductive reasoning.

(a) Our house is made of adobe. Both of my next-door neighbors have adobe houses. Therefore, all houses in our neighborhood are made of adobe.

(b) All keyboards have the symbol @. I have a keyboard. I can type the symbol @.

(c) Today is Tuesday. Tomorrow will be Wednesday.

SOLUTION

(a) The premises are "Our house is made of adobe" and "Both of my next-door neighbors have adobe houses." The conclusion is "Therefore, all houses in our neighborhood are made of adobe." Because the reasoning goes from specific examples to a general statement, the argument is an example of inductive reasoning (although it may very well have a false conclusion).

(b) Here, the premises are "All keyboards have the symbol @" and "I have a keyboard." The conclusion is "I can type the symbol @." This reasoning goes from general to specific, so deductive reasoning was used.

(c) There is only one premise here, "Today is Tuesday." The conclusion is "Tomorrow will be Wednesday." The fact that Wednesday immediately follows Tuesday is being used, even though this fact is not explicitly stated. Because the conclusion comes from general facts that apply to this special case, deductive reasoning was used. ■■■

The earlier calendar example illustrated how inductive reasoning may, at times, lead to false conclusions. However, in many cases, inductive reasoning does provide correct results if we look for the most *probable* answer.

■■ **EXAMPLE 2** Predicting the Next Number in a Sequence

Use inductive reasoning to determine the *probable* next number in each list below.

(a) 5, 9, 13, 17, 21, 25, 29   **(b)** 1, 1, 2, 3, 5, 8, 13, 21   **(c)** 2, 4, 8, 16, 32

SOLUTION

(a) Each number in the list is obtained by adding 4 to the previous number. The probable next number is $29 + 4 = 33$. (This is an example of an *arithmetic sequence*.)

(b) Beginning with the third number in the list, 2, each number is obtained by adding the two previous numbers in the list. That is,

$$1 + 1 = 2, \quad 1 + 2 = 3, \quad 2 + 3 = 5,$$

and so on. The probable next number in the list is $13 + 21 = 34$. (These are the first few terms of the famous *Fibonacci sequence*.)

(c) It appears here that to obtain each number after the first, we must double the previous number. Therefore, the most probable next number is $32 \times 2 = 64$. (This is an example of a *geometric sequence*.) ■■■

In the 2003 movie *A Wrinkle in Time*, young Charles Wallace, played by David Dorfman, is challenged to identify a particular sequence of numbers. He correctly identifies it as the **Fibonacci sequence.**

Inductive reasoning often can be used to predict an answer in a list of similarly constructed computation exercises, as shown in the next example.

▮▮ **EXAMPLE 3**   Predicting the Product of Two Numbers

Consider the list of equations. Predict the next multiplication fact in the list.

$$37 \times 3 = 111$$
$$37 \times 6 = 222$$
$$37 \times 9 = 333$$
$$37 \times 12 = 444$$

SOLUTION

The left side of each equation has two factors, the first 37 and the second a multiple of 3, beginning with 3. Each product (answer) consists of three digits, all the same, beginning with 111 for 37×3. Thus, the next multiplication fact would be

$$37 \times 15 = 555, \quad \text{which is indeed true.} \qquad ▮▮▮$$

Pitfalls of Inductive Reasoning

There are pitfalls associated with inductive reasoning. A classic example involves the maximum number of regions formed when chords are constructed in a circle. When two points on a circle are joined with a line segment, a *chord* is formed.

Locate a single point on a circle. Because no chords are formed, a single interior region is formed. See **Figure 2(a)**. Locate two points and draw a chord. Two interior regions are formed, as shown in **Figure 2(b)**. Continue this pattern. Locate three points, and draw all possible chords. Four interior regions are formed, as shown in **Figure 2(c)**. Four points yield 8 regions and five points yield 16 regions. See **Figures 2(d) and 2(e)**.

Table 1

Number of Points	Number of Regions
1	1
2	2
3	4
4	8
5	16

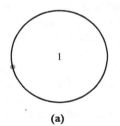   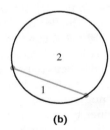   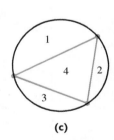   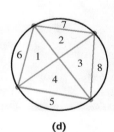   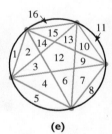

(a)   (b)   (c)   (d)   (e)

Figure 2

The results of the preceding observations are summarized in **Table 1** in the margin. The pattern formed in the column headed "Number of Regions" is the same one we saw in **Example 2(c)**, where we predicted that the next number would be 64. It seems here that for each additional point on the circle, the number of regions doubles. A reasonable inductive conjecture would be that for six points, 32 regions would be formed. But as **Figure 3** indicates, there are *only 31 regions*. The pattern of doubling ends when the sixth point is considered. Adding a seventh point would yield 57 regions. The numbers obtained here are

$$1, 2, 4, 8, 16, 31, 57.$$

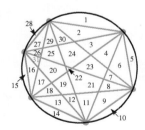

Figure 3

For *n* points on the circle, the number of regions is given by the formula

$$\frac{n^4 - 6n^3 + 23n^2 - 18n + 24}{24}.^*$$

_____

*For more information on this and other similar patterns, see "Counting Pizza Pieces and Other Combinatorial Problems," by Eugene Maier, in the January 1988 issue of *Mathematics Teacher*, pp. 22–26.

We can use a graphing calculator to construct a table of values that indicates the number of regions for various numbers of points. Using X rather than *n*, we can define Y_1 using the expression given on the previous page. (see **Figure 4(a)**). Then, creating a table of values, as in **Figure 4(b)**, we see how many regions (indicated by Y_1) there are for any number of points (X).

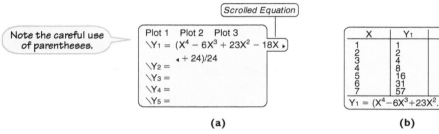

Note the careful use of parentheses.

Scrolled Equation

Plot 1   Plot 2   Plot 3
$\backslash Y_1 = (X^4 - 6X^3 + 23X^2 - 18X$ ▸
     ◂ $+ 24)/24$
$\backslash Y_2 =$
$\backslash Y_3 =$
$\backslash Y_4 =$
$\backslash Y_5 =$

X	Y_1	
1	1	
2	2	
3	4	
4	8	
5	16	
6	31	
7	57	

$Y_1 = (X^4 - 6X^3 + 23X^2...$

(a)   (b)

Figure 4

For Further Thought

Inductive Reasoning Anecdote

The following anecdote concerning inductive reasoning appears in the first volume of the *In Mathematical Circles* series by Howard Eves.

A scientist had two large jars before him on the laboratory table. The jar on his left contained 100 fleas; the jar on his right was empty. The scientist carefully lifted a flea from the jar on the left, placed the flea on the table between the two jars, stepped back, and in a loud voice said, "Jump." The flea jumped and was put in the jar on the right. A second flea was carefully lifted from the jar on the left and placed on the table between the two jars. Again the scientist stepped back and in a loud voice said, "Jump." The flea jumped and was put in the jar on the right. In the same manner, the scientist treated each of the 100 fleas in the jar on the left, and each flea jumped as ordered.

The two jars were then interchanged and the experiment continued with a slight difference. This time the scientist carefully lifted a flea from the jar on the left, yanked off its hind legs, placed the flea on the table between the jars, stepped back, and in a loud voice said, "Jump." The flea did not jump, and was put in the jar on the right. A second flea was carefully lifted from the jar on the left, its hind legs yanked off, and then placed on the table between the two jars. Again the scientist stepped back and in a loud voice said, "Jump." The flea did not jump, and was put in the jar on the right. In this manner, the scientist treated each of the 100 fleas in the jar on the left, and in no case did a flea jump when ordered. The scientist recorded the following induction:

"A flea, if its hind legs are yanked off, cannot hear."

For Group or Individual Investigation

Discuss or research examples from advertising that lead consumers to draw incorrect conclusions.

1.1 EXERCISES

In Exercises 1–12, determine whether the reasoning is an example of deductive or inductive reasoning.

1. If the mechanic says that it will take seven days to repair your car, then it will actually take ten days. The mechanic says, "I figure it'll take a week to fix it, ma'am." Then you can expect it to be ready ten days from now.

2. If you take your vitamins, you'll feel a lot better. You take your vitamins. Therefore, you'll feel a lot better.

3. It has rained every day for the past six days, and it is raining today as well. So it will also rain tomorrow.

4. Carrie's first three children were boys. If she has another baby, it will be a boy.

5. Finley had 85 baseball cards. His mom gave him 20 more for his birthday. Therefore, he now has 105 of them.

6. If the same number is subtracted from both sides of a true equation, the new equation is also true. I know that $9 + 18 = 27$. Therefore, $(9 + 18) - 13 = 27 - 13$.

7. If you build it, they will come. You build it. Therefore, they will come.

8. All men are mortal. Socrates is a man. Therefore, Socrates is mortal.

9. It is a fact that every student who ever attended Delgado University was accepted into graduate school. Because I am attending Delgado, I can expect to be accepted to graduate school, too.

10. For the past 97 years, a rare plant has bloomed in Columbia each summer, alternating between yellow and green flowers. Last summer, it bloomed with green flowers, so this summer it will bloom with yellow flowers.

11. In the sequence 5, 10, 15, 20, 25, ..., the most probable next number is 30.

12. Lady Gaga's last four single releases have reached the Top Ten in the pop charts, so her current release will also reach the Top Ten.

13. Discuss the differences between inductive and deductive reasoning. Give an example of each.

14. Give an example of faulty inductive reasoning.

Determine the most probable next term in each of the following lists of numbers.

15. 6, 9, 12, 15, 18

16. 13, 18, 23, 28, 33

17. 3, 12, 48, 192, 768

18. 32, 16, 8, 4, 2

19. 3, 6, 9, 15, 24, 39

20. $\dfrac{1}{3}, \dfrac{3}{5}, \dfrac{5}{7}, \dfrac{7}{9}, \dfrac{9}{11}$

21. $\dfrac{1}{2}, \dfrac{3}{4}, \dfrac{5}{6}, \dfrac{7}{8}, \dfrac{9}{10}$

22. 1, 4, 9, 16, 25

23. 1, 8, 27, 64, 125

24. 2, 6, 12, 20, 30, 42

25. 4, 7, 12, 19, 28, 39

26. $-1, 2, -3, 4, -5, 6$

27. 5, 3, 5, 5, 3, 5, 5, 5, 3, 5, 5, 5, 5, 3, 5, 5, 5, 5

28. 8, 2, 8, 2, 2, 8, 2, 2, 2, 8, 2, 2, 2, 2, 8, 2, 2, 2, 2

29. Construct a list of numbers similar to those in **Exercise 15** such that the most probable next number in the list is 60.

30. Construct a list of numbers similar to those in **Exercise 26** such that the most probable next number in the list is 9.

Use the list of equations and inductive reasoning to predict the next equation, and then verify your conjecture.

31.
$$(9 \times 9) + 7 = 88$$
$$(98 \times 9) + 6 = 888$$
$$(987 \times 9) + 5 = 8888$$
$$(9876 \times 9) + 4 = 88{,}888$$

32.
$$(1 \times 9) + 2 = 11$$
$$(12 \times 9) + 3 = 111$$
$$(123 \times 9) + 4 = 1111$$
$$(1234 \times 9) + 5 = 11{,}111$$

33.
$$3367 \times 3 = 10{,}101$$
$$3367 \times 6 = 20{,}202$$
$$3367 \times 9 = 30{,}303$$
$$3367 \times 12 = 40{,}404$$

34.
$$15873 \times 7 = 111{,}111$$
$$15873 \times 14 = 222{,}222$$
$$15873 \times 21 = 333{,}333$$
$$15873 \times 28 = 444{,}444$$

35.
$$34 \times 34 = 1156$$
$$334 \times 334 = 111{,}556$$
$$3334 \times 3334 = 11{,}115{,}556$$

36.
$$11 \times 11 = 121$$
$$111 \times 111 = 12{,}321$$
$$1111 \times 1111 = 1{,}234{,}321$$

37.
$$3 = \frac{3(2)}{2}$$
$$3 + 6 = \frac{6(3)}{2}$$
$$3 + 6 + 9 = \frac{9(4)}{2}$$
$$3 + 6 + 9 + 12 = \frac{12(5)}{2}$$

38.
$$2 = 4 - 2$$
$$2 + 4 = 8 - 2$$
$$2 + 4 + 8 = 16 - 2$$
$$2 + 4 + 8 + 16 = 32 - 2$$

39.
$$5(6) = 6(6 - 1)$$
$$5(6) + 5(36) = 6(36 - 1)$$
$$5(6) + 5(36) + 5(216) = 6(216 - 1)$$
$$5(6) + 5(36) + 5(216) + 5(1296) = 6(1296 - 1)$$

40.
$$3 = \frac{3(3-1)}{2}$$

$$3 + 9 = \frac{3(9-1)}{2}$$

$$3 + 9 + 27 = \frac{3(27-1)}{2}$$

$$3 + 9 + 27 + 81 = \frac{3(81-1)}{2}$$

41.
$$\frac{1}{2} = 1 - \frac{1}{2}$$

$$\frac{1}{2} + \frac{1}{4} = 1 - \frac{1}{4}$$

$$\frac{1}{2} + \frac{1}{4} + \frac{1}{8} = 1 - \frac{1}{8}$$

$$\frac{1}{2} + \frac{1}{4} + \frac{1}{8} + \frac{1}{16} = 1 - \frac{1}{16}$$

42.
$$\frac{1}{1 \cdot 2} = \frac{1}{2}$$

$$\frac{1}{1 \cdot 2} + \frac{1}{2 \cdot 3} = \frac{2}{3}$$

$$\frac{1}{1 \cdot 2} + \frac{1}{2 \cdot 3} + \frac{1}{3 \cdot 4} = \frac{3}{4}$$

$$\frac{1}{1 \cdot 2} + \frac{1}{2 \cdot 3} + \frac{1}{3 \cdot 4} + \frac{1}{4 \cdot 5} = \frac{4}{5}$$

A story is often told about how the great mathematician Carl Friedrich Gauss (1777–1855) at a very young age was told by his teacher to find the sum of the first 100 counting numbers. While his classmates toiled at the problem, Carl simply wrote down a single number and handed it in to his teacher. His answer was correct. When asked how he did it, the young Carl explained that he observed that there were 50 pairs of numbers that each added up to 101. (See below.) So the sum of all the numbers must be 50 × 101 = 5050.

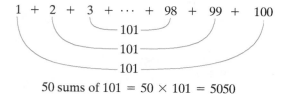

$$1 + 2 + 3 + \cdots + 98 + 99 + 100$$

50 sums of 101 = 50 × 101 = 5050

Use the method of Gauss to find each sum.

43. $1 + 2 + 3 + \cdots + 200$ **44.** $1 + 2 + 3 + \cdots + 400$

45. $1 + 2 + 3 + \cdots + 800$ **46.** $1 + 2 + 3 + \cdots + 2000$

47. Modify the procedure of Gauss to find the sum $1 + 2 + 3 + \cdots + 175$.

48. Explain in your own words how the procedure of Gauss can be modified to find the sum $1 + 2 + 3 + \cdots + n$, where n is an odd natural number. (When an odd natural number is divided by 2, it leaves a remainder of 1.)

49. Modify the procedure of Gauss to find the sum $2 + 4 + 6 + \cdots + 100$.

50. Use the result of **Exercise 49** to find the sum $4 + 8 + 12 + \cdots + 200$.

51. What is the most probable next number in this list?

12, 1, 1, 1, 2, 1, 3

(*Hint:* Think about a clock with chimes.)

52. What is the next term in this list?

O, T, T, F, F, S, S, E, N, T

(*Hint:* Think about words and their relationship to numbers.)

53. (a) Choose any three-digit number with all different digits. Now reverse the digits, and subtract the smaller from the larger. Record your result. Choose another three-digit number and repeat this process. Do this as many times as it takes for you to see a pattern in the different results you obtain. (*Hint:* What is the middle digit? What is the sum of the first and third digits?)

(b) Write an explanation of this pattern.

54. Choose any number, and follow these steps.
   (a) Multiply by 2.
   (b) Add 6.
   (c) Divide by 2.
   (d) Subtract the number you started with.
   (e) Record your result.

   Repeat the process, except in Step (b), add 8. Record your final result. Repeat the process once more, except in Step (b), add 10. Record your final result.

   (f) Observe what you have done. Then use inductive reasoning to explain how to predict the final result.

55. Complete the following.

$$142,857 \times 1 = \underline{\hspace{1.5cm}}$$
$$142,857 \times 2 = \underline{\hspace{1.5cm}}$$
$$142,857 \times 3 = \underline{\hspace{1.5cm}}$$
$$142,857 \times 4 = \underline{\hspace{1.5cm}}$$
$$142,857 \times 5 = \underline{\hspace{1.5cm}}$$
$$142,857 \times 6 = \underline{\hspace{1.5cm}}$$

What pattern exists in the successive answers? Now multiply 142,857 by 7 to obtain an interesting result.

56. Refer to **Figures 2(b)–(e)** and **Figure 3**. Instead of counting interior regions of the circle, count the chords formed. Use inductive reasoning to predict the number of chords that would be formed if seven points were used.

1.2 AN APPLICATION OF INDUCTIVE REASONING: NUMBER PATTERNS

Number Sequences • Successive Differences • Number Patterns and Sum Formulas • Figurate Numbers

Number Sequences

An ordered list of numbers such as

$$3, 9, 15, 21, 27, \ldots$$

is called a *sequence.* A **number sequence** is a list of numbers having a first number, a second number, a third number, and so on, called the **terms** of the sequence.

The sequence that begins

$$5, 9, 13, 17, 21, \ldots$$

is an *arithmetic sequence,* or *arithmetic progression.* In an **arithmetic sequence,** each term after the first is obtained by adding the same number, called the **common difference.** To find the common difference, choose any term after the first and subtract from it the preceding term. If we choose $9 - 5$ (the second term minus the first term), for example, we see that the common difference is 4. To find the term following 21, we add 4 to get $21 + 4 = 25$.

Similarly, the sequence that begins

$$2, 4, 8, 16, 32, \ldots$$

is a *geometric sequence,* or *geometric progression.* In a **geometric sequence,** each term after the first is obtained by multiplying by the same number, called the **common ratio.** To find the common ratio, choose any term after the first and divide it by the preceding term. If we choose $\frac{4}{2}$ (the second term divided by the first term), for example, we see that the common ratio is 2. To find the term following 32, we multiply by 2 to get $32 \cdot 2 = 64$.

EXAMPLE 1 Identifying Arithmetic and Geometric Sequences

For each sequence, determine if it is an *arithmetic sequence,* a *geometric sequence,* or *neither.* If it is either arithmetic or geometric, give the next term in the sequence.

(a) $5, 10, 15, 20, 25, \ldots$ **(b)** $3, 12, 48, 192, 768, \ldots$ **(c)** $1, 4, 9, 16, 25, \ldots$

SOLUTION

(a) If we choose *any* term after the first term, and subtract the preceding term, we find that the common difference is 5.

$$10 - 5 = 5 \quad 15 - 10 = 5 \quad 20 - 15 = 5 \quad 25 - 20 = 5$$

Therefore, this is an arithmetic sequence. The next term in the sequence is

$$25 + 5 = 30.$$

(b) If any term after the first is multiplied by 4, the following term is obtained.

$$\frac{12}{3} = 4 \quad \frac{48}{12} = 4 \quad \frac{192}{48} = 4 \quad \frac{768}{192} = 4$$

Therefore, this is a geometric sequence. The next term in the sequence is

$$768 \cdot 4 = 3072.$$

(c) While there is a pattern here (the terms are the squares of the first five counting numbers), there is neither a common difference nor a common ratio. (Verify this) This is neither an arithmetic nor a geometric sequence. ▌▌▌

Successive Differences

Some sequences may provide more difficulty in making a conjecture about the next term. Often the **method of successive differences** may be applied in such cases. Consider the sequence

$$2, 6, 22, 56, 114, \ldots .$$

Because the next term is not obvious, subtract the first term from the second term, the second from the third, the third from the fourth, and so on.

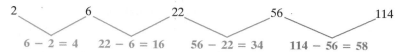

Now repeat the process with the sequence 4, 16, 34, 58 and continue repeating until the difference is a constant value, as shown in line (4).

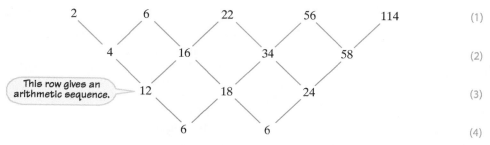

Once a line of constant values is obtained, simply work "backward" by adding until the desired term of the given sequence is obtained. Thus, for this pattern to continue, another 6 should appear in line (4), meaning that the next term in line (3) would have to be $24 + 6 = 30$. The next term in line (2) would be $58 + 30 = 88$. Finally, the next term in the given sequence would be $114 + 88 = \mathbf{202}$.

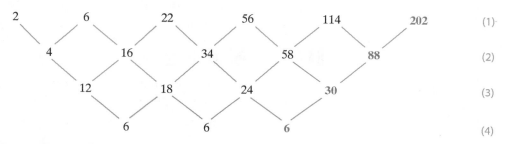

▮▮ **EXAMPLE 2** Using Successive Differences

Determine the next number in each sequence.

(a) 14, 22, 32, 44, . . .   **(b)** 5, 15, 37, 77, 141, . . .

SOLUTION

(a) Use the method of successive differences to obtain the following.

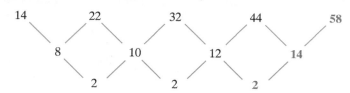

Once the row of 2s was obtained and extended, we were able to get $12 + 2 = 14$, and $44 + 14 = 58$, as shown above. The next number in the sequence is **58**.

(b) Proceeding as before, obtain the following diagram.

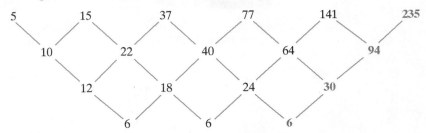

The numbers in the "diagonal" at the far right were obtained by adding: $24 + 6 = 30$, $64 + 30 = 94$, and $141 + 94 = 235$. The next number in the sequence is **235**.   ███

The method of successive differences will not always work. For example, try it on the Fibonacci sequence in **Example 2(b)** of **Section 1.1** and see what happens.

Number Patterns and Sum Formulas

Mathematics features a seemingly endless variety of number patterns. Observe the following pattern.

$$1 = 1^2$$
$$1 + 3 = 2^2$$
$$1 + 3 + 5 = 3^2$$
$$1 + 3 + 5 + 7 = 4^2$$
$$1 + 3 + 5 + 7 + 9 = 5^2$$

In each case, the left side of the equation is the indicated sum of consecutive odd counting numbers beginning with 1, and the right side is the square of the number of terms on the left side. Inductive reasoning would suggest that the next line in this pattern is as follows.

$$1 + 3 + 5 + 7 + 9 + 11 = 6^2$$

Evaluating each side shows that each side simplifies to 36.

We cannot conclude that this pattern will continue indefinitely, because observation of a finite number of examples does *not* guarantee that the pattern will continue. However, mathematicians have proved that this pattern does indeed continue indefinitely, using a method of proof called **mathematical induction.** (See any standard college algebra text.)

Any even counting number may be written in the form $2k$, where k is a counting number. It follows that the kth odd counting number is written $2k - 1$. For example, the **third** odd counting number, 5, can be written

$$2(3) - 1.$$

Using these ideas, we can write the result obtained above as follows.

Sum of the First *n* Odd Counting Numbers

If n is any counting number, then the following is true.

$$\mathbf{1 + 3 + 5 + \cdots + (2n - 1) = n^2}$$

▮▮ **EXAMPLE 3** Predicting the Next Equation in a List

In each of the following, several equations are given illustrating a suspected number pattern. Determine what the next equation would be, and verify that it is indeed a true statement.

(a)
$$1^2 = 1^3$$
$$(1 + 2)^2 = 1^3 + 2^3$$
$$(1 + 2 + 3)^2 = 1^3 + 2^3 + 3^3$$
$$(1 + 2 + 3 + 4)^2 = 1^3 + 2^3 + 3^3 + 4^3$$

(b)
$$1 = 1^3$$
$$3 + 5 = 2^3$$
$$7 + 9 + 11 = 3^3$$
$$13 + 15 + 17 + 19 = 4^3$$

(c)
$$1 = \frac{1 \cdot 2}{2}$$
$$1 + 2 = \frac{2 \cdot 3}{2}$$
$$1 + 2 + 3 = \frac{3 \cdot 4}{2}$$
$$1 + 2 + 3 + 4 = \frac{4 \cdot 5}{2}$$

(d)
$$12{,}345{,}679 \times 9 = 111{,}111{,}111$$
$$12{,}345{,}679 \times 18 = 222{,}222{,}222$$
$$12{,}345{,}679 \times 27 = 333{,}333{,}333$$
$$12{,}345{,}679 \times 36 = 444{,}444{,}444$$

SOLUTION

(a) The left side of each equation is the square of the sum of the first n counting numbers, while the right side is the sum of their cubes. The next equation in the pattern would be

$$(1 + 2 + 3 + 4 + 5)^2 = 1^3 + 2^3 + 3^3 + 4^3 + 5^3.$$

Each side simplifies to 225, so the pattern is true for this equation.

(b) The left sides of the equations contain the sum of odd counting numbers, starting with the first (1) in the first equation, the second and third (3 and 5) in the second equation, the fourth, fifth, and sixth (7, 9, and 11) in the third equation, and so on. The right side contains the cube (third power) of the number of terms on the left side in each case. Following this pattern, the next equation would be

$$21 + 23 + 25 + 27 + 29 = 5^3,$$

which can be verified by computation.

(c) The left side of each equation gives the indicated sum of the first n counting numbers, and the right side is always of the form

$$\frac{n(n + 1)}{2}.$$

For the pattern to continue, the next equation would be

$$1 + 2 + 3 + 4 + 5 = \frac{5 \cdot 6}{2}.$$

Because each side simplifies to 15, the pattern is true for this equation.

(d) In each case, the first factor on the left is 12,345,679 and the second factor is a multiple of 9 (that is, 9, 18, 27, 36). The right side consists of a nine-digit number, all digits of which are the same (that is, 1, 2, 3, 4). For the pattern to continue, the next equation would be as follows.

$$12{,}345{,}679 \times 45 = 555{,}555{,}555$$

Verify that this is a true statement.   ▮▮▮

The patterns established in **Examples 3(a) and 3(c)** can be written as follows.

Special Sum Formulas

For any counting number n, the following are true.

$$(1 + 2 + 3 + \cdots + n)^2 = 1^3 + 2^3 + 3^3 + \cdots + n^3$$

and

$$1 + 2 + 3 + \cdots + n = \frac{n(n + 1)}{2}$$

We can provide a general deductive argument showing how the second equation is obtained.

Let S represent the sum $1 + 2 + 3 + \cdots + n$. This sum can also be written as $S = n + (n - 1) + (n - 2) + \cdots + 1$. Write these two equations as follows.

$$
\begin{array}{l}
S = 1 \quad\;\; + 2 \quad\;\; + 3 \quad\;\; + \cdots + n \\
\underline{S = n \quad\;\; + (n - 1) + (n - 2) + \cdots + 1} \\
2S = (n + 1) + (n + 1) + (n + 1) + \cdots + (n + 1) \qquad \text{Add the corresponding sides.}
\end{array}
$$

$2S = n(n + 1)$ There are n terms of $n + 1$.

$S = \dfrac{n(n + 1)}{2}$ Divide both sides by 2.

Figurate Numbers

Pythagoras and his Pythagorean brotherhood studied numbers of geometric arrangements of points, such as **triangular numbers, square numbers,** and **pentagonal numbers. Figure 5** illustrates the first few of each of these types of numbers.

The **figurate numbers** possess numerous interesting patterns. Every square number greater than 1 is the sum of two consecutive triangular numbers. (For example, $9 = 3 + 6$ and $25 = 10 + 15$.)

In the 1959 Disney animation *Donald in Mathmagic Land*, Donald Duck travels back in time to meet the Greek mathematician **Pythagoras** (c. 540 B.C.), who with his fellow mathematicians formed the Pythagorean brotherhood. The brotherhood devoted its time to the study of mathematics and music.
© Disney Enterprises, Inc.

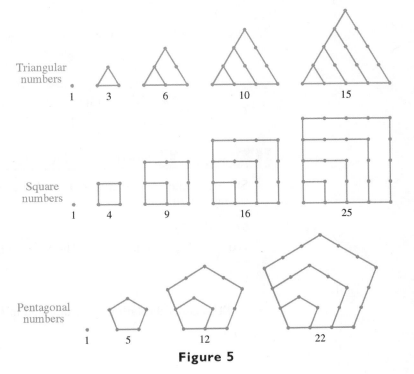

Figure 5

Every pentagonal number can be represented as the sum of a square number and a triangular number. (For example, $5 = 4 + 1$ and $12 = 9 + 3$.) Many other such relationships exist.

In the expression T_n, n is called a **subscript**. T_n is read **"T sub n,"** and it represents the triangular number in the nth position in the sequence. For example,

$$T_1 = 1, \quad T_2 = 3, \quad T_3 = 6, \quad \text{and} \quad T_4 = 10.$$

S_n and P_n represent the nth square and pentagonal numbers, respectively.

Formulas for Triangular, Square, and Pentagonal Numbers

For any natural number n, the following are true.

The nth triangular number is given by $T_n = \dfrac{n(n + 1)}{2}$.

The nth square number is given by $S_n = n^2$.

The nth pentagonal number is given by $P_n = \dfrac{n(3n - 1)}{2}$.

▮▮ **EXAMPLE 4** Using the Formulas for Figurate Numbers

Use the formulas to find each of the following.

(a) seventh triangular number

(b) twelfth square number

(c) sixth pentagonal number

SOLUTION

(a) $T_7 = \dfrac{n(n + 1)}{2} = \dfrac{7(7 + 1)}{2} = \dfrac{7(8)}{2} = \dfrac{56}{2} = 28$ Formula for a triangular number, $n = 7$

(b) $S_{12} = n^2 = 12^2 = 144$ Formula for a square number, $n = 12$

$12^2 = 12 \cdot 12$

Inside the brackets, multiply first and then subtract.

(c) $P_6 = \dfrac{n(3n - 1)}{2} = \dfrac{6[3(6) - 1]}{2} = \dfrac{6(18 - 1)}{2} = \dfrac{6(17)}{2} = 51$ ▮▮▮

▮▮ **EXAMPLE 5** Illustrating a Figurate Number Relationship

Show that the sixth pentagonal number is equal to the sum of 6 and 3 times the fifth triangular number.

SOLUTION

From **Example 4(c)**, $P_6 = 51$. The fifth triangular number is 15. Thus,

$$51 = 6 + 3(15) = 6 + 45 = 51.$$ ▮▮▮

The general relationship examined in **Example 5** can be written as follows.

$$P_n = n + 3 \cdot T_{n-1} \quad (n \geq 2)$$

▮▮ **EXAMPLE 6** Predicting the Value of a Pentagonal Number

The first five pentagonal numbers are 1, 5, 12, 22, 35. Use the method of successive differences to predict the sixth pentagonal number.

SOLUTION

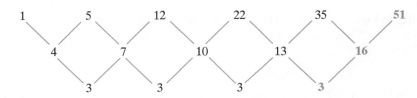

After the second line of successive differences, we work backward to find that the sixth pentagonal number is 51, which was also found in **Example 4(c).** ▮▮▮

For Further Thought

Kaprekar Constants

Take any three-digit number whose digits are not all the same. Arrange the digits in decreasing order, and then arrange them in increasing order. Now subtract. Repeat the process, using a 0 if necessary in the event that the difference consists of only two digits. For example, suppose that we choose a number whose digits are 1, 4, and 8, such as 841.

$$
\begin{array}{ccc}
841 & 963 & 954 \\
-148 & -369 & -459 \\
\hline
693 & 594 & 495
\end{array}
$$

Notice that we have obtained the number 495, and the process will lead to 495 again.

The number 495 is called a **Kaprekar constant.** The number 495 will eventually always be generated if this process is applied to such a three-digit number.

For Group or Individual Investigation

1. Apply the process of Kaprekar to a two-digit number, in which the digits are not the same. (Interpret 9 as 09 if necessary.) Compare the results. What seems to be true?

2. Repeat the process for four digits, comparing results after several steps. What conjecture can be made for this situation?

1.2 EXERCISES

For each sequence, determine if it is an arithmetic *sequence, a* geometric *sequence, or* neither. *If it is either arithmetic or geometric, give the next term in the sequence.*

1. 6, 16, 26, 36, 46, . . .

2. 8, 16, 24, 32, 40, . . .

3. 5, 15, 45, 135, 405, . . .

4. 2, 12, 72, 432, 2592, . . .

5. 1, 8, 27, 81, 243, . . .

6. 2, 8, 18, 32, 50, . . .

7. 256, 128, 64, 32, 16, . . .

8. 4096, 1024, 256, 64, 16, . . .

9. 1, 3, 4, 7, 11, . . .

10. 0, 1, 1, 2, 3, . . .

11. 12, 14, 16, 18, 20, . . .

12. 10, 50, 90, 130, 170, . . .

Use the method of successive differences to determine the next number in each sequence.

13. 1, 4, 11, 22, 37, 56, . . .

14. 3, 14, 31, 54, 83, 118, . . .

15. 6, 20, 50, 102, 182, 296, . . .

16. 1, 11, 35, 79, 149, 251, . . .

17. 0, 12, 72, 240, 600, 1260, 2352, ...

18. 2, 57, 220, 575, 1230, 2317, ...

19. 5, 34, 243, 1022, 3121, 7770, 16799, ...

20. 3, 19, 165, 771, 2503, 6483, 14409, ...

21. Refer to **Figures 2 and 3** in **Section 1.1.** The method of successive differences can be applied to the sequence of interior regions,

$$1, 2, 4, 8, 16, 31,$$

to find the number of regions determined by seven points on the circle. What is the next term in this sequence? How many regions would be determined by eight points? Verify this using the formula given at the end of that section.

22. Suppose that the expression $n^2 + 3n + 1$ determines the nth term in a sequence. That is, to find the first term, let $n = 1$. To find the second term, let $n = 2$, and so on.

(a) Find the first four terms of the sequence.

(b) Use the method of successive differences to predict the fifth term of the sequence.

(c) Find the fifth term by letting $n = 5$ in the expression $n^2 + 3n + 1$. Does your result agree with the one you found in part (b)?

In Exercises 23–32, several equations are given illustrating a suspected number pattern. Determine what the next equation would be, and verify that it is indeed a true statement.

23. $(1 \times 9) - 1 = 8$
$(21 \times 9) - 1 = 188$
$(321 \times 9) - 1 = 2888$

24. $(1 \times 8) + 1 = 9$
$(12 \times 8) + 2 = 98$
$(123 \times 8) + 3 = 987$

25. $999,999 \times 2 = 1,999,998$
$999,999 \times 3 = 2,999,997$

26. $101 \times 101 = 10,201$
$10,101 \times 10,101 = 102,030,201$

27. $3^2 - 1^2 = 2^3$
$6^2 - 3^2 = 3^3$
$10^2 - 6^2 = 4^3$
$15^2 - 10^2 = 5^3$

28. $1 = 1^2$
$1 + 2 + 1 = 2^2$
$1 + 2 + 3 + 2 + 1 = 3^2$
$1 + 2 + 3 + 4 + 3 + 2 + 1 = 4^2$

29. $2^2 - 1^2 = 2 + 1$
$3^2 - 2^2 = 3 + 2$
$4^2 - 3^2 = 4 + 3$

30. $1^2 + 1 = 2^2 - 2$
$2^2 + 2 = 3^2 - 3$
$3^2 + 3 = 4^2 - 4$

31. $1 = 1 \times 1$
$1 + 5 = 2 \times 3$
$1 + 5 + 9 = 3 \times 5$

32. $1 + 2 = 3$
$4 + 5 + 6 = 7 + 8$
$9 + 10 + 11 + 12 = 13 + 14 + 15$

Use the formula $S = \dfrac{n(n+1)}{2}$ to find each sum.

33. $1 + 2 + 3 + \cdots + 300$

34. $1 + 2 + 3 + \cdots + 500$

35. $1 + 2 + 3 + \cdots + 675$

36. $1 + 2 + 3 + \cdots + 825$

Use the formula $S = n^2$ to find each sum. (Hint: To find n, add 1 to the last term and divide by 2.)

37. $1 + 3 + 5 + \cdots + 101$

38. $1 + 3 + 5 + \cdots + 49$

39. $1 + 3 + 5 + \cdots + 999$

40. $1 + 3 + 5 + \cdots + 301$

41. Use the formula for finding the sum

$$1 + 2 + 3 + \cdots + n$$

to discover a formula for finding the sum

$$2 + 4 + 6 + \cdots + 2n.$$

42. State in your own words the following formula discussed in this section.

$$(1 + 2 + 3 + \cdots + n)^2 = 1^3 + 2^3 + 3^3 + \cdots + n^3$$

43. Explain how the following diagram geometrically illustrates the formula $1 + 3 + 5 + 7 + 9 = 5^2$.

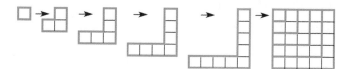

44. Explain how the following diagram geometrically illustrates the formula $1 + 2 + 3 + 4 = \dfrac{4 \times 5}{2}$.

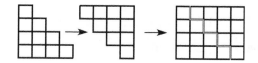

45. Use patterns to complete the table below.

Figurate Number	1st	2nd	3rd	4th	5th	6th	7th	8th
Triangular	1	3	6	10	15	21		
Square	1	4	9	16	25			
Pentagonal	1	5	12	22				
Hexagonal	1	6	15					
Heptagonal	1	7						
Octagonal	1							

46. The first five triangular, square, and pentagonal numbers may be obtained using sums of terms of sequences, as shown below.

Triangular	Square	Pentagonal
1 = 1	1 = 1	1 = 1
3 = 1 + 2	4 = 1 + 3	5 = 1 + 4
6 = 1 + 2 + 3	9 = 1 + 3 + 5	12 = 1 + 4 + 7
10 = 1 + 2 + 3 + 4	16 = 1 + 3 + 5 + 7	22 = 1 + 4 + 7 + 10
15 = 1 + 2 + 3 + 4 + 5	25 = 1 + 3 + 5 + 7 + 9	35 = 1 + 4 + 7 + 10 + 13

Notice the successive differences of the added terms on the right sides of the equations. The next type of figurate number is the **hexagonal** number. (A hexagon has six sides.) Use the patterns above to predict the first five hexagonal numbers.

47. Eight times any triangular number, plus 1, is a square number. Show that this is true for the first four triangular numbers.

48. Divide the first triangular number by 3 and record the remainder. Divide the second triangular number by 3 and record the remainder. Repeat this procedure several more times. Do you notice a pattern?

49. Repeat **Exercise 48,** but instead use square numbers and divide by 4. What pattern is determined?

50. **Exercises 48 and 49** are specific cases of the following: When the numbers in the sequence of n-agonal numbers are divided by n, the sequence of remainders obtained is a repeating sequence. Verify this for $n = 5$ and $n = 6$.

51. Every square number can be written as the sum of two triangular numbers. For example, $16 = 6 + 10$. This can be represented geometrically by dividing a square array of dots with a line as shown.

The triangular arrangement above the line represents 6, the one below the line represents 10, and the whole arrangement represents 16. Show how the square numbers 25 and 36 may likewise be geometrically represented as the sum of two triangular numbers.

52. A fraction is in **lowest terms** if the greatest common factor of its numerator and its denominator is 1. For example, $\frac{3}{8}$ is in lowest terms, but $\frac{4}{12}$ is not.

(a) For $n = 2$ to $n = 8$, form the fractions

$$\frac{n\text{th square number}}{(n + 1)\text{st square number}}.$$

(b) Repeat part (a) with triangular numbers.

(c) Use inductive reasoning to make a conjecture based on your results from parts (a) and (b), observing whether the fractions are in lowest terms.

*In addition to the formulas for T_n, S_n, and P_n, the following formulas are true for **hexagonal** numbers (H), **heptagonal** numbers (Hp), and **octagonal** numbers (O):*

$$\mathbf{H}_n = \frac{n(4n - 2)}{2}, \quad \mathbf{Hp}_n = \frac{n(5n - 3)}{2}, \quad \mathbf{O}_n = \frac{n(6n - 4)}{2}.$$

Use these formulas to find each of the following.

53. the sixteenth square number

54. the eleventh triangular number

55. the ninth pentagonal number

56. the seventh hexagonal number

57. the tenth heptagonal number

58. the twelfth octagonal number

59. Observe the formulas given for H_n, Hp_n, and O_n, and use patterns and inductive reasoning to predict the formula for N_n, the nth **nonagonal** number. (A nonagon has nine sides.) Then use the fact that the sixth nonagonal number is 111 to further confirm your conjecture.

60. Use the result of **Exercise 59** to find the tenth nonagonal number.

Use inductive reasoning to answer each question.

61. If you add two consecutive triangular numbers, what kind of figurate number do you get?

62. If you add the squares of two consecutive triangular numbers, what kind of figurate number do you get?

63. Square a triangular number. Square the next triangular number. Subtract the smaller result from the larger. What kind of number do you get?

64. Choose a value of n greater than or equal to 2. Find T_{n-1}, multiply it by 3, and add n. What kind of figurate number do you get?

In an arithmetic sequence, the nth term a_n is given by the formula

$$a_n = a_1 + (n - 1)d,$$

where a_1 is the first term and d is the common difference. Similarly, in a geometric sequence, the nth term is given by

$$a_n = a_1 \cdot r^{n-1}.$$

Here r is the common ratio. Use these formulas to determine the indicated term in the given sequence.

65. The eleventh term of 2, 6, 10, 14, . . .

66. The sixteenth term of 5, 15, 25, 35, . . .

67. The 21st term of 19, 39, 59, 79, . . .

68. The 36th term of 8, 38, 68, 98, . . .

69. The 101st term of $\frac{1}{2}$, 1, $\frac{3}{2}$, 2, . . .

70. The 151st term of 0.75, 1.50, 2.25, 3.00, . . .

71. The eleventh term of 2, 4, 8, 16, . . .

72. The ninth term of 1, 4, 16, 64, . . .

73. The 12th term of 1, $\frac{1}{2}$, $\frac{1}{4}$, $\frac{1}{8}$, . . .

74. The 10th term of 1, $\frac{1}{3}$, $\frac{1}{9}$, $\frac{1}{27}$, . . .

75. The 8th term of 40, 10, $\frac{5}{2}$, $\frac{5}{8}$, . . .

76. The 9th term of 10, 2, $\frac{2}{5}$, $\frac{2}{25}$, . . .

THE BASIC CONCEPTS OF SET THEORY

2

In the movie *I.Q.*, Meg Ryan plays Catherine Boyd, Alfred Einstein's brilliant niece, who is attracted to blue-collar worker Ed Walters (Tim Robbins). Ed pretends to be a physicist.

ED: I think your uncle wants us to dance.

CATHERINE: Oh, now, don't be irrelevant, Ed. You can't get from there to here.

ED: Why not?

CATHERINE: Now don't tell me that a famous and brilliant scientist such as yourself doesn't know about Zeno's paradox.

ED: Remind me.

CATHERINE: You can't get from there to here because you always have to cover half the remaining distance, like from me to you. I have to cover half of it. Then, see, I still have half of that remaining, so I cover half that . . . and since there are infinite halves left, I can't ever get there.

ED (taking her in his arms and starting to dance): So how did that happen?

CATHERINE: I don't know.

Prior to the twentieth century, some ideas in *set theory* were considered *paradoxes* (wrong opinions). *Zeno's paradox,* as described by Catherine and seen in **Exercises 51 and 52** of the **Extension,** has been around in several forms for thousands of years.

2.1 SYMBOLS AND TERMINOLOGY

Designating Sets • Sets of Numbers and Cardinality • Finite and Infinite Sets • Equality of Sets

Designating Sets

A **set** is a collection of objects. The objects belonging to the set are called the **elements,** or **members,** of the set. Sets are designated using the following three methods: (1) *word description,* (2) the *listing method,* and (3) *set-builder notation.*

The set of even counting numbers less than 10	Word description
$\{2, 4, 6, 8\}$	Listing method
$\{x \mid x$ is an even counting number less than 10$\}$	Set-builder notation

The set-builder notation above is read "the set of all x such that x is an even counting number less than 10." Set-builder notation uses the algebraic idea of a *variable.* (Any symbol would do, but just as in other algebraic applications, the letter x is a common choice.)

The basic ideas of set theory were developed by the German mathematician **Georg Cantor** (1845–1918) in about 1875. Cantor created a new field of theory and at the same time continued the long debate over infinity that began in ancient times. He developed counting by one-to-one correspondence to determine how many objects are contained in a set. Infinite sets differ from finite sets by not obeying the familiar law that the whole is greater than any of its parts.

Variable representing an element in general
↓
$\{x \mid x$ is an even counting number less than 10$\}$
↑
Criteria by which an element qualifies for membership in the set

Sets are commonly given names (usually capital letters), such as E for the set of all letters of the English alphabet.

$$E = \{a, b, c, d, e, f, g, h, i, j, k, l, m, n, o, p, q, r, s, t, u, v, w, x, y, z\}$$

The listing notation can often be shortened by establishing the pattern of elements included and using ellipsis points to indicate a continuation of the pattern.

$$E = \{a, b, c, d, \ldots, x, y, z\}, \quad \text{or} \quad E = \{a, b, c, d, e, \ldots, z\}.$$

The set containing no elements is called the **empty set,** or **null set.** The symbol ∅ is used to denote the empty set, so ∅ and { } have the same meaning. We do *not* denote the empty set with the symbol {∅} because this notation represents a set with one element (that element being the empty set).

▌▌ **EXAMPLE 1** Listing Elements of Sets

Give a complete listing of all the elements of each set.

(a) the set of counting numbers between six and thirteen

(b) $\{5, 6, 7, \ldots, 13\}$

(c) $\{x \mid x$ is a counting number between 6 and 7$\}$

SOLUTION

(a) This set can be denoted $\{7, 8, 9, 10, 11, 12\}$. (Notice that the word *between* excludes the endpoint values.)

(b) This set begins with the element 5, then 6, then 7, and so on, with each element obtained by adding 1 to the previous element in the list. This pattern stops at 13, so a complete listing is $\{5, 6, 7, 8, 9, 10, 11, 12, 13\}$.

(c) There are no counting numbers between 6 and 7, so this is the empty set $\{\ \}$, or $\emptyset$. ▮▮▮

For a set to be useful, it must be well defined. For example, the preceding set E of the letters of the English alphabet is well defined. Given the letter q, we know that q is an element of E. Given the Greek letter θ (theta), we know that it is not an element of set E.

However, given the set C of all good singers, and a particular singer, Raeanna, it may not be possible to say whether

Raeanna is an element of C or   Raeanna is *not* an element of C.

The problem is the word "good"; how good is good? Because we cannot necessarily decide whether a given singer belongs to set C, set C is not well defined.

The letter q is an element of set E, where E is the set of all the letters of the English alphabet. To show this, the symbol $\in$ is used.

$q \in E$ This is read "q is an element of set E."

The letter θ is not an element of E. To show this, $\in$ with a slash mark is used.

$\theta \notin E$ This is read "θ is not an element of set E."

▍▍ **EXAMPLE 2** Applying the Symbol $\in$

Decide whether each statement is *true* or *false*.

(a) $3 \in \{1, 2, 5, 9, 13\}$ **(b)** $0 \in \{0, 1, 2, 3\}$ **(c)** $\frac{1}{5} \notin \left\{\frac{1}{3}, \frac{1}{4}, \frac{1}{6}\right\}$

SOLUTION

(a) Because 3 is *not* an element of the set $\{1, 2, 5, 9, 13\}$, the statement is *false*.

(b) Because 0 is indeed an element of the set $\{0, 1, 2, 3\}$, the statement is *true*.

(c) This statement says that $\frac{1}{5}$ is not an element of the set $\left\{\frac{1}{3}, \frac{1}{4}, \frac{1}{6}\right\}$, which is *true*. ▮▮▮

Sets of Numbers and Cardinality

Important categories of numbers are summarized below.

Sets of Numbers

Natural or Counting numbers $\{1, 2, 3, 4, \dots\}$

Whole numbers $\{0, 1, 2, 3, 4, \dots\}$

Integers $\{\dots, -3, -2, -1, 0, 1, 2, 3, \dots\}$

Rational numbers $\left\{\frac{p}{q} \middle| p \text{ and } q \text{ are integers, and } q \neq 0\right\}$

(*Examples:* $\frac{3}{5}, -\frac{7}{9}, 5, 0$. Any rational number may be written as a terminating decimal number, such as 0.25, or a repeating decimal number, such as $0.666\dots$)

Real numbers $\{x \mid x \text{ is a number that can be expressed as a decimal}\}$

Irrational numbers $\{x \mid x \text{ is a real number and } x \text{ cannot be expressed as a quotient of integers}\}$

(*Examples:* $\sqrt{2}, \sqrt[3]{4}, \pi$. Decimal representations of irrational numbers are neither terminating nor repeating.)

The number of elements in a set is called the **cardinal number,** or **cardinality,** of the set. The symbol

$$n(A), \quad \text{which is read } \textbf{“n of A,”}$$

represents the cardinal number of set A. If elements are repeated in a set listing, they should not be counted more than once when determining the cardinal number of the set.

▋▋ **EXAMPLE 3** Finding Cardinal Numbers

Find the cardinal number of each set.

(a) $K = \{2, 4, 8, 16\}$ **(b)** $M = \{0\}$ **(c)** $B = \{1, 1, 2, 2, 3\}$

(d) $R = \{4, 5, \ldots, 12, 13\}$ **(e)** $\emptyset$

SOLUTION

(a) Set K contains four elements, so the cardinal number of set K is 4, and $n(K) = 4$.

(b) Set M contains only one element, 0, so $n(M) = 1$.

(c) If elements are repeated in a set listing, they should not be counted more than once when determining the cardinal number of the set. Set B has only three *distinct* elements, so $n(B) = 3$.

(d) Although only four elements are listed, the ellipsis points indicate that there are other elements in the set. Counting them all, we find that there are ten elements, so $n(R) = 10$.

(e) The empty set, $\emptyset$, contains no elements, so $n(\emptyset) = 0$.   ▋▋▋

A close-up of a camera lens shows the **infinity symbol, ∞,** defined in this case as any distance greater than 1000 times the focal length of a lens.

The sign was invented by the mathematician John Wallis in 1655. Wallis used $1/\infty$ to represent an infinitely small quantity.

Finite and Infinite Sets

If the cardinal number of a set is a particular whole number (0 or a counting number), as in all parts of **Example 3,** we call that set a **finite set.** Given enough time, we could finish counting all the elements of any finite set and arrive at its cardinal number.

Some sets, however, are so large that we could never finish the counting process. The counting numbers themselves are such a set. Whenever a set is so large that its cardinal number is not found among the whole numbers, we call that set an **infinite set.**

▋▋ **EXAMPLE 4** Designating an Infinite Set

Designate all odd counting numbers by the three common methods of set notation.

SOLUTION

The set of all odd counting numbers	Word description
$\{1, 3, 5, 7, 9, \ldots\}$	Listing method
$\{x \mid x \text{ is an odd counting number}\}$	Set-builder notation

▋▋▋

Equality of Sets

Set Equality

Set A is **equal** to set B provided the following two conditions are met:

1. Every element of A is an element of B, and
2. Every element of B is an element of A.

Two sets are equal if they contain exactly the same elements, regardless of order.

$$\{a, b, c, d\} = \{a, c, d, b\}$$ Both sets contain exactly the same elements.

Repetition of elements in a set listing does not add new elements.

$$\{1, 0, 1, 2, 3, 3\} = \{0, 1, 2, 3\}$$ Both sets contain exactly the same elements.

▮▮ **EXAMPLE 5** Determining Whether Two Sets Are Equal

Are $\{-4, 3, 2, 5\}$ and $\{-4, 0, 3, 2, 5\}$ equal sets?

SOLUTION

Every element of the first set is an element of the second. However, 0 is an element of the second and not of the first. The sets do not contain exactly the same elements, so they are not equal.

$$\{-4, 3, 2, 5\} \neq \{-4, 0, 3, 2, 5\}$$ ▮▮▮

▮▮ **EXAMPLE 6** Determining Whether Two Sets Are Equal

Decide whether each statement is *true* or *false*.

(a) $\{3\} = \{x \mid x$ is a counting number between 1 and 5$\}$

(b) $\{x \mid x$ is a negative natural number$\} = \{y \mid y$ is a number that is both rational and irrational$\}$

SOLUTION

(a) The set on the right contains *all* counting numbers between 1 and 5, namely 2, 3, and 4, while the set on the left contains *only* the number 3. Because the sets do not contain exactly the same elements, they are not equal. The statement is *false*.

(b) All natural numbers are positive, so the set on the left is $\emptyset$. By definition, if a number is rational, it cannot be irrational, so the set on the right is also $\emptyset$. Because each set is the empty set, the sets are equal. The statement is *true*.   ▮▮▮

2.1 EXERCISES

Match each set in Column I with the appropriate description in Column II.

I

1. $\{1, 3, 5, 7, 9\}$

2. $\{x \mid x$ is an even integer greater than 4 and less than 6$\}$

3. $\{\ldots, -4, -3, -2, -1\}$

4. $\{\ldots, -5, -3, -1, 1, 3, 5, \ldots\}$

5. $\{2, 4, 8, 16, 32\}$

6. $\{\ldots, -4, -2, 0, 2, 4, \ldots\}$

7. $\{2, 4, 6, 8, 10\}$

8. $\{2, 4, 6, 8\}$

II

A. the set of all even integers

B. the set of the five least positive integer powers of 2

C. the set of even positive integers less than 10

D. the set of all odd integers

E. the set of all negative integers

F. the set of odd positive integers less than 10

G. $\emptyset$

H. the set of the five least positive integer multiples of 2

List all the elements of each set. Use set notation and the listing method to describe the set.

9. the set of all counting numbers less than or equal to 6

10. the set of all whole numbers greater than 8 and less than 18

11. the set of all whole numbers not greater than 4

12. the set of all counting numbers between 4 and 14

13. $\{6, 7, 8, \ldots, 14\}$

14. $\{3, 6, 9, 12, \ldots, 30\}$

15. $\{-15, -13, -11, \ldots, -1\}$

16. $\{-4, -3, -2, \ldots, 4\}$

17. $\{2, 4, 8, \ldots, 256\}$

18. $\{90, 87, 84, \ldots, 69\}$

19. $\{x \mid x \text{ is an even whole number less than 11}\}$

20. $\{x \mid x \text{ is an odd integer between } -8 \text{ and 7}\}$

Denote each set by the listing method. There may be more than one correct answer.

21. the set of all counting numbers greater than 20

22. the set of all integers between -200 and 500

23. the set of Great Lakes

24. the set of U.S. presidents who served after Richard Nixon and before Barack Obama

25. $\{x \mid x \text{ is a positive multiple of 5}\}$

26. $\{x \mid x \text{ is a negative multiple of 6}\}$

27. $\{x \mid x \text{ is the reciprocal of a natural number}\}$

28. $\{x \mid x \text{ is a positive integer power of 4}\}$

Denote each set by set-builder notation, using x as the variable. There may be more than one correct answer.

29. the set of all rational numbers

30. the set of all even natural numbers

31. $\{1, 3, 5, \ldots, 75\}$

32. $\{35, 40, 45, \ldots, 95\}$

Give a word description for each set. There may be more than one correct answer.

33. $\{-9, -8, -7, \ldots, 7, 8, 9\}$

34. $\left\{1, \dfrac{1}{2}, \dfrac{1}{3}, \dfrac{1}{4}, \ldots\right\}$

35. $\{\text{Alabama, Alaska, Arizona}, \ldots, \text{Wisconsin, Wyoming}\}$

36. $\{\text{Alaska, California, Hawaii, Oregon, Washington}\}$

Identify each set as finite *or* infinite.

37. $\{2, 4, 6, \ldots, 932\}$ **38.** $\{6, 12, 18\}$

39. $\left\{\dfrac{1}{2}, \dfrac{2}{3}, \dfrac{3}{4}, \ldots\right\}$

40. $\{\ldots, -100, -80, -60, -40, \ldots\}$

41. $\{x \mid x \text{ is a natural number greater than 50}\}$

42. $\{x \mid x \text{ is a natural number less than 50}\}$

43. $\{x \mid x \text{ is a rational number}\}$

44. $\{x \mid x \text{ is a rational number between 0 and 1}\}$

Find $n(A)$ for each set.

45. $A = \{0, 1, 2, 3, 4, 5, 6, 7\}$

46. $A = \{-3, -1, 1, 3, 5, 7, 9\}$

47. $A = \{2, 4, 6, \ldots, 1000\}$

48. $A = \{0, 1, 2, 3, \ldots, 3000\}$

49. $A = \{a, b, c, \ldots, z\}$

50. $A = \{x \mid x \text{ is a vowel in the English alphabet}\}$

51. $A = $ the set of integers between -20 and 20

52. $A = $ the set of sanctioned U.S. senate seats

53. $A = \left\{\dfrac{1}{3}, \dfrac{2}{4}, \dfrac{3}{5}, \dfrac{4}{6}, \ldots, \dfrac{27}{29}, \dfrac{28}{30}\right\}$

54. $A = \left\{\dfrac{1}{2}, -\dfrac{1}{2}, \dfrac{1}{3}, -\dfrac{1}{3}, \ldots, \dfrac{1}{10}, -\dfrac{1}{10}\right\}$

55. Although x is a consonant, why can we write "x is a vowel in the English alphabet" in **Exercise 50?**

56. Explain how **Exercise 53** can be answered without actually listing and then counting all the elements.

Identify each set as well defined *or* not well defined.

57. $\{x \mid x \text{ is a real number}\}$

58. $\{x \mid x \text{ is a good athlete}\}$

59. $\{x \mid x \text{ is a difficult course}\}$

60. $\{x \mid x \text{ is a counting number less than 2}\}$

Fill each blank with either ∈ or ∉ to make each statement true.

61. 5 ____ {2, 4, 5, 7}   **62.** −4 ____ {4, 7, 8, 12}

63. −12 ____ {3, 8, 12, 18}   **64.** 0 ____ {−2, 0, 5, 9}

65. {3} ____ {2, 3, 4, 6}   **66.** {6} ____ {5 + 1, 6 + 1}

67. 8 ____ {11 − 2, 10 − 2, 9 − 2, 8 − 2}

68. The statement 3 ∈ {9 − 6, 8 − 6, 7 − 6} is true even though the *symbol* 3 does not appear in the set. Explain.

Write true or false for each statement.

69. 3 ∈ {2, 5, 6, 8}   **70.** 6 ∈ {−2, 5, 8, 9}

71. b ∈ {h, c, d, a, b}   **72.** m ∈ {l, m, n, o, p}

73. 9 ∉ {6, 3, 4, 8}   **74.** 2 ∉ {7, 6, 5, 4}

75. {k, c, r, a} = {k, c, a, r}

76. {e, h, a, n} = {a, h, e, n}   **77.** {5, 8, 9} = {5, 8, 9, 0}

78. {3, 7, 12, 14} = {3, 7, 12, 14, 0}

79. {4} ∈ {{3}, {4}, {5}}   **80.** 4 ∈ {{3}, {4}, {5}}

81. {x|x is a natural number less than 3} = {1, 2}

82. {x|x is a natural number greater than 10} = {11, 12, 13, . . . }

Write true or false for each statement.

Let *A* = {2, 4, 6, 8, 10, 12}, *B* = {2, 4, 8, 10}, and *C* = {4, 10, 12}.

83. 4 ∈ A   **84.** 8 ∈ B

85. 4 ∉ C   **86.** 8 ∉ B

87. Every element of *C* is also an element of *A*.

88. Every element of *C* is also an element of *B*.

89. The human mind likes to create collections. Why do you suppose this is so? In your explanation, use one or more particular "collections," mathematical or otherwise.

90. Explain the difference between a well-defined set and a not well-defined set. Give examples and use terms introduced in this section.

*Two sets are **equal** if they contain identical elements. However, two sets are **equivalent** if they contain the same number of elements (but not necessarily the same elements). For each condition, give an example or explain why it is impossible.*

91. two sets that are neither equal nor equivalent

92. two sets that are equal but not equivalent

93. two sets that are equivalent but not equal

94. two sets that are both equal and equivalent

95. **Overpaid Actors** A *Forbes* magazine survey of a recent five-year period considered 100 featured Hollywood actors. The table shows the "worst" ten actors, in terms of how much their films returned per dollar that the actor earned.

MOST OVERPAID ACTORS

Rank	Actor	Return per Dollar to Actor
1.	Will Ferrell	$3.29
2.	Ewan McGregor	$3.75
3.	Billy Bob Thornton	$4.00
4.	Eddie Murphy	$4.43
5.	Ice Cube	$4.77
6.	Tom Cruise	$7.18
7.	Drew Barrymore	$7.43
8.	Leonardo DiCaprio	$7.52
9.	Samuel L. Jackson	$8.59
10.	Jim Carrey	$8.62

Source: Forbes.com

(a) List the set of actors with a return of at least $7.40.

(b) List the set of actors with a return of at most $3.75.

96. **Burning Calories** Candice Cotton likes cotton candy, each serving of which contains 220 calories. To burn off unwanted calories, Candice participates in her favorite activities, shown below, in increments of 1 hour and never repeats a given activity on a given day.

Activity	Symbol	Calories Burned per Hour
Volleyball	*v*	160
Golf	*g*	260
Canoeing	*c*	340
Swimming	*s*	410
Running	*r*	680

(a) On Monday, Candice has time for no more than two hours of activities. List all possible sets of activities that would burn off at least the number of calories obtained from three cotton candies.

(b) Assume that Candice can afford up to three hours of time for activities on Wednesday. List all sets of activities that would burn off at least the number of calories in five cotton candies.

(c) Candice can spend up to four hours in activities on Saturday. List all sets of activities that would burn off at least the number of calories in seven cotton candies.

2.2 VENN DIAGRAMS AND SUBSETS

Venn Diagrams • Complement of a Set • Subsets of a Set • Proper Subsets
• Counting Subsets

Venn Diagrams

In the statement of a problem, there is either a stated or implied **universe of discourse.** The universe of discourse includes all things under discussion at a given time. For example, in studying reactions to a proposal that a certain campus raise the minimum age of individuals to whom beer may be sold, the universe of discourse might be all the students at the school, the nearby members of the public, the board of trustees of the school, or perhaps all these groups of people.

In set theory, the universe of discourse is called the **universal set,** typically designated by the letter **U.** The universal set might change from problem to problem.

Also in set theory, we commonly use **Venn diagrams,** developed by the logician John Venn (1834–1923). In these diagrams, the universal set is represented by a rectangle, and other sets of interest within the universal set are depicted by circular regions (sometimes ovals or other shapes). See **Figure 1.**

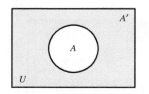

The entire region bounded by the rectangle represents the universal set *U,* while the portion bounded by the circle represents set *A.*

Figure 1

Complement of a Set

The colored region inside *U* and outside the circle in **Figure 1** is labeled *A′* (read **"A prime"**). This set, called the *complement* of *A*, contains all elements that are contained in *U* but not contained in *A*.

> **The Complement of a Set**
>
> For any set *A* within the universal set *U*, the **complement** of *A*, written *A′*, is the set of elements of *U* that are not elements of *A*. That is,
>
> $$A' = \{x \mid x \in U \text{ and } x \notin A\}.$$

▮▮ **EXAMPLE 1** Finding Complements

Find each set.

Let $U = \{a, b, c, d, e, f, g, h\}$, $M = \{a, b, e, f\}$,   and $N = \{b, d, e, g, h\}$.

(a) M' **(b)** N'

SOLUTION

(a) Set *M′* contains all the elements of set *U* that are *not* in set *M*. Because set *M* contains a, b, e, and f, these elements will be disqualified from belonging to set *M′*.

$$M' = \{c, d, g, h\}$$

(b) Set *N′* contains all the elements of *U* that are not in set *N*, so $N' = \{a, c, f\}$. ▮▮▮

Consider the complement of the universal set, **U′.** The set **U′** is found by selecting all the elements of *U* that do not belong to *U*. There are no such elements, so there can be no elements in set **U′.** This means that for any universal set *U*,

$$U' = \emptyset.$$

Now consider the complement of the empty set, $\emptyset'$. Because $\emptyset' = \{x \mid x \in U$ and $x \notin \emptyset\}$ and set $\emptyset$ contains no elements, every member of the universal set *U* satisfies this description. Therefore, for any universal set *U*,

$$\emptyset' = U.$$

Subsets of a Set

Suppose that we are given the universal set $U = \{1, 2, 3, 4, 5\}$, while $A = \{1, 2, 3\}$. Every element of set A is also an element of set U. Because of this, set A is called a *subset* of set U, written

$$A \subseteq U.$$

("A is not a subset of set U" would be written $A \nsubseteq U$.)

A Venn diagram showing that set M is a subset of set N is shown in **Figure 2**.

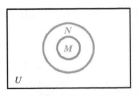

Figure 2

> **Subset of a Set**
>
> Set A is a **subset** of set B if every element of A is also an element of B. In symbols, this is written $A \subseteq B$.

‖ EXAMPLE 2 Determining Whether One Set is a Subset of Another

Write $\subseteq$ or $\nsubseteq$ in each blank to make a true statement.

(a) $\{3, 4, 5, 6\}$ _____ $\{3, 4, 5, 6, 8\}$ **(b)** $\{1, 2, 6\}$ _____ $\{2, 4, 6, 8\}$

(c) $\{5, 6, 7, 8\}$ _____ $\{5, 6, 7, 8\}$

SOLUTION

(a) Because every element of $\{3, 4, 5, 6\}$ is also an element of $\{3, 4, 5, 6, 8\}$, the first set is a subset of the second, so $\subseteq$ goes in the blank.

$$\{3, 4, 5, 6\} \subseteq \{3, 4, 5, 6, 8\}$$

(b) $\{1, 2, 6\} \nsubseteq \{2, 4, 6, 8\}$ 1 does not belong to $\{2, 4, 6, 8\}$.

(c) $\{5, 6, 7, 8\} \subseteq \{5, 6, 7, 8\}$ ■■■

As **Example 2(c)** suggests, every set is a subset of itself.

$$B \subseteq B, \quad \text{for any set } B.$$

The statement of set equality in **Section 2.1** can be formally presented.

> **Set Equality (Alternative definition)**
>
> Suppose A and B are sets. Then $A = B$ if $A \subseteq B$ and $B \subseteq A$ are both true.

Proper Subsets

Suppose that we are given the following sets.

$$B = \{5, 6, 7, 8\} \quad \text{and} \quad A = \{6, 7\}$$

A is a subset of B, but A is not all of B. There is at least one element in B that is not in A. (Actually, in this case there are two such elements, 5 and 8.) In this situation, A is called a *proper subset* of B. To indicate that A is a proper subset of B, write

$$A \subset B.$$

Notice the similarity of the subset symbols, $\subset$ and $\subseteq$, to the inequality symbols from algebra, $<$ and $\leq$.

> **Proper Subset of a Set**
>
> Set A is a **proper subset** of set B if $A \subseteq B$ and $A \neq B$. In symbols, this is written $A \subset B.$

▌▌ **EXAMPLE 3** Determining Subset and Proper Subset Relationships

Decide whether ⊂, ⊆, or both could be placed in each blank to make a true statement.

(a) $\{5, 6, 7\}$ _____ $\{5, 6, 7, 8\}$ **(b)** $\{a, b, c\}$ _____ $\{a, b, c\}$

SOLUTION

(a) Every element of $\{5, 6, 7\}$ is contained in $\{5, 6, 7, 8\}$, so ⊆ could be placed in the blank. Also, the element 8 belongs to $\{5, 6, 7, 8\}$ but not to $\{5, 6, 7\}$, making $\{5, 6, 7\}$ a proper subset of $\{5, 6, 7, 8\}$. Place ⊂ in the blank.

(b) The set $\{a, b, c\}$ is a subset of $\{a, b, c\}$. Because the two sets are equal, $\{a, b, c\}$ is not a proper subset of $\{a, b, c\}$. Only ⊆ may be placed in the blank.   ▌▌▌

Set A is a subset of set B if every element of set A is also an element of set B. This definition can be reworded by saying that set A is a subset of set B if there are no elements of A that are not also elements of B. This second form of the definition shows that the empty set is a subset of any set.

$$\emptyset \subseteq B, \quad \text{for any set } B.$$

This is true because it is not possible to find any elements of $\emptyset$ that are not also in B. (There are no elements in $\emptyset$.) The empty set $\emptyset$ is a proper subset of every set except itself.

$$\emptyset \subset B \quad \text{if } B \text{ is any set other than } \emptyset.$$

Every set (except $\emptyset$) has at least two subsets, $\emptyset$ and the set itself.

▌▌ **EXAMPLE 4** Listing All Subsets of a Set

Find all possible subsets of each set.

(a) $\{7, 8\}$ **(b)** $\{a, b, c\}$

SOLUTION

(a) By trial and error, the set $\{7, 8\}$ has four subsets: $\emptyset, \{7\}, \{8\}, \{7, 8\}$.

(b) Here, trial and error leads to eight subsets for $\{a, b, c\}$:

$$\emptyset, \{a\}, \{b\}, \{c\}, \{a, b\}, \{a, c\}, \{b, c\}, \{a, b, c\}.$$ ▌▌▌

Counting Subsets

In **Example 4,** the subsets of $\{7, 8\}$ and the subsets of $\{a, b, c\}$ were found by trial and error. An alternative method involves drawing a **tree diagram,** a systematic way of listing all the subsets of a given set. See **Figure 3.**

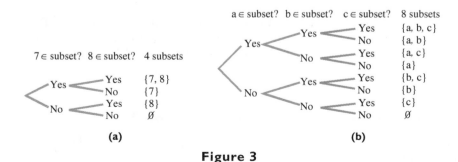

(a)   **(b)**

Figure 3

Powers of 2

$2^0 = 1$

$2^1 = 2$

$2^2 = 2 \cdot 2 = 4$

$2^3 = 2 \cdot 2 \cdot 2 = 8$

$2^4 = 2 \cdot 2 \cdot 2 \cdot 2 = 16$

$2^5 = 32$

$2^6 = 64$

$2^7 = 128$

$2^8 = 256$

$2^9 = 512$

$2^{10} = 1024$

$2^{11} = 2048$

$2^{12} = 4096$

$2^{15} = 32{,}768$

$2^{20} = 1{,}048{,}576$

$2^{25} = 33{,}554{,}432$

$2^{30} = 1{,}073{,}741{,}824$

In **Example 4,** we determined the number of subsets of a given set by making a list of all such subsets and then counting them. The tree diagram method also produced a list of all possible subsets. To obtain a formula for finding the number of subsets, we use inductive reasoning. That is, we observe particular cases to try to discover a general pattern.

Begin with the set containing the least number of elements possible—the empty set. This set, $\emptyset$, has only one subset, $\emptyset$ itself. Next, a set with one element has only two subsets, itself and $\emptyset$. These facts, together with those obtained in **Example 4** for sets with two and three elements, are summarized here.

Number of elements	0	1	2	3
Number of subsets	1	2	4	8

This chart suggests that as the number of elements of the set increases by one, the number of subsets doubles. If so, then the number of subsets in each case might be a power of 2. Since every number in the second row of the chart is indeed a power of 2, add this information to the chart.

Number of elements	0	1	2	3
Number of subsets	$1 = 2^0$	$2 = 2^1$	$4 = 2^2$	$8 = 2^3$

This chart shows that the number of elements in each case is the same as the exponent on the base 2. Inductive reasoning gives the following generalization.

Number of Subsets

The number of subsets of a set with n elements is 2^n.

Because the value 2^n includes the set itself, we must subtract 1 from this value to obtain the number of proper subsets of a set containing n elements.

Number of Proper Subsets

The number of proper subsets of a set with n elements is $2^n - 1$.

As shown in **Chapter 1,** although inductive reasoning is a good way of *discovering* principles or arriving at a *conjecture,* it does not provide a proof that the conjecture is true in general. The two formulas above are true, by observation, for $n = 0, 1, 2,$ or 3. (For a general proof, see **Exercise 69** at the end of this section.)

▌▌ **EXAMPLE 5** Finding the Numbers of Subsets and Proper Subsets

Find the number of subsets and the number of proper subsets of each set.

(a) $\{3, 4, 5, 6, 7\}$ **(b)** $\{1, 2, 3, 4, 5, 9, 12, 14\}$

SOLUTION

(a) This set has 5 elements and $2^5 = 2 \cdot 2 \cdot 2 \cdot 2 \cdot 2 = 32$ subsets. Of these, $2^5 - 1 = 32 - 1 = 31$ are proper subsets.

(b) This set has 8 elements. There are $2^8 = 256$ subsets and 255 proper subsets. ▌▌▌

2.2 EXERCISES

Match each set or sets in Column I with the appropriate description in Column II.

I	**II**
1. {p}, {q}, {p, q}, ∅	**A.** the proper subsets of {p, q}
2. {p}, {q}, ∅	**B.** the complement of {c, d}, if $U = \{a, b, c, d\}$
3. {a, b}	**C.** the complement of U
4. ∅	**D.** the subsets of {p, q}

Insert ⊆ or ⊄ in each blank so that the resulting statement is true.

5. {−2, 0, 2} _____ {−2, −1, 1, 2}

6. {M, W, F} _____ {S, M, T, W, Th}

7. {2, 5} _____ {0, 1, 5, 3, 7, 2}

8. {a, n, d} _____ {r, a, n, d, y}

9. ∅ _____ {a, b, c, d, e}

10. ∅ _____ ∅

11. {−5, 2, 9} _____ {x | x is an odd integer}

12. $\left\{1, 2, \dfrac{9}{3}\right\}$ _____ the set of rational numbers

Decide whether ⊂, ⊆, both, or neither can be placed in each blank to make the statement true.

13. {P, Q, R} _____ {P, Q, R, S}

14. {red, blue, yellow} _____ {yellow, blue, red}

15. {9, 1, 7, 3, 5} _____ {1, 3, 5, 7, 9}

16. {S, M, T, W, Th} _____ {W, E, E, K}

17. ∅ _____ {0}

18. ∅ _____ ∅

19. {0, 1, 2, 3} _____ {1, 2, 3, 4}

20. $\left\{\dfrac{5}{6}, \dfrac{9}{8}\right\}$ _____ $\left\{\dfrac{6}{5}, \dfrac{8}{9}\right\}$

For Exercises 21–40, tell whether each statement is true *or* false. *U is the universal set.*

Let $U = \{a, b, c, d, e, f, g\}$, $A = \{a, e\}$, $B = \{a, b, e, f, g\}$, $C = \{b, f, g\}$, and $D = \{d, e\}$.

21. $A \subset U$

22. $C \not\subset U$

23. $D \subseteq B$

24. $D \not\subseteq A$

25. $A \subset B$

26. $B \subseteq C$

27. $\emptyset \not\subset A$

28. $\emptyset \subseteq D$

29. $\emptyset \subseteq \emptyset$

30. $D \subset B$

31. $D \not\subseteq B$

32. $A \not\subseteq B$

33. There are exactly 6 subsets of C.

34. There are exactly 31 subsets of B.

35. There are exactly 3 proper subsets of A.

36. There are exactly 4 subsets of D.

37. There is exactly 1 subset of ∅.

38. There are exactly 128 proper subsets of U.

39. The Venn diagram below correctly represents the relationship among sets A, D, and U.

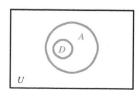

40. The Venn diagram below correctly represents the relationship among sets B, C, and U.

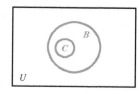

Find **(a)** *the number of subsets and* **(b)** *the number of proper subsets of each set.*

41. {a, b, c, d, e, f}

42. the set of days of the week

43. {x | x is an odd integer between −4 and 6}

44. {x | x is an odd whole number less than 4}

Let $U = \{1, 2, 3, 4, 5, 6, 7, 8, 9, 10\}$ *and find the complement of each set.*

45. {1, 2, 3, 4, 6, 8}

46. {2, 5, 9, 10}

47. {1, 3, 4, 5, 6, 7, 8, 9, 10}

48. {1, 2, 3, 4, 5, 6, 7, 8, 9}

49. U

50. ∅

Vacationing in California Terry McGinnis is planning a trip with her two sons to California. In weighing her options concerning whether to fly or drive from their home in Iowa, she has listed the following characteristics.

Fly to California	Drive to California
Higher cost	Lower cost
Educational	Educational
More time to see the sights in California	Less time to see the sights in California
Cannot visit relatives along the way	Can visit relatives along the way

Refer to these characteristics in Exercises 51–56.

51. Find the smallest universal set *U* that contains all listed characteristics of both options.

*Let F represent the set of characteristics of the flying option and let D represent the set of characteristics of the driving option. Use the universal set from **Exercise 51**.*

52. Give the set *F′*.

53. Give the set *D′*.

Find the set of elements common to both sets in Exercises 54–56.

54. *F* and *D*

55. *F′* and *D′*

56. *F* and *D′*

Meeting in a Hospitality Suite Amie Carobrese, Bruce Collin, Corey Chapman, Dwayne Coy, and Eric Cobbe plan to meet at the hospitality suite after the CEO makes his speech at the January sales meeting of their publishing company. Denoting these five people by A, B, C, D, and E, list all the possible sets of this group in which the given number of them can gather.

57. five people

58. four people

59. three people

60. two people

61. one person

62. no people

63. Find the total number of ways that members of this group can gather in the suite. (*Hint:* Find the total number of sets in your answers to **Exercises 57–62**.)

64. How does your answer in **Exercise 63** compare with the number of subsets of a set of five elements? Interpret the answer to **Exercise 63** in terms of subsets.

65. The twenty-five members of the mathematics club must send a delegation to a meeting for student groups at their school. The delegation can include as many members of the club as desired, but at least one member must attend. How many different delegations are possible? (*Mathematics Teacher* calendar problem)

66. In **Exercise 65,** suppose ten of the club members say they do not want to be part of the delegation. Now how many delegations are possible?

67. *Selecting Bills* Suppose you have the bills shown here.

(a) If you must select at least one bill, and you may select up to all of the bills, how many different sums of money could you make?

(b) In part (a), remove the condition "you must select at least one bill." How many sums are possible?

68. *Selecting Coins* The photo shows a group of obsolete U.S. coins, consisting of one each of the penny, nickel, dime, quarter, and half dollar. Repeat **Exercise 65,** replacing "bill(s)" with "coin(s)."

69. In discovering the expression (2^n) for finding the number of subsets of a set with *n* elements, we observed that for the first few values of *n*, increasing the number of elements by one doubles the number of subsets. Here, you can prove the formula in general by showing that the same is true for any value of *n*. Assume set *A* has *n* elements and *s* subsets. Now add one additional element, say *e*, to the set *A*. (We now have a new set, say *B*, with *n* + 1 elements.) Divide the subsets of *B* into those that do not contain *e* and those that do.

(a) How many subsets of *B* do not contain *e*? (*Hint:* Each of these is a subset of the original set *A*.)

(b) How many subsets of *B* do contain *e*? (*Hint:* Each of these would be a subset of the original set *A*, with the element *e* inserted.)

(c) What is the total number of subsets of *B*?

(d) What do you conclude?

70. Explain why ∅ is both a subset and an element of {∅}.

2.3 SET OPERATIONS AND CARTESIAN PRODUCTS

Intersection of Sets • Union of Sets • Difference of Sets • Ordered Pairs
• Cartesian Product of Sets • Venn Diagrams • De Morgan's Laws

Intersection of Sets

Two candidates, Aimee Berger and Darien Estes, are running for a seat on the city council. A voter deciding for whom she should vote recalled the campaign promises, each given a code letter, made by the candidates.

Honest Aimee Berger	Determined Darien Estes
Spend less money, m	Spend less money, m
Emphasize traffic law enforcement, t	Crack down on crooked politicians, p
Increase service to suburban areas, s	Increase service to the city, c

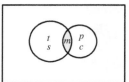

Figure 4

The only promise common to both candidates is promise m, to spend less money. Suppose we take each candidate's promises to be a set. The promises of Berger give the set $\{m, t, s\}$, while the promises of Estes give $\{m, p, c\}$. The common element m belongs to the *intersection* of the two sets, as shown in color in the Venn diagram in **Figure 4**.

$$\{m, t, s\} \cap \{m, p, c\} = \{m\} \quad \cap \text{ represents set intersection.}$$

The intersection of two sets is itself a set.

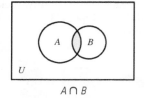

$A \cap B$

Figure 5

> **Intersection of Sets**
>
> The **intersection** of sets A and B, written $A \cap B$, is the set of elements common to both A and B.
>
> $$A \cap B = \{x \mid x \in A \text{ and } x \in B\}$$

Form the intersection of sets A and B by taking all the elements included in both sets, as shown in color in **Figure 5**.

▮▮ **EXAMPLE 1** Finding Intersections

Find each intersection.

(a) $\{3, 4, 5, 6, 7\} \cap \{4, 6, 8, 10\}$　　**(b)** $\{9, 14, 25, 30\} \cap \{10, 17, 19, 38, 52\}$

(c) $\{5, 9, 11\} \cap \emptyset$

SOLUTION

(a) The elements common to both sets are 4 and 6.

$$\{3, 4, 5, 6, 7\} \cap \{4, 6, 8, 10\} = \{4, 6\}$$

(b) These two sets have no elements in common.

$$\{9, 14, 25, 30\} \cap \{10, 17, 19, 38, 52\} = \emptyset$$

(c) There are no elements in $\emptyset$, so there can be no elements belonging to both $\{5, 9, 11\}$ and $\emptyset$.

$$\{5, 9, 11\} \cap \emptyset = \emptyset$$

▮▮▮

White light can be viewed as the intersection of the three primary colors.

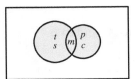

Disjoint sets

Figure 6

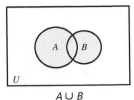

Figure 7

Examples **1(b)** and **1(c)** show two sets that have no elements in common. Sets with no elements in common are called **disjoint sets.** (See **Figure 6.**) A set of dogs and a set of cats would be disjoint sets.

$$\text{Sets } A \text{ and } B \text{ are disjoint if } A \cap B = \emptyset.$$

Union of Sets

Referring again to the lists of campaign promises, suppose a pollster wants to summarize the types of promises made by the candidates. The pollster would need to study *all* the promises made by *either* candidate, or the set $\{m, t, s, p, c\}$. This set is the *union* of the sets of promises, as shown in color in the Venn diagram in **Figure 7.**

> Be careful not to confuse this symbol with the universal set U.

$$\{m, t, s\} \cup \{m, p, c\} = \{m, t, s, p, c\} \qquad \cup \text{ denotes set union.}$$

Again, the union of two sets is a set.

Union of Sets

The **union** of sets A and B, written $A \cup B$, is the set of all elements belonging to either A or B.

$$A \cup B = \{x \mid x \in A \text{ or } x \in B\}$$

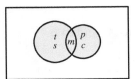

$A \cup B$

Figure 8

*Form the union of sets A and B by taking all the elements of set A and then including the elements of set B that are not already listed. See **Figure 8**.*

▌▌ **EXAMPLE 2** Finding Unions

Find each union.

(a) $\{2, 4, 6\} \cup \{4, 6, 8, 10, 12\}$

(b) $\{a, b, d, f, g, h\} \cup \{c, f, g, h, k\}$

(c) $\{3, 4, 5\} \cup \emptyset$

SOLUTION

(a) Start by listing all the elements from the first set, 2, 4, and 6. Then list all the elements from the second set that are not in the first set, 8, 10, and 12. The union is made up of *all* these elements.

$$\{2, 4, 6\} \cup \{4, 6, 8, 10, 12\} = \{2, 4, 6, 8, 10, 12\}$$

(b) $\{a, b, d, f, g, h\} \cup \{c, f, g, h, k\} = \{a, b, c, d, f, g, h, k\}$

(c) Because there are no elements in $\emptyset$, the union of $\{3, 4, 5\}$ and $\emptyset$ contains only the elements 3, 4, and 5.

$$\{3, 4, 5\} \cup \emptyset = \{3, 4, 5\} \qquad\qquad ▌▌▌$$

Recall from the previous section that A' represents the *complement* of set A. *Set A' is formed by taking all the elements of the universal set U that are not in set A.*

▐▐ **EXAMPLE 3** Finding Intersections and Unions of Complements

Find each set. Let

$$U = \{1, 2, 3, 4, 5, 6, 9\}, \quad A = \{1, 2, 3, 4\}, \quad B = \{2, 4, 6\}, \text{ and } C = \{1, 3, 6, 9\}.$$

(a) $A' \cap B$ **(b)** $B' \cup C'$ **(c)** $A \cap (B \cup C')$ **(d)** $(A' \cup C') \cap B'$

SOLUTION

(a) First identify the elements of set A', the elements of U that are not in set A.

$$A' = \{5, 6, 9\}$$

Now, find $A' \cap B$, the set of elements belonging both to A' and to B.

$$A' \cap B = \{5, 6, 9\} \cap \{2, 4, 6\} = \{6\}$$

(b) $B' \cup C' = \{1, 3, 5, 9\} \cup \{2, 4, 5\} = \{1, 2, 3, 4, 5, 9\}$

(c) First find the set inside the parentheses.

$$B \cup C' = \{2, 4, 6\} \cup \{2, 4, 5\} = \{2, 4, 5, 6\}$$

Now, find the intersection of this set with A.

$$\begin{aligned} A \cap (B \cup C') &= A \cap \{2, 4, 5, 6\} \\ &= \{1, 2, 3, 4\} \cap \{2, 4, 5, 6\} \\ &= \{2, 4\} \end{aligned}$$

(d) $A' = \{5, 6, 9\}$ and $C' = \{2, 4, 5\}$, so

$$A' \cup C' = \{5, 6, 9\} \cup \{2, 4, 5\} = \{2, 4, 5, 6, 9\}.$$

$B' = \{1, 3, 5, 9\}$, so

$$(A' \cup C') \cap B' = \{2, 4, 5, 6, 9\} \cap \{1, 3, 5, 9\} = \{5, 9\}.$$ ▐▐▐

For Further Thought

Comparing Properties

The arithmetic operations of addition and multiplication, when applied to numbers, have some familiar properties. If $a, b,$ and c are *real numbers,* then the **commutative property of addition** says that the order of the numbers being added makes no difference:

$$a + b = b + a.$$

(Is there a **commutative property of multiplication?**) The **associative property of addition** says that when three numbers are added, the grouping used makes no difference:

$$(a + b) + c = a + (b + c).$$

(Is there an **associative property of multiplication?**) The number 0 is called the **identity element for addition** since adding it to any number does not change that number:

$$a + 0 = a.$$

(What is the **identity element for multiplication?**) Finally, the **distributive property of multiplication over addition** says that

$$a(b + c) = ab + ac.$$

(Is there a distributive property of addition over multiplication?)

For Group or Individual Investigation

Now consider the operations of union and intersection, applied to sets. By recalling definitions, or by trying examples, answer the following questions.

1. Is set union commutative? Set intersection?

2. Is set union associative? Set intersection?

3. Is there an identity element for set union? If so, what is it? How about set intersection?

4. Is set intersection distributive over set union? Is set union distributive over set intersection?

▮▮ **EXAMPLE 4** Describing Sets in Words

Describe each set in words.

(a) $A \cap (B \cup C')$ **(b)** $(A' \cup C') \cap B'$

SOLUTION

(a) This set might be described as "the set of all elements that are in A, and also are in B or not in C."

(b) One possibility is "the set of all elements that are not in A or not in C, and also are not in B." ▮▮▮

Difference of Sets

Suppose that $A = \{1, 2, 3, \ldots, 10\}$ and $B = \{2, 4, 6, 8, 10\}$. If the elements of B are excluded (or taken away) from A, the set $C = \{1, 3, 5, 7, 9\}$ is obtained. C is called the *difference* of sets A and B.

> **Difference of Sets**
>
> The **difference** of sets A and B, written $A - B$, is the set of all elements belonging to set A and not to set B.
>
> $$A - B = \{x \mid x \in A \text{ and } x \notin B\}$$

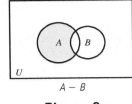

$A - B$

Figure 9

Because $x \notin B$ has the same meaning as $x \in B'$ the set difference $A - B$ can also be described as

$$\{x \mid x \in A \text{ and } x \in B'\}, \quad \text{or} \quad A \cap B'.$$

Figure 9 illustrates the idea of set difference. The region in color represents $A - B$.

▮▮ **EXAMPLE 5** Finding Set Differences

Find each set.

$$\text{Let} \quad U = \{1, 2, 3, 4, 5, 6, 7\}, \quad A = \{1, 2, 3, 4, 5, 6\},$$
$$B = \{2, 3, 6\}, \quad \text{and} \quad C = \{3, 5, 7\}.$$

(a) $A - B$ **(b)** $B - A$ **(c)** $(A - B) \cup C'$

SOLUTION

(a) Begin with set A and exclude any elements found also in set B.

$$A - B = \{1, 2, 3, 4, 5, 6\} - \{2, 3, 6\} = \{1, 4, 5\}$$

(b) To be in $B - A$, an element must be in set B and not in set A. But all elements of B are also in A. Thus, $B - A = \emptyset$.

(c) From part (a), $A - B = \{1, 4, 5\}$. Also, $C' = \{1, 2, 4, 6\}$.

$$(A - B) \cup C' = \{1, 2, 4, 5, 6\}$$ ▮▮▮

The results in **Examples 5(a) and 5(b)** illustrate that, in general,

$$A - B \neq B - A.$$

Ordered Pairs

When writing a set that contains several elements, the order in which the elements appear is not relevant. For example,

$$\{1, 5\} = \{5, 1\}.$$

However, there are many instances in mathematics where, when two objects are paired, the order in which the objects are written is important. This leads to the idea of the *ordered pair.* When writing ordered pairs, use parentheses rather than braces, which are reserved for writing sets.

Ordered Pairs

In the **ordered pair** (a, b), a is called the **first component** and b is called the **second component.** In general, $(a, b) \neq (b, a)$.

Two ordered pairs (a, b) and (c, d) are **equal** provided that their first components are equal and their second components are equal.

$$(a, b) = (c, d) \quad \textit{if and only if} \quad a = c \textit{ and } b = d.$$

◼◼ **EXAMPLE 6**   Determining Equality of Sets and of Ordered Pairs

Decide whether each statement is *true* or *false.*

(a) $(3, 4) = (5 - 2, 1 + 3)$ **(b)** $\{3, 4\} \neq \{4, 3\}$ **(c)** $(7, 4) = (4, 7)$

SOLUTION

(a) Because $3 = 5 - 2$ and $4 = 1 + 3$, the first components are equal and the second components are equal. The statement is *true.*

(b) Because these are sets and not ordered pairs, the order in which the elements are listed is not important. Because these sets are equal, the statement is *false.*

(c) The ordered pairs $(7, 4)$ and $(4, 7)$ are not equal because they do not satisfy the requirements for equality of ordered pairs. The statement is *false.*   ◼◼◼

Cartesian Product of Sets

A set may contain ordered pairs as elements. If A and B are sets, then each element of A can be paired with each element of B, and the results can be written as ordered pairs. The set of all such ordered pairs is called the *Cartesian product* of A and B, written $A \times B$ and read **"A cross B."** The name comes from that of the French mathematician René Descartes.

Cartesian Product of Sets

The **Cartesian product** of sets A and B is defined as follows.

$$A \times B = \{(a, b) \mid a \in A \text{ and } b \in B\}$$

◼◼ **EXAMPLE 7**   Finding Cartesian Products

Let $A = \{1, 5, 9\}$ and $B = \{6, 7\}$. Find each set.

(a) $A \times B$ **(b)** $B \times A$

SOLUTION

(a) Pair each element of A with each element of B. Write the results as ordered pairs, with the element of A written first and the element of B written second. Write as a set.

$$A \times B = \{(1, 6), (1, 7), (5, 6), (5, 7), (9, 6), (9, 7)\}$$

(b) Because B is listed first, this set will consist of ordered pairs that have their components interchanged when compared to those in part (a).

$$B \times A = \{(6, 1), (7, 1), (6, 5), (7, 5), (6, 9), (7, 9)\}$$ ▮▮▮

The order in which the ordered pairs themselves are listed is not important.
For example, another way to write $B \times A$ in **Example 7(b)** would be

$$\{(6, 1), (6, 5), (6, 9), (7, 1), (7, 5), (7, 9)\}.$$

▮▮ **EXAMPLE 8** Finding the Cartesian Product of a Set with Itself

Let $A = \{1, 2, 3, 4, 5, 6\}$. Find $A \times A$.

SOLUTION
Pair 1 with each element in the set, 2 with each element, and so on.

$$\begin{aligned} A \times A = \{ &(1, 1), (1, 2), (1, 3), (1, 4), (1, 5), (1, 6), \\ &(2, 1), (2, 2), (2, 3), (2, 4), (2, 5), (2, 6), \\ &(3, 1), (3, 2), (3, 3), (3, 4), (3, 5), (3, 6), \\ &(4, 1), (4, 2), (4, 3), (4, 4), (4, 5), (4, 6), \\ &(5, 1), (5, 2), (5, 3), (5, 4), (5, 5), (5, 6), \\ &(6, 1), (6, 2), (6, 3), (6, 4), (6, 5), (6, 6)\} \end{aligned}$$ ▮▮▮

The **Cartesian product** in **Example 8** represents all possible results that are obtained when two distinguishable dice are rolled. This Cartesian product is important when studying certain problems in counting techniques and probability.

From **Example 7** it can be seen that, in general,

$$A \times B \neq B \times A,$$

because they do not contain exactly the same ordered pairs. However, each set contains the same number of elements, six. Furthermore, $n(A) = 3$, $n(B) = 2$, and $n(A \times B) = n(B \times A) = 6$. Because $3 \cdot 2 = 6$, one might conclude that the cardinal number of the Cartesian product of two sets is equal to the product of the cardinal numbers of the sets. In general, this conclusion is correct.

Cardinal Number of a Cartesian Product

If $n(A) = a$ and $n(B) = b$, then the following is true.

$$n(A \times B) = n(B \times A) = n(A) \cdot n(B) = n(B) \cdot n(A) = ab = ba$$

▮▮ **EXAMPLE 9** Finding Cardinal Numbers of Cartesian Products

Find $n(A \times B)$ and $n(B \times A)$ from the given information.

(a) $A = \{a, b, c, d, e, f, g\}$ and $B = \{2, 4, 6\}$ **(b)** $n(A) = 24$ and $n(B) = 5$

SOLUTION

(a) Because $n(A) = 7$ and $n(B) = 3$, $n(A \times B)$ and $n(B \times A)$ both equal $7 \cdot 3$, or 21.

(b) $n(A \times B) = n(B \times A) = 24 \cdot 5 = 5 \cdot 24 = 120$ ▮▮▮

An **operation** is a rule or procedure by which one or more objects are used to obtain another object. The most common operations on sets are summarized in the box on the next page.

Set Operations

Let A and B be any sets, with U the universal set.

The **complement** of A, written A', is

$$A' = \{x \mid x \in U \text{ and } x \notin A\}.$$

The **intersection** of A and B is

$$A \cap B = \{x \mid x \in A \text{ and } x \in B\}.$$

The **union** of A and B is

$$A \cup B = \{x \mid x \in A \text{ or } x \in B\}.$$

The **difference** of A and B is

$$A - B = \{x \mid x \in A \text{ and } x \notin B\}.$$

The **Cartesian product** of A and B is

$$A \times B = \{(x, y) \mid x \in A \text{ and } y \in B\}.$$

Venn Diagrams

With a single set, we can use a Venn diagram as in **Figure 10**. The universal set U is divided into two regions, one representing set A and the other representing set A'.

Two sets A and B within the universal set suggest a Venn diagram as in **Figure 11**. Region 1 includes those elements outside of both set A and set B. Region 2 includes the elements belonging to A but not to B. Region 3 includes those elements belonging to both A and B. How would you describe the elements of region 4?

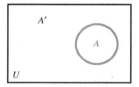

Figure 10

▍▊ **EXAMPLE 10** Shading Venn Diagrams to Represent Sets

Draw a Venn diagram similar to **Figure 11** and shade the region or regions representing each set.

(a) $A' \cap B$ **(b)** $A' \cup B'$

SOLUTION

(a) Refer to **Figure 11**. Set A' contains all the elements outside of set A—in other words, the elements in regions 1 and 4. Set B is made up of the elements in regions 3 and 4. The intersection of sets A' and B is made up of the elements in the region common to (1 and 4) and (3 and 4), which is region 4. Thus, $A' \cap B$ is represented by region 4, shown in color in **Figure 12**. This region can also be described as $B - A$.

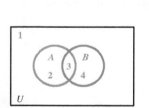

Numbering is arbitrary. The numbers indicate four regions, not cardinal numbers or elements.

Figure 11

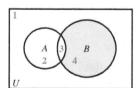   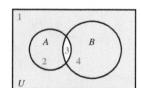

Figure 12   **Figure 13**

(b) Again, set A' is represented by regions 1 and 4, while B' is made up of regions 1 and 2. The union of A' and B', the set $A' \cup B'$, is made up of the elements belonging to the union of regions 1, 2, and 4, which are in color in **Figure 13**.   ▍▊▋

▮▮ **EXAMPLE 11** Locating Elements in a Venn Diagram

Place the elements of the sets in their proper locations in a Venn diagram.

Let $U = \{q, r, s, t, u, v, w, x, y, z\}$, $A = \{r, s, t, u, v\}$, and $B = \{t, v, x\}$.

SOLUTION

Because $A \cap B = \{t, v\}$, elements t and v are placed in region 3 in **Figure 14**. The remaining elements of A, that is r, s, and u, go in region 2. The figure shows the proper placement of all other elements.

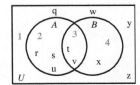

Figure 14 ▮▮▮

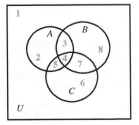

Numbering is arbitrary. The numbers indicate regions, not cardinal numbers or elements.

Figure 15

To include three sets A, B, and C within a universal set, draw a Venn diagram as in **Figure 15**, where again an arbitrary numbering of the regions is shown.

▮▮ **EXAMPLE 12** Shading a Set in a Venn Diagram

Shade the set $(A' \cap B') \cap C$ in a Venn diagram similar to the one in **Figure 15**.

SOLUTION

Work first inside the parentheses. As shown in **Figure 16**, set A' is made up of the regions outside set A, or regions 1, 6, 7, and 8. Set B' is made up of regions 1, 2, 5, and 6. The intersection of these sets is given by the overlap of regions 1, 6, 7, 8 and 1, 2, 5, 6, or regions 1 and 6.

For the final Venn diagram, find the intersection of regions 1 and 6 with set C. As seen in **Figure 16**, set C is made up of regions 4, 5, 6, and 7. The overlap of regions 1, 6 and 4, 5, 6, 7 is region 6, the region in color in **Figure 16**. ▮▮▮

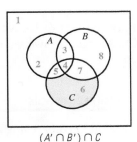

$(A' \cap B') \cap C$

Figure 16

▮▮ **EXAMPLE 13** Verifying a Statement Using a Venn Diagram

Is the statement $(A \cap B)' = A' \cup B'$ true for every choice of sets A and B?

SOLUTION

To help decide, use the regions labeled in **Figure 11**. Set $A \cap B$ is made up of region 3, so that $(A \cap B)'$ is made up of regions 1, 2, and 4. These regions are in color in **Figure 17(a)**.

To find a Venn diagram for set $A' \cup B'$, first check that A' is made up of regions 1 and 4, while set B' includes regions 1 and 2. Finally, $A' \cup B'$ is made up of regions 1 and 4, or 1 and 2, that is, regions 1, 2, and 4. These regions are in color in **Figure 17(b)**.

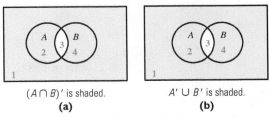

$(A \cap B)'$ is shaded. $A' \cup B'$ is shaded.
(a)   **(b)**

Figure 17

The fact that the same regions are in color in both Venn diagrams suggests that

$$(A \cap B)' = A' \cup B'.$$

▮▮▮

De Morgan's Laws

The result of **Example 13** can be stated in words.

> *The complement of the intersection of two sets is equal to the union of the complements of the two sets.*

As a result, it is natural to ask ourselves whether it is also true that the complement of the *union* of two sets is equal to the *intersection* of the complements of the two sets (where the words "intersection" and "union" are substituted for each other). This was investigated by the British logician Augustus De Morgan (1806–1871) and was found to be true. (See the margin note on **page 21.**) DeMorgan's two laws for sets follow.

De Morgan's Laws for Sets

For any sets A and B,

$$(A \cap B)' = A' \cup B' \quad \text{and} \quad (A \cup B)' = A' \cap B'.$$

The Venn diagrams in **Figure 17** strongly suggest the truth of the first of De Morgan's laws. They provide a *conjecture*. Actual proofs of De Morgan's laws would require methods used in more advanced courses on set theory.

▮▮ **EXAMPLE 14** Describing Regions in Venn Diagrams Using Symbols

For the Venn diagrams, write a symbolic description of the region in color, using A, B, C, $\cap$, $\cup$, $-$, and $'$ as necessary.

(a)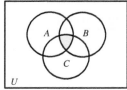

(b)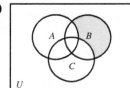

(c) Refer to the figure in part (b) and give two additional ways of describing the region in color.

SOLUTION

(a) The region in color belongs to all three sets, A and B and C. Therefore, the region corresponds to

$$A \cap B \cap C.$$

(b) The region in color is in set B and is not in A and is not in C. Because it is not in A, it is in A', and similarly it is in C'. The region is, therefore, in B and in A' and in C', and corresponds to

$$B \cap A' \cap C'.$$

(c) The region in color includes all of B, except for the regions belonging to either A or C. This suggests the idea of set difference. The region may be described as

$$B - (A \cup C), \quad \text{or equivalently,} \quad B \cap (A \cup C)'. \quad ▮▮▮$$

2.3 EXERCISES

Match each term in Group I with the appropriate description A–F in Group II. Assume that A and B are sets.

I

1. the intersection of A and B

2. the union of A and B

3. the difference of A and B

4. the complement of A

5. the Cartesian product of A and B

6. the difference of B and A

II

A. the set of elements in A that are not in B

B. the set of elements common to both A and B

C. the set of elements in the universal set that are not in A

D. the set of elements in B that are not in A

E. the set of ordered pairs such that each first element is from A and each second element is from B, with every element of A paired with every element of B

F. the set of elements that are in A or in B or in both A and B

Perform the indicated operations, and designate each answer using the listing method.

$$Let \quad U = \{a, b, c, d, e, f, g\}, \quad X = \{a, c, e, g\},$$
$$Y = \{a, b, c\}, \quad and \quad Z = \{b, c, d, e, f\}.$$

7. $X \cap Y$ **8.** $X \cup Y$ **9.** $Y \cup Z$

10. $Y \cap Z$ **11.** $X \cup U$ **12.** $Y \cap U$

13. X' **14.** Y'

15. $X' \cap Y'$ **16.** $X' \cap Z$

17. $X \cup (Y \cap Z)$ **18.** $Y \cap (X \cup Z)$

19. $(Y \cap Z') \cup X$ **20.** $(X' \cup Y') \cup Z$

21. $(Z \cup X')' \cap Y$ **22.** $(Y \cap X')' \cup Z'$

23. $X - Y$ **24.** $Y - X$

25. $X \cap (X - Y)$ **26.** $Y \cup (Y - X)$

27. $X' - Y$ **28.** $Y' - X$

29. $(X \cap Y') \cup (Y \cap X')$ **30.** $(X \cap Y') \cap (Y \cap X')$

Describe each set in words.

31. $A \cup (B' \cap C')$ **32.** $(A \cap B') \cup (B \cap A')$

33. $(C - B) \cup A$ **34.** $B \cap (A' - C)$

35. $(A - C) \cup (B - C)$ **36.** $(A' \cap B') \cup C'$

Adverse Effects of Alcohol and Tobacco *The table lists some common adverse effects of prolonged tobacco and alcohol use.*

Tobacco	Alcohol
Emphysema, e	Liver damage, l
Heart damage, h	Brain damage, b
Cancer, c	Heart damage, h

Let T be the set of listed effects of tobacco and A be the set of listed effects of alcohol. Find each set.

37. the smallest possible universal set U that includes all the effects listed

38. A' **39.** T' **40.** $T \cap A$

41. $T \cup A$ **42.** $T \cap A'$

Describe in words each set in Exercises 43–48.

Let U = the set of all tax returns,
    A = the set of all tax returns with itemized deductions,
    B = the set of all tax returns showing business income,
    C = the set of all tax returns filed in 2009,
    D = the set of all tax returns selected for audit.

43. $B \cup C$ **44.** $A \cap D$ **45.** $C - A$

46. $D \cup A'$ **47.** $(A \cup B) - D$ **48.** $(C \cap A) \cap B'$

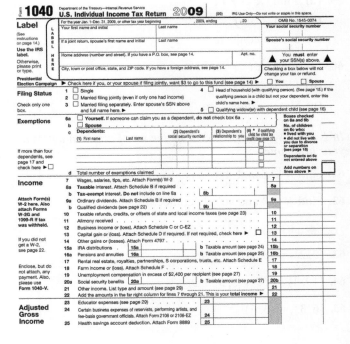

Assuming that A and B represent any two sets, identify each statement as either always true *or* not always true.

49. $A \subseteq (A \cup B)$

50. $A \subseteq (A \cap B)$

51. $(A \cap B) \subseteq A$

52. $(A \cup B) \subseteq A$

53. $n(A \cup B) = n(A) + n(B)$

54. $n(A \cup B) = n(A) + n(B) - n(A \cap B)$

For Exercises 55–60, use your results in parts (a) and (b) to answer part (c).

Let $U = \{1, 2, 3, 4, 5\}$, $X = \{1, 3, 5\}$, $Y = \{1, 2, 3\}$, and $Z = \{3, 4, 5\}$.

55. (a) Find $X \cup Y$.
  (b) Find $Y \cup X$.
  (c) State a conjecture.

56. (a) Find $X \cap Y$.
  (b) Find $Y \cap X$.
  (c) State a conjecture.

57. (a) Find $X \cup (Y \cup Z)$.
  (b) Find $(X \cup Y) \cup Z$.
  (c) State a conjecture.

58. (a) Find $X \cap (Y \cap Z)$.
  (b) Find $(X \cap Y) \cap Z$.
  (c) State a conjecture.

59. (a) Find $(X \cup Y)'$.
  (b) Find $X' \cap Y'$.
  (c) State a conjecture.

60. (a) Find $(X \cap Y)'$.
  (b) Find $X' \cup Y'$.
  (c) State a conjecture.

In Exercises 61 and 62, let X be the set of different letters in your last name.

61. Find $X \cup \emptyset$ and state a conjecture.

62. Find $X \cap \emptyset$ and state a conjecture.

Decide whether each statement is true or false.

63. $(3, 2) = (5 - 2, 1 + 1)$

64. $(10, 4) = (7 + 3, 5 - 1)$

65. $(6, 3) = (3, 6)$

66. $(2, 13) = (13, 2)$

67. $\{6, 3\} = \{3, 6\}$

68. $\{2, 13\} = \{13, 2\}$

69. $\{(1, 2), (3, 4)\} = \{(3, 4), (1, 2)\}$

70. $\{(5, 9), (4, 8), (4, 2)\} = \{(4, 8), (5, 9), (4, 2)\}$

Find $A \times B$ and $B \times A$, for A and B defined as follows.

71. $A = \{2, 8, 12\}$, $B = \{4, 9\}$

72. $A = \{3, 6, 9, 12\}$, $B = \{6, 8\}$

73. $A = \{d, o, g\}$, $B = \{p, i, g\}$

74. $A = \{b, l, u, e\}$, $B = \{r, e, d\}$

For the sets specified in Exercises 75–78, use the given information to find $n(A \times B)$ and $n(B \times A)$.

75. the sets in **Exercise 71**

76. the sets in **Exercise 73**

77. $n(A) = 35$ and $n(B) = 6$

78. $n(A) = 13$ and $n(B) = 5$

Find the cardinal number specified.

79. If $n(A \times B) = 72$ and $n(A) = 12$, find $n(B)$.

80. If $n(A \times B) = 300$ and $n(B) = 30$, find $n(A)$.

Place the elements of these sets in the proper locations in the given Venn diagram.

81. Let $U = \{a, b, c, d, e, f, g\}$,
  $A = \{b, d, f, g\}$,
  $B = \{a, b, d, e, g\}$.

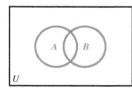

82. Let $U = \{5, 6, 7, 8, 9, 10, 11, 12, 13\}$,
  $M = \{5, 8, 10, 11\}$,
  $N = \{5, 6, 7, 9, 10\}$.

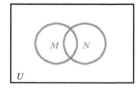

Use a Venn diagram similar to the one shown below to shade each set.

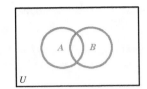

83. $B \cap A'$

84. $A \cup B$

85. $A' \cup B$

86. $A' \cap B'$

87. $B' \cup A$

88. $A' \cup A$

89. $B' \cap B$

90. $A \cap B'$

91. $B' \cup (A' \cap B')$

92. $(A \cap B) \cup B$

93. U'

94. $\emptyset'$

In Exercises 95 and 96, place the elements of the sets in the proper location in a Venn diagram similar to the one shown below.

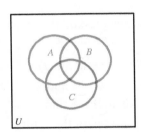

95. Let $U = \{m, n, o, p, q, r, s, t, u, v, w\}$,
$A = \{m, n, p, q, r, t\}$,
$B = \{m, o, p, q, s, u\}$,
$C = \{m, o, p, r, s, t, u, v\}$.

96. Let $U = \{1, 2, 3, 4, 5, 6, 7, 8, 9\}$,
$A = \{1, 3, 5, 7\}$,
$B = \{1, 3, 4, 6, 8\}$,
$C = \{1, 4, 5, 6, 7, 9\}$.

Use a Venn diagram to shade each set.

97. $(A \cap B) \cap C$

98. $(A \cap C') \cup B$

99. $(A \cap B) \cup C'$

100. $(A' \cap B) \cap C$

101. $(A' \cap B') \cap C$

102. $(A \cup B) \cup C$

103. $(A \cap B') \cup C$

104. $(A \cap C') \cap B$

105. $(A \cap B') \cap C'$

106. $(A' \cap B') \cup C$

107. $(A' \cap B') \cup C'$

108. $(A \cap B)' \cup C$

Write a symbolic description of each shaded area. Use the symbols A, B, C, $\cap$, $\cup$, $-$, and ' as necessary. More than one answer may be possible.

109.

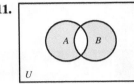

110.

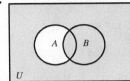

111.

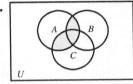

112.

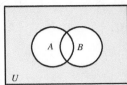

113.

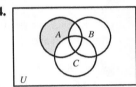

114.

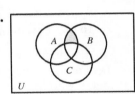

115.

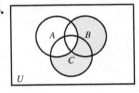

116.

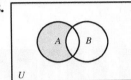

Suppose A and B are sets. Describe the conditions under which each statement would be true.

117. $A = A - B$

118. $A = B - A$

119. $A = A - \emptyset$

120. $A = \emptyset - A$

121. $A \cup \emptyset = \emptyset$

122. $A \cap \emptyset = \emptyset$

123. $A \cap \emptyset = A$

124. $A \cup \emptyset = A$

125. $A \cup A = \emptyset$

126. $A \cap A = \emptyset$

127. $A \cup B = A$

128. $A \cap B = B$

For Exercises 129–135, draw two appropriate Venn diagrams to decide whether the given statement is always true *or* not always true.

129. $A \cap A' = \emptyset$

130. $A \cup A' = U$

131. $(A \cap B) \subseteq A$

132. $(A \cup B) \subseteq A$

133. If $A \subseteq B$, then $A \cup B = A$.

134. If $A \subseteq B$, then $A \cap B = B$.

135. $(A \cup B)' = A' \cap B'$
(De Morgan's second law)

136. If A and B are sets, is it necessarily true that $n(A - B) = n(A) - n(B)$?

137. If $Q = \{x | x$ is a rational number$\}$ and $H = \{x | x$ is an irrational number$\}$, describe each set.

(a) $Q \cup H$

(b) $Q \cap H$

▍▍▍▍▍▍▍ 2.4 SURVEYS AND CARDINAL NUMBERS

Surveys • Cardinal Number Formula • Tables

Surveys

Problems involving sets of people (or objects) sometimes require analyzing known information about certain subsets to obtain cardinal numbers of other subsets. In this section, we apply three problem-solving techniques to such problems: Venn diagrams, cardinal number formulas, and tables. The "known information" is quite often (although not always) obtained by conducting a survey.

Suppose a group of students on a college campus is asked to compare some animated feature films, and the following information is produced.

34 like *Up*	12 like *Up* and *Mr. Fox*
29 like *The Princess and the Frog*	10 like *Princess* and *Mr. Fox*
26 like *Fantastic Mr. Fox*	4 like all three films
16 like *Up* and *Princess*	5 like none of these films.

To determine the total number of students surveyed, we cannot just add the eight numbers above because there is some overlap. For example, in **Figure 18**, the 34 students who like *Up* should not be positioned in region *b* but should be distributed among regions *b*, *c*, *d*, and *e*, in a way that is consistent with all of the given data. (Region *b* actually contains those students who like *Up* but do not like *The Princess and the Frog* and do not like *Fantastic Mr. Fox*.)

Because, at the start, we do not know how to distribute the 34 who like *Up*, we look first for some more manageable data. The smallest total listed, the 4 students who like all three films, can be placed in region *d* (the intersection of the three sets). The 5 who like none of the three must go into region *a*. Then, the 16 who like *Up* and *Princess* must go into regions *d* and *e*. Because region *d* already contains 4 students, we must place

$$16 - 4 = 12 \quad \text{in region } e.$$

Because 12 like *Up* and *Mr. Fox* (regions *c* and *d*), we place

$$12 - 4 = 8 \quad \text{in region } c.$$

Now that regions *c*, *d*, and *e* contain 8, 4, and 12 students, respectively, we must place

$$34 - 8 - 4 - 12 = 10 \quad \text{in region } b.$$

By similar reasoning, all regions are assigned their correct numbers. See **Figure 19** on the next page.

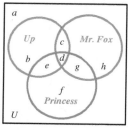

Figure 18

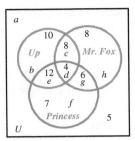

Figure 19

▋▋ **EXAMPLE 1** Analyzing a Survey

Using the survey data on student preferences for animated feature films, as summarized in **Figure 19**, answer each question.

(a) How many students like *Fantastic Mr. Fox* only?

(b) How many students like exactly two films?

(c) How many students were surveyed?

SOLUTION

(a) A student who likes *Mr. Fox* only does not like *Up* and does not like *Princess*. These students are inside the regions for *Mr. Fox* and outside the regions for *Up* and *Princess*. Region h is the appropriate region in **Figure 19**, and we see that eight students like *Fantastic Mr. Fox* only.

(b) The students in regions c, e, and g like exactly two films. The total number of such students is

$$8 + 12 + 6 = 26.$$

(c) Each student surveyed has been placed in exactly one region of **Figure 19**, so the total number surveyed is the sum of the numbers in all eight regions:

$$5 + 10 + 8 + 4 + 12 + 7 + 6 + 8 = 60. \quad ■■■$$

Cardinal Number Formula

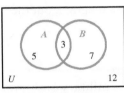

Figure 20

If the numbers shown in **Figure 20** are the cardinal numbers of the individual regions, then

$$n(A) = 5 + 3 = 8, \quad n(B) = 3 + 7 = 10, \quad n(A \cap B) = 3,$$

and

$$n(A \cup B) = 5 + 3 + 7 = 15.$$

Notice that $n(A \cup B) = n(A) + n(B) - n(A \cap B)$ because $15 = 8 + 10 - 3$. This relationship is true for any two sets A and B.

Cardinal Number Formula

For any two sets A and B, the following is true.

$$n(A \cup B) = n(A) + n(B) - n(A \cap B)$$

This formula can be rearranged to find any one of its four terms when the others are known.

▋▋ **EXAMPLE 2** Applying the Cardinal Number Formula

Find $n(A)$ if $n(A \cup B) = 22, n(A \cap B) = 8$, and $n(B) = 12$.

SOLUTION

We solve the cardinal number formula for $n(A)$.

$$n(A) = n(A \cup B) - n(B) + n(A \cap B)$$
$$= 22 - 12 + 8$$
$$= 18 \quad ■■■$$

Sometimes, even when information is presented as in **Example 2**, it is more convenient to fit that information into a Venn diagram as in **Example 1.**

▌▌ **EXAMPLE 3** Analyzing Data in a Report

Scott Heeren, who leads a group of software engineers who investigate illegal activities on social networking sites, reported the following information.

T = the set of group members following patterns on Twitter

F = the set of group members following patterns on Facebook

L = the set of group members following patterns on LinkedIn

$n(T) = 13$	$n(T \cap F) = 9$	$n(T \cap F \cap L) = 5$
$n(F) = 16$	$n(F \cap L) = 10$	$n(T' \cap F' \cap L') = 3$
$n(L) = 13$	$n(T \cap L) = 6$	

How many engineers are in Scott's group?

SOLUTION

The data supplied by Scott are reflected in **Figure 21**. The sum of the numbers in the diagram gives the total number of engineers in the group.

$$3 + 3 + 1 + 2 + 5 + 5 + 4 + 2 = 25$$ ▌▌▌

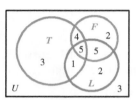

Figure 21

Tables

Sometimes information appears in a table rather than a Venn diagram, but the basic ideas of union and intersection still apply.

▌▌ **EXAMPLE 4** Analyzing Data in a Table

Melanie Cutler, the officer in charge of the cafeteria on a military base, wanted to know if the beverage that enlisted men and women preferred with lunch depended on their ages. On a given day, Melanie categorized her lunch patrons according to age and preferred beverage, recording the results in a table.

		Beverage			
		Cola (*C*)	Iced Tea (*I*)	Sweet Tea (*S*)	**Totals**
	18–25 (*Y*)	45	10	35	90
Age	**26–33 (*M*)**	20	25	30	75
	Over 33 (*O*)	5	30	20	55
	Totals	70	65	85	220

Using the letters in the table, find the number of people in each set.

(a) $Y \cap C$ **(b)** $O' \cup I$

SOLUTION

(a) The set Y includes all personnel represented across the top row of the table (90 in all), while C includes the 70 down the left column. The intersection of these two sets is just the upper left entry, 45 people.

(b) The set O' excludes the bottom row, so it includes the first and second rows. The set I includes the middle column only. The union of the two sets represents

$$45 + 10 + 35 + 20 + 25 + 30 + 30 = 195 \text{ people.}$$ ▌▌▌

2.4 EXERCISES

Use the numerals representing cardinalities in the Venn diagrams to give the cardinality of each set specified.

1.
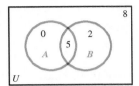

(a) $A \cap B$ (b) $A \cup B$
(c) $A \cap B'$ (d) $A' \cap B$
(e) $A' \cap B'$

2.
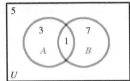

(a) $A \cap B$ (b) $A \cup B$
(c) $A \cap B'$ (d) $A' \cap B$
(e) $A' \cap B'$

3.
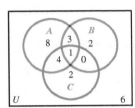

(a) $A \cap B \cap C$ (b) $A \cap B \cap C'$
(c) $A \cap B' \cap C$ (d) $A' \cap B \cap C$
(e) $A' \cap B' \cap C$ (f) $A \cap B' \cap C'$
(g) $A' \cap B \cap C'$ (h) $A' \cap B' \cap C'$

4.
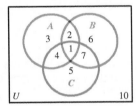

(a) $A \cap B \cap C$ (b) $A \cap B \cap C'$
(c) $A \cap B' \cap C$ (d) $A' \cap B \cap C$
(e) $A' \cap B' \cap C$ (f) $A \cap B' \cap C'$
(g) $A' \cap B \cap C'$ (h) $A' \cap B' \cap C'$

In Exercises 5–10, make use of an appropriate formula.

5. Find the value of $n(A \cup B)$ if $n(A) = 12, n(B) = 14$, and $n(A \cap B) = 5$.

6. Find the value of $n(A \cup B)$ if $n(A) = 16, n(B) = 28$, and $n(A \cap B) = 5$.

7. Find the value of $n(A \cap B)$ if $n(A) = 20, n(B) = 12$, and $n(A \cup B) = 25$.

8. Find the value of $n(A \cap B)$ if $n(A) = 20, n(B) = 24$, and $n(A \cup B) = 30$.

9. Find the value of $n(A)$ if $n(B) = 35, n(A \cap B) = 15$, and $n(A \cup B) = 55$.

10. Find the value of $n(B)$ if $n(A) = 20, n(A \cap B) = 6$, and $n(A \cup B) = 30$.

Draw an appropriate Venn diagram and use the given information to fill in the number of elements in each region.

11. $n(A) = 19, n(B) = 13, n(A \cup B) = 25, n(A') = 11$

12. $n(U) = 43, n(A) = 25, n(A \cap B) = 5, n(B') = 30$

13. $n(A') = 25, n(B) = 28, n(A' \cup B') = 40$, $n(A \cap B) = 10$

14. $n(A \cup B) = 15, n(A \cap B) = 8, n(A) = 13$, $n(A' \cup B') = 11$

15. $n(A) = 57, n(A \cap B) = 35, n(A \cup B) = 81$, $n(A \cap B \cap C) = 15, n(A \cap C) = 21, n(B \cap C) = 25$, $n(C) = 49, n(B') = 52$

16. $n(A) = 24, n(B) = 24, n(C) = 26, n(A \cap B) = 10$, $n(B \cap C) = 8, n(A \cap C) = 15, n(A \cap B \cap C) = 6$, $n(U) = 50$

17. $n(A) = 15, n(A \cap B \cap C) = 5, n(A \cap C) = 13$, $n(A \cap B') = 9, n(B \cap C) = 8, n(A' \cap B' \cap C') = 21$, $n(B \cap C') = 3, n(B \cup C) = 32$

18. $n(A \cap B) = 21, n(A \cap B \cap C) = 6, n(A \cap C) = 26$, $n(B \cap C) = 7, n(A \cap C') = 20, n(B \cap C') = 25$, $n(C) = 40, n(A' \cap B' \cap C') = 2$

Use Venn diagrams to work each problem.

19. ***Writing and Producing Music*** Joe Long worked on 9 music projects last year.

Joe Long, Bob Gaudio, Tommy DeVito, and Frankie Valli
The Four Seasons

He wrote and produced 3 projects.
He wrote a total of 5 projects.
He produced a total of 7 projects.

(a) How many projects did he write but not produce?
(b) How many projects did he produce but not write?

20. *Compact Disc Collection* Gitti Lindner is a fan of the music of Paul Simon and Art Garfunkel. In her collection of 25 compact discs, she has the following:

 5 on which both Simon and Garfunkel sing
 7 on which Simon sings
 8 on which Garfunkel sings
 15 on which neither Simon nor Garfunkel sings.

(a) How many of her compact discs feature only Paul Simon?

(b) How many of her compact discs feature only Art Garfunkel?

(c) How many feature at least one of these two artists?

(d) How many feature at most one of these two artists?

21. *Fan Response to Singers* Julie Davis, a pop culture analyst, wanted to evaluate the relative appeal of different singers. She interviewed 65 fans and determined the following:

 37 like Jazmine Sullivan
 36 like Carrie Underwood
 31 like Brad Paisley
 14 like Jazmine and Carrie
 21 like Jazmine and Brad
 14 like Carrie and Brad
 8 like all three singers.

How many of these fans like:

(a) exactly two of these singers?

(b) exactly one of these singers?

(c) none of these singers?

(d) Jazmine, but neither Carrie nor Brad?

(e) Brad and exactly one of the other two?

22. *Financial Aid for Students* At the University of Louisiana, half of the 48 mathematics majors were receiving federal financial aid as follows:

 5 had Pell Grants
 14 participated in the College Work Study Program
 4 had TOPS scholarships
 2 had TOPS scholarships and participated in Work Study.

Those with Pell Grants had no other federal aid.

How many of the 48 math majors had:

(a) no federal aid?

(b) more than one of these three forms of aid?

(c) federal aid other than these three forms?

(d) a TOPS scholarship or Work Study?

(e) exactly one of these three forms of aid?

23. *Cooking Habits* Eric Dangerfield interviewed 140 people in a suburban shopping center to find out some of their cooking habits. He obtained the results given at the top of the next column.

 58 use microwave ovens
 63 use electric ranges
 58 use gas ranges
 19 use microwave ovens and electric ranges
 17 use microwave ovens and gas ranges
 4 use both gas and electric ranges
 1 uses all three

(a) How many use exactly two of these kinds of appliances?

(b) How many use at least two of these kinds of appliances?

24. *Non-Mainline Religious Beliefs* 140 U.S. adults were surveyed.

Let $A =$ the set of respondents who believe in astrology,
 $R =$ the set of respondents who believe in reincarnation,
 $Y =$ the set of respondents who believe in the spirituality of yoga.

The survey revealed the following information:

$$n(A) = 35 \qquad n(R \cap Y) = 8$$
$$n(R) = 36 \qquad n(A \cap Y) = 10$$
$$n(Y) = 32 \qquad n(A \cap R \cap Y) = 6$$
$$n(A \cap R) = 19$$

How many of the respondents believe in:

(a) astrology, but not reincarnation?

(b) at least one of these three things?

(c) reincarnation but neither of the others?

(d) exactly two of these three things?

(e) none of the three?

25. *Survey on Attitudes Toward Religion* Researchers interviewed a number of people and recorded the following data. Of all the respondents:

 240 think Hollywood is unfriendly toward religion
 160 think the media are unfriendly toward religion
 181 think scientists are unfriendly toward religion
 145 think both Hollywood and the media are unfriendly toward religion
 122 think both scientists and the media are unfriendly toward religion
 80 think exactly two of these groups are unfriendly toward religion
 110 think all three groups are unfriendly toward religion
 219 think none of these three groups is unfriendly toward religion.

How many respondents:

(a) were surveyed?

(b) think exactly one of these three groups is unfriendly toward religion?

26. *Student Goals* Carol Britz, who sells college textbooks, interviewed freshmen on a community college campus to find out the main goals of today's students.

Let W = the set of those who want to be wealthy,
  F = the set of those who want to raise a family,
  E = the set of those who want to become experts in their fields.

Carol's findings are summarized here.

$$n(W) = 160 \qquad n(E \cap F) = 90$$

$$n(F) = 140 \qquad n(W \cap F \cap E) = 80$$

$$n(E) = 130 \qquad n(E') = 95$$

$$n(W \cap F) = 95 \qquad n[(W \cup F \cup E)'] = 10$$

Find the total number of students interviewed.

27. *Hospital Patient Symptoms* Jesse Fisher conducted a survey among 75 patients admitted to the cardiac unit of a Santa Fe hospital during a two-week period.

Let B = the set of patients with high blood pressure,
  C = the set of patients with high cholesterol levels,
  S = the set of patients who smoke cigarettes.

Jesse's data are as follows.

$$n(B) = 47 \qquad n(B \cap S) = 33$$

$$n(C) = 46 \qquad n(B \cap C) = 31$$

$$n(S) = 52 \qquad n(B \cap C \cap S) = 21$$

$$n[(B \cap C) \cup (B \cap S) \cup (C \cap S)] = 51$$

Find the number of these patients who:

(a) had either high blood pressure or high cholesterol levels, but not both

(b) had fewer than two of the indications listed

(c) were smokers but had neither high blood pressure nor high cholesterol levels

(d) did not have exactly two of the indications listed.

28. *Song Themes* It was once said that country-western songs emphasize three basic themes: love, prison, and trucks. A survey of the local country-western radio station produced the following data.

  12 songs about a truck driver who is in love while in prison
  13 about a prisoner in love
  28 about a person in love
  18 about a truck driver in love
   3 about a truck driver in prison who is not in love
   2 about people in prison who are not in love and do not drive trucks
   8 about people who are out of prison, are not in love, and do not drive trucks
  16 about truck drivers who are not in prison

(a) How many songs were surveyed?

Find the number of songs about:

(b) truck drivers   **(c)** prisoners

(d) truck drivers in prison

(e) people not in prison

(f) people not in love.

29. Use the figure below to find the numbers of the regions belonging to each set.

(a) $A \cap B \cap C \cap D$

(b) $A \cup B \cup C \cup D$

(c) $(A \cap B) \cup (C \cap D)$

(d) $(A' \cap B') \cap (C \cup D)$

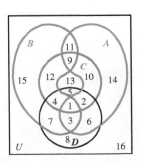

30. *Sports Viewing* A survey of 130 TV viewers was taken.

  52 watch football
  56 watch basketball
  62 watch tennis
  60 watch golf
  21 watch football and basketball
  19 watch football and tennis
  22 watch basketball and tennis
  27 watch football and golf
  30 watch basketball and golf
  21 watch tennis and golf
   3 watch football, basketball, and tennis
  15 watch football, basketball, and golf
  10 watch football, tennis, and golf
  10 watch basketball, tennis, and golf
   3 watch all four of these sports
   5 don't watch any of these four sports

Use a Venn diagram to answer each question.

(a) How many of these viewers watch football, basketball, and tennis, but not golf?

(b) How many watch exactly one of these four sports?

(c) How many watch exactly two of these four sports?

Solve each problem.

31. Basketball Positions Donna DePaulis runs a basketball program in California. On the first day of the season, 60 young women showed up and were categorized by age level and by preferred basketball position, as shown in the following table.

		Position			
		Guard (G)	Forward (F)	Center (N)	Totals
Age	Junior High (J)	9	6	4	19
	Senior High (S)	12	5	9	26
	College (C)	5	8	2	15
	Totals	26	19	15	60

Using the set labels (letters) in the table, find the number of players in each of the following sets.

(a) $J \cap G$ **(b)** $S \cap N$ **(c)** $N \cup (S \cap F)$

(d) $S' \cap (G \cup N)$ **(e)** $(S \cap N') \cup (C \cap G')$

(f) $N' \cap (S' \cap C')$

32. Army Housing A study of U.S. Army housing trends categorized personnel as commissioned officers (C), warrant officers (W), or enlisted (E), and categorized their living facilities as on-base (B), rented off-base (R), or owned off-base (O). One survey yielded the following data.

		Facilities			
		B	R	O	Totals
Personnel	C	12	29	54	95
	W	4	5	6	15
	E	374	71	285	730
	Totals	390	105	345	840

Find the number of personnel in each of the following sets.

(a) $W \cap O$ **(b)** $C \cup B$

(c) $R' \cup W'$ **(d)** $(C \cup W) \cap (B \cup R)$

(e) $(C \cap B) \cup (E \cap O)$ **(f)** $B \cap (W \cup R)'$

33. Could the information of **Example 4** have been presented in a Venn diagram similar to those in **Examples 1 and 3?** If so, construct such a diagram. Otherwise, explain the essential difference of **Example 4**.

34. Explain how a cardinal number formula can be derived for the case where *three* sets occur. Specifically, give a formula relating $n(A \cup B \cup C)$ to

$$n(A), \ n(B), \ n(C), \ n(A \cap B), \ n(A \cap C),$$
$$n(B \cap C), \ \text{and} \ n(A \cap B \cap C).$$

Illustrate with a Venn diagram.

EXTENSION Infinite Sets and Their Cardinalities

One-to-One Correspondence and Equivalent Sets • The Cardinal Number $\aleph_0$ • Infinite Sets • Sets That Are Not Countable

One-to-One Correspondence and Equivalent Sets Georg Cantor, profiled on **page 44,** met with much resistance in the late 1800s when he first developed modern set theory because of his ideas on infinite sets. The results discussed here, however, are commonly accepted today. Recall the following from **Section 2.1.**

1. The cardinal number of a set is the number of elements it contains.

2. Two sets are *equivalent* if their cardinal numbers are equal.

3. A set is *infinite* if its cardinal number is "too large" to be found among the whole numbers.

We can easily establish the equivalence of two finite sets by counting their elements and comparing their cardinal numbers. But the elements of an infinite set cannot be counted in the same sense. Cantor addressed this difficulty using the idea of a **one-to-one correspondence** between sets. The sets $A = \{1, 2, 3\}$ and $B = \{3, 6, 9\}$, for example, can be placed in such correspondence as follows (among other ways):

$$\{1, \quad 2, \quad 3\}$$
$$\updownarrow \quad \updownarrow \quad \updownarrow$$
$$\{3, \quad 6, \quad 9\}.$$

This correspondence is "one-to-one" because each element of each set is paired with exactly one element of the other set. The equivalence of A and B is denoted $A \sim B$.

On the other hand, the sets $C = \{1, 8, 12\}$ and $D = \{6, 11\}$ are *not* equivalent. Any correspondence between them, such as

$$\{1, \quad 8, \quad 12\}$$
$$\updownarrow \quad \searrow \swarrow$$
$$\{6, \quad 11\}$$

is not one-to-one. (Two different elements from C must be paired with a single element of D.)

Cantor extended this idea that one-to-one correspondence establishes equivalence to his study of infinite sets.

The Cardinal Number $\aleph_0$

The most basic infinite set is the set of counting numbers, $\{1, 2, 3, 4, 5, \ldots\}$. The counting numbers are said to have the infinite cardinal number $\aleph_0$ (the first Hebrew letter, aleph, with a zero subscript, read "aleph-null"). Think of $\aleph_0$ as being the "smallest" infinite cardinal number. To the question "How many counting numbers are there?", we answer "There are $\aleph_0$ of them."

Now, any set that can be placed in a one-to-one correspondence with the counting numbers will have the same cardinal number, or $\aleph_0$. There are many such sets.

The word **paradox** in Greek originally meant "wrong opinion" as opposed to orthodox, which meant "right opinion." Over the years, the word came to mean self-contradiction.

Before the twentieth century it was considered a paradox that any set could be placed into one-to-one correspondence with a proper subset of itself. This paradox, called **Galileo's paradox** after the sixteenth-century mathematician and scientist **Galileo** (see the picture), is now explained by saying that the ability to make such a correspondence is how we distinguish infinite sets from finite sets. What is true for finite sets is not necessarily true for infinite sets.

▮▮ **EXAMPLE 1** Showing that $\{0, 1, 2, 3, \ldots\}$ Has Cardinal Number $\aleph_0$

Verify that the set of whole numbers $\{0, 1, 2, 3, \ldots\}$ has cardinal number $\aleph_0$.

SOLUTION

We know that $\aleph_0$ is the cardinal number of the set of counting numbers (by definition). To show that another set, such as the whole numbers, also has $\aleph_0$ as its cardinal number, we must show that set to be equivalent to the set of counting numbers. Equivalence is established by a one-to-one correspondence between the two sets.

$$\{1, \quad 2, \quad 3, \quad 4, \quad 5, \quad 6, \ldots, \quad n, \quad \ldots\} \text{ Counting numbers}$$
$$\updownarrow \quad \updownarrow \quad \updownarrow \quad \updownarrow \quad \updownarrow \quad \updownarrow \quad \updownarrow \quad \updownarrow$$
$$\{0, \quad 1, \quad 2, \quad 3, \quad 4, \quad 5, \ldots, \quad n-1, \quad \ldots\} \text{ Whole numbers}$$

The pairing of the counting number n with the whole number $n - 1$ continues indefinitely, with neither set containing any element not used up in the pairing process. Even though the set of whole numbers has an additional element (the number 0) compared to the set of counting numbers, the correspondence proves that both sets have the same cardinal number, $\aleph_0$. ▮▮▮

The result in **Example 1** shows that intuition is a poor guide for dealing with infinite sets. Because the sets of counting numbers and whole numbers can be placed in a one-to-one correspondence, the two sets have the same cardinal number.

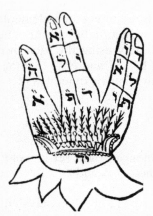

Aleph and other letters of the **Hebrew alphabet** are shown on a Kabbalistic diagram representing one of the ten emanations of God during Creation. Kabbalah, the ultramystical tradition within Judaism, arose in the fifth century and peaked in the sixteenth century in both Palestine and Poland.

Kabbalists believed that the Bible held mysteries that could be discovered in permutations, combinations, and anagrams of its very letters. Each letter in the aleph-bet has a numerical value (aleph = 1), and thus a numeration system exists. The letter Y stands for 10, so 15 should be YH (10 + 5). However, YH is a form of the Holy Name, so instead TW (9 + 6) is the symbol.

Infinite Sets The set $\{5, 6, 7\}$ is a proper subset of the set $\{5, 6, 7, 8\}$, and there is no way to place these two sets in a one-to-one correspondence. However, the set of counting numbers is a proper subset of the set of whole numbers, and **Example 1** showed that these two sets *can* be placed in a one-to-one correspondence. This important property is used in the formal definition of an infinite set.

> **Infinite Set**
>
> A set is **infinite** if it can be placed in a one-to-one correspondence with a proper subset of itself.

▮ **EXAMPLE 2** Showing that $\{\ldots, -3, -2, -1, 0, 1, 2, 3, \ldots\}$ Has Cardinal Number $\aleph_0$

Verify that the set of integers $\{\ldots, -3, -2, -1, 0, 1, 2, 3, \ldots\}$ has cardinal number $\aleph_0$.

SOLUTION

A one-to-one correspondence can be set up between the set of integers and the set of counting numbers.

$$\{1, \quad 2, \quad 3, \quad 4, \quad 5, \quad 6, \quad 7, \quad \ldots, \quad 2n, \quad 2n + 1, \quad \ldots\}$$
$$\updownarrow \ \updownarrow \ \updownarrow \ \updownarrow \ \updownarrow \ \updownarrow \ \updownarrow \qquad\quad \updownarrow \qquad\quad \updownarrow$$
$$\{0, \quad 1, \quad -1, \quad 2, \quad -2, \quad 3, \quad -3, \quad \ldots, \quad n, \quad -n, \quad \ldots\}$$

Because of this one-to-one correspondence, the cardinal number of the set of integers is the same as the cardinal number of the set of counting numbers, $\aleph_0$. ▮▮▮

The one-to-one correspondence of **Example 2** proves that the set of integers is infinite—it was placed in one-to-one correspondence with a proper subset of itself.

As shown by **Example 2,** there are just as many integers as there are counting numbers. This result is not at all intuitive, and the next result is even less so. There is an infinite number of fractions between any two counting numbers. For example, there is an infinite set of fractions $\left\{\frac{1}{2}, \frac{3}{4}, \frac{7}{8}, \frac{15}{16}, \frac{31}{32}, \ldots\right\}$ between the counting numbers 0 and 1. This should imply that there are "more" fractions than counting numbers. However, there are just as many fractions as counting numbers.

▮ **EXAMPLE 3** Showing that the Set of Rational Numbers Has Cardinal Number $\aleph_0$

Verify that the cardinal number of the set of rational numbers is $\aleph_0$.

SOLUTION

First show that a one-to-one correspondence may be set up between the set of nonnegative rational numbers and the counting numbers. This is done by the following ingenious scheme, devised by Georg Cantor.

Look at **Figure 22** on the next page. The nonnegative rational numbers whose denominators are 1 are written in the first row. Those whose denominators are 2 are written in the second row, and so on. Every nonnegative rational number appears in this list sooner or later. For example, $\frac{327}{189}$ is in row 189 and column 327.

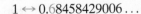

$$\frac{0}{1} \rightarrow \frac{1}{1} \rightarrow \frac{2}{1} \quad \frac{3}{1} \rightarrow \frac{4}{1} \quad \frac{5}{1} \rightarrow \frac{6}{1} \quad \frac{7}{1} \quad \cdots$$

$$\frac{1}{2} \rightarrow \frac{2}{2} \quad \frac{3}{2} \quad \frac{4}{2} \quad \frac{5}{2} \quad \frac{6}{2} \quad \frac{7}{2} \quad \cdots$$

$$\frac{1}{3} \quad \frac{2}{3} \quad \frac{3}{3} \quad \frac{4}{3} \quad \frac{5}{3} \quad \frac{6}{3} \quad \frac{7}{3} \quad \cdots$$

$$\frac{1}{4} \quad \frac{2}{4} \quad \frac{3}{4} \quad \frac{4}{4} \quad \frac{5}{4} \quad \frac{6}{4} \quad \frac{7}{4} \quad \cdots$$

$$\frac{1}{5} \quad \frac{2}{5} \quad \frac{3}{5} \quad \frac{4}{5} \quad \frac{5}{5} \quad \frac{6}{5} \quad \frac{7}{5} \quad \cdots$$

$$\frac{1}{6} \quad \frac{2}{6} \quad \frac{3}{6} \quad \frac{4}{6} \quad \frac{5}{6} \quad \frac{6}{6} \quad \frac{7}{6} \quad \cdots$$

$$\vdots \qquad \vdots \qquad \vdots \qquad \vdots \qquad \vdots \qquad \vdots$$

Figure 22

To set up a one-to-one correspondence between the set of nonnegative rationals and the set of counting numbers, follow the path drawn in **Figure 22**. Let $\frac{0}{1}$ correspond to 1, let $\frac{1}{1}$ correspond to 2, $\frac{2}{1}$ to 3, $\frac{1}{2}$ to 4 $\left(\text{skip } \frac{2}{2}, \text{ since } \frac{2}{2} = \frac{1}{1}\right)$, $\frac{1}{3}$ to 5, $\frac{1}{4}$ to 6, and so on. The numbers under the colored disks are omitted because they can be reduced to lower terms, and were thus included earlier in the listing.

This procedure sets up a one-to-one correspondence between the set of nonnegative rationals and the counting numbers, showing that both of these sets have the same cardinal number, $\aleph_0$. Now by using the method of **Example 2** (i.e., letting each negative number follow its corresponding positive number), we can extend this correspondence to include negative rational numbers as well. Thus, the set of all rational numbers has cardinal number $\aleph_0$. ▮▮▮

A set is called **countable** if it is finite or if it has cardinal number $\aleph_0$. All the infinite sets of numbers discussed so far—the counting numbers, the whole numbers, the integers, and the rational numbers—are countable.

Sets That Are Not Countable

▮▮ **EXAMPLE 4** Showing that the Set of Real Numbers Does Not Have Cardinal Number $\aleph_0$

Verify that the set of all real numbers does not have cardinal number $\aleph_0$.

SOLUTION

There are two possibilities:

1. The set of real numbers has cardinal number $\aleph_0$.
2. The set of real numbers does not have cardinal number $\aleph_0$.

If we assume that the first statement is true, then a one-to-one correspondence can be set up between the set of real numbers and the set of counting numbers.

In a later chapter, we show that every real number can be written as a decimal number (or simply "decimal"). Thus, in the one-to-one correspondence we are assuming, some decimal corresponds to the counting number 1, some decimal corresponds to 2, and so on. Suppose the correspondence begins as follows:

$$1 \leftrightarrow 0.68458429006\ldots$$
$$2 \leftrightarrow 0.13479201038\ldots$$
$$3 \leftrightarrow 0.37291568341\ldots$$
$$4 \leftrightarrow 0.935223671611\ldots$$
and so on.

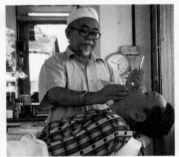

The Barber Paradox is a version of a paradox of set theory that Bertrand Russell proposed in the early twentieth century.

1. The men in a village are of two types: men who do not shave themselves and men who do.
2. The village barber shaves all men who do not shave themselves and he shaves only those men.

But who shaves the barber?
The barber cannot shave himself. If he did, he would fall into the category of men who shave themselves. However, (2) above states that the barber does not shave such men.

So the barber does not shave himself. But then he falls into the category of men who do not shave themselves. According to (2), the barber shaves all of these men; hence, the barber shaves himself, too.

We find that the barber cannot shave himself, yet the barber does shave himself—a paradox.

Zeno's paradox of the Tortoise and Achilles was given in its original form by Zeno of Elea.

In the original story, the Tortoise is able to convince Achilles (the Greek hero of Homer's *The Illiad*) that in a race, given a small head start, the Tortoise is always able to defeat Achilles. (See the **Chapter Opener** and **Exercises 51 and 52** in this **Extension**.) The resolution of this paradox is discussed on the Web site www.mathacademy.com.

Assuming the existence of a one-to-one correspondence between the counting numbers and the real numbers means that every decimal is in the list above. Let's construct a new decimal K as follows. The first decimal in the above list has 6 as its first digit. Let K start as $K = 0.4.\ldots$ We picked 4 because $4 \neq 6$. (We could have used any other digit except 6.) Because the second digit of the second decimal in the list is 3, we let $K = 0.45\ldots$ (because $5 \neq 3$). The third digit of the third decimal is 2, so let $K = 0.457\ldots$ (because $7 \neq 2$). The fourth digit of the fourth decimal is 2, so let $K = 0.4573\ldots$ (because $3 \neq 2$). Continue defining K in this way.

Is K in the list that we assumed to contain all decimals? The first decimal in the list differs from K in at least the first position (K starts with 4, and the first decimal in the list starts with 6). The second decimal in the list differs from K in at least the second position, and the nth decimal in the list differs from K in at least the nth position. Every decimal in the list differs from K in at least one position, so that K cannot possibly be in the list. In summary:

> We assume every decimal is in the list above.
> The decimal K is not in the list.

Because these statements cannot both be true, the original assumption has led to a contradiction. This forces the acceptance of the only possible alternative to the original assumption: It is not possible to set up a one-to-one correspondence between the set of reals and the set of counting numbers. The cardinal number of the set of reals is not equal to $\aleph_0$. ∎∎∎

The set of counting numbers is a proper subset of the set of real numbers. Because of this, it would seem reasonable to say that the cardinal number of the set of reals, commonly written c, is greater than $\aleph_0$. (The letter c here represents *continuum*.) Other, even larger, infinite cardinal numbers can be constructed. For example, the set of all subsets of the set of real numbers has a cardinal number larger than c. Continuing this process of finding cardinal numbers of sets of subsets, more and more, larger and larger infinite cardinal numbers are produced.

The six most important infinite sets of numbers were listed in **Section 2.1.** All of them have been dealt with in this **Extension,** except the irrational numbers. The irrationals have decimal representations, so they are all included among the real numbers. Because the irrationals are a subset of the reals, you might guess that the irrationals have cardinal number $\aleph_0$, just like the rationals. However, because the union of the rationals and the irrationals is all the reals, that would imply that the cardinality of the union of two disjoint countable sets is c. But **Example 2** showed that this is not the case. A better guess is that the cardinal number of the irrationals is c (the same as that of the reals). This is, in fact, true.

Cardinal Numbers of Infinite Number Sets

Infinite Set	Cardinal Number
Natural or counting numbers	$\aleph_0$
Whole numbers	$\aleph_0$
Integers	$\aleph_0$
Rational numbers	$\aleph_0$
Irrational numbers	c
Real numbers	c

EXTENSION EXERCISES

Match each set in Column I with the set in Column II that has the same cardinality. Give the cardinal number.

I	**II**
1. $\{6\}$	**A.** $\{x \mid x \text{ is a rational number}\}$
2. $\{-16, 14, 3\}$	**B.** $\{26\}$
3. $\{x \mid x \text{ is a natural number}\}$	**C.** $\{x \mid x \text{ is an irrational number}\}$
4. $\{x \mid x \text{ is a real number}\}$	**D.** $\{x, y, z\}$
5. $\{x \mid x \text{ is an integer between } 5 \text{ and } 6\}$	**E.** $\{x \mid x \text{ is a real number that satisfies } x^2 = 25\}$
6. $\{x \mid x \text{ is an integer that satisfies } x^2 = 100\}$	**F.** $\{x \mid x \text{ is an integer that is both even and odd}\}$

Place each pair of sets into a one-to-one correspondence, if possible.

7. $\{I, II, III\}$ and $\{x, y, z\}$

8. $\{a, b, c, d\}$ and $\{2, 4, 6\}$

9. $\{a, d, d, i, t, i, o, n\}$ and $\{a, n, s, w, e, r\}$

10. $\{$Obama, Clinton, Bush$\}$ and $\{$Michelle, Hillary, Laura$\}$

Give the cardinal number of each set.

11. $\{a, b, c, d, \ldots, k\}$

12. $\{9, 12, 15, \ldots, 36\}$

13. $\emptyset$

14. $\{0\}$

15. $\{300, 400, 500, \ldots\}$

16. $\{-35, -28, -21, \ldots, 56\}$

17. $\left\{-\dfrac{1}{4}, -\dfrac{1}{8}, -\dfrac{1}{12}, \ldots\right\}$

18. $\{x \mid x \text{ is an even integer}\}$

19. $\{x \mid x \text{ is an odd counting number}\}$

20. $\{b, a, 1, 1, a, d\}$

21. $\{$Jan, Feb, Mar, $\ldots$, Dec$\}$

22. $\{$Alabama, Alaska, Arizona, $\ldots$, Wisconsin, Wyoming$\}$

23. Lew Lefton has revised the old song "100 Bottles of Beer on the Wall" to illustrate a property of infinite cardinal numbers.

Fill in the blank in the first verse of Lefton's composition:

$\aleph_0$ bottles of beer on the wall, $\aleph_0$ bottles of beer, take one down and pass it around, _____ bottles of beer on the wall.
(*Source:* http://people.math.gatech.edu/~llefton)

$\aleph_0 - 1 = \;?$

24. Two one-to-one correspondences are considered "different" if some elements are paired differently in one than in the other.

$$
\begin{array}{ccc}
\{a, & b, & c\} \\
\updownarrow & \updownarrow & \updownarrow \\
\{a, & b, & c\}
\end{array}
\text{ and }
\begin{array}{ccc}
\{a, & b, & c\} \\
\updownarrow & \updownarrow & \updownarrow \\
\{c, & b, & a\}
\end{array}
\text{ are different,}
$$

$$
\text{while }
\begin{array}{ccc}
\{a, & b, & c\} \\
\updownarrow & \updownarrow & \updownarrow \\
\{c, & a, & b\}
\end{array}
\text{ and }
\begin{array}{ccc}
\{b, & c, & a\} \\
\updownarrow & \updownarrow & \updownarrow \\
\{a, & b, & c\}
\end{array}
\text{ are not.}
$$

(a) How many *different* correspondences can be set up between the two sets $\{$Jamie Foxx, Mike Myers, Madonna$\}$ and $\{$Austin Powers, Ray Charles, Eva Peron$\}$?

(b) Which one of these correspondences pairs each person with the appropriate famous movie role?

Determine whether each pair of sets is equal, equivalent, both, *or* neither.

25. $\{u, v, w\}$, $\{v, u, w\}$

26. $\{48, 6\}$, $\{4, 86\}$

27. $\{X, Y, Z\}$, $\{x, y, z\}$

28. $\{$top$\}$, $\{$pot$\}$

29. $\{x \mid x \text{ is a positive real number}\}$, $\{x \mid x \text{ is a negative real number}\}$

30. $\{x \mid x \text{ is a positive rational number}\}$, $\{x \mid x \text{ is a negative real number}\}$

Show that each set has cardinal number $\aleph_0$ by setting up a one-to-one correspondence between the given set and the set of counting numbers.

31. the set of positive even integers

32. $\{-10, -20, -30, -40, \ldots\}$

33. $\{1,000,000,\ 2,000,000,\ 3,000,000,\ \dots\}$

34. the set of odd integers

35. $\{2, 4, 8, 16, 32, \dots\}$
(*Hint*: $4 = 2^2$, $8 = 2^3$, $16 = 2^4$, and so on)

36. $\{-17, -22, -27, -32, \dots\}$

In Exercises 37–40, identify the given statement as always true *or* not always true. *If* not always true, *give a counterexample.*

37. If A and B are infinite sets, then A is equivalent to B.

38. If set A is an infinite set and set B can be put in a one-to-one correspondence with a proper subset of A, then B must be infinite.

39. If A is an infinite set and A is not equivalent to the set of counting numbers, then $n(A) = c$.

40. If A and B are both countably infinite sets, then $n(A \cup B) = \aleph_0$.

Exercises 41 and 42 are geometric applications of the concept of infinity.

41. The set of real numbers can be represented by an infinite line, extending indefinitely in both directions. Each point on the line corresponds to a unique real number, and each real number corresponds to a unique point on the line.

(a) Use the figure below, where the line segment between 0 and 1 has been bent into a semicircle and positioned above the line, to prove that

$\{x \mid x$ is a real number between 0 and 1$\}$ *is equivalent to* $\{x \mid x$ is a real number$\}$.

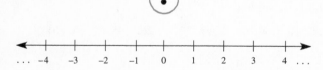

(b) What fact does part (a) establish about the set of real numbers?

42. Show that the two vertical line segments shown here both have the same number of points.

Show that each set can be placed in a one-to-one correspondence with a proper subset of itself to prove that the set is infinite.

43. $\{3, 6, 9, 12, \dots\}$

44. $\{4, 7, 10, 13, 16, \dots\}$

45. $\left\{\dfrac{3}{4}, \dfrac{3}{8}, \dfrac{3}{12}, \dfrac{3}{16}, \dots\right\}$

46. $\left\{1, \dfrac{4}{3}, \dfrac{5}{3}, 2, \dots\right\}$

47. $\left\{\dfrac{1}{9}, \dfrac{1}{18}, \dfrac{1}{27}, \dfrac{1}{36}, \dots\right\}$

48. $\{-3, -5, -9, -17, \dots\}$

49. Describe the distinction between *equal* and *equivalent* sets.

50. Explain how the correspondence suggested in **Example 4** shows that the set of real numbers between 0 and 1 is not countable.

The Paradoxes of Zeno *The* **Chapter Opener** *discussed the scene in the movie* I.Q. *that deals with Zeno's paradox. Zeno was born about 496* B.C. *in southern Italy. Two forms of his paradox are given below. What is your explanation for the following two examples of Zeno's paradoxes?*

51. Achilles, if he starts out behind a tortoise, can never overtake the tortoise even if he runs faster.

Suppose Tortoise has a head start of one meter and goes one-tenth as fast as Achilles. When Achilles reaches the point where Tortoise started, Tortoise is then one-tenth meter ahead. When Achilles reaches *that* point, Tortoise is one-hundredth meter ahead. And so on. Achilles gets closer but can never catch up.

52. Motion itself cannot occur.

You cannot travel one meter until after you have first gone a half meter. But you cannot go a half meter until after you have first gone a quarter meter. And so on. Even the tiniest motion cannot occur because a tinier motion would have to occur first.

COLLABORATIVE INVESTIGATION

Surveying the Members of Your Class

This group activity is designed to determine the number of students present in your class without actually counting the members one by one. This will be accomplished by having each member of the class determine one particular set in which he or she belongs, and then finding the sum of the cardinal numbers of the subsets.

For this activity, we designate three sets: X, Y, and Z.

$X = \{$students in the class registered with the Republican party$\}$

$Y = \{$students in the class 24 years of age or younger$\}$

$Z = \{$students who have never been married$\}$

Each student in the class will belong to one of the sets X, X', one of the sets Y, Y', and one of the sets Z, Z'. (The complement of a set consists of all elements in the universe (class) that are not in the set.)

As an example, suppose that a student is a 23-year-old divorced Democrat. The student belongs to the sets X', Y, and Z'. The set to which the student belongs is

$$X' \cap Y \cap Z'.$$

In the Venn diagram that follows, the eight subsets are identified by lowercase letters (a)–(h).

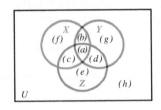

The final column in the following table will be completed when a survey is made. Each student should now determine to which set he or she belongs. (The student described earlier belongs to (g).)

Region	Description in Terms of Set Notation	Number of Class Members in the Set
(a)	$X \cap Y \cap Z$	
(b)	$X \cap Y \cap Z'$	
(c)	$X \cap Y' \cap Z$	
(d)	$X' \cap Y \cap Z$	
(e)	$X' \cap Y' \cap Z$	
(f)	$X \cap Y' \cap Z'$	
(g)	$X' \cap Y \cap Z'$	
(h)	$X' \cap Y' \cap Z'$	

The instructor will now poll the class to see how many members are in each set. *Remember that each class member will belong to one and only one set.*

After the survey is made, find the sum of the numbers in the final column. They should add up to *exactly* the number of students present. Count the class members individually to verify this.

Topics for Discussion

1. Suppose that the final column entries do not add up to the total number of class members. What might have gone wrong?

2. Why can't a class member be a member of more than one of the eight subsets listed?

CHAPTER 2 TEST

In Exercises 1–14, let

$U = \{a, b, c, d, e, f, g, h\}, \quad A = \{a, b, c, d\},$

$B = \{b, e, a, d\}, \quad and \quad C = \{a, e\}.$

Find each set.

1. $A \cup C$

2. $B \cap A$

3. B'

4. $A - (B \cap C')$

Identify each statement as true *or* false.

5. $b \in A$

6. $C \subseteq A$

7. $B \subset (A \cup C)$

8. $c \notin C$

9. $n[(A \cup B) - C] = 4$

10. $\emptyset \subset C$

11. $A \cap B'$ is equivalent to $B \cap A'$

12. $(A \cup B)' = A' \cap B'$

Find each of the following.

13. $n(A \times C)$

14. the number of proper subsets of A

Give a word description for each set.

15. $\{-3, -1, 1, 3, 5, 7, 9\}$

16. $\{$January, February, March, . . . , December$\}$

Express each set in set-builder notation.

17. $\{-1, -2, -3, -4, \ldots\}$

18. $\{24, 32, 40, 48, \ldots, 88\}$

Place $\subset$, $\subseteq$, both, or neither in each blank to make a true statement.

19. $\emptyset$ _____ $\{x \mid x$ is a counting number between 20 and 21$\}$

20. $\{4, 9, 16\}$ _____ $\{4, 5, 6, 7, 8, 9, 10\}$

Shade each set in an appropriate Venn diagram.

21. $X \cup Y'$ **22.** $X' \cap Y'$

23. $(X \cup Y) - Z$

24. $[(X \cap Y) \cup (Y \cap Z) \cup (X \cap Z)] - (X \cap Y \cap Z)$

Facts About Inventions *The table lists ten inventions, together with other pertinent data.*

Invention	Date	Inventor	Nation
Adding machine	1642	Pascal	France
Barometer	1643	Torricelli	Italy
Electric razor	1917	Schick	U.S.
Fiber optics	1955	Kapany	England
Geiger counter	1913	Geiger	Germany
Pendulum clock	1657	Huygens	Holland
Radar	1940	Watson-Watt	Scotland
Telegraph	1837	Morse	U.S.
Thermometer	1593	Galileo	Italy
Zipper	1891	Judson	U.S.

Let U = the set of all ten inventions,
      A = the set of items invented in the United States,
and T = the set of items invented in the twentieth century.

List the elements of each set.

25. $A \cap T$

26. $(A \cup T)'$

27. $A - T'$

28. State De Morgan's laws for sets in words rather than symbols.

29. The numerals in the Venn diagram indicate the number of elements in each particular subset.

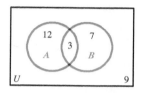

Determine the number of elements in each set.

(a) $A \cup B$ **(b)** $A \cap B'$ **(c)** $(A \cap B)'$

30. *Financial Aid to College Students*   Three major sources of financial aid are government grants, private scholarships, and the colleges themselves. Susan Brilling, Financial Aid Director of a small private Southern college, surveyed the records of 100 sophomores and found the following:

     49 receive government grants
     55 receive private scholarships
     43 receive aid from the college
     23 receive government grants and private scholarships
     18 receive government grants and aid from the college
     28 receive private scholarships and aid from the college
      8 receive help from all three sources.

How many of the students in the survey:

(a) have government grants only?

(b) have private scholarships but not government grants?

(c) receive financial aid from only one of these sources?

(d) receive aid from exactly two of these sources?

(e) receive no financial aid from any of these sources?

(f) receive no aid from the college or from the government?

INTRODUCTION TO LOGIC 3

In the 2007 movie *Shrek the Third*, Shrek searches for the rightful heir to the throne of the Kingdom of Far Far Away, while Prince Charming schemes to gain the throne for himself. The Prince, knowing that Pinocchio's nose grows if he lies, questions Pinocchio.

PRINCE CHARMING: So tell me puppet, where is Shrek?

PINOCCHIO: Well, I don't know where he's not.

PRINCE CHARMING: You're telling me you don't know where Shrek is?

PINOCCHIO: It wouldn't be inaccurate to assume that I couldn't exactly not say that is or isn't almost partially incorrect.

PRINCE CHARMING: So you do know where he is!

PINOCCHIO: On the contrary, I'm possibly more or less not definitely rejecting the idea that in no way, with any amount of uncertainty, that I undeniably do or do not know where he shouldn't probably be. If that indeed wasn't where he isn't. Even if he wasn't not where I knew he was, it could mean. . . .

Unable to contain his frustration with Pinocchio's roundabout answer, one of the Three Little Pigs blurts out that Shrek has gone to search for the rightful heir. The pig was unable to follow Pinocchio's logic, or lack of it. In this chapter, we examine the basics of the study of logic.

3.1 STATEMENTS AND QUANTIFIERS

Statements • Negations • Symbols • Quantifiers • Quantifiers and Number Sets

Statements

This section introduces the study of **symbolic logic,** which uses letters to represent statements, and symbols for words such as *and, or, not.* Logic is used in the study of the **truth value** (that is, the truth or falsity) of statements with multiple parts. The truth value of such statements depends on their components.

Many kinds of sentences occur in ordinary language, including factual statements, opinions, commands, and questions. Symbolic logic discusses only the type that involves facts. A **statement** is a declarative sentence that is either true or false, but not both simultaneously.

Gottfried Leibniz (1646–1716) was a wide-ranging philosopher and a universalist who tried to patch up Catholic–Protestant conflicts. He promoted cultural exchange between Europe and the East. Chinese ideograms led him to search for a universal symbolism. He was an early inventor of **symbolic logic.**

Electronic mail provides a means of communication. } Statements
$$12 + 6 = 13$$ Each is either true or false.

Access the file.
Did the Saints win the Super Bowl? } Not statements
Tim Lincecum is a better baseball player than Cliff Lee. Each cannot be identified as being either true or false.
This sentence is false.

Of the sentences that are not statements, the first is a command, and the second is a question. The third is an opinion. "This sentence is false" is a paradox: If we assume it is true, then it is false, and if we assume it is false, then it is true.

A **compound statement** may be formed by combining two or more statements. The statements making up a compound statement are called **component statements.** Various **logical connectives,** or simply **connectives,** such as *and, or, not,* and *if . . . then,* can be used in forming compound statements. (While a statement such as "Today is not Tuesday" does not consist of two component statements, for convenience it is considered compound, because its truth value is determined by noting the truth value of a different statement, "Today is Tuesday.")

▮▮ **EXAMPLE 1** Deciding Whether a Statement Is Compound

Decide whether each statement is compound. If so, identify the connective.

(a) Lord Byron wrote sonnets, and the poem exhibits iambic pentameter.

(b) You can pay me now, or you can pay me later.

(c) If he said it, then it must be true.

(d) My pistol was made by Smith and Wesson.

SOLUTION

(a) This statement is compound, because it is made up of the component statements "Lord Byron wrote sonnets" and "the poem exhibits iambic pentameter." The connective is *and.*

(b) The connective here is *or.* The statement is compound.

(c) The connective here is *if . . . then,* discussed in more detail in **Section 3.3.** The statement is compound.

(d) While the word "and" is used in this statement, it is not used as a *logical* connective. It is part of the name of the manufacturer. The statement is not compound. ▄▄▄

Negations

The sentence "Anthony Mansella has a red truck" is a statement. The **negation** of this statement is "Anthony Mansella does not have a red truck." ***The negation of a true statement is false, and the negation of a false statement is true.***

▌▌ **EXAMPLE 2** Forming Negations

Form the negation of each statement.

(a) That city has a mayor.　　**(b)** The moon is not a planet.

SOLUTION

(a) To negate this statement, we introduce *not* into the sentence: "That city does not have a mayor."

(b) The negation is "The moon is a planet." ▄▄▄

One way to detect incorrect negations is to check truth values. *A negation must have the opposite truth value from the original statement.*

The next example uses some of the inequality symbols in **Table 1.** In the case of an inequality involving a variable, the negation must have the opposite truth value for *any* replacement of the variable.

```
TEST  LOGIC
1: =
2: ≠
3: >
4: ≥
5: <
6: ≤
```

The TEST menu of the TI-83/84 Plus calculator allows the user to test the truth or falsity of statements involving $=$, $\neq$, $>$, $\geq$, $<$, and $\leq$. If a statement is true, it returns a 1. If it is false, it returns a 0.

Table 1

Symbolism	Meaning	Examples	
$a < b$	a is less than b	$4 < 9$	$\frac{1}{2} < \frac{3}{4}$
$a > b$	a is greater than b	$6 > 2$	$-5 > -11$
$a \leq b$	a is less than or equal to b	$8 \leq 10$	$3 \leq 3$
$a \geq b$	a is greater than or equal to b	$-2 \geq -3$	$-5 \geq -5$

▌▌ **EXAMPLE 3** Negating Inequalities

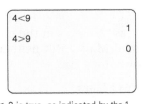

```
4<9
                    1
4>9
                    0
```

$4 < 9$ is true, as indicated by the 1.
$4 > 9$ is false, as indicated by the 0.

Give a negation of each inequality. Do *not* use a slash symbol.

(a) $x < 9$　　**(b)** $7x + 11y \geq 77$

SOLUTION

(a) The negation of "x is less than 9" is "x is *not* less than 9." Because we cannot use "not," which would require writing $x \nless 9$, phrase the negation as "x is greater than or equal to 9," or

$$x \geq 9.$$

(b) The negation, with no slash, is

$$7x + 11y < 77.$$ ▄▄▄

Symbols

The study of logic uses symbols. Statements are represented with letters, such as p, q, or r. Several symbols for connectives are shown in **Table 2**.

Table 2		
Connective	**Symbol**	**Type of Statement**
and	$\wedge$	Conjunction
or	$\vee$	Disjunction
not	$\sim$	Negation

The symbol $\sim$ represents the connective *not*. If p represents the statement "Barack Obama was president in 2009" then $\sim p$ represents "Barack Obama was not president in 2009."

▪▪ **EXAMPLE 4** Translating from Symbols to Words

Let p represent "It is 70° today," and let q represent "It is Tuesday." Write each symbolic statement in words.

(a) $p \vee q$ **(b)** $\sim p \wedge q$ **(c)** $\sim(p \vee q)$ **(d)** $\sim(p \wedge q)$

SOLUTION

(a) From the table, $\vee$ symbolizes *or*. Thus, $p \vee q$ represents

It is 70° today or it is Tuesday.

(b) It is not 70° today and it is Tuesday.

(c) It is not the case that it is 70° today or it is Tuesday.

(d) It is not the case that it is 70° today and it is Tuesday. ▪▪▪

The statement in **Example 4(c)** usually is translated as **"Neither p nor q."**

Quantifiers

Quantifiers are used to indicate *how many* cases of a particular situation exist. The words *all, each, every,* and *no(ne)* are called **universal quantifiers,** while words and phrases such as *some, there exists,* and *(for) at least one* are called **existential quantifiers.** *Be careful when forming the negation of a statement involving quantifiers.*

The negation of a statement must be false if the given statement is true and must be true if the given statement is false, in all possible cases. Consider this statement.

All girls in the group are named Mary.

Many people would write the negation of this statement as "No girls in the group are named Mary" or "All girls in the group are not named Mary." But neither of these is correct. To see why, look at the three groups below.

Group I: Mary Jane Payne, Mary Meyer, Mary O'Hara
Group II: Mary Johnson, Lisa Pollak, Margaret Watson
Group III: Donna Garbarino, Paula Story, Rhonda Alessi, Kim Falgout

Aristotle, the first to systematize the logic we use in everyday life, appears above in a detail from the painting *The School of Athens,* by Raphael. He is shown debating a point with his teacher **Plato.**

These groups contain all possibilities that need to be considered. In Group I, *all* girls are named Mary. In Group II, *some* girls are named Mary (and some are not). In Group III, *no* girls are named Mary. Look at the truth values in **Table 3** on the next page, and keep in mind that "some" means "at least one (and possibly all)."

Table 3   Truth Value as Applied to:

	Group I	Group II	Group III
(1) All girls in the group are named Mary. (Given)	T	F	F
(2) No girls in the group are named Mary. (Possible negation)	F	F	T
(3) All girls in the group are not named Mary. (Possible negation)	F	F	T
(4) Some girls in the group are not named Mary. (Possible negation)	F	T	T

Negation

The negation of the given statement (1) must have opposite truth values in *all* cases. It can be seen that statements (2) and (3) do not satisfy this condition (for Group II), but statement (4) does. It may be concluded that the correct negation for "All girls in the group are named Mary" is "Some girls in the group are not named Mary." Other ways of stating the negation include the following.

> Not all girls in the group are named Mary.
>
> It is not the case that all girls in the group are named Mary.
>
> At least one girl in the group is not named Mary.

Table 4 shows how to find the negation of a statement involving quantifiers.

Table 4   Negations of Quantified Statements

Statement	Negation
All do.	Some do not. (Equivalently: Not all do.)
Some do.	None do. (Equivalently: All do not.)

The negation of the negation of a statement is simply the statement itself. For instance, the negations of the statements in the Negation column are simply the corresponding original statements in the Statement column. As an example, the negation of "Some do not" is "All do."

▌▌ **EXAMPLE 5** Forming Negations of Quantified Statements

Form the negation of each statement.

(a) Some cats have fleas.   **(b)** Some cats do not have fleas.

(c) No cats have fleas.

SOLUTION

(a) Because *some* means "at least one," the statement "Some cats have fleas" is really the same as "At least one cat has fleas." The negation of this is

"No cat has fleas."

(b) The statement "Some cats do not have fleas" claims that at least one cat, somewhere, does not have fleas. The negation of this is

"All cats have fleas."

(c) The negation is   "Some cats have fleas."

> Avoid the incorrect answer
> "All cats have fleas."

▐▐▐

Quantifiers and Number Sets

Earlier we introduced sets of numbers.

Sets of Numbers

Natural or Counting numbers $\{1, 2, 3, 4, \ldots\}$

Whole numbers $\{0, 1, 2, 3, 4, \ldots\}$

Integers $\{\ldots, -3, -2, -1, 0, 1, 2, 3, \ldots\}$

Rational numbers $\left\{\frac{p}{q} \mid p \text{ and } q \text{ are integers, and } q \neq 0\right\}$

(*Examples:* $\frac{3}{5}$, $-\frac{7}{9}$, 5, 0. Any rational number may be expressed as a terminating decimal number, such as 0.25, or a repeating decimal number, such as 0.666 . . . .)

Real numbers $\{x \mid x \text{ is a number that can be written as a decimal}\}$

Irrational numbers $\{x \mid x \text{ is a real number and } x \text{ cannot be written as a quotient of integers}\}$

(*Examples:* $\sqrt{2}$, $\sqrt[3]{4}$, π. Decimal representations of irrational numbers are neither terminating nor repeating.)

▌▌▌ **EXAMPLE 6**   Deciding Whether Quantified Statements Are True or False

Decide whether each statement involving a quantifier is *true* or *false*.

(a) There exists a whole number that is not a natural number.

(b) Every integer is a natural number.

(c) Every natural number is a rational number.

(d) There exists an irrational number that is not real.

SOLUTION

(a) Because there is such a whole number (it is 0), this statement is true.

(b) This statement is false, because we can find at least one integer that is not a natural number. For example, −1 is an integer but is not a natural number.

(c) Because every natural number can be written as a fraction with denominator 1, this statement is true.

(d) In order to be an irrational number, a number must first be real. Because we cannot give an irrational number that is not real, this statement is false. (Had we been able to find at least one, the statement would have then been true.)   ▉▉▉

3.1 EXERCISES

Decide whether each is a statement or is not a statement.

1. February 2, 2009, was a Monday.

2. The ZIP code for Oscar, LA, is 70762.

3. Listen, my children, and you shall hear of the midnight ride of Paul Revere.

4. Yield to oncoming traffic.

5. $5 + 9 \neq 14$ and $4 - 1 = 12$

6. $5 + 9 \neq 12$ or $4 - 2 = 5$

7. Some numbers are positive.

8. Millard Fillmore was president of the United States in 1851.

9. Accidents are the main cause of deaths of children under the age of 7.

10. *The Dark Knight* was the top-grossing movie of 2008.

11. Where are you going tomorrow?

12. Behave yourself and sit down.

13. Kevin "Catfish" McCarthy once took a prolonged continuous shower for 340 hours, 40 minutes.

14. One gallon of milk weighs more than 3 pounds.

Decide whether each statement is compound.

15. I read the *Detroit Free Press*, and I read the *Sacramento Bee*.

16. My brother got married in Copenhagen.

17. Tomorrow is Saturday.

18. Mamie Zwettler is younger than 18 years of age, and so is her friend Emma Lister.

19. Jay Beckenstein's wife loves Ben and Jerry's ice cream.

20. The sign on the back of the car read "Canada or bust!"

21. If Lorri Morgan sells her quota, then Michelle Cook will be happy.

22. If Bobby is a politician, then Mitch is a crook.

Write a negation for each statement.

23. Her aunt's name is Hermione.

24. The flowers are to be watered.

25. Every dog has its day.

26. No rain fell in southern California today.

27. Some books are longer than this book.

28. All students present will get another chance.

29. No computer repairman can play blackjack.

30. Some people have all the luck.

31. Everybody loves somebody sometime.

32. Everyone loves a winner.

Give a negation of each inequality. Do not use a slash symbol.

33. $x > 12$

34. $x < -6$

35. $x \geq 5$

36. $x \leq 19$

37. Try to negate the sentence "The exact number of words in this sentence is ten" and see what happens. Explain the problem that arises.

38. Explain why the negation of "$x > 5$" is not "$x < 5$."

Let p represent the statement "She has green eyes" and let q represent the statement "He is 60 years old." Translate each symbolic compound statement into words.

39. $\sim p$

40. $\sim q$

41. $p \wedge q$

42. $p \vee q$

43. $\sim p \vee q$

44. $p \wedge \sim q$

45. $\sim p \vee \sim q$

46. $\sim p \wedge \sim q$

47. $\sim(\sim p \wedge q)$

48. $\sim(p \vee \sim q)$

Let p represent the statement "Chris collects DVDs" and let q represent the statement "Josh is an art major." Convert each compound statement into symbols.

49. Chris collects DVDs and Josh is not an art major.

50. Chris does not collect DVDs or Josh is not an art major.

51. Chris does not collect DVDs or Josh is an art major.

52. Josh is an art major and Chris does not collect DVDs.

53. Neither Chris collects DVDs nor Josh is an art major.

54. Either Josh is an art major or Chris collects DVDs, and it is not the case that both Josh is an art major and Chris collects DVDs.

55. Incorrect use of quantifiers often is heard in everyday language. Suppose you hear that a local electronics chain is having a 40% off sale, and the radio advertisement states "All items are not available in all stores." Do you think that, literally translated, the ad really means what it says? What do you think is really meant? Explain your answer.

56. Repeat **Exercise 55** for the following: "All people don't have the time to devote to maintaining their vehicles properly."

Refer to the groups of art labeled A, B, *and* C, *and identify by letter the group or groups that are satisfied by the given statements involving quantifiers.*

A

B

C

57. All pictures have frames.

58. No picture has a frame.

59. At least one picture does not have a frame.

60. Not every picture has a frame.

61. At least one picture has a frame.

62. No picture does not have a frame.

63. All pictures do not have frames.

64. Not every picture does not have a frame.

Decide whether each statement in Exercises 65–74 involving a quantifier is true *or* false.

65. Every whole number is an integer.

66. Every natural number is an integer.

67. There exists a rational number that is not an integer.

68. There exists an integer that is not a natural number.

69. All rational numbers are real numbers.

70. All irrational numbers are real numbers.

71. Some rational numbers are not integers.

72. Some whole numbers are not rational numbers.

73. Each whole number is a positive number.

74. Each rational number is a positive number.

75. Explain the difference between the following statements.

> All students did not pass the test.
> Not all students passed the test.

76. The statement "For some real number x, $x^2 \geq 0$" is true. However, your friend does not understand why, because he claims that $x^2 \geq 0$ is true for *all* real numbers x (and not *some*). How would you explain his misconception to him?

77. Write the following statement using "every": There is no one here who has not done that at one time or another.

78. Only one of these statements is true. Which one is it?
A. For some real number x, $x \not< 0$.
B. For all real numbers x, $x^3 > 0$.
C. For all real numbers x less than 0, x^2 is also less than 0.
D. For some real number x, $x^2 < 0$.

▮ ▮ ▮▮ ▮ ▮ ▮ **3.2 TRUTH TABLES AND EQUIVALENT STATEMENTS**

Conjunctions • Disjunctions • Negations • Mathematical Statements • Truth Tables • Alternative Method for Constructing Truth Tables • Equivalent Statements and De Morgan's Laws

Conjunctions

Truth values of component statements are used to find truth values of compound statements. To begin, we must decide on truth values of the **conjunction p and q,** symbolized **$p \wedge q$.** Here, the connective *and* implies the idea of "both." The following statement is true, because each component statement is true.

Monday immediately follows Sunday and March immediately follows February.

True

On the other hand, the following statement is false, even though part of the statement (Monday immediately follows Sunday) is true.

Monday immediately follows Sunday and March immediately follows January.

False

For the conjunction p ∧ q to be true, both p and q must be true. This result is summarized by a table, called a **truth table,** which shows all four of the possible combinations of truth values for the conjunction *p and q.*

Truth Table for the Conjunction   *p* and *q*

p and q

p	*q*	*p* ∧ *q*
T	T	T
T	F	F
F	T	F
F	F	F

▮▮ **EXAMPLE 1**   Finding the Truth Value of a Conjunction

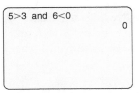

The calculator returns a "0" for 5 > 3 *and* 6 < 0, indicating that the statement is false.

Let *p* represent "5 > 3" and let *q* represent "6 < 0." Find the truth value of *p* ∧ *q*.

SOLUTION

Here *p* is true and *q* is false. Looking in the second row of the conjunction truth table shows that *p* ∧ *q* is false.   ▮▮▮

In some cases, the logical connective *but* is used in compound statements.

He wants to go to the mountains but she wants to go to the beach.

Here, *but* is used in place of *and* to give a different emphasis to the statement. We consider this statement as we would consider the conjunction using the word *and.* The truth table for the conjunction, given above, would apply.

Disjunctions

In ordinary language, the word *or* can be ambiguous. The expression "this or that" can mean either "this or that or both," or "this or that but not both." For example, consider the following statement.

I will paint the wall or I will paint the ceiling.

This statement probably means: "I will paint the wall or I will paint the ceiling or I will paint both." On the other hand, consider the following statement.

I will drive the Lexus or the BMW to the store.

It probably means "I will drive the Lexus, or I will drive the BMW, but I will not drive both."

The symbol ∨ represents the first *or* described. That is,

_p_ ∨ _q_   means   "_p_ or _q_ or both."   Disjunction

With this meaning of *or*, *p* ∨ *q* is called the **inclusive disjunction,** or just the **disjunction** of *p* and *q*. In everyday language, the disjunction implies the idea of "either." For example, consider the following disjunction.

I have a quarter or I have a dime.

It is true whenever I have either a quarter, a dime, or both. The only way this disjunction could be false would be if I had neither coin. ***The disjunction $p \lor q$ is false only if both component statements are false.***

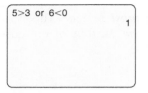

The calculator returns a "1" for $5 > 3$ *or* $6 < 0$, indicating that the statement is true.

Truth Table for the Disjunction *p or q*

	p or q	
p	*q*	$p \lor q$
T	T	T
T	F	T
F	T	T
F	F	F

███ **EXAMPLE 2** Finding the Truth Value of a Disjunction

Let *p* represent "$5 > 3$" and let *q* represent "$6 < 0$." Find the truth value of $p \lor q$.

SOLUTION

Here, as in **Example 1,** *p* is true and *q* is false. The second row of the disjunction truth table shows that $p \lor q$ is true. ███

The symbol $\geq$ is read **"is greater than or equal to,"** while $\leq$ is read **"is less than or equal to."** If *a* and *b* are real numbers, then $a \leq b$ is true if $a < b$ or $a = b$. **Table 5** in the margin shows several statements and the reasons they are true.

Table 5

Statement	Reason That It Is True
$8 \geq 8$	$8 = 8$
$3 \geq 1$	$3 > 1$
$-5 \leq -3$	$-5 < -3$
$-4 \leq -4$	$-4 = -4$

Negations

The **negation** of a statement *p*, symbolized $\sim p$, must have the opposite truth value from the statement *p* itself. This leads to the truth table for the negation.

Truth Table for the Negation *not p*

	not p
p	$\sim p$
T	F
F	T

███ **EXAMPLE 3** Finding the Truth Value of a Compound Statement

Suppose *p* is false, *q* is true, and *r* is false. What is the truth value of the compound statement $\sim p \land (q \lor \sim r)$?

SOLUTION

Here parentheses are used to group *q* and $\sim r$ together. Work first inside the parentheses. Because *r* is false, $\sim r$ will be true. Because $\sim r$ is true and *q* is true, find the truth value of $q \lor \sim r$ by looking in the first row of the *or* truth table. This row gives the result T.

Because *p* is false, $\sim p$ is true, and the final truth value of $\sim p \land (q \lor \sim r)$ is found in the top row of the *and* truth table. From the *and* truth table, when $\sim p$ is true, and $q \lor \sim r$ is true, the statement

$$\sim p \land (q \lor \sim r) \quad \text{is true.}$$

We can use a short-cut symbolic method that involves replacing the statements with their truth values, letting T represent a true statement and F represent a false statement.

$$\sim p \wedge (q \vee \sim r)$$
$$\sim F \wedge (T \vee \sim F) \quad \text{Work within parentheses first.}$$
$$T \wedge (T \vee T) \quad \sim F \text{ gives T.}$$
$$T \wedge T \quad T \vee T \text{ gives T.}$$

The compound statement is true. → T   T ∧ T gives T.   ▌▌▌

Mathematical Statements

We can use truth tables to determine the truth values of compound mathematical statements.

▌▌ **EXAMPLE 4** Deciding Whether a Compound Mathematical Statement Is True or False

Let p represent the statement $3 > 2$, q represent $5 < 4$, and r represent $3 < 8$. Decide whether each statement is *true* or *false*.

(a) $\sim p \wedge \sim q$ **(b)** $\sim(p \wedge q)$ **(c)** $(\sim p \wedge r) \vee (\sim q \wedge \sim p)$

SOLUTION

(a) Because p is true, $\sim p$ is false. By the *and* truth table, if one part of an "and" statement is false, the entire statement is false.

$$\sim p \wedge \sim q \quad \text{is false.}$$

(b) For $\sim(p \wedge q)$, first work within the parentheses. Because p is true and q is false, $p \wedge q$ is false by the *and* truth table. Next, apply the negation. The negation of a false statement is true.

$$\sim(p \wedge q) \quad \text{is true.}$$

(c) Here p is true, q is false, and r is true. This makes $\sim p$ false and $\sim q$ true. By the *and* truth table, $\sim p \wedge r$ is false, and $\sim q \wedge \sim p$ is also false. By the *or* truth table,

$$(\sim p \wedge r) \vee (\sim q \wedge \sim p) \quad \text{is false.}$$
$$\downarrow \qquad\qquad \downarrow$$
$$\text{F} \quad \vee \quad \text{F}$$

(Alternatively, see **Example 8(b)**.)   ▌▌▌

When a quantifier is used with a conjunction or a disjunction, we must be careful in determining the truth value, as shown in the following example.

▌▌ **EXAMPLE 5** Deciding Whether a Quantified Mathematical Statement Is True or False

Decide whether each statement is *true* or *false*.

(a) For some real number x, $x < 5$ and $x > 2$.

(b) For every real number x, $x > 0$ or $x < 1$.

(c) For all real numbers x, $x^2 > 0$.

SOLUTION

(a) Replacing x with 3 (as an example) gives $3 < 5$ and $3 > 2$. Because both $3 < 5$ and $3 > 2$ are true statements, the given statement is true by the *and* truth table. (Remember: *Some* means "at least one.")

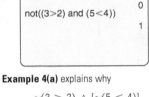

not(3>2) and not (5<4)	0
not((3>2) and (5<4))	1

Example 4(a) explains why

$$\sim(3 > 2) \wedge [\sim(5 < 4)]$$

is false. The calculator returns a 0. For a true statement such as

$$\sim[(3 > 2) \wedge (5 < 4)],$$

it returns a 1.

George Boole (1815–1864) grew up in poverty. His father, a London tradesman, gave him his first mathematics lessons and taught him to make optical instruments. Boole was largely self-educated. At 16 he worked in an elementary school and by age 20 had opened his own school. He studied mathematics in his spare time. He died of lung disease at age 49.

Boole's ideas have been used in the design of computers and telephone systems.

(b) No matter which real number might be tried as a replacement for x, at least one of the two statements

$$x > 0, \quad x < 1$$

will be true. Because an "or" statement is true if one or both component statements are true, the entire statement as given is true.

(c) Because the quantifier is a universal quantifier, we need only find one case in which the inequality is false to make the entire statement false. Can we find a real number whose square is not positive (that is, not greater than 0)? Yes, we can—0 is the *only* real number whose square is not positive. This statement is false.   ■■■

For Further Thought

Whose Picture Am I Looking At?

Raymond Smullyan is one of today's foremost writers of logic puzzles. This professor of mathematics and philosophy is now retired from Indiana University and has written several books on recreational logic, including *What Is the Name of This Book?*, *The Lady or the Tiger?*, and *Alice in Puzzleland*. The first of these includes the following puzzle, which has been around for many years.

For Group or Individual Investigation

A man is looking at a portrait. Someone asked him, "Whose picture are you looking at?" He replied: "Brothers and sisters, I have none, but this man's father is my father's son. ("This man's father" means, of course, the father of the man in the picture.)

Whose picture was the man looking at? (The answer is on page 96.)

p	q	Compound Statement
T	T	
T	F	
F	T	
F	F	

Truth Tables

In the preceding examples, the truth value for a given statement was found by going back to the basic truth tables. In the long run, it is easier to first create a complete truth table for the given statement itself. Then final truth values can be read directly from this table.

In this book we use the standard format shown in the margin for listing the possible truth values in compound statements involving two component statements.

■■ EXAMPLE 6 Constructing a Truth Table

Consider the statement $(\sim p \wedge q) \vee \sim q$.

(a) Construct a truth table.

(b) Suppose both p and q are true. Find the truth value of the compound statement.

SOLUTION

(a) Begin by listing all possible combinations of truth values for p and q, as above. Then list the truth values of $\sim p$, which are the opposite of those of p, as shown in the table in the margin.

p	q	$\sim p$
T	T	F
T	F	F
F	T	T
F	F	T

Use only the "~p" column and the "q" column, along with the *and* truth table, to find the truth values of $\sim p \wedge q$. List them in a separate column.

p	q	~p	~p ∧ q
T	T	F	F
T	F	F	F
F	T	T	T
F	F	T	F

Next include a column for $\sim q$.

p	q	~p	~p ∧ q	~q
T	T	F	F	F
T	F	F	F	T
F	T	T	T	F
F	F	T	F	T

Finally, make a column for the entire compound statement. To find the truth values, use *or* to combine $\sim p \wedge q$ with $\sim q$.

p	q	~p	~p ∧ q	~q	(~p ∧ q) ∨ ~q
T	T	F	F	F	F
T	F	F	F	T	T
F	T	T	T	F	T
F	F	T	F	T	T

(b) Look in the first row of the final truth table above, where both p and q have truth value T. Read across the row to find that the compound statement is false.   ▌▌▌

▌▌ **EXAMPLE 7** Constructing a Truth Table

Construct the truth table for $p \wedge (\sim p \vee \sim q)$.

SOLUTION
Proceed as shown.

p	q	~p	~q	~p ∨ ~q	p ∧ (~p ∨ ~q)
T	T	F	F	F	F
T	F	F	T	T	T
F	T	T	F	T	F
F	F	T	T	T	F

If a compound statement involves three component statements p, q, and r, we will use the following standard format in setting up the truth table.

p	q	r	Compound Statement
T	T	T	
T	T	F	
T	F	T	
T	F	F	
F	T	T	
F	T	F	
F	F	T	
F	F	F	

Emilie, Marquise du Châtelet
(1706–1749) participated in the scientific activity of the generation after Newton and Leibniz. Educated in science, music, and literature, she was studying mathematics at the time (1733) she began a long intellectual relationship with the philosopher **François Voltaire** (1694–1778). She and Voltaire competed independently in 1738 for a prize offered by the French Academy on the subject of fire. Although du Châtelet did not win, her dissertation was published by the academy in 1744.

▌▌▌

▐▐ **EXAMPLE 8** Constructing a Truth Table

Consider the statement $(\sim p \wedge r) \vee (\sim q \wedge \sim p)$.

(a) Construct a truth table.

(b) Suppose p is true, q is false, and r is true. Find the truth value of this statement.

SOLUTION

(a) There are three component statements: p, q, and r. The truth table thus requires eight rows to list all possible combinations of truth values of p, q, and r. The final truth table can be found in much the same way as the ones earlier.

p	q	r	$\sim p$	$\sim p \wedge r$	$\sim q$	$\sim q \wedge \sim p$	$(\sim p \wedge r) \vee (\sim q \wedge \sim p)$
T	T	T	F	F	F	F	F
T	T	F	F	F	F	F	F
T	F	T	F	F	T	F	F
T	F	F	F	F	T	F	F
F	T	T	T	T	F	F	T
F	T	F	T	T	F	F	F
F	F	T	T	T	T	T	T
F	F	F	T	F	T	T	T

(b) By the third row of the truth table in part (a), the compound statement is false. (This is an alternative method for working part (c) of **Example 4.**)   ▐▐▐

> **PROBLEM-SOLVING HINT** One strategy for problem solving is to notice a pattern and use inductive reasoning. This strategy is applied in the next example.

▐▐ **EXAMPLE 9** Using Inductive Reasoning

If n is a counting number, and a logical statement is composed of n component statements, how many rows will appear in the truth table for the compound statement?

SOLUTION

To answer this question, we examine some of the earlier truth tables in this section. The truth table for the negation has one statement and two rows. The truth tables for the conjunction and the disjunction have two component statements, and each has four rows. The truth table in **Example 8(a)** has three component statements and eight rows.

Summarizing these in **Table 6** (seen in the margin) reveals a pattern encountered earlier. Inductive reasoning leads us to the conjecture that if a logical statement is composed of n component statements, it will have 2^n rows. This can be proved using more advanced concepts.   ▐▐▐

The result of **Example 9** is reminiscent of the formula for the number of subsets of a set having n elements.

Number of Rows in a Truth Table

A logical statement having n component statements will have 2^n rows in its truth table.

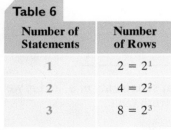

Table 6

Number of Statements	Number of Rows
1	$2 = 2^1$
2	$4 = 2^2$
3	$8 = 2^3$

Answer to the problem of *Whose Picture Am I Looking At?*

Most people give the incorrect answer that the man is looking at his own picture. The correct answer is that the man is looking at a picture of his son.

Smullyan helps the reader to understand why this is correct. Because he has no siblings, "my father's son" must refer to the man himself, so the second part of the problem can be reworded "This man's father is myself." Thus, the man in the picture must be his own son.

Alternative Method for Constructing Truth Tables

After making a reasonable number of truth tables, some people prefer the shortcut method shown in **Example 10,** which repeats **Examples 6 and 8.**

EXAMPLE 10 Constructing Truth Tables

Construct the truth table for each compound statement.

(a) $(\sim p \wedge q) \vee \sim q$ **(b)** $(\sim p \wedge r) \vee (\sim q \wedge \sim p)$

SOLUTION

(a) Start by inserting truth values for $\sim p$ and for q. Then, use the *and* truth table to obtain the truth values for $\sim p \wedge q$.

p	q	($\sim p$	$\wedge$	q)	$\vee$	$\sim q$
T	T	F		T		
T	F	F		F		
F	T	T		T		
F	F	T		F		

p	q	($\sim p$	$\wedge$	q)	$\vee$	$\sim q$
T	T	F	F	T		
T	F	F	F	F		
F	T	T	T	T		
F	F	T	F	F		

Now disregard the two preliminary columns of truth values for $\sim p$ and for q, and insert truth values for $\sim q$. Finally, use the *or* truth table.

p	q	($\sim p \wedge q$)	$\vee$	$\sim q$
T	T	F		F
T	F	F		T
F	T	T		F
F	F	F		T

p	q	($\sim p \wedge q$)	$\vee$	$\sim q$
T	T	F	F	F
T	F	F	T	T
F	T	T	T	F
F	F	F	T	T

These steps can be summarized as follows.

p	q	($\sim p$	$\wedge$	q)	$\vee$	$\sim q$
T	T	F	F	T	F	F
T	F	F	F	F	T	T
F	T	T	T	T	T	F
F	F	T	F	F	T	T
		①	②	①	④	③

The circled numbers indicate the order in which the various columns of the truth table were found.

(b) Work as follows.

p	q	r	($\sim p$	$\wedge$	r)	$\vee$	($\sim q$	$\wedge$	$\sim p$)
T	T	T	F	F	T	F	F	F	F
T	T	F	F	F	F	F	F	F	F
T	F	T	F	F	T	F	T	F	F
T	F	F	F	F	F	F	T	F	F
F	T	T	T	T	T	T	F	F	T
F	T	F	T	F	F	F	F	F	T
F	F	T	T	T	T	T	T	T	T
F	F	F	T	F	F	T	T	T	T
			①	②	①	⑤	③	④	③

The circled numbers indicate the order.

Equivalent Statements and De Morgan's Laws

Two statements are **equivalent** if they have the same truth value in *every* possible situation. The columns of the two truth tables that were the last to be completed will be the same for equivalent statements.

▮▮ **EXAMPLE 11** Deciding Whether Two Statements Are Equivalent

Are the following two statements equivalent?

$$\sim p \wedge \sim q \quad \text{and} \quad \sim(p \vee q)$$

SOLUTION

Construct a truth table for each statement.

p	q	$\sim p \wedge \sim q$	p	q	$\sim(p \vee q)$
T	T	F	T	T	F
T	F	F	T	F	F
F	T	F	F	T	F
F	F	T	F	F	T

Because the truth values are the same in all cases, as shown in the columns in color, the statements $\sim p \wedge \sim q$ and $\sim(p \vee q)$ are equivalent. Equivalence is written with a three-bar symbol, $\equiv$.

$$\sim p \wedge \sim q \equiv \sim(p \vee q)$$ ▮▮▮

In the same way, the statements $\sim p \vee \sim q$ and $\sim(p \wedge q)$ are equivalent. We call these equivalences *De Morgan's laws*.

De Morgan's Laws for Logical Statements

For any statements p and q, the following equivalences are valid.

$$\sim(p \vee q) \equiv \sim p \wedge \sim q \quad \text{and} \quad \sim(p \wedge q) \equiv \sim p \vee \sim q$$

(Compare the logic statements of De Morgan's laws with the set versions on **page 64.**) De Morgan's laws can be used to find the negations of certain compound statements.

▮▮ **EXAMPLE 12** Applying De Morgan's Laws

Find a negation of each statement by applying De Morgan's laws.

(a) I got an A or I got a B.   **(b)** She won't try and he will succeed.

(c) $\sim p \vee (q \wedge \sim p)$

SOLUTION

(a) If p represents "I got an A" and q represents "I got a B," then the compound statement is symbolized $p \vee q$. The negation of $p \vee q$ is $\sim(p \vee q)$. By one of De Morgan's laws, this is equivalent to

$$\sim p \wedge \sim q,$$

or, in words,   **I didn't get an A and I didn't get a B.**

This negation is reasonable—the original statement says that I got either an A or a B. The negation says that I didn't get *either* grade.

(b) From one of De Morgan's laws, $\sim(p \wedge q) \equiv \sim p \vee \sim q$, so the negation becomes

She will try or he won't succeed.

(c) Negate both component statements and change $\vee$ to $\wedge$.

$$\sim[\sim p \vee (q \wedge \sim p)] \equiv p \wedge \sim(q \wedge \sim p)$$

Now apply De Morgan's law again.

$$p \wedge \sim(q \wedge \sim p) \equiv p \wedge (\sim q \vee \sim(\sim p))$$
$$\equiv p \wedge (\sim q \vee p)$$

A truth table will show that the statements

$\sim p \vee (q \wedge \sim p)$ and $p \wedge (\sim q \vee p)$ are negations of each other. ▪▪▪

3.2 EXERCISES

Use the concepts introduced in this section to answer Exercises 1–6.

1. If q is false, what must be the truth value of the statement $(p \wedge \sim q) \wedge q$?

2. If q is true, what must be the truth value of the statement $q \vee (q \wedge \sim p)$?

3. If the statement $p \wedge q$ is true, and p is true, then q must be _____.

4. If the statement $p \vee q$ is false, and p is false, then q must be _____.

5. If $\sim(p \vee q)$ is true, what must be the truth values of the component statements?

6. If $\sim(p \wedge q)$ is false, what must be the truth values of the component statements?

Let p represent a false statement and let q represent a true statement. Find the truth value of the given compound statement.

7. $\sim p$ **8.** $\sim q$

9. $p \vee q$ **10.** $p \wedge q$

11. $p \vee \sim q$ **12.** $\sim p \wedge q$

13. $\sim p \vee \sim q$ **14.** $p \wedge \sim q$

15. $\sim(p \wedge \sim q)$ **16.** $\sim(\sim p \vee \sim q)$

17. $\sim[\sim p \wedge (\sim q \vee p)]$ **18.** $\sim[(\sim p \wedge \sim q) \vee \sim q]$

19. Is the statement $6 \geq 2$ a conjunction or a disjunction? Why?

20. Why is the statement $8 \geq 3$ true? Why is $5 \geq 5$ true?

Let p represent a true statement, and q and r represent false statements. Find the truth value of the given compound statement.

21. $(p \wedge r) \vee \sim q$ **22.** $(q \vee \sim r) \wedge p$

23. $p \wedge (q \vee r)$ **24.** $(\sim p \wedge q) \vee \sim r$

25. $\sim(p \wedge q) \wedge (r \vee \sim q)$ **26.** $(\sim r \wedge \sim q) \vee (\sim r \wedge q)$

27. $\sim[(\sim p \wedge q) \vee r]$ **28.** $\sim[r \vee (\sim q \wedge \sim p)]$

29. $\sim[\sim q \vee (r \wedge \sim p)]$

30. What is the only possible case in which the statement $(p \wedge \sim q) \wedge \sim r$ is true?

Let p represent the statement $16 < 8$, let q represent the statement $5 \not> 4$, and let r represent the statement $17 \leq 17$. Find the truth value of the given compound statement.

31. $p \wedge r$ **32.** $p \vee \sim q$

33. $\sim q \vee \sim r$ **34.** $\sim p \wedge \sim r$

35. $(p \wedge q) \vee r$ **36.** $\sim p \vee (\sim r \vee \sim q)$

37. $(\sim r \wedge q) \vee \sim p$ **38.** $\sim(p \vee \sim q) \vee \sim r$

Give the number of rows in the truth table for each compound statement.

39. $p \vee \sim r$ **40.** $p \wedge (r \wedge \sim s)$

41. $(\sim p \wedge q) \vee (\sim r \vee \sim s) \wedge r$

42. $[(p \vee q) \wedge (r \wedge s)] \wedge (t \vee \sim p)$

43. $[(\sim p \wedge \sim q) \wedge (\sim r \wedge s \wedge \sim t)] \wedge (\sim u \vee \sim v)$

44. $[(\sim p \wedge \sim q) \vee (\sim r \vee \sim s)]$
     $\vee [(\sim m \wedge \sim n) \wedge (u \wedge \sim v)]$

45. If the truth table for a certain compound statement has 128 rows, how many distinct component statements does it have?

46. Is it possible for the truth table of a compound statement to have exactly 54 rows? Why or why not?

Construct a truth table for each compound statement.

47. $\sim p \wedge q$ **48.** $\sim p \vee \sim q$

49. $\sim(p \wedge q)$ **50.** $p \vee \sim q$

51. $(q \vee \sim p) \vee \sim q$ **52.** $(p \wedge \sim q) \wedge p$

53. $\sim q \land (\sim p \lor q)$ **54.** $\sim p \lor (\sim q \land \sim p)$

55. $(p \lor \sim q) \land (p \land q)$

56. $(\sim p \land \sim q) \lor (\sim p \lor q)$

57. $(\sim p \land q) \land r$

58. $r \lor (p \land \sim q)$

59. $(\sim p \land \sim q) \lor (\sim r \lor \sim p)$

60. $(\sim r \lor \sim p) \land (\sim p \lor \sim q)$

61. $\sim(\sim p \land \sim q) \lor (\sim r \lor \sim s)$

62. $(\sim r \lor s) \land (\sim p \land q)$

Use one of De Morgan's laws to write the negation of each statement.

63. You can pay me now or you can pay me later.

64. I am not going or she is going.

65. It is summer and there is no snow.

66. $\frac{1}{2}$ is a positive number and -9 is less than zero.

67. I said yes but she said no.

68. Dan La Chapelle tried to sell the software, but he was unable to do so.

69. $6 - 1 = 5$ and $9 + 13 \neq 7$

70. $8 < 10$ or $5 \neq 2$

71. Prancer or Vixen will lead Santa's reindeer sleigh next Christmas.

72. The lawyer and the client appeared in court.

Identify each statement as true *or* false.

73. For every real number x, $x < 14$ or $x > 6$.

74. For every real number x, $x > 9$ or $x < 9$.

75. There exists an integer n such that $n > 0$ and $n < 0$.

76. For some integer n, $n \geq 3$ and $n \leq 3$.

77. Complete the truth table for *exclusive disjunction*. The symbol $\underline{\lor}$ represents "one or the other is true, but not both."

p	q	$p \underline{\lor} q$
T	T	
T	F	
F	T	
F	F	

Exclusive disjunction

78. Attorneys sometimes use the phrase "and/or." This phrase corresponds to which usage of the word *or*: inclusive or exclusive disjunction?

Decide whether each compound statement is true *or* false. *Remember that* $\underline{\lor}$ *is the* exclusive disjunction of **Exercise 77.**

79. $3 + 1 = 4 \underline{\lor} 2 + 5 = 7$

80. $3 + 1 = 4 \underline{\lor} 2 + 5 = 10$

81. $3 + 1 = 6 \underline{\lor} 2 + 5 = 7$

82. $3 + 1 = 12 \underline{\lor} 2 + 5 = 10$

83. In his book *The Lady or the Tiger and Other Logic Puzzles,* Raymond Smullyan proposes the following problem. It is taken from the classic Frank Stockton short story, in which a prisoner must make a choice between two doors: behind one is a beautiful lady, and behind the other is a hungry tiger.

    What if each door has a sign, and the man knows that only one sign is true?

    The sign on Door 1 reads:

IN THIS ROOM THERE IS A LADY AND IN THE OTHER ROOM THERE IS A TIGER.

    The sign on Door 2 reads:

IN ONE OF THESE ROOMS THERE IS A LADY AND IN ONE OF THESE ROOMS THERE IS A TIGER.

    With this information, the man is able to choose the correct door. Can you?

84. In Raymond Smullyan's books, he writes about an island in which certain inhabitants are called knights and others are called knaves. Knights always tell the truth, and knaves always lie. Every inhabitant is either a knight or a knave.

    Three inhabitants—A, B, and C—were standing together in a garden. A stranger passed by and asked A, "Are you a knight or a knave?" A answered, but rather indistinctly, so the stranger could not make out what he said. The stranger then asked B, "What did A say?" B replied "A said that he is a knave." At this point, the third inhabitant, C, said, "Don't believe B; he is lying!"

    The question is, what are B and C?

3.3 THE CONDITIONAL AND CIRCUITS

Conditionals • Negation of a Conditional • Circuits

In his April 21, 1989, five-star review of *Field of Dreams*, the *Chicago Sun-Times* movie critic Roger Ebert gave an explanation of why the movie has become an American classic.

There is a speech in this movie about baseball that is so simple and true that it is heartbreaking. And the whole attitude toward the players reflects that attitude. Why do they come back from the great beyond and play in this cornfield? Not to make any kind of vast, earthshattering statement, but simply to hit a few and field a few, and remind us of a good and innocent time.

The photo above was taken in 2007 in Dyersville, Iowa, at the actual scene of the filming. The carving "Ray Loves Annie" in the bleacher seats can be seen in a quick shot during the movie. It has weathered over time.

Conditionals

"If you build it, he will come."
— The Voice in the movie *Field of Dreams*

Ray Kinsella, an Iowa farmer in the movie *Field of Dreams*, hears a voice from the sky. No one else, including his wife Annie, can hear it. Ray interprets it as a promise that if he builds a baseball field in his cornfield, then the ghost of Shoeless Joe Jackson (a baseball star in the early days of the twentieth century) would come to play on it.

This promise came in the form of a conditional statement. A **conditional** statement is a compound statement that uses the connective *if . . . then*.

> *If* I read for too long, *then* I get tired.
> *If* looks could kill, *then* I would be dead.
> *If* he doesn't get back soon, *then* you should go look for him.

Conditional statements

In each of these conditional statements, the component coming after the word *if* gives a condition (but not necessarily the only condition) under which the statement coming after *then* will be true. For example, "If it is over 90°, then I'll go to the mountains" tells one possible condition under which I will go to the mountains—if the temperature is over 90°.

The conditional is written with an arrow, so "if p, then q" is symbolized as follows.

$$p \rightarrow q \qquad \text{If } p, \text{then } q.$$

We read $p \rightarrow q$ as "**p implies q**" or "**if p, then q.**" In the conditional $p \rightarrow q$, the statement p is the **antecedent,** while q is the **consequent.**

The conditional connective may not always be explicitly stated. That is, it may be "hidden" in an everyday expression. For example, consider the following statement.

$$\text{Big girls don't cry.}$$

It can be written in *if . . . then* form as

$$\textit{If } \text{you're a big girl, } \textit{then } \text{you don't cry.}$$

As another example, consider this statement.

$$\text{It is difficult to study when you are distracted.}$$

It can be written

$$\textit{If } \text{you are distracted, } \textit{then } \text{it is difficult to study.}$$

In the quotation "If you build it, he will come" from the movie *Field of Dreams*, the word "then" is not stated but understood from the context of the statement. "You build it" is the antecedent, and "he will come" is the consequent.

The conditional truth table is a little harder to define than the tables in the previous section. To see how to define the conditional truth table, we analyze a statement made by a politician, Senator Laura Kennedy.

$$\text{If I am elected, then taxes will go down.}$$

There are four possible combinations of truth values for the two component statements. Let p represent "I am elected," and let q represent "Taxes will go down."

$\sqrt[3]{250}$ $90°$ $(0, -3)$

θ $45.5 \div 2^{-1}$ ∞

$x = (4+8)-3$ $|a|$

$y = -x + 2$ $\frac{1}{4}$

10^2 $\geq$ $f(x) =$

The importance of **symbols** was emphasized by the American philosopher-logician **Charles Sanders Peirce** (1839–1914), who asserted the nature of humans as symbol-using or sign-using organisms. Symbolic notation is half of mathematics, Bertrand Russell once said.

As we analyze the four possibilities, it is helpful to think in terms of the following: "Did Senator Laura Kennedy lie?" If she lied, then the conditional statement is considered false. If she did not lie, then the conditional statement is considered true.

Possibility	Elected?	Taxes Go Down?	
1	Yes	Yes	p is T, q is T.
2	Yes	No	p is T, q is F.
3	No	Yes	p is F, q is T.
4	No	No	p is F, q is F.

The four possibilities are as follows.

1. In the first case assume that the senator was elected and taxes did go down (p is T, q is T). The senator told the truth, so place T in the first row of the truth table. (We do not claim that taxes went down *because* she was elected. It is possible that she had nothing to do with it at all.)

2. In the second case assume that the senator was elected and taxes did not go down (p is T, q is F). Then the senator did not tell the truth (that is, she lied). So we put F in the second row of the truth table.

3. In the third case assume that the senator was defeated, but taxes went down anyway (p is F, q is T). The senator did not lie. She only promised a tax reduction if she were elected. She said nothing about what would happen if she were not elected. In fact, her campaign promise gives no information about what would happen if she lost. Because we cannot say that the senator lied, place T in the third row of the truth table. (See the margin note.)

4. In the last case assume that the senator was defeated and taxes did not go down (p is F, q is F). We cannot blame her, because she only promised to reduce taxes if elected. Thus, T goes in the last row of the truth table.

You Lie! (or Do You?) Granted, the T for Case 3 is less obvious than the F for Case 2. However, the laws of symbolic logic permit only one of two truth values. Since no lie can be established in Case 3, we give the senator the benefit of the doubt. Likewise, *any* conditional statement is declared to be true whenever its antecedent is false.

The completed truth table for the conditional is defined as follows.

Truth Table for the Conditional If p, then q		
If p, then q		
p	q	$p \rightarrow q$
T	T	T
T	F	F
F	T	T
F	F	T

The use of the conditional connective in no way implies a cause-and-effect relationship. Any two statements may have an arrow placed between them to create a compound statement. Consider this example.

If I pass mathematics, then the sun will rise the next day.

It is true, because the consequent is true. (See the special characteristics following **Example 1** on the next page.) There is, however, no cause-and-effect connection between my passing mathematics and the rising of the sun. The sun will rise no matter what grade I get.

▌▌ **EXAMPLE 1** Finding the Truth Value of a Conditional

Given that p, q, and r are all false, find the truth value of the statement.

$$(p \rightarrow \sim q) \rightarrow (\sim r \rightarrow q)$$

SOLUTION

Using the short-cut method explained in **Example 3** of the previous section, we can replace p, q, and r with F (since each is false) and proceed as before, using the negation and conditional truth tables as necessary.

$$\begin{array}{ccc} (p \rightarrow \sim q) & \rightarrow & (\sim r \rightarrow q) \\ (F \rightarrow \sim F) & \rightarrow & (\sim F \rightarrow F) \\ (F \rightarrow T) & \rightarrow & (T \rightarrow F) \quad \text{Use the negation truth table.} \\ T & \rightarrow & F \quad \text{Use the conditional truth table.} \\ & F & \end{array}$$

The statement $(p \rightarrow \sim q) \rightarrow (\sim r \rightarrow q)$ is false when p, q, and r are all false. ▌▌▌

Special Characteristics of Conditional Statements

1. $p \rightarrow q$ is false only when the antecedent is *true* and the consequent is *false*.

2. If the antecedent is *false*, then $p \rightarrow q$ is automatically *true*.

3. If the consequent is *true*, then $p \rightarrow q$ is automatically *true*.

▌▌ **EXAMPLE 2** Determining Whether a Conditional Is True or False

Write *true* or *false* for each statement. Here T represents a true statement, and F represents a false statement.

(a) $T \rightarrow (7 = 3)$ **(b)** $(8 < 2) \rightarrow F$ **(c)** $(4 \neq 3 + 1) \rightarrow T$

SOLUTION

(a) Because the antecedent is true, while the consequent, $7 = 3$, is false, the given statement is false by the first point mentioned above.

(b) The antecedent is false, so the given statement is true by the second observation.

(c) The consequent is true, making the statement true by the third characteristic of conditional statements. ▌▌▌

▌▌ **EXAMPLE 3** Constructing Truth Tables

Construct a truth table for each statement.

(a) $(\sim p \rightarrow \sim q) \rightarrow (\sim p \wedge q)$ **(b)** $(p \rightarrow q) \rightarrow (\sim p \vee q)$

SOLUTION

(a) Insert the truth values of $\sim p$ and $\sim q$. Find the truth values of $\sim p \rightarrow \sim q$.

p	q	$\sim p$	$\sim q$	$\sim p \rightarrow \sim q$
T	T	F	F	T
T	F	F	T	T
F	T	T	F	F
F	F	T	T	T

PROGRAM:SIGN
: Input A
: If A>0
: Then
: Disp "POSITIVE"
:
:

PROGRAM:SIGN
:
: Else
: Disp "NOT POSITIVE"
: End
:

prgmSIGN
?3
POSITIVE
                    Done

prgmSIGN
?-5
NOT POSITIVE
                    Done

Conditional statements are useful in writing programs. The short program in the first two screens determines whether a number is positive. Notice the lines that begin with *If* and *Then*.

Next use $\sim p$ and q to find the truth values of $\sim p \land q$.

p	q	$\sim p$	$\sim q$	$\sim p \to \sim q$	$\sim p \land q$
T	T	F	F	T	F
T	F	F	T	T	F
F	T	T	F	F	T
F	F	T	T	T	F

Now find the truth values of $(\sim p \to \sim q) \to (\sim p \land q)$.

p	q	$\sim p$	$\sim q$	$\sim p \to \sim q$	$\sim p \land q$	$(\sim p \to \sim q) \to (\sim p \land q)$
T	T	F	F	T	F	F
T	F	F	T	T	F	F
F	T	T	F	F	T	T
F	F	T	T	T	F	F

(b) For $(p \to q) \to (\sim p \lor q)$, go through steps similar to the ones above.

p	q	$p \to q$	$\sim p$	$\sim p \lor q$	$(p \to q) \to (\sim p \lor q)$
T	T	T	F	T	T
T	F	F	F	F	T
F	T	T	T	T	T
F	F	T	T	T	T

▮▮▮

As the truth table in **Example 3(b)** shows, the statement

$$(p \to q) \to (\sim p \lor q)$$

is always true, no matter what the truth values of the components. Such a statement is called a **tautology.** Several other examples of tautologies (as can be checked by forming truth tables) are

$$p \lor \sim p, \quad p \to p, \quad \text{and} \quad (\sim p \lor \sim q) \to \sim (p \land q). \quad \text{Tautologies}$$

The truth tables in **Example 3** also could have been found by the alternative method shown in **Section 3.2.**

Negation of a Conditional

Suppose that someone makes the following conditional statement.

> "If it rains, then I take my umbrella."

When will the person have lied to you? The only case in which you would have been misled is when it rains *and* the person does *not* take the umbrella. Letting p represent "it rains" and q represent "I take my umbrella," you might suspect that the symbolic statement

$$p \land \sim q$$

is a candidate for the negation of $p \to q$. This would imply that

$$\sim (p \to q) \equiv p \land \sim q.$$

This is indeed the case, as the following truth table indicates.

p	q	$p \to q$	$\sim (p \to q)$	$\sim q$	$p \land \sim q$
T	T	T	F	F	F
T	F	F	T	T	T
F	T	T	F	F	F
F	F	T	F	T	F

↑ $\quad$ ↑
=

In the 1959 Disney short film *Donald in Mathmagicland,* Donald Duck, dressed as Alice from Lewis Carroll's *Through the Looking Glass,* is attacked by a "none-too-friendly group of chess pieces." Logic and **chess** have been paired for centuries. Most scholars agree that chess dates back at least 1500 years, coming from Northern India and Afghanistan following trade routes through Persia.

Good chess players rely on memory, imagination, determination, and inspiration. They are pattern thinkers that use long-established sets of consequences and probabilities.

In the end, logic does not necessarily dictate the final outcome of any chess game, for if it did, humans would not stand a chance when playing faceless, number-crunching computers.
© Disney Enterprises, Inc.

Sources: www.imdb.com, Walter A. Smart.

Negation of $p \rightarrow q$

The negation of $p \rightarrow q$ is $p \wedge \sim q$.

Because

$$\sim(p \rightarrow q) \equiv p \wedge \sim q,$$

by negating each expression we have

$$\sim[\sim(p \rightarrow q)] \equiv \sim(p \wedge \sim q).$$

The left side of the above equivalence is $p \rightarrow q$, and one of De Morgan's laws can be applied to the right side.

$$p \rightarrow q \equiv \sim p \vee \sim(\sim q)$$
$$p \rightarrow q \equiv \sim p \vee q$$

This final row indicates that a conditional may be written as a disjunction.

Writing a Conditional as a Disjunction

$p \rightarrow q$ is equivalent to $\sim p \vee q$.

▮▮ **EXAMPLE 4** Determining Negations

Determine the negation of each statement.

(a) If you build it, he will come.　　**(b)** All dogs have fleas.

> Do not try to negate a conditional with another conditional.

SOLUTION

(a) If b represents "you build it" and q represents "he will come," then the given statement can be symbolized by $b \rightarrow q$. The negation of $b \rightarrow q$, as shown earlier, is $b \wedge \sim q$, so the negation of the statement is

You build it and he will not come.

(b) First, we must restate the given statement in *if . . . then* form.

If it is a dog, then it has fleas.

Based on our earlier discussion, the negation is

It is a dog and it does not have fleas.　　▮▮▮

As seen in **Example 4,** the negation of a conditional statement is written as a conjunction.

▮▮ **EXAMPLE 5** Determining Statements Equivalent to Conditionals

Write each conditional as an equivalent statement without using *if . . . then*.

(a) If the Indians win the pennant, then Johnny will go to the World Series.

(b) If it's Borden's, it's got to be good.

SOLUTION

(a) Because the conditional $p \rightarrow q$ is equivalent to $\sim p \vee q$, let p represent "The Indians win the pennant" and q represent "Johnny will go to the World Series." Restate the conditional as

The Indians do not win the pennant or Johnny will go to the World Series.

(b) If p represents "it's Borden's" and if q represents "it's got to be good," the conditional may be restated as

It's not Borden's or it's got to be good. ▮▮▮

Circuits

Figure 1

Series circuit

Figure 2

Parallel circuit

Figure 3

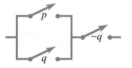

Figure 4

One of the first nonmathematical applications of symbolic logic was seen in the master's thesis of Claude Shannon in 1937. Shannon showed how logic could be used to design electrical circuits. His work was immediately used by computer designers. Then in the developmental stage, computers could be simplified and built for less money using the ideas of Shannon.

To see how Shannon's ideas work, look at the electrical switch shown in **Figure 1.** We assume that current will flow through this switch when it is closed and not when it is open.

Figure 2 shows two switches connected in *series.* In such a circuit, current will flow only when both switches are closed. Note how closely a series circuit corresponds to the conjunction $p \wedge q$. We know that $p \wedge q$ is true only when both p and q are true.

A circuit corresponding to the disjunction $p \vee q$ can be found by drawing a *parallel* circuit, as in **Figure 3.** Here, current flows if either p *or* q is closed or if both p *and* q are closed.

The circuit in **Figure 4** corresponds to the statement $(p \vee q) \wedge {\sim}q$, which is a compound statement involving both a conjunction and a disjunction.

Simplifying an electrical circuit depends on the idea of equivalent statements from **Section 3.2.** Recall that two statements are equivalent if they have the same truth table final column. The symbol $\equiv$ is used to indicate that the two statements are equivalent. Some equivalent statements are shown in the following box.

Equivalent Statements Used to Simplify Circuits

$$p \vee (q \wedge r) \equiv (p \vee q) \wedge (p \vee r) \qquad p \vee p \equiv p$$
$$p \wedge (q \vee r) \equiv (p \wedge q) \vee (p \wedge r) \qquad p \wedge p \equiv p$$
$$p \rightarrow q \equiv {\sim}q \rightarrow {\sim}p \qquad {\sim}(p \wedge q) \equiv {\sim}p \vee {\sim}q$$
$$p \rightarrow q \equiv {\sim}p \vee q \qquad {\sim}(p \vee q) \equiv {\sim}p \wedge {\sim}q$$

If T represents any true statement and F represents any false statement, then

$$p \vee \mathbf{T} \equiv \mathbf{T} \qquad p \vee {\sim}p \equiv \mathbf{T}$$
$$p \wedge \mathbf{F} \equiv \mathbf{F} \qquad p \wedge {\sim}p \equiv \mathbf{F}.$$

Circuits can be used as models of compound statements, with a closed switch corresponding to T, while an open switch corresponds to F.

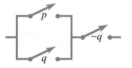

Figure 5

▮▮ **EXAMPLE 6** Simplifying a Circuit

Simplify the circuit of **Figure 5.**

SOLUTION

At the top of **Figure 5,** p and q are connected in series, and at the bottom, p and r are connected in series. These are interpreted as the compound statements $p \wedge q$ and $p \wedge r$, respectively. These two conjunctions are connected in parallel, as indicated by the figure treated as a whole.

Write the disjunction of the two conjunctions.

$$(p \wedge q) \vee (p \wedge r)$$

(Think of the two switches labeled "p" as being controlled by the same lever.) By one of the pairs of equivalent statements in the preceding box,

$$(p \wedge q) \vee (p \wedge r) \equiv p \wedge (q \vee r),$$

which has the circuit of **Figure 6.** This circuit is logically equivalent to the one in **Figure 5,** and yet it contains only three switches instead of four—which might well lead to a large savings in manufacturing costs. ▮▮▮

Figure 6

▮▮ **EXAMPLE 7** Drawing a Circuit for a Conditional Statement

Draw a circuit for $p \rightarrow (q \wedge \sim r)$.

SOLUTION

From the list of equivalent statements in the box, $p \rightarrow q$ is equivalent to $\sim p \vee q$. This equivalence gives $p \rightarrow (q \wedge \sim r) \equiv \sim p \vee (q \wedge \sim r)$, which has the circuit diagram in **Figure 7.** ▮▮▮

Figure 7

3.3 EXERCISES

Rewrite each statement using the if . . . then *connective. Rearrange the wording or add words as necessary.*

1. You can believe it if you see it on the Internet.

2. It must be alive if it is breathing.

3. Every integer divisible by 10 is divisible by 5.

4. All perfect square integers have units digit 0, 1, 4, 5, 6, or 9.

5. All Marines love boot camp.

6. Every picture tells a story.

7. No pandas live in Idaho.

8. No guinea pigs are scholars.

9. An opium eater cannot have self-command.

10. Running Bear loves Little White Dove.

Decide whether each statement is true *or* false.

11. If the antecedent of a conditional statement is false, the conditional statement is true.

12. If the consequent of a conditional statement is true, the conditional statement is true.

13. If q is true, then $(p \wedge q) \rightarrow q$ is true.

14. If p is true, then $\sim p \rightarrow (q \vee r)$ is true.

15. The negation of "If pigs fly, I'll believe it" is "If pigs don't fly, I won't believe it."

16. The statements "If it flies, then it's a bird" and "It does not fly or it's a bird" are logically equivalent.

17. Given that $\sim p$ is true and q is false, the conditional $p \rightarrow q$ is true.

18. Given that $\sim p$ is false and q is false, the conditional $p \rightarrow q$ is true.

19. Explain why the statement "If $3 = 5$, then $4 = 6$" is true.

20. In a few sentences, explain how to determine the truth value of a conditional statement.

Tell whether each conditional is true (T) *or* false (F).

21. $T \rightarrow (7 < 3)$

22. $F \rightarrow (4 \neq 8)$

23. $F \rightarrow (5 \neq 5)$

24. $(8 \geq 8) \rightarrow F$

25. $(5^2 \neq 25) \rightarrow (8 - 8 = 16)$

26. $(5 = 12 - 7) \rightarrow (9 > 0)$

Let s represent "She has a bird for a pet," *let p represent* "he trains dogs," *and let m represent* "they raise alpacas." *Express each compound statement in words.*

27. $\sim m \rightarrow p$

28. $p \rightarrow \sim m$

29. $s \rightarrow (m \wedge p)$

30. $(s \wedge p) \rightarrow m$

31. $\sim p \rightarrow (\sim m \vee s)$

32. $(\sim s \vee \sim m) \rightarrow \sim p$

Let b represent "I ride my bike," *let s represent* "it snows," *and let p represent* "the play is cancelled." *Write each compound statement in symbols.*

33. If I ride my bike, then the play is cancelled.

34. If it snows, then I ride my bike.

35. If the play is cancelled, then it does not snow.

36. If I do not ride my bike, then it does not snow.

37. The play is cancelled, and if it snows then I do not ride my bike.

38. I ride my bike, or if the play is cancelled then it snows.

39. It snows if the play is cancelled.

40. I'll ride my bike if it doesn't snow.

Find the truth value of each statement. Assume that p and r are false, and q is true.

41. $\sim r \rightarrow q$

42. $\sim p \rightarrow \sim r$

43. $q \rightarrow p$

44. $\sim r \rightarrow p$

45. $p \rightarrow q$

46. $\sim q \rightarrow r$

47. $\sim p \rightarrow (q \wedge r)$

48. $(\sim r \vee p) \rightarrow p$

49. $\sim q \rightarrow (p \wedge r)$

50. $(\sim p \wedge \sim q) \rightarrow (p \wedge \sim r)$

51. $(p \rightarrow \sim q) \rightarrow (\sim p \wedge \sim r)$

52. $(p \rightarrow \sim q) \wedge (p \rightarrow r)$

53. Explain why, if we know that p is true, we also know that

$$[r \vee (p \vee s)] \rightarrow (p \vee q)$$

is true, even if we are not given the truth values of q, r, and s.

54. Construct a true statement involving a conditional, a conjunction, a disjunction, and a negation (not necessarily in that order), that consists of component statements p, q, and r, with all of these component statements false.

Construct a truth table for each statement. Identify any tautologies.

55. $\sim q \rightarrow p$

56. $p \rightarrow \sim q$

57. $(\sim p \rightarrow q) \rightarrow p$

58. $(\sim q \rightarrow \sim p) \rightarrow \sim q$

59. $(p \vee q) \rightarrow (q \vee p)$

60. $(p \wedge q) \rightarrow (p \vee q)$

61. $(\sim p \rightarrow \sim q) \rightarrow (p \wedge q)$

62. $r \rightarrow (p \wedge \sim q)$

63. $[(r \vee p) \wedge \sim q] \rightarrow p$

64. $[(r \wedge p) \wedge (p \wedge q)] \rightarrow p$

65. $(\sim r \rightarrow s) \vee (p \rightarrow \sim q)$

66. $(\sim p \wedge \sim q) \rightarrow (s \rightarrow r)$

67. What is the minimum number of Fs that must appear in the final column of a truth table for us to be assured that the statement is not a tautology?

68. If all truth values in the final column of a truth table are F, how can we easily transform the statement into a tautology?

Write the negation of each statement. Remember that the negation of $p \rightarrow q$ is $p \wedge \sim q$.

69. If that is an authentic Rolex watch, I'll be surprised.

70. If Minnie Ripperton reaches that note, she will shatter glass.

71. If the English measures are not converted to metric measures, then the spacecraft will crash on the surface of Saturn.

72. If you say "I do," then you'll be happy for the rest of your life.

73. "If you want to be happy for the rest of your life, never make a pretty woman your wife." *Jimmy Soul*

74. "If loving you is wrong, I don't want to be right." *Luther Ingram*

Write each statement as an equivalent statement that does not use the if . . . then *connective. Remember that*

$$p \to q \quad \text{is equivalent to} \quad {\sim}p \lor q.$$

75. If you give your plants tender, loving care, they flourish.

76. If the check is in the mail, I will buy you lunch.

77. If she doesn't, he will.

78. If I say "black," she says "white."

79. All residents of Pensacola are residents of Florida.

80. All women were once girls.

Use truth tables to decide which of the pairs of statements are equivalent.

81. $p \to q$; ${\sim}p \lor q$ **82.** ${\sim}(p \to q)$; $p \land {\sim}q$

83. $p \to q$; ${\sim}q \to {\sim}p$ **84.** $q \to p$; ${\sim}p \to {\sim}q$

85. $p \land {\sim}q$; ${\sim}q \to {\sim}p$ **86.** $p \to q$; $q \to p$

87. $p \to {\sim}q$; ${\sim}p \lor {\sim}q$ **88.** ${\sim}p \land q$; ${\sim}p \to q$

89. $q \to {\sim}p$; $p \to {\sim}q$ **90.** ${\sim}p \to q$; $p \lor q$

Write a logical statement representing each of the following circuits. Simplify each circuit when possible.

91.

92.

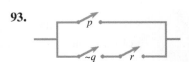

93.

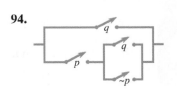

94.

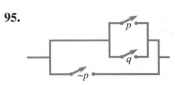

95.

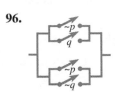

96.

Draw circuits representing the following statements as they are given. Simplify if possible.

97. $p \land (q \lor {\sim}p)$ **98.** $({\sim}p \land {\sim}q) \land {\sim}r$

99. $(p \lor q) \land ({\sim}p \land {\sim}q)$

100. $({\sim}q \land {\sim}p) \lor ({\sim}p \lor q)$

101. $[(p \lor q) \land r] \land {\sim}p$

102. $[({\sim}p \land {\sim}r) \lor {\sim}q] \land ({\sim}p \land r)$

103. ${\sim}q \to ({\sim}p \to q)$ **104.** ${\sim}p \to ({\sim}p \lor {\sim}q)$

105. Refer to **Figures 5 and 6** in **Example 6.** Suppose the cost of the use of one switch for an hour is $0.06. By using the circuit in **Figure 6** rather than the circuit in **Figure 5,** what is the savings for a year of 365 days, assuming that the circuit is in continuous use?

106. Explain why the circuit shown will always have exactly one open switch. What does this circuit simplify to?

3.4 THE CONDITIONAL AND RELATED STATEMENTS

Converse, Inverse, and Contrapositive • Alternative Forms of "If p, then q"
• Biconditionals • Summary of Truth Tables

Alfred North Whitehead (1861–1947) and Bertrand Russell worked together on *Principia Mathematica*. During that time, Whitehead was teaching mathematics at Cambridge University and had written *Universal Algebra*. In 1910 he went to the University of London, exploring not only the philosophical basis of science but also the "aims of education" (as he called one of his books). It was as a philosopher that he was invited to Harvard University in 1924. Whitehead died at the age of 86 in Cambridge, Massachusetts.

Converse, Inverse, and Contrapositive

Many mathematical properties and theorems are stated in *if . . . then* form. Any conditional statement $p \rightarrow q$ is made up of an antecedent p and a consequent q. If they are interchanged, negated, or both, a new conditional statement is formed. Suppose that we begin with a conditional statement.

If you stay, then I go.   Conditional Statement

By interchanging the antecedent ("you stay") and the consequent ("I go"), we obtain a new conditional statement.

If I go, then you stay.   Converse

This new conditional is called the **converse** of the given conditional statement.

By negating both the antecedent and the consequent, we obtain the **inverse** of the given conditional statement.

If you do not stay, then I do not go.   Inverse

If the antecedent and the consequent are both interchanged *and* negated, the **contrapositive** of the given conditional statement is formed.

If I do not go, then you do not stay.   Contrapositive

These three related statements for the conditional $p \rightarrow q$ are summarized below. (***The inverse is the contrapositive of the converse.***)

Related Conditional Statements		
Conditional Statement	$p \rightarrow q$	(If p, then q.)
Converse	$q \rightarrow p$	(If q, then p.)
Inverse	$\sim p \rightarrow \sim q$	(If not p, then not q.)
Contrapositive	$\sim q \rightarrow \sim p$	(If not q, then not p.)

▐▐ **EXAMPLE 1** Determining Related Conditional Statements

Determine each of the following, given the conditional statement

If I live in Orlando, then I live in Florida.

(a) the converse   **(b)** the inverse   **(c)** the contrapositive

SOLUTION

(a) Let p represent "I live in Orlando" and q represent "I live in Florida." Then the given statement may be written $p \rightarrow q$. The converse, $q \rightarrow p$, is

If I live in Florida, then I live in Orlando.

Notice that for this statement, the converse is not necessarily true, even though the given statement is true.

(b) The inverse of $p \rightarrow q$ is $\sim p \rightarrow \sim q$. Thus, the inverse is

If I don't live in Orlando, then I don't live in Florida.

Again, this is not necessarily true.

Bertrand Russell (1872–1970) was a student of Whitehead's before they wrote the *Principia*. Like his teacher, Russell turned toward philosophy. His works include a critique of Leibniz, analyses of mind and of matter, and a history of Western thought.

Russell became a public figure because of his involvement in social issues. Deeply aware of human loneliness, he was "passionately desirous of finding ways of diminishing this tragic isolation." During World War I he was an antiwar crusader, and he was imprisoned briefly. Again in the 1960s he championed peace. He wrote many books on social issues, winning the Nobel Prize for Literature in 1950.

(c) The contrapositive, $\sim q \rightarrow \sim p$, is

> If I don't live in Florida, then I don't live in Orlando.

The contrapositive, like the given conditional statement, is true.   ▪▪▪

Example 1 shows that the converse and inverse of a true statement need not be true. They *can* be true, but they need not be. The relationships between the related conditionals are shown in the truth table that follows.

		Conditional	Converse	Inverse	Contrapositive
p	q	$p \rightarrow q$	$q \rightarrow p$	$\sim p \rightarrow \sim q$	$\sim q \rightarrow \sim p$
T	T	T	T	T	T
T	F	F	T	T	F
F	T	T	F	F	T
F	F	T	T	T	T

Equivalent (Conditional and Contrapositive); *Equivalent* (Converse and Inverse)

As this truth table shows,

1. ***A conditional statement and its contrapositive always have the same truth values,*** making it possible to replace any statement with its contrapositive without affecting the logical meaning.

2. ***The converse and inverse always have the same truth values.***

Equivalences

A conditional statement and its contrapositive are equivalent. Also, the converse and the inverse are equivalent.

▌▌ **EXAMPLE 2** Determining Related Conditional Statements

For the conditional statement $\sim p \rightarrow q$, write each of the following.

(a) the converse   **(b)** the inverse   **(c)** the contrapositive

SOLUTION

(a) The converse of $\sim p \rightarrow q$ is $q \rightarrow \sim p$.

(b) The inverse is $\sim(\sim p) \rightarrow \sim q$, which simplifies to $p \rightarrow \sim q$.

(c) The contrapositive is $\sim q \rightarrow \sim(\sim p)$, which simplifies to $\sim q \rightarrow p$.   ▪▪▪

Alternative Forms of "If p, then q"

The conditional statement "if p, then q" can be stated in several other ways in English. Consider this statement.

> If you go to the outlet mall, then you will find a place to park.

It can also be written as follows.

> Going to the outlet mall is *sufficient* for finding a place to park.

According to this statement, going to the outlet mall is enough to guarantee finding a place to park. Going to other places, such as schools or office buildings, *might* also guarantee a place to park, but at least we *know* that going to the outlet mall does. Thus, $p \rightarrow q$ can be written "p is sufficient for q." Knowing that p has occurred is sufficient to guarantee that q will also occur.

On the other hand, consider this statement, which has a different meaning.

Having the set on is necessary for watching television. (∗)

Here, we are saying that one condition that is necessary for watching television is that the set be turned on. This may not be enough. The set might be broken, for example. The statement labeled (∗) could be written as

If you watch television, then the set was turned on.

As this example suggests, $p \rightarrow q$ is the same as "q is necessary for p." In other words, if q doesn't happen, then neither will p. Notice how this idea is closely related to the idea of equivalence between a conditional statement and its contrapositive.

Common Translations of $p \rightarrow q$

The conditional $p \rightarrow q$ can be translated in any of the following ways, none of which depends on the truth or falsity of $p \rightarrow q$.

If p, then q.	**p is sufficient for q.**
If p, q.	**q is necessary for p.**
p implies q.	**All p are q.**
p only if q.	**q if p.**

Example: If you live in Dubuque, then you live in Iowa.   Statement

You live in Iowa if you live in Dubuque.
You live in Dubuque only if you live in Iowa.
Living in Iowa is necessary for living in Dubuque. } Common translations
Living in Dubuque is sufficient for living in Iowa.
All residents of Dubuque are residents of Iowa.
Being a resident of Dubuque implies residency in Iowa.

▮▮ **EXAMPLE 3** Rewording Conditional Statements

Write each statement in the form "if p, then q."

(a) You'll be sorry if I go.   **(b)** Today is Tuesday only if yesterday was Monday.

(c) All nurses wear white shoes.

SOLUTION

(a) If I go, then you'll be sorry.

(b) If today is Tuesday, then yesterday was Monday.

(c) If you are a nurse, then you wear white shoes.   ▮▮▮

▮▮ **EXAMPLE 4** Translating from Words to Symbols

Let p represent "A triangle is equilateral," and let q represent "A triangle has three sides of equal length." Write each of the following in symbols.

(a) A triangle is equilateral if it has three sides of equal length.

(b) A triangle is equilateral only if it has three sides of equal length.

SOLUTION

(a) $q \rightarrow p$ **(b)** $p \rightarrow q$ ▮▮▮

Biconditionals

The compound statement *p if and only if q* (often abbreviated *p iff q*) is called a **biconditional.** It is symbolized $p \leftrightarrow q$, and is interpreted as the conjunction of the two conditionals $p \rightarrow q$ and $q \rightarrow p$. Using symbols, this conjunction is written $(q \rightarrow p) \wedge (p \rightarrow q)$ so that, by definition,

$$p \leftrightarrow q \equiv (q \rightarrow p) \wedge (p \rightarrow q). \quad \text{Biconditional}$$

The truth table for the biconditional $p \leftrightarrow q$ can be determined using this definition.

Principia Mathematica, the title chosen by Whitehead and Russell, was a deliberate reference to *Philosophiae naturalis principia mathematica,* or "mathematical principles of the philosophy of nature," Isaac Newton's epochal work of 1687. Newton's *Principia* pictured a kind of "clockwork universe" that ran via his Law of Gravitation. Newton independently invented the calculus, unaware that Leibniz had published his own formulation of it earlier.

Truth Table for the Biconditional *p if and only if q*

p if and only if q		
p	*q*	$p \leftrightarrow q$
T	T	T
T	F	F
F	T	F
F	F	T

A biconditional is true when both component statements have the same truth value. It is false when they have different truth values.

▌▌ **EXAMPLE 5** Determining Whether Biconditionals Are True or False

Determine whether each biconditional statement is *true* or *false*.

(a) $6 + 8 = 14$ if and only if $11 + 5 = 16$

(b) $6 = 5$ if and only if $12 \neq 12$

(c) $5 + 2 = 10$ if and only if $17 + 19 = 36$

SOLUTION

(a) Both $6 + 8 = 14$ and $11 + 5 = 16$ are true. By the truth table for the biconditional, this biconditional is true.

(b) Both component statements are false, so by the last line of the truth table for the biconditional, this biconditional statement is true.

(c) Because the first component ($5 + 2 = 10$) is false, and the second is true, this biconditional statement is false. ▄▄▄

Summary of Truth Tables

Truth tables have been derived for several important types of compound statements.

Summary of Basic Truth Tables

1. $\sim p$, the **negation** of p, has truth value opposite that of p.
2. $p \wedge q$, the **conjunction,** is true only when both p and q are true.
3. $p \vee q$, the **disjunction,** is false only when both p and q are false.
4. $p \rightarrow q$, the **conditional,** is false only when p is true and q is false.
5. $p \leftrightarrow q$, the **biconditional,** is true only when both p and q have the same truth value.

3.4 EXERCISES

*For each given conditional statement (or statement that can be written as a conditional), write (**a**) the converse, (**b**) the inverse, and (**c**) the contrapositive in* if . . . then *form. In some of the exercises, it may be helpful to first restate the given statement in* if . . . then *form.*

1. If beauty were a minute, then you would be an hour.

2. If you lead, then I will follow.

3. If it ain't broke, don't fix it.

4. If I had a nickel for each time that happened, I would be rich.

5. Walking in front of a moving car is dangerous to your health.

6. Milk contains calcium.

7. Birds of a feather flock together.

8. A rolling stone gathers no moss.

9. If you build it, he will come.

10. Where there's smoke, there's fire.

11. $p \to \sim q$

12. $\sim p \to q$

13. $\sim p \to \sim q$

14. $\sim q \to \sim p$

15. $p \to (q \lor r)$ (*Hint:* Use one of De Morgan's laws as necessary.)

16. $(r \lor \sim q) \to p$ (*Hint:* Use one of De Morgan's laws as necessary.)

17. Discuss the equivalences that exist among a given conditional statement, its converse, its inverse, and its contrapositive.

18. State the contrapositive of "If the square of a natural number is even, then the natural number is even." The two statements must have the same truth value. Use several examples and inductive reasoning to decide whether both are true or both are false.

Write each statement in the form "if p, then q."

19. If it is muddy, I'll wear my galoshes.

20. If I finish studying, I'll go to the party.

21. "19 is positive" implies that $19 + 1$ is positive.

22. "Today is Wednesday" implies that yesterday was Tuesday.

23. All integers are rational numbers.

24. All whole numbers are integers.

25. Doing logic puzzles is sufficient for driving me crazy.

26. Being in Kalamazoo is sufficient for being in Michigan.

27. A day's growth of beard is necessary for Jeff Marsalis to shave.

28. Being an environmentalist is necessary for being elected.

29. I can go from Boardwalk to Baltic Avenue only if I pass GO.

30. The principal will hire more teachers only if the school board approves.

31. No whole numbers are not integers.

32. No integers are irrational numbers.

33. The Nationals will win the pennant when their pitching improves.

34. Sarah will be a liberal when pigs fly.

35. A rectangle is a parallelogram with a right angle.

36. A parallelogram is a four-sided figure with opposite sides parallel.

37. A triangle with two perpendicular sides is a right triangle.

38. A square is a rectangle with two adjacent sides equal.

39. The square of a two-digit number whose units digit is 5 will end in 25.

40. An integer whose units digit is 0 or 5 is divisible by 5.

41. One of the following statements is not equivalent to all the others. Which one is it?
    A. r only if s.   **B.** r implies s.
    C. If r, then s.   **D.** r is necessary for s.

42. Many students have difficulty interpreting *necessary* and *sufficient*. Use the statement "Being in Vancouver is sufficient for being in North America" to explain why "p is sufficient for q" translates as "if p, then q."

43. Use the statement "To be an integer, it is necessary that a number be rational" to explain why "p is necessary for q" translates as "if q, then p."

44. Explain why the statement "A week has eight days if and only if October has forty days" is true.

Identify each statement as true *or* false.

45. $6 = 9 - 3$ if and only if $8 + 2 = 10$.

46. $3 + 1 \neq 7$ if and only if $8 \neq 8$.

47. $8 + 7 \neq 15$ if and only if $3 \times 5 \neq 8$.

48. $6 \times 2 = 18$ if and only if $9 + 7 \neq 16$.

49. George H. W. Bush was president if and only if George W. Bush was not president.

50. Burger King sells Big Macs if and only if Apple manufactures Ipods.

Two statements that can both be true about the same object are **consistent.** *For example, "It is green" and "It weighs 60 pounds" are consistent statements. Statements that cannot both be true about the same object are called* **contrary.** *"It is a Nissan" and "It is a Mazda" are contrary. In Exercises 51–56, label each pair of statements as either* contrary *or* consistent.

51. Michael Jackson is alive. Michael Jackson is dead.

52. Barack Obama is a Democrat. Barack Obama is a Republican.

53. That animal has four legs. That same animal is a cat.

54. That book is nonfiction. That book costs more than $150.

55. This number is a whole number. This same number is irrational.

56. This number is positive. This same number is a natural number.

57. This number is an integer. This same number is a rational number.

58. This number is a whole number. This same number is a negative number.

59. Make up two statements that are consistent.

60. Make up two statements that are contrary.

3.5 ANALYZING ARGUMENTS WITH EULER DIAGRAMS

Logical Arguments • Arguments with Universal Quantifiers • Arguments with Existential Quantifiers

Leonhard Euler (1707–1783) won the Academy prize and edged out du Châtelet and Voltaire. That was a minor achievement, as was the invention of "Euler circles" (which antedated Venn diagrams). Euler was the most prolific mathematician of his generation despite blindness that forced him to dictate from memory.

Logical Arguments

With inductive reasoning we observe patterns to solve problems. Now we study how deductive reasoning may be used to determine whether logical arguments are valid or invalid.

A logical argument is made up of **premises** (assumptions, laws, rules, widely held ideas, or observations) and a **conclusion.** Recall that *deductive* reasoning involves drawing specific conclusions from given general premises. When reasoning from the premises of an argument to obtain a conclusion, we want the argument to be valid.

> **Valid and Invalid Arguments**
>
> An argument is **valid** if the fact that all the premises are true forces the conclusion to be true. An argument that is not valid is **invalid.** It is called a **fallacy.**

"Valid" and "true" do not have the same meaning—an argument can be valid even though the conclusion is false. **(See Example 4.)**

Arguments with Universal Quantifiers

Several techniques can be used to check whether an argument is valid. One such technique is based on **Euler diagrams.**

Leonhard Euler (pronounced "Oiler") was one of the greatest mathematicians who ever lived. He is immortalized in mathematics history with the important irrational number e, named in his honor. This number appears throughout mathematics, and is discussed in **Chapters 6 and 8.**

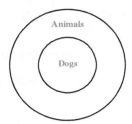

Figure 8

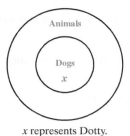

x represents Dotty.

Figure 9

▐▐ **EXAMPLE 1** Using an Euler Diagram to Determine Validity

Is the following argument valid?

> All dogs are animals.
> Dotty is a dog.
> _____
> Dotty is an animal.

SOLUTION

To begin, draw regions to represent the first premise. Because all dogs are animals, the region for "dogs" goes inside the region for "animals," as in **Figure 8.**

The second premise, "Dotty is a dog," suggests that "Dotty" would go inside the region representing "dogs." Let *x* represent "Dotty." **Figure 9** shows that "Dotty" is also inside the region for "animals." If both premises are true, the conclusion that Dotty is an animal must be true also. The argument is valid. ▐▐▐

▐▐ **EXAMPLE 2** Using an Euler Diagram to Determine Validity

Is the following argument valid?

> All rainy days are cloudy.
> Today is not cloudy.
> _____
> Today is not rainy.

SOLUTION

In **Figure 10,** the region for "rainy days" is drawn entirely inside the region for "cloudy days." Since "Today is *not* cloudy," place an *x* for "today" *outside* the region for "cloudy days." See **Figure 11.** Placing the *x* outside the region for "cloudy days" forces it also to be outside the region for "rainy days." Thus, if the two premises are true, then it is also true that today is not rainy. The argument is valid.

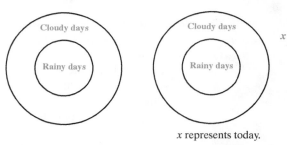

x represents today.

Figure 10   **Figure 11**   ▐▐▐

▐▐ **EXAMPLE 3** Using an Euler Diagram to Determine Validity

Is the following argument valid?

> All magnolia trees have green leaves.
> That plant has green leaves.
> _____
> That plant is a magnolia tree.

SOLUTION

The region for "magnolia trees" goes entirely inside the region for "things that have green leaves." See **Figure 12.** The *x* that represents "that plant" must go inside the region for "things that have green leaves," but can go either inside or outside the region for "magnolia trees." Even if the premises are true, we are not forced to accept the conclusion as true. This argument is invalid. It is a fallacy. ▐▐▐

Figure 12

▮▮   **EXAMPLE 4**   Using an Euler Diagram to Determine Validity

Is the following argument valid?

> All expensive things are desirable.
> All desirable things make you feel good.
> All things that make you feel good make you live longer.
>
> All expensive things make you live longer.

SOLUTION

A diagram for the argument is given in **Figure 13.**

  If each premise is true, then the conclusion must be true because the region for "expensive things" lies completely within the region for "things that make you live longer." Thus, the argument is valid. (This argument is an example of the fact that a *valid* argument need *not* have a true conclusion.)

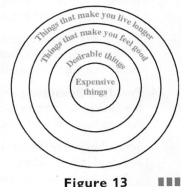

Figure 13   ▮▮▮

Arguments with Existential Quantifiers

▮▮   **EXAMPLE 5**   Using an Euler Diagram to Determine Validity

Is the following argument valid?

> Some students go to the beach for Spring Break.
> I am a student.
>
> I go to the beach for Spring Break.

SOLUTION

The first premise is sketched in **Figure 14,** where some (but not necessarily *all*) students go to the beach. There are two possibilities for *I*, as shown in **Figure 15.** One possibility is that *I* go to the beach. The other is that *I* don't. Since the truth of the premises does not force the conclusion to be true, the argument is invalid.   ▮▮▮

Figure 14

Figure 15

For Further Thought (*cont.*)

3. **Loaded Question and Complex Claims** This fallacy involves one person asking a question or making a statement that is constructed in such a way as to obtain an answer in which the responder agrees to something with which he does not actually agree.

   Teenager Beth to her father: I hope you enjoyed embarrassing me in front of my friends.

   If Beth gets the expected response "No, I didn't enjoy it," the answer allows Beth to interpret that while her father didn't enjoy it, he did indeed embarrass her.

4. *Post Hoc* **Reasoning** An argument that is based on the false belief that if event A preceded event B, then A must have caused B is called *post hoc* reasoning.

   Johnny: I wore my Hawaiian shirt while watching all three playoff games, and my team won all three games. So I am going to wear that shirt every time I watch them.

   The fact that Johnny put the same shirt on before each game has nothing to do with the outcomes of the games.

5. **Red Herring** (also called *Smoke Screen,* or *Wild Goose Chase*) This fallacy involves introducing an irrelevant topic to divert attention away from the original topic, allowing the person making the argument to seemingly prevail.

   (From the movie *Field of Dreams,* in a scene where Annie and Beulah are arguing at a town meeting about the banning of books)

   Beulah: I say smut and filth like this has no place in our schools. . . . The so-called novels of Terence Mann endorse promiscuity, godlessness, the mongrelization of the races, and disrespect to high-ranking officers of the United States army. And that is why school boards across the country have been banning his books since 1969.
   Annie: Excuse me, madam. Terence Mann was a warm and gentle voice of reason in a time of great madness. He coined the phrase "Make love, not war." . . . He was talking about peace, and love, and understanding . . .
   Beulah: Oh yeah, well your husband plowed under his corn and built a baseball field . . . the weirdo. . . .
   Annie: Now there's an intelligent response.

   While most of the people in the audience agreed that Annie's husband Ray was doing strange things, those things had nothing to do with banning books.

6. **Shifting the Burden of Proof** A person making a claim usually is required to support that claim. In this fallacy, if the claim is difficult to support, that person turns the burden of proof of that claim over to someone else.

   Employee: You accuse me of embezzling money? That's ridiculous.
   Employer: Well, until you can prove otherwise, you will just have to accept it as true.

   If money has been disappearing, it is up to the employer to prove that this employee is guilty. The burden of proof is on the employer, but he is insinuating that the employee must prove that he is not the one taking the money.

7. **Straw Man** This fallacy involves creating a false image (like a scarecrow, or straw man) of someone else's position in an argument.

   Dan Quayle: I have as much experience in the Congress as Jack Kennedy did when he sought the presidency.
   Lloyd Bentsen: Senator, I served with Jack Kennedy. I knew Jack Kennedy. Jack Kennedy was a friend of mine. And Senator, you're no Jack Kennedy.
   Dan Quayle: That was really uncalled for, Senator.
   Lloyd Bentsen: You're the one that was making the comparison, Senator.

   While this was the defining moment of the 1988 vice-presidential debate, Bentsen expertly used the straw man fallacy. Quayle did not compare himself or his accomplishments to those of Kennedy, but merely stated that he had spent as much time in Congress as Kennedy had when the latter ran for president.

For Group or Individual Investigation

Use the Internet to investigate the following additional logical fallacies.

Appeal to Authority	Appeal to Common	Common Practice
Two Wrongs	Belief	Wishful Thinking
Appeal to Fear	Indirect Consequences	Appeal to Pity
Appeal to Prejudice	Appeal to Loyalty	Appeal to Vanity
Guilt by Association	Appeal to Spite	Hasty Generalization
	Slippery Slope	

3.5 EXERCISES

Decide whether each argument is valid *or* invalid.

1. All amusement parks have thrill rides.
   <u>*Universal Orlando* is an amusement park.</u>
   Universal Orlando has thrill rides.

2. All disc jockeys play music.
   <u>Phlash Phelps is a disc jockey.</u>
   Phlash Phelps plays music.

3. All politicians lie, cheat, and steal.
   <u>That man lies, cheats, and steals.</u>
   That man is a politician.

4. All Southerners speak with an accent.
   <u>Bill Leonard speaks with an accent.</u>
   Bill Leonard is a Southerner.

5. All dogs love to bury bones.
   <u>Puddles does not love to bury bones.</u>
   Puddles is not a dog.

6. All vice-presidents use cell phones.
   <u>Bob DeBiasio does not use a cell phone.</u>
   Bob DeBiasio is not a vice-president.

7. All residents of Minnesota know how to live in freezing temperatures.
   <u>Jessica Rockswold knows how to live in freezing temperatures.</u>
   Jessica Rockswold lives in Minnesota.

8. All people who apply for a loan must pay for a title search.
   <u>Kurt Massey paid for a title search.</u>
   Kurt Massey applied for a loan.

9. Some dinosaurs were plant eaters.
   <u>Danny was a plant eater.</u>
   Danny was a dinosaur.

10. Some philosophers are absent minded.
    <u>Nicole Mallon is a philosopher.</u>
    Nicole Mallon is absent minded.

11. Some nurses wear blue uniforms.
    <u>Dee Boyle is a nurse.</u>
    Dee Boyle wears a blue uniform.

12. Some trucks have sound systems.
    <u>Some trucks have gun racks.</u>
    Some trucks with sound systems have gun racks.

13. Refer to **Example 3.** If the second premise and the conclusion were interchanged, would the argument then be valid?

14. Refer to **Example 4.** Give a different conclusion than the one given there so that the argument is still valid.

Construct a valid argument based on the Euler diagram shown.

15.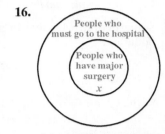

16.

x represents Natalie Graham   *x* represents Mark Robinson

As mentioned in the text, an argument can have a true conclusion yet be invalid. In these exercises, each argument has a true conclusion. Identify each argument as valid *or* invalid.

17. All birds fly.
    <u>All planes fly.</u>
    A bird is not a plane.

18. All cars have tires.
    <u>All tires are rubber.</u>
    All cars have rubber.

19. All chickens have beaks.
    <u>All hens are chickens.</u>
    All hens have beaks.

20. All chickens have beaks.
    <u>All birds have beaks.</u>
    All chickens are birds.

21. Little Rock is northeast of Texarkana.
    <u>Little Rock is northeast of Austin.</u>
    Texarkana is northeast of Austin.

22. Veracruz is south of Tampico.
    <u>Tampico is south of Monterrey.</u>
    Veracruz is south of Monterrey.

23. No whole numbers are negative.
    <u>−3 is negative.</u>
    −3 is not a whole number.

24. A scalene triangle has a longest side.
    <u>A scalene triangle has a largest angle.</u>
    The largest angle in a scalene triangle is opposite the longest side.

In Exercises 25–30, the premises marked A, B, and C are followed by several possible conclusions. Take each conclusion in turn, and check whether the resulting argument is valid or *invalid.*

A. *All people who drive contribute to air pollution.*

B. *All people who contribute to air pollution make life a little worse.*

C. *Some people who live in a suburb make life a little worse.*

25. Some people who live in a suburb contribute to air pollution.

26. Some people who live in a suburb drive.

27. Suburban residents never drive.

28. Some people who contribute to air pollution live in a suburb.

29. Some people who make life a little worse live in a suburb.

30. All people who drive make life a little worse.

EXTENSION Logic Problems and Sudoku

How to Solve Logic Problems • How to Solve Sudoku

Logic problems, which are based on deductive reasoning, appear in periodicals such as *Original Logic Problems, World-Class Logic Problems,* and *England's Best Logic Problems* (all PennyPress), and *Logic Puzzles* (Dell). The following explanation on solving such problems appeared in the February 2010 issue of *Original Logic Problems.*

How to Solve Logic Problems

Solving logic problems is entertaining and challenging. All the information you need to solve a logic problem is given in the introduction and clues, and in illustrations, when provided. If you've never solved a logic problem before, our sample should help you get started. Fill in the Sample Solving Chart as you follow our explanation. We use a "•" to signify "Yes" and an "X" to signify "No."

Sample Logic Problem

Five couples were married last week, each on a different weekday. From the information provided, determine the woman (one is Cathy) and man (one is Paul) who make up each couple, as well as the day on which each couple was married.

1. Anne was married on Monday, but not to Wally.

2. Stan's wedding was on Wednesday. Rob was married on Friday, but not to Ida.

3. Vern (who married Fran) was married the day after Eve.

Sample Solving Chart:	PAUL	ROB	STAN	VERN	WALLY	MONDAY	TUESDAY	WEDNESDAY	THURSDAY	FRIDAY
ANNE										
CATHY										
EVE										
FRAN										
IDA										
MONDAY										
TUESDAY										
WEDNESDAY										
THURSDAY										
FRIDAY										

1	PAUL	ROB	STAN	VERN	WALLY	MONDAY	TUESDAY	WEDNESDAY	THURSDAY	FRIDAY
ANNE	X	X			X	•	X	X	X	X
CATHY						X				
EVE						X				
FRAN						X				
IDA		X				X				X
MONDAY	X	X								
TUESDAY	X	X								
WEDNESDAY	X	X	•	X	X					
THURSDAY	X	X								
FRIDAY	X	•	X	X	X					

Explanation

Anne was married Mon. (1), so put a "•" at the intersection of Anne and Mon. Put "X"s in all the other days in Anne's row and all the other names in the Mon. column. (Whenever you establish a relationship, as we did here, be sure to place "X"s at the intersections of all relationships that become impossible as a result.) Anne wasn't married to Wally (1), so put an "X" at the intersection of Anne and Wally. Stan's wedding was Wed. (2), so put a "•" at the intersection of Stan and Wed. (Don't forget the "X"s.) Stan didn't marry Anne, who was married Mon., so put an "X" at the intersection of Anne and Stan. Rob was married Fri., but not to Ida (2), so put a "•" at the intersection of Rob and Fri., and "X"s at the intersections of Rob and Ida and Ida and Fri. Rob also didn't marry Anne, who was married Mon., so put an "X" at the intersection of Anne and Rob. Now your chart should look like **chart 1.**

Vern married Fran (3), so put a "•" at the intersection of Vern and Fran. This leaves Anne's only possible husband as Paul, so put a "•" at the intersection of Anne and Paul and Paul and Mon. Vern and Fran's wedding was the day after Eve's (3), which wasn't Mon. [Anne], so Vern's wasn't Tue. It must have been Thu. [see chart], so Eve's was Wed. (3). Put "•"s at the intersections of Vern and Thu., Fran and Thu., and Eve and Wed. Now your chart should look like **chart 2.**

2	PAUL	ROB	STAN	VERN	WALLY	MONDAY	TUESDAY	WEDNESDAY	THURSDAY	FRIDAY
ANNE	•	×	×	×	×	•	×	×	×	×
CATHY	×		×		×	×			×	×
EVE	×		×			×	×	•	×	×
FRAN	×	×	×	•	×	×	×	×	•	×
IDA	×	×	×		×		×		×	×
MONDAY	•	×	×	×	×					
TUESDAY	×	×	×	×						
WEDNESDAY	×	×	•	×	×					
THURSDAY	×	×	×	•	×					
FRIDAY	×	•	×	×	×					

3	PAUL	ROB	STAN	VERN	WALLY	MONDAY	TUESDAY	WEDNESDAY	THURSDAY	FRIDAY
ANNE	•	×	×	×	×	•	×	×	×	×
CATHY	×	•	×	×	×	×	×	×	×	•
EVE	×	×	•	×	×	×	×	•	×	×
FRAN	×	×	×	•	×	×	×	×	•	×
IDA	×	×	×	×	•	×	•	×	×	×
MONDAY	•	×	×	×	×					
TUESDAY	×	×	×	×	•					
WEDNESDAY	×	×	•	×	×					
THURSDAY	×	×	×	•	×					
FRIDAY	×	•	×	×	×					

The chart shows that Cathy was married Fri., Ida was married Tue., and Wally was married Tue. Ida married Wally, and Cathy's wedding was Fri., so she married Rob. After this information is filled in, Eve could only have married Stan. You've completed the puzzle, and your chart should now look like **chart 3.**

In summary: Anne and Paul, Mon.; Cathy and Rob, Fri.; Eve and Stan, Wed.; Fran and Vern, Thu.; Ida and Wally, Tue.

In some problems, it may be necessary to make a logical guess based on facts you've established. When you do, always look for clues or other facts that disprove it. If you find that your guess is incorrect, eliminate it as a possibility.

How to Solve Sudoku

Sudoku is a simple game that has gained great popularity in the United States during the past few years. It is believed that the game originated as Number Place in the United States over 25 years ago, but gained in popularity only after it became a sensation in Japan, where it was renamed Sudoku, meaning "single number." (*Source: Sudoku #13*, 2005, Platinum Magazine Group.)

There is only one rule in Sudoku: **"Fill in the grid so that every row, every column, and every 3 × 3 box contains the digits 1 through 9."** This involves scanning the given digits, marking up the grid, and analyzing. Here is a sample Sudoku.

Given Form

Solved Form

You can find Sudoku puzzles and solving strategies online at www.sudoku.org.uk and at www.pennydellsudokusolver.com.

EXTENSION EXERCISES

Follow the guidelines to solve each logic problem, which appeared in the February 2010 issue of Original Logic Problems, *published by PennyPress.*

1. *Breath Taking* As part of a weekly tradition, Drew and four of his friends met for lunch at Aristotle's Grill. Each person enjoyed a different lunch special, but when it came time for the post-meal conversation, the five quickly realized that they were all in need of a mint or two. Luckily, each person had a container of mints on his or her person. No two friends had the same brand of mint (one is Inti-mints), and no two friends had mints with the same flavor. A few seconds later they were all ready to talk, but they agreed that next week, they'll be a little more careful about what they order for lunch! From the information provided, can you determine the meal enjoyed by each friend, as well as the brand and flavor of mint each person used afterward?

(a) The friend who had garlic shrimp ate a couple of orange-flavored mints (which weren't Fresh Air mints). The person who ordered the spanakopita isn't the one who had wintergreen-flavored TKO mints.

(b) The friend who ate French onion soup followed it with a few Liplickers mints. Nash (who didn't have the spearmint-flavored mints) didn't order garlic shrimp.

(c) Neither Nash nor Xerxes is the one who ate a tuna-salad sandwich. The friend who had a buffalo-chicken sandwich isn't the one who freshened his or her breath with spearmint-flavored mints.

(d) One friend had a couple of cinnamon-flavored Deltoids mints. The Liplickers mints were vanilla-flavored.

(e) Ilse (who ate a buffalo-chicken sandwich) didn't have wintergreen-flavored mints. Neither Uma nor Xerxes is the friend who had a couple of Fresh Air mints.

2. *Kings of Hearts* Although the exact origins of the holiday are murky, the tradition of Valentine's Day probably harkens back to the Middle Ages, when it was better known as the feast of Saint Valentine. Couples exchanged gifts on this February holiday even back then, and no one gave more expensive and elaborate valentines than the royalty of that time. One Valentine's Day, each of four kings, each whom ruled a different small kingdom, gave his queen a different valuable gift. It just goes to show that love (or at least the idea of it) stands the test of time! From the information provided, can you determine the king and queen of each kingdom, as well as the gift each king gave his wife for the feast of Saint Valentine?

(a) King Jacobus didn't give his queen a platinum crown.

(b) Neither the jeweled scepter nor the platinum crown was the gift given to Queen Meyla (who was married to either King Kevrick or King Vermond).

(c) Queen Dejah (who was married to either King Fedris or King Jacobus) wasn't the ruler of Undervale.

(d) King Kevrick wasn't the ruler of the Dalelands.

(e) Neither the platinum crown nor the set of velvet robes was the gift given by King Vermond.

(f) The queen of Undervale (who was married to either King Fedris or King Jacobus) was given a golden throne by her husband.

(g) Queen Tilnara wasn't given a jeweled scepter by her husband. Queen Aasta ruled Hightop.

		QUEEN				KINGDOM				GIFT			
		AASTA	DEJAH	MEYLA	TILNARA	DALELANDS	HIGHTOP	SHADOW COAST	UNDERVALE	GOLDEN THRONE	JEWELED SCEPTER	PLATINUM CROWN	VELVET ROBES
KING	FEDRIS												
	JACOBUS												
	KEVRICK												
	VERMOND												
GIFT	GOLDEN THRONE												
	JEWELED SCEPTER												
	PLATINUM CROWN												
	VELVET ROBES												
KINGDOM	DALELANDS												
	HIGHTOP												
	SHADOW COAST												
	UNDERVALE												

3. New Year's Revelations Lucy and four of her friends met at the Golden Panda for dinner one evening in January. Much to their surprise, they had wandered in to the restaurant during a celebration of the Chinese New Year. Luckily for the five, this meant a discount on their meals and a free session with the mysterious medium Madame Wau Pei. The five friends had their fortunes told, one at a time. Each person told the mystic the date and year of his or her birth and learned that, according to Chinese astrology, each friend's birth year is designated by a different animal. Also, each of the five was told that he or she has a different lucky element. Before leaving the restaurant, the five friends compared their predictions, noticing that all of them had a long journey in their future—the trip back home! From the information provided, determine the order in which the five friends had their fortunes told, the year in which each person was born, and each person's lucky element.

(a) Toni was the third person to get her fortune told. The person whose lucky element is wood was the last person to see the fortune-teller.

(b) Earl (whose lucky element is fire) had his fortune told immediately before the person who was born in the Year of the Rooster. The fourth person to visit the fortune-teller was born in the Year of the Dragon.

(c) The person born in the Year of the Ox had his or her fortune told at some point before the one whose lucky element is metal. Ivana was born in the Year of the Horse.

(d) The person whose lucky element is water (who was born in the Year of the Cow) wasn't the first person to have his or her fortune told.

(e) The person whose lucky element is earth had his or her fortune told exactly two after Philip.

		FRIEND					YEAR				ELEMENT				
		EARL	IVANA	LUCY	PHILIP	TONI	COW	DRAGON	HORSE	OX	ROOSTER	EARTH	FIRE	METAL	WATER	WOOD
ORDER	FIRST															
	SECOND															
	THIRD															
	FOURTH															
	FIFTH															
ELEMENT	EARTH															
	FIRE															
	METAL															
	WATER															
	WOOD															
YEAR	COW															
	DRAGON															
	HORSE															
	OX															
	ROOSTER															

4. Barn Again For as long as I can remember, I've dreamed of owning my own bed-and-breakfast, and it looks like my dream is about to come true! We'd like our inn to be distinctive, so my husband and I have decided to purchase a barn and convert it into unique living quarters. We viewed five barns recently, each of which had once served a different purpose. My husband and I visited each barn with a different contractor, each of whom gave us a different estimate ($50,000, $60,000, $70,000, $80,000, or $100,000) for the conversion. Each barn has a different feature that makes it appealing (one has a functioning hoist), but we still haven't decided which one to buy—we're starting to go a little haywire! From the information provided, determine the contractor who visited each barn with us and the special feature of each structure, as well as the estimate given for the renovation of each barn.

(a) The apple barn (which has distinctive octagonal windows) will cost exactly $20,000 less to convert than the barn we visited with a Bill's Building representative. The estimate for renovating the hay barn is higher than the estimate for converting the potato barn.

(b) The barn we visited with the person from AB Contracting (which isn't the barn that has fabulous heavy beams) will cost more to renovate than the barn we viewed with the contractor from Pine Valley but exactly $10,000 less to convert than the horse barn.

(c) The estimates for converting the apple barn and the barn with lovely board-and-batten siding are the lowest and highest estimates, in some order.

(d) The barn we visited with the contractor from Dekker Ltd. will cost exactly $20,000 more to renovate than the barn with insulation worth preserving.

(e) The old dairy barn will cost more to renovate than the one we visited with the representative from Vander Estates.

		APPLE	DAIRY	HAY	HORSE	POTATO	BEAMS	HOIST	INSULATION	SIDING	WINDOWS	$50,000	$60,000	$70,000	$80,000	$100,000
		BARN					FEATURE					ESTIMATE				
CONTRACTOR	AB CONTRACTING															
	BILL'S BUILDING															
	DEKKER LTD.															
	PINE VALLEY															
	VANDER ESTATES															
ESTIMATE	$50,000															
	$60,000															
	$70,000															
	$80,000															
	$100,000															
FEATURE	BEAMS															
	HOIST															
	INSULATION															
	SIDING															
	WINDOWS															

Solve each Sudoku, which appeared in Dell Original Sudoku, *March 2010, Penny Publications. (They are categorized according to difficulty level.)*

5. *Easy*

	4		1	6	8			5
		9		5			2	8
	6		9					4
		4	7		9			
	3	8		4		2	9	
			2		3	8		
2				1		6		
9	7			2		5		
4			6	9	5		7	

6. *Easy*

2		3			8	1	4	
	7		6	2	4			
	8			3				7
8	4	7	2				6	
			8		6			
	1				9	4	8	2
7			6			2		
			9	5	7		1	
	6	9	3			5		4

7. *Medium*

8	3		6					1
	1			4			5	6
		6			8			
		7	1				3	8
		1		2		4		
5	4				6	1		
		5			7			
9	8			7			1	
6				1			2	3

8. *Medium*

			4	5		6		
4	5					3		9
	6	1			3			8
5	8			1		6		
		9		3		2		
	4		9				1	7
8			1			7	3	
1		5					9	2
		6		7	2			

9. *Hard*

	1			2				4
4		9			1		7	
		8			9			
	3		6				2	
7				3				9
	9				8		5	
		2				4		
	8		2			6		5
9				8			3	

10. *Hard*

	2			9		6	7	
	5	6						
			6		4			5
	6	9						1
			3	6	9			
8						9	4	
1			4		7			
						4	2	
	4	8		2			3	

3.6 ANALYZING ARGUMENTS WITH TRUTH TABLES

Truth Tables (Two Premises) • Valid and Invalid Argument Forms • Truth Tables (More Than Two Premises) • Arguments of Lewis Carroll

In the 2007 Spanish film *La Habitacion de Fermat (Fermat's Room)*, four mathematicians are invited to dinner, only to discover that the room in which they are meeting is designed to eventually crush them as walls creep in closer and closer. The only way for them to delay the inevitable is to answer enigmas, questions, puzzles, problems, and riddles that they are receiving on a cell phone.

One of the enigmas deals with a hermetically sealed room that contains a single light bulb. There are three switches outside the room, and only one of the switches controls the bulb. You are allowed to push any or all of the buttons as many times as you wish before you enter the room, but once you enter you cannot return to the switches outside. How can you determine which one controls the bulb? (The answer is on **page 126**.)

Truth Tables (Two Premises)

In **Section 3.5** we used Euler diagrams to test the validity of arguments. While Euler diagrams often work well for simple arguments, difficulties can develop with more complex ones, because Euler diagrams require a sketch showing every possible case. In complex arguments, it is hard to be sure that all cases have been considered.

In deciding whether to use Euler diagrams to test the validity of an argument, look for quantifiers such as "all," "some," or "no." These words often indicate arguments best tested by Euler diagrams. If these words are absent, it may be better to use truth tables to test the validity of an argument.

As an example of this method, consider the following argument:

> If the floor is dirty, then I must mop it.
> The floor is dirty.
> _____
> I must mop it.

To test the validity of this argument, we begin by identifying the *component* statements found in the argument. They are "the floor is dirty" and "I must mop it." We assign the letters p and q to represent these statements:

> p represents "the floor is dirty";
> q represents "I must mop it."

Now we write the two premises and the conclusion in symbols.

> Premise 1: $p \rightarrow q$
> Premise 2: p
> _____
> Conclusion: q

To decide if this argument is valid, we must determine whether the conjunction of both premises implies the conclusion for all possible cases of truth values for p and q. Therefore, write the conjunction of the premises as the antecedent of a conditional statement, and the conclusion as the consequent.

$$[(p \rightarrow q) \quad \wedge \quad p] \quad \rightarrow \quad q$$

premise   and   premise   implies   conclusion

Finally, construct the truth table for this conditional statement, as shown below.

p	q	$p \rightarrow q$	$(p \rightarrow q) \wedge p$	$[(p \rightarrow q) \wedge p] \rightarrow q$
T	T	T	T	T
T	F	F	F	T
F	T	T	F	T
F	F	T	F	T

Because the final column, shown in color, indicates that the conditional statement that represents the argument is true for all possible truth values of p and q, the statement is a tautology. Thus, the argument is valid.

Answer to the Light Bulb question on **page 125**.

Label the switches 1, 2, and 3. Turn switch 1 on and leave it on for several minutes. Then turn switch 1 off, turn switch 2 on, and then immediately enter the room. If the bulb is on, then you know that switch 2 controls it. If the bulb is off, touch it to see if it is still warm. If it is, then switch 1 controls it. If the bulb is not warm, then switch 3 controls it.

The pattern of the argument in the floor-mopping example

$$p \rightarrow q$$
$$\underline{p}$$
$$q$$

is called **modus ponens,** or the *law of detachment.*

To test the validity of an argument using a truth table, follow the steps in the box.

Testing the Validity of an Argument with a Truth Table

Step 1   Assign a letter to represent each component statement in the argument.

Step 2   Express each premise and the conclusion symbolically.

Step 3   Form the symbolic statement of the entire argument by writing the *conjunction* of *all* the premises as the antecedent of a conditional statement, and the conclusion of the argument as the consequent.

Step 4   Complete the truth table for the conditional statement formed in Step 3. If it is a tautology, then the argument is valid; otherwise, it is invalid.

▮▮ **EXAMPLE 1**   Using a Truth Table to Determine Validity

Determine whether the argument is *valid* or *invalid*.

If my check arrives in time, I'll register for the fall semester.
I've registered for the fall semester.

My check arrived in time.

SOLUTION

Let p represent "my check arrives (arrived) in time" and let q represent "I'll register (I've registered) for the fall semester." The argument can be written as follows.

$$p \rightarrow q$$
$$\underline{q}$$
$$p$$

To test for validity, construct a truth table for the statement $[(p \rightarrow q) \wedge q] \rightarrow p$.

p	q	$p \rightarrow q$	$(p \rightarrow q) \wedge q$	$[(p \rightarrow q) \wedge q] \rightarrow p$
T	T	T	T	T
T	F	F	F	T
F	T	T	T	F
F	F	T	F	T

The third row of the final column of the truth table shows F, and this is enough to conclude that the argument is invalid.   ▮▮▮

If a conditional and its converse were logically equivalent, then an argument of the type found in **Example 1** would be valid. Because a conditional and its converse are *not* equivalent, the argument is an example of what is sometimes called the **fallacy of the converse.**

▮▮ **EXAMPLE 2**   Using a Truth Table to Determine Validity

Determine whether the argument is *valid* or *invalid*.

If a man could be in two places at one time, I'd be with you.
I am not with you.

A man can't be in two places at one time.

SOLUTION

If p represents "a man could be in two places at one time" and q represents "I'd be with you," the argument is written as follows.

$$p \rightarrow q$$
$$\underline{\sim q}$$
$$\sim p$$

The symbolic statement of the entire argument is as follows.

$$[(p \rightarrow q) \wedge \sim q] \rightarrow \sim p$$

The truth table for this argument indicates a tautology, and the argument is valid.

p	q	$p \rightarrow q$	$\sim q$	$(p \rightarrow q) \wedge \sim q$	$\sim p$	$[(p \rightarrow q) \wedge \sim q] \rightarrow \sim p$
T	T	T	F	F	F	T
T	F	F	T	F	F	T
F	T	T	F	F	T	T
F	F	T	T	T	T	T

The pattern of reasoning of this example is called **modus tollens,** or the *law of contraposition,* or *indirect reasoning.* ■■■

With reasoning similar to that used to name the fallacy of the converse, the fallacy

$$p \rightarrow q$$
$$\underline{\sim p}$$
$$\sim q$$

is called the **fallacy of the inverse.** An example of such a fallacy is "If it rains, I get wet. It doesn't rain. Therefore, I don't get wet."

‖ EXAMPLE 3   Using a Truth Table to Determine Validity

Determine whether the argument is *valid* or *invalid.*

I'll buy a car or I'll take a vacation.
I won't buy a car.
I'll take a vacation.

SOLUTION

If p represents "I'll buy a car" and q represents "I'll take a vacation," the argument is symbolized as follows.

$$p \vee q$$
$$\underline{\sim p}$$
$$q$$

We must set up a truth table for the statement $[(p \vee q) \wedge \sim p] \rightarrow q$.

p	q	$p \vee q$	$\sim p$	$(p \vee q) \wedge \sim p$	$[(p \vee q) \wedge \sim p] \rightarrow q$
T	T	T	F	F	T
T	F	T	F	F	T
F	T	T	T	T	T
F	F	F	T	F	T

The statement is a tautology and the argument is valid. Any argument of this form is valid by the law of **disjunctive syllogism.** ■■■

▮▮ **EXAMPLE 4** Using a Truth Table to Determine Validity

Determine whether the argument is *valid* or *invalid*.

> If it squeaks, then I use WD-40.
> If I use WD-40, then I must go to the hardware store.
> If it squeaks, then I must go to the hardware store.

SOLUTION

Let p represent "it squeaks," let q represent "I use WD-40," and let r represent "I must go to the hardware store." The argument takes on the following general form.

$$p \rightarrow q$$
$$q \rightarrow r$$
$$\overline{p \rightarrow r}$$

Make a truth table for this statement, which requires eight rows.

$$[(p \rightarrow q) \wedge (q \rightarrow r)] \rightarrow (p \rightarrow r)$$

p	q	r	$p \rightarrow q$	$q \rightarrow r$	$p \rightarrow r$	$(p \rightarrow q) \wedge (q \rightarrow r)$	$[(p \rightarrow q) \wedge (q \rightarrow r)] \rightarrow (p \rightarrow r)$
T	T	T	T	T	T	T	T
T	T	F	T	F	F	F	T
T	F	T	F	T	T	F	T
T	F	F	F	T	F	F	T
F	T	T	T	T	T	T	T
F	T	F	T	F	T	F	T
F	F	T	T	T	T	T	T
F	F	F	T	T	T	T	T

This argument is valid because the final statement is a tautology. This pattern of argument is called **reasoning by transitivity,** or the *law of hypothetical syllogism.* ▮▮▮

Valid and Invalid Argument Forms

A summary of the valid and invalid forms of argument presented so far in this section follows.

In a scene near the beginning of the 1974 film *Monty Python and the Holy Grail,* an amazing application of **poor logic** leads to the apparent demise of a supposed witch. Some peasants have forced a young woman to wear a nose made of wood. The convoluted argument they make is this: Witches and wood are both burned, and because witches are made of wood, and wood floats, and ducks also float, if she weighs the same as a duck, then she is made of wood and, therefore, is a witch!

Valid Argument Forms

Modus Ponens	Modus Tollens	Disjunctive Syllogism	Reasoning by Transitivity
$p \rightarrow q$	$p \rightarrow q$	$p \vee q$	$p \rightarrow q$
p	$\sim q$	$\sim p$	$q \rightarrow r$
q	$\sim p$	q	$p \rightarrow r$

Invalid Argument Forms (Fallacies)

Fallacy of the Converse	Fallacy of the Inverse
$p \rightarrow q$	$p \rightarrow q$
q	$\sim p$
p	$\sim q$

Truth Tables (More Than Two Premises)

When an argument contains more than two premises, it is necessary to determine the truth values of the conjunction of *all* of them. *If at least one premise in a conjunction of several premises is false, then the entire conjunction is false.*

▮▮ **EXAMPLE 5** Using a Truth Table to Determine Validity

Determine whether the argument is *valid* or *invalid*.

If Eddie goes to town, then Mabel stays at home. If Mabel does not stay at home, then Rita will cook. Rita will not cook. Therefore, Eddie does not go to town.

SOLUTION

In an argument written in this manner, the premises are given first, and the conclusion is the statement that follows the word "Therefore." Let p represent "Eddie goes to town," let q represent "Mabel stays at home," and let r represent "Rita will cook."

$$p \rightarrow q$$
$$\sim q \rightarrow r$$
$$\underline{\sim r}$$
$$\sim p$$

To test validity, set up a truth table for this statement.

$$[(p \rightarrow q) \land (\sim q \rightarrow r) \land \sim r] \rightarrow \sim p$$

p	q	r	$p \rightarrow q$	$\sim q$	$\sim q \rightarrow r$	$\sim r$	$(p \rightarrow q) \land (\sim q \rightarrow r) \land \sim r$	$\sim p$	$[(p \rightarrow q) \land (\sim q \rightarrow r) \land \sim r] \rightarrow \sim p$
T	T	T	T	F	T	F	F	F	T
T	T	F	T	F	T	T	T	F	F
T	F	T	F	T	T	F	F	F	T
T	F	F	F	T	F	T	F	F	T
F	T	T	T	F	T	F	F	T	T
F	T	F	T	F	T	T	T	T	T
F	F	T	T	T	T	F	F	T	T
F	F	F	T	T	F	T	F	T	T

Because the final column does not contain all Ts, the statement is not a tautology. The argument is invalid. ▮▮▮

Arguments of Lewis Carroll

Consider the following verse, which has been around for many years.

For want of a nail, the shoe was lost. For want of a shoe, the horse was lost. For want of a horse, the rider was lost. For want of a rider, the battle was lost. For want of a battle, the war was lost.
Therefore, for want of a nail, the war was lost.

Each line of the verse may be written as an *if . . . then* statement. For example, the first line may be restated as "if a nail is lost, then the shoe is lost." The conclusion, "for want of a nail, the war was lost," follows from the premises, because repeated use of the law of transitivity applies. Arguments such as the one used by Lewis Carroll in the next example often take on a similar form.

Alice in the Forest of Forgetfulness
When Alice entered the Forest of Forgetfulness, she often forgot what day of the week it was. She encountered a Lion and a Unicorn, two strange creatures. The Lion lies on Mondays, Tuesdays, and Wednesdays and tells the truth on the other days of the week. The Unicorn, on the other hand, lies on Thursdays, Fridays, and Saturdays, but tells the truth on the other days of the week.

One day Alice met the Lion and the Unicorn resting under a tree. They made the following statements:

Lion: Yesterday was one of my lying days.
Unicorn: Yesterday was one of my lying days, too.

From these two statements, Alice was able to deduce the day of the week. What day was it? (The answer is on **page 133**.)

(Adapted from a problem in Raymond Smullyan's *What Is the Name of This Book?*)

██ **EXAMPLE 6** Supplying a Conclusion to Assure Validity

Supply a conclusion that yields a valid argument for the following premises.

> Babies are illogical.
> Nobody is despised who can manage a crocodile.
> Illogical persons are despised.

SOLUTION

First, write each premise in the form *if . . . then. . . .*

> If you are a baby, then you are illogical.
> If you can manage a crocodile, then you are not despised.
> If you are illogical, then you are despised.

Let *p* be "you are a baby," let *q* be "you are logical," let *r* be "you can manage a crocodile," and let *s* be "you are despised." The statements can be written symbolically.

$$p \rightarrow \sim q$$
$$r \rightarrow \sim s$$
$$\sim q \rightarrow s$$

Begin with any letter that appears only once. Here *p* appears only once. Using the contrapositive of $r \rightarrow \sim s$, which is $s \rightarrow \sim r$, rearrange the statements as follows.

$$p \rightarrow \sim q$$
$$\sim q \rightarrow s$$
$$s \rightarrow \sim r$$

From the three statements, repeated use of reasoning by transitivity gives the conclusion

$$p \rightarrow \sim r, \quad \text{which leads to a valid argument.}$$

In words, the conclusion is "If you are a baby, then you cannot manage a crocodile," or, as Lewis Carroll would have written it, "Babies cannot manage crocodiles." ███

3.6 EXERCISES

Each argument is either valid by one of the forms of valid arguments discussed in this section, or it is a fallacy by one of the forms of invalid arguments discussed. (See the summary boxes.) Decide whether the argument is valid *or a* fallacy, *and give the form that applies.*

1. If James Taylor comes to town, then I will go to the concert.
If I go to the concert, then I'll call in sick for work.

If James Taylor comes to town, then I'll call in sick for work.

2. If you use binoculars, then you get a glimpse of the space shuttle.
If you get a glimpse of the space shuttle, then you'll be amazed.

If you use binoculars, then you'll be amazed.

3. If Julie Nhem works hard enough, she will get a promotion.
Julie Nhem works hard enough.

She gets a promotion.

4. If Andrew Noble sells his quota, he'll get a bonus.
Andrew Noble sells his quota.

He gets a bonus.

5. If he doesn't have to get up at 3:00 A.M., he's ecstatic.
He's ecstatic.

He doesn't have to get up at 3:00 A.M.

6. If she buys another pair of shoes, her closet will overflow.
Her closet will overflow.

She buys another pair of shoes.

7. If Mariano Rivera pitches, the Yankees win.
The Yankees do not win.

Mariano Rivera does not pitch.

8. If Nelson Dida plays, the opponent gets shut out.
The opponent does not get shut out.

Nelson Dida does not play.

9. "If we evolved a race of Isaac Newtons, that would not be progress." (quote from Aldous Huxley)
We have not evolved a race of Isaac Newtons.

That is progress.

10. "If I have seen farther than others, it is because I stood on the shoulders of giants." (quote from Sir Isaac Newton)
I have not seen farther than others.

I have not stood on the shoulders of giants.

11. She uses e-commerce or she pays by credit card.
She does not pay by credit card.

She uses e-commerce.

12. Mia kicks or Drew passes.
Drew does not pass.

Mia kicks.

Use a truth table to determine whether the argument is valid *or* invalid.

13. $p \lor q$
p

$\sim q$

14. $p \land \sim q$
p

$\sim q$

15. $\sim p \to \sim q$
q

p

16. $p \lor \sim q$
p

$\sim q$

17. $p \to q$
$q \to p$

$p \land q$

18. $\sim p \to q$
p

$\sim q$

19. $p \to \sim q$
q

$\sim p$

20. $p \to \sim q$
$\sim p$

$\sim q$

21. $(p \land q) \lor (p \lor q)$
q

p

22. $(p \to q) \land (q \to p)$
p

$p \lor q$

23. $(\sim p \lor q) \land (\sim p \to q)$
p

$\sim q$

24. $(r \land p) \to (r \lor q)$
$q \land p$

$r \lor p$

25. $(\sim p \land r) \to (p \lor q)$
$\sim r \to p$

$q \to r$

26. $(p \to \sim q) \lor (q \to \sim r)$
$p \lor \sim r$

$r \to p$

27. Earlier we showed how to analyze arguments using Euler diagrams. Refer to **Example 4** in this section, restate each premise and the conclusion using a quantifier, and then draw an Euler diagram to illustrate the relationship.

28. Explain in a few sentences how to determine the statement for which a truth table will be constructed so that the arguments that follow in **Exercises 29–38** can be analyzed for validity.

Determine whether each argument is valid *or* invalid.

29. Joey loves to watch movies. If Terry likes to jog, then Joey does not love to watch movies. If Terry does not like to jog, then Carrie drives a school bus. Therefore, Carrie drives a school bus.

30. If Hurricane Gustave hit that grove of trees, then the trees are devastated. People plant trees when disasters strike and the trees are not devastated. Therefore, if people plant trees when disasters strike, then Hurricane Gustave did not hit that grove of trees.

31. If the social networking craze continues, then downloading music will remain popular. American Girl dolls are favorites or downloading music will remain popular. American Girl dolls are not favorites. Therefore, the social networking craze does not continue.

32. Carrie Underwood sings or Joe Jonas is not a teen idol. If Joe Jonas is not a teen idol, then Jennifer Hudson does not win a Grammy. Jennifer Hudson wins a Grammy. Therefore, Carrie Underwood does not sing.

33. The Dolphins will be in the playoffs if and only if Chad leads the league in passing. Tony coaches the Dolphins or Chad leads the league in passing. Tony does not coach the Dolphins. Therefore, the Dolphins will not be in the playoffs.

34. If I've got you under my skin, then you are deep in the heart of me. If you are deep in the heart of me, then you are not really a part of me. You are deep in the heart of me or you are really a part of me. Therefore, if I've got you under my skin, then you are really a part of me.

35. If Dr. Hardy is a department chairman, then he lives in Atlanta. He lives in Atlanta and his first name is Larry. Therefore, if his first name is not Larry, then he is not a department chairman.

36. If I were your woman and you were my man, then I'd never stop loving you. I've stopped loving you. Therefore, I am not your woman or you are not my man.

37. All men are created equal. All people who are created equal are women. Therefore, all men are women.

38. All men are mortal. Socrates is a man. Therefore, Socrates is mortal.

39. Suppose that you ask a stranger for the time and you get the following response:

> "If I tell you the time, then we'll start chatting. If we start chatting, then you'll want to meet me at a truck stop. If we meet at a truck stop, then we'll discuss my family. If we discuss my family, then you'll find out that my daughter is available for marriage. If you find out that she is available for marriage, then you'll want to marry her. If you want to marry her, then my life will be miserable since I don't want my daughter married to some fool who can't afford a $10 watch."

Use reasoning by transitivity to draw a valid conclusion.

40. Molly Riggs made the following observation: "If I want to determine whether an argument leading to the statement

$$[(p \rightarrow q) \wedge \sim q] \rightarrow \sim p$$

is valid, I only need to consider the lines of the truth table which lead to T for the column headed $(p \rightarrow q) \wedge \sim q$." Molly was very perceptive. Can you explain why her observation was correct?

In the arguments used by Lewis Carroll, it is helpful to restate a premise in if . . . then *form in order to more easily identify a valid conclusion. The following premises come from Lewis Carroll. Write each premise in* if . . . then *form.*

41. All my poultry are ducks.

42. None of your sons can do logic.

43. Guinea pigs are hopelessly ignorant of music.

44. No teetotalers are pawnbrokers.

45. No teachable kitten has green eyes.

46. Opium-eaters have no self-command.

47. I have not filed any of them that I can read.

48. All of them written on blue paper are filed.

Exercises 49–54 involve premises from Lewis Carroll. Write each premise in symbols, and then in the final part, give a conclusion that yields a valid argument.

49. Let *p* be "it is a duck," *q* be "it is my poultry," *r* be "one is an officer," and *s* be "one is willing to waltz."

 (a) No ducks are willing to waltz.

 (b) No officers ever decline to waltz.

 (c) All my poultry are ducks.

 (d) Give a conclusion that yields a valid argument.

50. Let *p* be "one is able to do logic," *q* be "one is fit to serve on a jury," *r* be "one is sane," and *s* be "he is your son."

 (a) Everyone who is sane can do logic.

 (b) No lunatics are fit to serve on a jury.

 (c) None of your sons can do logic.

 (d) Give a conclusion that yields a valid argument.

51. Let *p* be "one is honest," *q* be "one is a pawnbroker," *r* be "one is a promise-breaker," *s* be "one is trustworthy," *t* be "one is very communicative," and *u* be "one is a wine-drinker."

 (a) Promise-breakers are untrustworthy.

 (b) Wine-drinkers are very communicative.

 (c) A person who keeps a promise is honest.

 (d) No teetotalers are pawnbrokers. (*Hint:* Assume "teetotaler" is the opposite of "wine-drinker.")

 (e) One can always trust a very communicative person.

 (f) Give a conclusion that yields a valid argument.

52. Let *p* be "it is a guinea pig," *q* be "it is hopelessly ignorant of music," *r* be "it keeps silent while the *Moonlight Sonata* is being played," and *s* be "it appreciates Beethoven."

 (a) Nobody who really appreciates Beethoven fails to keep silent while the *Moonlight Sonata* is being played.

 (b) Guinea pigs are hopelessly ignorant of music.

 (c) No one who is hopelessly ignorant of music ever keeps silent while the *Moonlight Sonata* is being played.

 (d) Give a conclusion that yields a valid argument.

53. Let *p* be "it begins with 'Dear Sir'," *q* be "it is crossed," *r* be "it is dated," *s* be "it is filed," *t* be "it is in black ink," *u* be "it is in the third person," *v* be "I can read it," *w* be "it is on blue paper," *x* be "it is on one sheet," and *y* be "it is written by Brown."

(a) All the dated letters are written on blue paper.

(b) None of them are in black ink, except those that are written in the third person.

(c) I have not filed any of them that I can read.

(d) None of them that are written on one sheet are undated.

(e) All of them that are not crossed are in black ink.

(f) All of them written by Brown begin with "Dear Sir."

(g) All of them written on blue paper are filed.

(h) None of them written on more than one sheet are crossed.

(i) None of them that begin with "Dear Sir" are written in the third person.

(j) Give a conclusion that yields a valid argument.

54. Let *p* be "he is going to a party," *q* be "he brushes his hair," *r* be "he has self-command," *s* be "he looks fascinating," *t* be "he is an opium-eater," *u* be "he is tidy," and *v* be "he wears white kid gloves."

(a) No one who is going to a party ever fails to brush his hair.

(b) No one looks fascinating if he is untidy.

(c) Opium-eaters have no self-command.

(d) Everyone who has brushed his hair looks fascinating.

(e) No one wears white kid gloves unless he is going to a party. (*Hint:* "*a* unless *b*" ≡ ~*b* → *a*.)

(f) A man is always untidy if he has no self-command.

(g) Give a conclusion that yields a valid argument.

Answer to Alice in the Forest of Forgetfulness problem on **page 130:**

The only days the Lion can say, "I lied yesterday" are Mondays and Thursdays. The only days the Unicorn can say "I lied yesterday" are Thursdays and Sundays. Therefore the only day they can both say that is Thursday.

COLLABORATIVE INVESTIGATION

Logic Problems and Sudoku Revisited

Logic problems and Sudoku were first discussed in the **Extension** on **pages 120–124.** The problems here require more time and reasoning skills than the ones appearing in the **Extension.** They are taken from *Original Logic*

Problems, February 2010, and *Dell Original Sudoku*, March 2010.

The class may wish to divide up into groups and see which group can solve these problems fastest.

EXERCISES

Note: As an exception to our usual style, answers to these Collaborative Investigation Exercises are given in the back of the book.

1. ***Out to Launch*** The National Space Association has scheduled five rockets for launch early next year. Each rocket (including the *Penchant*) will take off in a different month (January through May) on a different date (the 1st through the 5th). Each rocket will launch from a different site (including the San Simeon Launch Center) and engage in a different mission. For fans of the space program, next year will be a real blast! From the information provided, determine the month and date of the launch of the rocket from each launch site, as well as each rocket's mission.

		DATE					LAUNCH SITE					ROCKET					MISSION				
		1ST	2ND	3RD	4TH	5TH	CAPE CARNIVAL	EDDINGS A. F. B.	SAN SIMEON L. C.	VANDYKE FACILITY	WILLARD ISLAND	BRAVURA	FALCONER	LIBERTY	PENCHANT	TWILIGHT	INVESTIGATE	LAND ON MOON	MEASURE	REPAIR SATELLITE	TEST PROPULSION
MONTH	JANUARY																				
	FEBRUARY																				
	MARCH																				
	APRIL																				
	MAY																				
MISSION	INVESTIGATE																				
	LAND ON MOON																				
	MEASURE																				
	REPAIR																				
	TEST																				
ROCKET	BRAVURA																				
	FALCONER																				
	LIBERTY																				
	PENCHANT																				
	TWILIGHT																				
LAUNCH SITE	CAPE CARNIVAL																				
	EDDINGS AIR																				
	SAN SIMEON																				
	VANDYKE																				
	WILLARD ISLAND																				

(a) The date of the May launch is numbered exactly two lower than the date of the Willard Island launch. None of the rockets will launch on February 1. The mission to test a new propulsion system won't be launching in January.

(b) The *Liberty* and the rocket that will blast off in April will launch from Cape Carnival and Willard Island in some order. Neither the rocket on a mission to measure magnetic fields (which won't launch on the 1st of a month) nor the Willard Island rocket will blast off on the 3rd of a month.

(c) The *Bravura* will launch the month after the rocket that will blast off on the 4th of a month (which will launch later than the rocket that will land on the moon). The *Liberty* won't blast off on the 2nd of a month.

(d) The rocket that will launch from Cape Carnival won't be testing a new propulsion system. The *Twilight*'s mission (which isn't the mission to repair a satellite) won't begin on the 5th of a month.

(e) The rocket on a mission to investigate strange radiation will launch at some point earlier in the year than the *Liberty* (which won't be repairing a satellite) but at some point later in the year than the vessel that will blast off from the Vandyke Facility.

(f) The rocket that will blast off from Eddings Air Force Base will launch on a lower-numbered date than the one that will launch in March (which won't be testing a new propulsion system), which will blast off on a lower-numbered date than the *Falconer*.

2. *Super Challenger Puzzle* To solve the following Super Challenger puzzle, place a number into every box so that each row across, each column down, each small 16-box square (there are 16 of these), and each of the two diagonals contains each number from 1 to 16. No number may appear more than once in any one row or column, in either diagonal, or within any small 16-box square.

CHAPTER 3 TEST

Write a negation for each statement.

1. $6 - 3 = 3$

2. All men are created equal.

3. Some members of the class went on the field trip.

4. If that's the way you feel, then I will accept it.

5. She applied and got a student loan.

Let p represent "You will love me" and let q represent "I will love you." Write each statement in symbols.

6. If you won't love me, then I will love you.

7. I will love you if you will love me.

8. I won't love you if and only if you won't love me.

Using the same statements as for Exercises 6–8, write each of the following in words.

9. $\sim p \land q$

10. $\sim(p \lor \sim q)$

In each of the following, assume that p is true and that q and r are false. Find the truth value of each statement.

11. $\sim q \land \sim r$

12. $r \lor (p \land \sim q)$

13. $r \rightarrow (s \lor r)$ (The truth value of the statement s is unknown.)

14. $p \leftrightarrow (p \rightarrow q)$

15. Explain in your own words why, if p is a statement, the biconditional $p \leftrightarrow \sim p$ must be false.

16. State the necessary conditions for each of the following.
   (a) a conditional statement to be false
   (b) a conjunction to be true
   (c) a disjunction to be false

Construct a truth table for each of the following.

17. $p \land (\sim p \lor q)$

18. $\sim(p \land q) \rightarrow (\sim p \lor \sim q)$

Decide whether each statement is true *or* false.

19. Some negative integers are whole numbers.

20. All irrational numbers are real numbers.

Write each conditional statement in if . . . then *form.*

21. All integers are rational numbers.

22. Being a rhombus is sufficient for a polygon to be a quadrilateral.

23. Being divisible by 2 is necessary for a number to be divisible by 4.

24. She digs dinosaur bones only if she is a paleontologist.

For each statement, write (**a**) *the converse,* (**b**) *the inverse, and* (**c**) *the contrapositive.*

25. If a picture paints a thousand words, the graph will help me understand it.

26. $\sim p \rightarrow (q \wedge r)$ (Use one of De Morgan's laws as necessary.)

27. Use an Euler diagram to determine whether the argument is *valid* or *invalid*.

All members of that athletic club save money.
Don O'Neal is a member of that athletic club.

Don O'Neal saves money.

28. Match each argument in parts (a)–(d) in the next column with the law that justifies its validity, or the fallacy of which it is an example, in choices A–F.

A. Modus ponens
B. Modus tollens
C. Reasoning by transitivity
D. Disjunctive syllogism
E. Fallacy of the converse
F. Fallacy of the inverse

(a) If he eats liver, then he'll eat anything.
He eats liver.

He'll eat anything.

(b) If you use your seat belt, you will be safer.
You don't use your seat belt.

You won't be safer.

(c) If I hear *Mr. Bojangles*, I think of her.
If I think of her, I smile.

If I hear *Mr. Bojangles*, I smile.

(d) She sings or she dances.
She does not sing.

She dances.

Use a truth table to determine whether each argument is valid *or* invalid.

29. If I write a check, it will bounce. If the bank guarantees it, then it does not bounce. The bank guarantees it. Therefore, I don't write a check.

30. $\sim p \rightarrow \sim q$
$q \rightarrow p$
$p \vee q$

6.5 APPLICATIONS OF DECIMALS AND PERCENTS

Operations with Decimals • Rounding Decimals • Percent • Applications

Operations with Decimals

Because calculators have, for the most part, replaced paper-and-pencil methods for operations with decimals and percent, we will only briefly mention these latter methods. *We strongly suggest that the work in this section be done with a calculator at hand.*

Addition and Subtraction of Decimals

To add or subtract decimal numbers, line up the decimal points in a column and perform the operation.

▪▪ **EXAMPLE 1** Adding and Subtracting Decimal Numbers

Find each of the following.

(a) $0.46 + 3.9 + 12.58$ **(b)** $12.1 - 8.723$

SOLUTION

```
.46+3.9+12.58
                16.94
12.1−8.723
                3.377
```

This screen supports the results in
Example 1.

(a)
$$
\begin{array}{r}
0.46 \\
3.90 \\
+12.58 \\
\hline
16.94
\end{array}
$$
Line up decimal points.
Attach a zero as a placeholder.
← Sum

(b)
$$
\begin{array}{r}
12.100 \\
-8.723 \\
\hline
3.377
\end{array}
$$
Attach zeros.
← Difference

▪▪▪

Recall that when two numbers are multiplied, the numbers are called **factors** and the answer is called the **product.** When two numbers are divided, the number being divided is called the **dividend,** the number doing the dividing is called the **divisor,** and the answer is called the **quotient.**

Multiplication and Division of Decimals

Multiplication To multiply decimals, multiply in the same manner as integers are multiplied. The number of decimal places to the right of the decimal point in the product is the *sum* of the numbers of places to the right of the decimal points in the factors.

Division To divide decimals, move the decimal point to the right the same number of places in the divisor and the dividend so as to obtain a whole number in the divisor. Divide in the same manner as integers are divided. The number of decimal places to the right of the decimal point in the quotient is the same as the number of places to the right in the dividend.

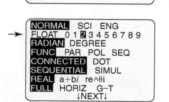

Here the TI-83/84 Plus is set to round the answer to two decimal places.

▐▐ **EXAMPLE 2** Multiplying and Dividing Decimal Numbers

Find each of the following.

(a) 4.613×2.52 **(b)** $65.175 \div 8.25$

SOLUTION

(a)
$$
\begin{array}{r}
4.613 \quad \leftarrow \text{3 decimal places} \\
\times \quad 2.52 \quad \leftarrow \text{2 decimal places} \\
\hline
9226 \\
23065 \\
9226 \\
\hline
11.62476 \quad \leftarrow 3 + 2 = 5 \text{ decimal places}
\end{array}
$$

(b)

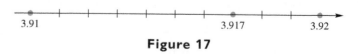

Bring the decimal point straight up in the answer.

▐▐▐

Rounding Decimals

▐▐ **EXAMPLE 3** Rounding a Decimal Number

Round 3.917 to the nearest hundredth.

SOLUTION

The hundredths place in 3.917 contains the digit 1.

3.917
↑ Hundredths place

To round this decimal, locate 3.91 and 3.92 on a number line as in **Figure 17**.

The calculator rounds 3.917 to the nearest hundredth.

Figure 17

The distance from 3.91 to 3.92 is divided into ten equal parts. The seventh of these ten parts locates the number 3.917. As the number line shows, 3.917 is closer to 3.92 than it is to 3.91, so 3.917 rounded to the nearest hundredth is 3.92. ▐▐▐

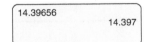

The calculator rounds 3.915 *up* to 3.92.

If the number line method of **Example 3** were used to round 3.915 to the nearest hundredth, a problem would develop—the number 3.915 is exactly halfway between 3.91 and 3.92. An arbitrary decision is then made to round *up:* 3.915 rounded to the nearest hundredth is 3.92. (Some disciplines have guidelines so that in certain cases, a *downward* roundoff is made. We will not investigate these.)

Rules for Rounding Decimals

Step 1   Locate the **place** to which the number is being rounded.

Step 2   Look at the next **digit to the right** of the place to which the number is being rounded.

Step 3A   If this digit is **less than 5,** drop all digits to the right of the place to which the number is being rounded. Do *not change* the digit in the place to which the number is being rounded.

Step 3B   If this digit is **5 or greater,** drop all digits to the right of the place to which the number is being rounded. *Add one* to the digit in the place to which the number is being rounded.

■■ **EXAMPLE 4** Rounding a Decimal Number

Round 14.39656 to the nearest thousandth.

SOLUTION

Step 1   Use an arrow to locate the place to which the number is being rounded.

Step 2   Check to see if the first digit to the right of the arrow is 5 or greater.

14.396 ⑤ 6   Digit to the right of the arrow is 5.

Step 3   Since the digit to the right of the arrow is 5 or greater, increase by 1 the digit to which the arrow is pointing. Drop all digits to the right of the arrow.

14.39656   Drop.

14.397   Increase by 1.

Finally, 14.39656 rounded to the nearest thousandth is 14.397.   ■■■

With the calculator set to round to three decimal places, the result of **Example 4** is supported.

Percent

One of the main applications of decimals comes from problems involving percents. The word **percent** means **"per hundred."** The symbol % represents "percent."

Percent

$$1\% = \frac{1}{100} = 0.01$$

In *The Producers*, Leo Bloom (Gene Wilder) and Max Bialystock (Zero Mostel) scheme to make a fortune by overfinancing what they think will be a Broadway flop. After enumerating the **percent** of profits all of Max's little old ladies have been offered in the production, reality sets in.

MAX: Leo, how much percentage of a play can there be altogether?

LEO: Max, you can only sell 100% of anything.

MAX: And how much for *Springtime for Hitler* have we sold?

LEO: 25,000%.

MAX (reaching for Leo's blue security blanket): 25,000% . . . . Give me that blue thing.

   In *Willy Wonka and the Chocolate Factory,* upon preparing a mixture in his laboratory, Wilder delivers the following impossible **percent** analysis as he drinks his latest concoction.

WILLY WONKA: Invention, my dear friends, is 93% perspiration, 6% electricity, 4% evaporation, and 2% butterscotch ripple.

FEMALE VOICE: That's 105%.

MALE VOICE: Any good?

WILLY WONKA: Yes!

EXAMPLE 5   Converting Percents to Decimals

Convert each percent to a decimal.

(a) 98%   **(b)** 3.4%   **(c)** 0.2%   **(d)** 150%

SOLUTION

(a) $98\% = 98(1\%) = 98(0.01) = 0.98$

(b) $3.4\% = 3.4(1\%) = 3.4(0.01) = 0.034$

(c) $0.2\% = 0.2(1\%) = 0.2(0.01) = 0.002$

(d) $150\% = 150(1\%) = 150(0.01) = 1.5$ ■■■

EXAMPLE 6   Converting Decimals to Percents

Convert each decimal to a percent.

(a) 0.13   **(b)** 0.532   **(c)** 2.3   **(d)** 0.07

SOLUTION

(a) $0.13 = 13(0.01) = 13(1\%) = 13\%$

(b) $0.532 = 53.2(0.01) = 53.2(1\%) = 53.2\%$

(c) $2.3 = 230(0.01) = 230(1\%) = 230\%$

(d) $0.07 = 7(0.01) = 7(1\%) = 7\%$ ■■■

Converting between Decimals and Percents

To convert a percent to a decimal, drop the percent symbol (%) and move the decimal point two places to the left, inserting zeros as placeholders if necessary.

To convert a decimal to a percent, move the decimal point two places to the right, inserting zeros as placeholders if necessary, and attach the percent symbol (%).

EXAMPLE 7   Converting Fractions to Percents

Convert each fraction to a percent.

(a) $\dfrac{3}{5}$ **(b)** $\dfrac{14}{25}$

SOLUTION

(a) First write $\frac{3}{5}$ as a decimal. Dividing 3 by 5 gives $\frac{3}{5} = 0.6 = 60\%$.

(b) $\dfrac{14}{25} = \dfrac{14 \cdot 4}{25 \cdot 4} = \dfrac{56}{100} = 0.56 = 56\%$ ■■■

Converting a Fraction to a Percent

To convert a fraction to a percent, convert the fraction to a decimal, and then convert the decimal to a percent.

In the following examples involving percents, three methods are shown. The second method in each case involves using cross-products. The third method involves the percent key of a basic calculator. (Keystrokes may vary among models.)

▮▮ **EXAMPLE 8** Finding a Percent of a Number

Find 18% of 250.

SOLUTION

Method 1 The key word "of" translates as "times."

$$(18\%)(250) = (0.18)(250) = 45$$

Method 2 Think "18 is to 100 as what (x) is to 250?" This translates as follows.

$$\frac{18}{100} = \frac{x}{250}$$

$$100x = 18 \cdot 250 \quad \text{\small $\frac{a}{b} = \frac{c}{d}$ if and only if $ad = bc$.}$$

$$x = \frac{18 \cdot 250}{100} \quad \text{\small Divide by 100.}$$

$$x = 45 \quad \text{\small Simplify.}$$

Method 3 Use the percent key on a calculator with the following keystrokes.

With any of these methods, we find that 18% of 250 is 45. ▮▮▮

▮▮ **EXAMPLE 9** Finding What Percent One Number Is of Another

What percent of 500 is 75?

SOLUTION

Method 1 Let the phrase "what percent" be represented by $x \cdot 1\%$ or $0.01x$. Again the word "of" translates as "times," while "is" translates as "equals."

$$0.01x \cdot 500 = 75$$

$$5x = 75 \quad \text{\small Multiply on the left side.}$$

$$x = 15 \quad \text{\small Divide by 5.}$$

Method 2 Think "What (x) is to 100 as 75 is to 500?"

$$\frac{x}{100} = \frac{75}{500}$$

$$500x = 7500 \quad \text{\small Cross-products}$$

$$x = 15 \quad \text{\small Divide by 500.}$$

Method 3 Use the following keystrokes on a calculator.

In each case, 15 is the percent, so we conclude that 75 is 15% of 500. ▮▮▮

EXAMPLE 10   Finding a Number of Which a Given Number Is a Given Percent

38 is 5% of what number?

SOLUTION

Method 1

$$38 = 0.05x$$

$$x = \frac{38}{0.05} \qquad \text{Divide by 0.05.}$$

$$x = 760 \qquad \text{Simplify.}$$

Method 2   Think "38 is to what number (x) as 5 is to 100?"

$$\frac{38}{x} = \frac{5}{100}$$

$$5x = 3800 \qquad \text{Cross-products}$$

$$x = 760 \qquad \text{Divide by 5.}$$

Method 3   Use the following keystrokes on a calculator.

$\boxed{3}\ \boxed{8}\ \boxed{\div}\ \boxed{5}\ \boxed{\%}$ **760** ◁ Final display

Each method shows us that 38 is 5% of 760.   ▮▮▮

There are various shortcuts that can be used to work with percents. Suppose that you need to compute 20% of 50. Here are two such shortcuts.

1. You think "20% means $\frac{1}{5}$, and to find $\frac{1}{5}$ of something I divide by 5, so 50 divided by 5 is 10. The answer is 10."

2. You think "20% is twice 10%, and to find 10% of something I move the decimal point one place to the left. So, 10% of 50 is 5, and 20% is twice 5, or 10. The answer is 10."

Applications

EXAMPLE 11   Interpreting Percents from a Graph

In 2007, Americans spent about $41.2 billion on their pets. Use the graph in **Figure 18** to determine how much of this amount was spent on pet food.

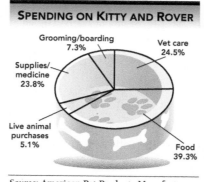

SPENDING ON KITTY AND ROVER

Grooming/boarding 7.3%
Vet care 24.5%
Supplies/medicine 23.8%
Live animal purchases 5.1%
Food 39.3%

Source: American Pet Products Manufacturers Association, Inc.

Figure 18

Dotty

SOLUTION

According to the graph on the preceding page, 39.3% was spent on food. Let x represent this amount in billions of dollars. We use Method 2 of **Example 8.**

$$\frac{x}{41.2} = 0.393 \qquad \text{\small 39.3\% = 0.393}$$

$$x = 41.2(0.393) \qquad \text{\small Multiply by 41.2.}$$

$$x \approx 16.2 \qquad \text{\small Nearest tenth}$$

Therefore, about $16.2 billion was spent on pet food.   ▮▮▮

In many applications we are asked to find the percent increase or percent decrease from one quantity to another. The following guidelines are helpful.

> **Finding Percent Increase or Decrease**
>
> 1. To find the **percent increase from a to b,** where $b > a$, subtract a from b, and divide this result by a. Convert to a percent.
>
>   *Example:*   The percent increase from 4 to 7 is $\frac{7-4}{4} = \frac{3}{4} = 75\%$.
>
> 2. To find the **percent decrease from a to b,** where $b < a$, subtract b from a, and divide this result by a. Convert to a percent.
>
>   *Example:*   The percent decrease from 8 to 6 is $\frac{8-6}{8} = \frac{2}{8} = \frac{1}{4} = 25\%$.

▮▮ **EXAMPLE 12** Solving Problems about Percent Increase or Decrease

(a) An electronics store marked up a laptop computer from their cost of $1200 to a selling price of $1464. What was the percent markup?

(b) The enrollment in a community college declined from 12,750 during one school year to 11,350 the following year. Find the percent decrease to the nearest tenth.

SOLUTION

(a) "Markup" is a name for an increase. Let x = the percent increase (as a decimal).

$$x = \frac{1464 - 1200}{1200} \qquad \text{\small Substitute the given values.}$$

Subtract to find the amount of increase.   *Use the original cost.*

$$x = \frac{264}{1200}$$

$$x = 0.22 \qquad \text{\small Use a calculator.}$$

The computer was marked up 22%.

(b) Let x = the percent decrease (as a decimal).

$$\text{percent decrease} = \frac{\text{amount of decrease}}{\text{original amount}}$$

Subtract to find the amount of decrease.

$$x = \frac{12{,}750 - 11{,}350}{12{,}750} \qquad \text{\small Substitute the given values.}$$

Use the original enrollment.

$$x = \frac{1400}{12{,}750}$$

$$x \approx 0.11 \qquad \text{\small Use a calculator.}$$

The college enrollment decreased by about 11%.   ▮▮▮

When calculating a percent increase or a percent decrease, be sure to use the original number (before the increase or decrease) as the base. A common error is to use the final number (*after* the increase or decrease) in the denominator of the fraction.

For Further Thought

It's Time to End Decimal Point Abuse

Using a decimal point erroneously with a ¢ symbol is seen almost on a daily basis. Think about it . . . $.99 represents $\frac{99}{100}$ of a dollar, or 99 cents, while 99¢ also represents 99 cents (since ¢ is the symbol for *cent*). So what does .99¢ represent? That's right, $\frac{99}{100}$ of one cent!

Look at the photos provided by one of the authors. An order of spicy nuggets at Wendy's is advertised for .99¢. What do you think would happen if you gave the clerk a dime and asked for ten orders and change? You would most likely get a dumbfounded look. A similar response would probably be forthcoming if you asked for Sierra Mist, which costs even less: .79¢. To vacuum your car, it costs .50¢, a mere half cent. At The Floor Place, fabulous floors really do cost less . . . a lot less: less than half a cent per square foot for Berber flooring. Now here's a deal: a 2-liter bottle of Coca Cola for .09¢! (No doubt, the 1 preceding the decimal point fell off. Even then, one such bottle would cost only a tiny bit more than one penny.) At Winn Dixie, one pound of bananas costs .69¢.

For Group or Individual Investigation

Assume that the products shown in the photos are actually being sold for the indicated prices. Answer each of the following.

1. How many orders of spicy nuggets should you get for $1.00? How much change would Wendy's owe you?

2. How much does one ounce of Sierra Mist cost?

3. If you deposit two quarters to have your car vacuumed, how many times should you be able to vacuum?

4. You want to cover your room area with 400 square feet of Berber flooring. How much will this cost?

5. How many 2 liter bottles of Coca Cola would nine cents get you?

6. If 3 bananas weigh a total of 1 pound, how many can you get for a penny?

6.5 EXERCISES

Decide whether each statement is true *or* false.

1. 300% of 12 is 36.

2. 25% of a quantity is the same as $\frac{1}{4}$ of that quantity.

3. When 759.367 is rounded to the nearest hundredth, the result is 759.40.

4. When 759.367 is rounded to the nearest hundred, the result is 759.37.

5. To find 50% of a quantity, we may simply divide the quantity by 2.

6. A soccer team that has won 12 games and lost 8 games has a winning percentage of 60%.

7. If 70% is the lowest passing grade on a quiz that has 50 items of equal value, then answering at least 35 items correctly will assure you of a passing grade.

8. 30 is more than 40% of 120.

9. .99¢ = 99 cents

10. If an item usually costs $70.00 and it is discounted 10%, then the discount price is $7.00.

Calculate each of the following using either a calculator or paper-and-pencil methods, as directed by your instructor.

11. 8.53 + 2.785

12. 9.358 + 7.2137

13. 8.74 − 12.955

14. 2.41 − 3.997

15. 25.7 × 0.032

16. 45.1 × 8.344

17. 1019.825 ÷ 21.47

18. −262.563 ÷ 125.03

19. $\dfrac{118.5}{1.45 + 2.3}$

20. 2.45(1.2 + 3.4 − 5.6)

Government Spending *For 2005, total U.S. government spending was about $2500 billion (or $2.5 trillion). The circle graph shows how the spending was divided.*

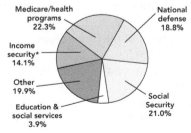

2005 U.S. GOVERNMENT SPENDING

Medicare/health programs 22.3%

National defense 18.8%

Income security* 14.1%

Other 19.9%

Education & social services 3.9%

Social Security 21.0%

*Includes pensions for government workers, unemployment compensation, food stamps, and other such programs.

Source: Office of Management and Budget.

21. About how much was spent on Social Security?

22. About how much did the U.S. government spend on education and social services in 2005?

Postage Stamp Pricing *Refer to* **For Further Thought** *on decimal point abuse. At one time, the United States Postal Service sold rolls of 33-cent stamps that featured fruit berries. One such stamp is shown on the left. On the right is a photo of the pricing information found on the cellophane wrapper of such a roll.*

100 STAMPS PSA
.33¢ ea. TOTAL $33.00
FRUIT BERRIES
ITEM 7757
BCA

23. Look at the second line of the pricing information. According to the price listed *per stamp,* how many stamps should you be able to purchase for one cent?

24. The total price listed is the amount the Postal Service actually charges. If you were to multiply the listed price *per stamp* by the number of stamps, what should the total price be?

Pricing of Pie and Coffee *The photos here were taken at a flea market near Natchez, MS. The handwritten signs indicate that a piece of pie costs .10¢ and a cup of coffee ("ffee") costs .5¢. Assuming these are the actual prices, answer the questions in Exercises 25–28.*

25. How much will 10 pieces of pie and 10 cups of coffee cost?

26. How much will 20 pieces of pie and 10 cups of coffee cost?

27. How many pieces of pie can you get for $1.00?

28. How many cups of coffee can you get for $1.00?

Exercises 29–32 are based on formulas found in Auto Math Handbook: Mathematical Calculations, Theory, and Formulas for Automotive Enthusiasts, *by John Lawlor (1991, HP Books).*

29. *Blood Alcohol Concentration* The Blood Alcohol Concentration (BAC) of a person who has been drinking is given by the formula

$$BAC = \frac{(\text{ounces} \times \text{percent alcohol} \times 0.075)}{\text{body weight in lb}}$$
$$- (\text{hours of drinking} \times 0.015).$$

Suppose a policeman stops a 190-pound man who, in two hours, has ingested four 12-ounce beers, each having a 3.2 percent alcohol content. The formula would then read

$$BAC = \frac{[(4 \times 12) \times 3.2 \times 0.075]}{190} - (2 \times 0.015).$$

(a) Find this BAC.

(b) Find the BAC for a 135-pound woman who, in three hours, has drunk three 12-ounce beers, each having a 4.0 percent alcohol content.

30. *Approximate Automobile Speed* The approximate speed of an automobile in miles per hour (MPH) can be found in terms of the engine's revolutions per minute (rpm), the tire diameter in inches, and the overall gear ratio by the formula

$$MPH = \frac{\text{rpm} \times \text{tire diameter}}{\text{gear ratio} \times 336}.$$

If a certain automobile has an rpm of 5600, a tire diameter of 26 inches, and a gear ratio of 3.12, what is its approximate speed (MPH)?

31. *Engine Horsepower* Horsepower can be found from indicated mean effective pressure (mep) in pounds per square inch, engine displacement in cubic inches, and revolutions per minute (rpm) using the formula

$$\text{Horsepower} = \frac{\text{mep} \times \text{displacement} \times \text{rpm}}{792,000}.$$

Suppose that an engine has displacement of 302 cubic inches and indicated mep of 195 pounds per square inch at 4000 rpm. What is its approximate horsepower?

32. *Torque Approximation* To determine the torque at a given value of rpm, the formula below applies:

$$\text{Torque} = \frac{5252 \times \text{horsepower}}{\text{rpm}}.$$

If the horsepower of a certain vehicle is 400 at 4500 rpm, what is the approximate torque?

Round each number to the nearest **(a)** *tenth;* **(b)** *hundredth. Always round from the original number.*

33. 78.414   **34.** 3689.537   **35.** 0.0837

36. 0.0658   **37.** 12.68925   **38.** 43.99613

Convert each decimal to a percent.

39. 0.42   **40.** 0.87   **41.** 0.365   **42.** 0.792

43. 0.008   **44.** 0.0093   **45.** 2.1   **46.** 8.9

Convert each fraction to a percent.

47. $\frac{1}{5}$ **48.** $\frac{2}{5}$ **49.** $\frac{1}{100}$ **50.** $\frac{1}{50}$

51. $\frac{3}{8}$ **52.** $\frac{5}{6}$ **53.** $\frac{3}{2}$ **54.** $\frac{7}{4}$

55. Explain the difference between $\frac{1}{2}$ of a quantity and $\frac{1}{2}\%$ of the quantity.

56. Group I shows some common percents, found in many everyday situations. In Group II are fractional equivalents of these percents. Match the fractions in Group II with their equivalent percents in Group I.

I		II	
(a) 25%	**(b)** 10%	**A.** $\frac{1}{3}$	**B.** $\frac{1}{50}$
(c) 2%	**(d)** 20%	**C.** $\frac{3}{4}$	**D.** $\frac{1}{10}$
(e) 75%	**(f)** $33\frac{1}{3}\%$	**E.** $\frac{1}{4}$	**F.** $\frac{1}{5}$

57. Fill in each blank with the correct numerical response.

(a) 5% means ———— in every 100.

(b) 25% means 6 in every ————.

(c) 200% means ———— for every 4.

(d) 0.5% means ———— in every 100.

(e) ———— % means 12 for every 2.

58. The Venn diagram shows the number of elements in the four regions formed.

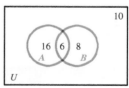

(a) What percent of the elements in the universe are in $A \cap B$?

(b) What percent of the elements in the universe are in A but not in B?

(c) What percent of the elements in $A \cup B$ are in $A \cap B$?

(d) What percent of the elements in the universe are in neither A nor B?

59. *Discount and Markup* Suppose that an item regularly costs $60.00 and it is discounted 20%. If it is then marked up 20%, is the resulting price $60.00? If not, what is it?

60. The figures in **Exercise 13** of **Section 6.3** are reproduced here. Express the fractional parts represented by the shaded areas as percents.

(a)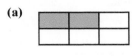

(b)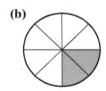

(c)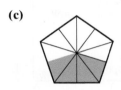

(d)

Win-Loss Record *Exercises 61 and 62 deal with winning percentage in the standings of sports teams.*

61. At the end of the regular 2009 Major League Baseball season, the standings of the East Division of the American League were as shown. Winning percentage is commonly expressed as a decimal rounded to the nearest thousandth. To find the winning percentage of a team, divide the number of wins (W) by the total number of games played (W + L). Find the winning percentage of each team.

Team	W	L	Pct.
New York Yankees	103	59	.636
Boston	95	67	
Tampa Bay	84	78	
Toronto	75	87	
Baltimore	64	98	

Source: World Almanac and Book of Facts.

(a) Boston   **(b)** Tampa Bay

(c) Toronto   **(d)** Baltimore

62. Repeat **Exercise 61** for the following standings for the East Division of the National League.

Team	W	L	Pct.
Philadelphia	93	69	
Florida	87	75	.537
Atlanta	86	76	
New York Mets	70	92	
Washington	59	103	

Source: World Almanac and Book of Facts.

(a) Philadelphia   **(b)** Atlanta

(c) New York Mets   **(d)** Washington

Work each problem involving percent.

63. What is 26% of 480?   **64.** Find 38% of 12.

65. Find 10.5% of 28.   **66.** What is 48.6% of 19?

67. What percent of 30 is 45?

68. What percent of 48 is 20?

69. 25% of what number is 150?

70. 12% of what number is 3600?

71. 0.392 is what percent of 28?

72. 78.84 is what percent of 292?

Solve each problem involving percent increase or decrease.

73. **Percent Increase** After 1 year on the job, Grady got a raise from $10.50 per hour to $11.34 per hour. What was the percent increase in his hourly wage?

74. **Percent Discount** Clayton bought a ticket to a rock concert at a discount. The regular price of the ticket was $70.00, but he paid only $59.50. What was the percent discount?

75. **Percent Decrease** Between July 1, 2000, and July 1, 2007, the estimated population of Pittsfield, Massachusetts declined from 134,953 to 129,798. What was the percent decrease to the nearest tenth? (*Source:* U.S. Census Bureau.)

76. **Percent Increase** Between July 1, 2000, and July 1, 2007, the estimated population of Anchorage, Alaska grew from 320,391 to 362,340. What was the percent increase to the nearest tenth? (*Source:* U.S. Census Bureau.)

77. **Percent Discount** In April 2008, the audio CD of the Original Broadway Cast Recording of the musical *Wicked* was available at www.amazon.com for $9.97. The list price (full price) of this CD was $18.98. To the nearest tenth, what was the percent discount? (*Source:* www.amazon.com)

78. **Percent Discount** In April 2008, the DVD of the movie *Alvin and the Chipmunks* was released. This DVD had a list price of $29.99 and was for sale at www.amazon.com at $15.99. To the nearest tenth, what was the percent discount? (*Source:* www.amazon.com)

Use mental techniques to answer the questions in Exercises 79–82. Try to avoid using paper and pencil or a calculator.

79. **Allowance Increase** Carly Murray's allowance was raised from $4.00 per week to $5.00 per week. What was the percent of the increase?

     A. 25%   **B.** 20%   **C.** 50%   **D.** 30%

80. **Boat Purchase and Sale** Susan Nassy bought a boat five years ago for $5000 and sold it this year for $2000. What percent of her original purchase did she lose on the sale?

     A. 40%   **B.** 50%   **C.** 20%   **D.** 60%

81. *Population of Alabama* The 2000 U.S. census showed that the population of Alabama was 4,447,000, with 26.0% represented by African Americans. What is the best estimate of the African American population in Alabama? (*Source:* U.S. Census Bureau.)

 A. 500,000   **B.** 1,500,000

 C. 1,100,000   **D.** 750,000

82. *Population of Hawaii* The 2000 U.S. census showed that the population of Hawaii was 1,212,000, with 21.4% of the population being of two or more races. What is the best estimate of this population of Hawaii? (*Source:* U.S. Census Bureau.)

 A. 240,000   **B.** 300,000

 C. 21,400   **D.** 24,000

Gasoline Prices *The line graph shows the average price, adjusted for inflation, that Americans have paid for a gallon of gasoline for selected years between 1958 and 2008. Use this information in Exercises 83 and 84.*

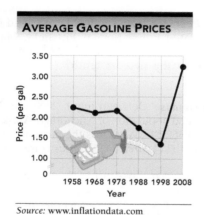

AVERAGE GASOLINE PRICES

Source: www.inflationdata.com

83. By what percent did prices increase from 1998 to 2008?

84. By what percent did prices decrease from 1978 to 1988?

Metabolic Units *One way to measure a person's cardio fitness is to calculate how many METs, or metabolic units, he or she can reach at peak exertion. One MET is the amount of energy used when sitting quietly. To calculate ideal METs, we can use one of the following expressions.*

$$14.7 - \text{age} \cdot 0.13 \quad \text{For women}$$

$$14.7 - \text{age} \cdot 0.11 \quad \text{For men}$$

(*Source: New England Journal of Medicine,* August, 2005.)

85. A 40-year-old woman wishes to calculate her ideal MET.

 (a) Write the expression using her age.

 (b) Calculate her ideal MET. (*Hint:* Use the order of operations.)

(c) Researchers recommend that a person reach approximately 85% of their MET when exercising. Calculate 85% of the ideal MET from part (b). Then refer to the following table. What activity can the woman do that is approximately this value?

Activity	METs	Activity	METs
Golf (with cart)	2.5	Skiing (water or downhill)	6.8
Walking (3 mph)	3.3	Swimming	7.0
Mowing lawn (power mower)	4.5	Walking (5 mph)	8.0
Ballroom or square dancing	5.5	Jogging	10.2
Cycling	5.7	Rope skipping	12.0

Source: Harvard School of Public Health.

86. Repeat parts **(a)–(c)** of **Exercise 85** for a 55-year-old man.

87. *Value of 1916-D Mercury Dime* The 1916 Mercury dime minted in Denver is quite rare. In 1979 its value in Extremely Fine condition was $625. The 2010 value had increased to $6200. What was the percent increase in the value of this coin from 1979 to 2010? (*Sources: A Guide Book of United States Coins; Coin World Coin Values.*)

88. *Value of 1903-O Morgan Dollar* In 1963, the value of a 1903 Morgan dollar minted in New Orleans in typical Uncirculated condition was $1500. Due to a discovery of a large hoard of these dollars late that year, the value plummeted. Its value in 2010 was $550. What was the percent decrease in its value from 1963 to 2010? (*Sources: A Guide Book of United States Coins; Coin World Coin Values.*)

Tipping Procedure *It is customary in our society to "tip" waiters and waitresses when dining in restaurants. One common rate for tipping is 15%. A quick way of figuring a tip that will give a close approximation of 15% is as follows:*

Step 1 *Round off the bill to the nearest dollar.*

Step 2 *Find 10% of this amount by moving the decimal point one place to the left.*

Step 3 *Take half of the amount obtained in Step 2 and add it to the result of Step 2.*

This will give you approximately 15% of the bill. The amount obtained in Step 3 is 5%, and 10% + 5% = 15%. Use the method above to find an approximation of 15% for each restaurant bill.

89. $29.57 **90.** $38.32

91. $5.15 **92.** $7.89

Suppose that you get extremely good service and decide to tip 20%. You can use the first two steps listed, and then in Step 3, double the amount you obtained in Step 2. Use this method to find an approximation of 20% for each restaurant bill.

93. $59.96 **94.** $40.24

95. $180.43 **96.** $199.86

97. Say Again? A television reporter once asked a professional wrist-wrestler what percent of his sport was physical and what percent was mental. The athlete responded "I would say it's 50% physical and 90% mental." Comment on this response.

98. Are You Sure? According to *The Yogi Book,* consisting of quotations by baseball Hall-of-Famer Yogi Berra, he claims that "90% of the game is half mental." Comment on this statement.

THE BASIC CONCEPTS OF ALGEBRA

7

The 2004 movie *Mean Girls* stars Lindsay Lohan as Cady Heron. A scene in the school cafeteria features Cady sitting with The Plastics (the "mean girls" of the title). Regina George, played by Rachel McAdams, is reading a candy bar wrapper.

REGINA: 120 calories and 48 calories from fat. What percent is that? I'm only eating food with less than 30% calories from fat.

CADY: It's 40%. (Responding to a quizzical look from Regina.) Well, 48 over 120 equals x over 100, and then you cross-multiply and get the value of x.

REGINA: Whatever. I'm getting cheese fries.

In her correct solution, Cady turns a percent problem into a proportion, which is an example of a linear equation. In this chapter, we learn how to solve linear equations and investigate other topics from elementary algebra.

7.1 LINEAR EQUATIONS

Solving Linear Equations • Special Kinds of Linear Equations • Literal Equations and Formulas • Models

al-jabr, algebrista, algebra The word **algebra** comes from the title of the work *Hisâb al-jabr w'al muquâbalah*, a ninth-century treatise by the Arab Mohammed ibn Mûsâ al-Khowârizmî. The title translates as "the science of reunion and reduction," or more generally, "the science of transposition and cancellation."

In the title of Khowârizmî's book, *jabr* ("restoration") refers to transposing negative quantities across the equals symbol in solving equations. From Latin versions of Khowârizmî's text, **"al-jabr"** became the broad term covering the art of equation solving. (The prefix *al* means "the.")

Solving Linear Equations

An **algebraic expression** involves only the basic operations of addition, subtraction, multiplication, division (except by 0), raising to powers, or taking roots on any collection of variables and numbers.

$$8x + 9, \quad \sqrt{y} + 4, \quad \text{and} \quad \frac{x^3 y^8}{z} \qquad \text{Examples of algebraic expressions}$$

An **equation** is a statement that two algebraic expressions are equal. A *linear equation in one variable* involves only real numbers and one variable.

$$x + 1 = -2, \quad x - 3 = 5, \quad \text{and} \quad 2x + 5 = 10 \qquad \text{Examples of linear equations}$$

Linear Equation in One Variable

An equation in the variable x is **linear** if it can be written in the form

$$Ax + B = C,$$

where A, B, and C are real numbers, with $A \neq 0$.

A linear equation in one variable is also called a **first-degree equation,** because the greatest power on the variable is one.

If the variable in an equation is replaced by a real number that makes the statement true, then that number is a **solution** of the equation. For example, 8 is a solution of the equation

$$x - 3 = 5,$$

because replacing x with 8 gives a true statement. An equation is **solved** by finding its **solution set,** the set of all solutions. The solution set of the equation $x - 3 = 5$ is $\{8\}$.

Equivalent equations are equations with the same solution set. Equations generally are solved by starting with a given equation and producing a series of simpler equivalent equations. For example,

$$8x + 1 = 17, \quad 8x = 16, \quad \text{and} \quad x = 2 \qquad \text{Equivalent equations}$$

are equivalent equations because each has the same solution set, {2}. We use the addition and multiplication properties of equality to produce equivalent equations.

Addition Property of Equality

For all real numbers A, B, and C, the equations

$$A = B \qquad \text{and} \qquad A + C = B + C$$

are equivalent. (The same number may be added to both sides of an equation without changing the solution set.)

algebrista, algebra In Spain under Moslem rule, the word **algebrista** referred to the person who restored (reset) broken bones. Signs outside barber shops read *Algebrista y Sangrador* (bonesetter and bloodletter). Such services were part of the barber's trade. The traditional red-and-white striped barber pole symbolizes blood and bandages.

Multiplication Property of Equality

For all real numbers A, B, and C, where $C \neq 0$, the equations

$$A = B \quad \text{and} \quad AC = BC$$

are equivalent. (Both sides of an equation may be multiplied by the same nonzero number without changing the solution set.)

EXAMPLE 1 Using the Addition and Multiplication Properties to Solve a Linear Equation

Solve $4x - 2x - 5 = 4 + 6x + 3$.

SOLUTION

The distributive property allows us to combine *like terms*, such as $4x$ and $2x$.

$4x - 2x - 5 = 4 + 6x + 3$	Our goal is to isolate x on one side.
$2x - 5 = 7 + 6x$	Combine like terms; $4x - 2x = (4 - 2)x = 2x$
$2x - 5 + 5 = 7 + 6x + 5$	Add 5.
$2x = 12 + 6x$	Combine like terms.
$2x - 6x = 12 + 6x - 6x$	Subtract 6x.
$-4x = 12$	Combine like terms.
$\dfrac{-4x}{-4} = \dfrac{12}{-4}$	Divide by -4.
$x = -3$	Simplify.

Check that -3 is the solution by substituting it for x in the *original* equation.

Check:

$4x - 2x - 5 = 4 + 6x + 3$	Original equation
$4(-3) - 2(-3) - 5 \overset{?}{=} 4 + 6(-3) + 3$	Let $x = -3$.
$-12 + 6 - 5 \overset{?}{=} 4 - 18 + 3$	Multiply.
This is not the solution. $\quad -11 = -11 \checkmark$	True

The true statement indicates that $\{-3\}$ is the solution set. ▮▮▮

Solving a Linear Equation in One Variable

Step 1 **Clear fractions.** Eliminate any fractions by multiplying both sides of the equation by a common denominator.

Step 2 **Simplify each side separately.** Use the distributive property to clear parentheses, and combine like terms as needed.

Step 3 **Isolate the variable terms on one side.** Use the addition property of equality to transform the equation so that all terms with variables are on one side and all numbers are on the other.

Step 4 **Transform so that the coefficient of the variable is 1.** Use the multiplication property of equality to obtain an equation with only the variable (with coefficient 1) on one side.

Step 5 **Check.** Substitute the solution into the original equation.

Notice in **Example 1** that because subtraction and division are defined in terms of addition and multiplication, respectively, we were able to subtract the same number from both sides of the equation, and divide both sides by the same nonzero number, without affecting the solution set.

▐▐ **EXAMPLE 2** Using the Distributive Property to Solve a Linear Equation

Solve $2(x - 5) + 3x = x + 6$.

The problem-solving strategy of guessing and checking, discussed in **Chapter 1,** was actually used by the early Egyptians in equation solving. This method, called the **Rule of False Position,** involved making an initial guess at the solution of an equation, and then following up with an adjustment in the likely event that the guess was incorrect. For example (using our modern notation), if the equation

$$6x + 2x = 32$$

was to be solved, an initial guess might have been $x = 3$. Substituting 3 for x gives

$$6(3) + 2(3) \overset{?}{=} 32$$
$$18 + 6 \overset{?}{=} 32$$
$$24 = 32. \quad \textbf{False}$$

The guess, 3, gives a value (24) which is smaller than the desired value (32). Since 24 is $\frac{3}{4}$ of 32, the guess, 3, is $\frac{3}{4}$ of the actual solution. The actual solution, therefore, must be 4, since 3 is $\frac{3}{4}$ of 4.

Use the methods explained in this section to verify this result.

SOLUTION

Step 1 Because there are no fractions in this equation, Step 1 does not apply.

Step 2 Use the distributive property to simplify and combine terms on the left side.

$$2(x - 5) + 3x = x + 6$$
$$2x - 10 + 3x = x + 6 \quad \text{Distributive property}$$
$$5x - 10 = x + 6 \quad \text{Combine like terms.}$$

Step 3 Next, use the addition property of equality.

$$5x - 10 + 10 = x + 6 + 10 \quad \text{Add 10.}$$
$$5x = x + 16 \quad \text{Combine like terms.}$$
$$5x - x = x + 16 - x \quad \text{Subtract } x.$$
$$4x = 16 \quad \text{Combine like terms.}$$

Step 4 Use the multiplication property of equality to isolate x on the left.

$$\frac{4x}{4} = \frac{16}{4} \quad \text{Divide by 4.}$$
$$x = 4 \quad \text{Simplify.}$$

Step 5 Check that the solution set is $\{4\}$ by substituting 4 for x in the original equation. ***You should always check your work.*** ▐▐▐

▐▐ **EXAMPLE 3** Solving a Linear Equation with Fractions

Solve $\dfrac{x + 7}{6} + \dfrac{2x - 8}{2} = -4$.

SOLUTION

Step 1 $\quad 6\left(\dfrac{x + 7}{6} + \dfrac{2x - 8}{2}\right) = 6(-4)$ Multiply each side by the least common denominator (LCD), 6, to eliminate the fractions.

Step 2 $\quad 6\left(\dfrac{x + 7}{6}\right) + 6\left(\dfrac{2x - 8}{2}\right) = 6(-4)$ Distributive property

Multiply each term by 6.

$$x + 7 + 3(2x - 8) = -24 \quad \text{Multiply.}$$
$$x + 7 + 6x - 24 = -24 \quad \text{Distributive property}$$
$$7x - 17 = -24 \quad \text{Combine like terms.}$$

François Viète (1540–1603) was a lawyer at the court of Henry IV of France and studied equations. Viète simplified the notation of algebra and was among the first to use letters to represent numbers.

Step 3

$$7x - 17 + 17 = -24 + 17 \quad \text{Add 17.}$$
$$7x = -7 \quad \text{Combine like terms.}$$

Step 4

$$\frac{7x}{7} = \frac{-7}{7} \quad \text{Divide by 7.}$$
$$x = -1 \quad \text{Simplify.}$$

Step 5 *Check:*

$$\frac{x + 7}{6} + \frac{2x - 8}{2} = -4 \quad \text{Original equation}$$
$$\frac{-1 + 7}{6} + \frac{2(-1) - 8}{2} \overset{?}{=} -4 \quad \text{Let } x = -1.$$
$$\frac{6}{6} + \frac{-10}{2} \overset{?}{=} -4 \quad \text{Simplify each fraction.}$$
$$1 - 5 \overset{?}{=} -4$$
$$-4 = -4 \quad \checkmark \quad \text{True}$$

The solution -1 checks, so the solution set is $\{-1\}$. ▌▌▌

▌▌ **EXAMPLE 4** Solving a Linear Equation with Decimals

Solve $0.06x + 0.09(15 - x) = 0.07(15)$.

SOLUTION

Because each decimal number is in hundredths, multiply both sides of the equation by 100. This is done by moving the decimal points two places to the right. (To multiply the second term, $0.09(15 - x)$, by 100, multiply $100(0.09)$ first to get 9, so the product $100(0.09)(15 - x)$ becomes $9(15 - x)$.)

$$0.06x + 0.09(15 - x) = 0.07(15) \quad \text{Original equation}$$
$$0.06x + 0.09(15 - x) = 0.07(15) \quad \text{Multiply each term by 100.}$$
$$6x + 9(15 - x) = 7(15)$$
$$6x + 9(15) - 9x = 105 \quad \text{Distributive property; multiply.}$$
$$-3x + 135 = 105 \quad \text{Combine like terms; multiply.}$$
$$-3x + 135 - 135 = 105 - 135 \quad \text{Subtract 135.}$$
$$-3x = -30 \quad \text{Combine like terms.}$$
$$\frac{-3x}{-3} = \frac{-30}{-3} \quad \text{Divide by } -3.$$
$$x = 10 \quad \text{Simplify.}$$

Check to verify that the solution set is $\{10\}$. ▌▌▌

Special Kinds of Linear Equations

The preceding equations had solution sets containing one element. For example,

$$2(x - 5) + 3x = x + 6 \quad \text{has solution set} \quad \{4\}.$$

Some equations that appear to be linear have no solutions, while others have an infinite number of solutions. **Table 1** on the next page gives the names of these types of equations.

Algebra dates back to the Babylonians of 2000 B.C. The Egyptians also worked problems in algebra, but the problems were not as complex as those of the Babylonians. In about the sixth century, the Hindus developed methods for solving problems involving interest, discounts, and partnerships.

Many Hindu and Greek works on mathematics were preserved only because Moslem scholars from about 750 to 1250 made translations of them. For example, Mohammed ibn Mûsâ al-Khowârizmî wrote books on algebra and on the Hindu numeration system (the one we use) that had tremendous influence in Western Europe. His name is remembered today in the word *algorithm*.

Sofia Kovalevskaya (1850–1891) was the most widely known Russian mathematician in the late nineteenth century. She did most of her work in the theory of **differential equations**— equations invaluable for expressing rates of change. For example, in biology, the rate of growth of a population, say of microbes, can be precisely stated by differential equations.

Kovalevskaya studied privately because public lectures were not open to women. She eventually received a degree (1874) from the University of Göttingen, Germany. In 1884 she became a lecturer at the University of Stockholm and later was appointed professor of higher mathematics.

Table 1   Types of Equations

Type of Equation	Number of Solutions	Indication When Solving
Conditional	One	Final line is $x =$ a number. (See **Example 5(a)**.)
Identity	Infinite; solution set {all real numbers}	Final line is true, such as $0 = 0$. (See **Example 5(b)**.)
Contradiction	None; solution set $\emptyset$	Final line is false, such as $0 = 1$. (See **Example 5(c)**.)

EXAMPLE 5   Recognizing Conditional Equations, Identities, and Contradictions

Solve each equation. Decide whether it is a *conditional equation*, an *identity*, or a *contradiction*.

(a) $5x - 9 = 4(x - 3)$ **(b)** $5x - 15 = 5(x - 3)$ **(c)** $5x - 15 = 5(x - 4)$

SOLUTION

(a)

$$5x - 9 = 4(x - 3)$$
$$5x - 9 = 4x - 12 \qquad \text{Distributive property}$$
$$5x - 9 - 4x = 4x - 12 - 4x \qquad \text{Subtract } 4x.$$
$$x - 9 = -12 \qquad \text{Combine like terms.}$$
$$x - 9 + 9 = -12 + 9 \qquad \text{Add 9.}$$
$$x = -3 \qquad \text{Solution set } \{-3\}$$

The solution set has one element, so $5x - 9 = 4(x - 3)$ is a conditional equation.

(b)

$$5x - 15 = 5(x - 3)$$
$$5x - 15 = 5x - 15 \qquad \text{Distributive property}$$
$$0 = 0 \qquad \text{Subtract } 5x \text{ and add 15.}$$

The final line, $0 = 0$, indicates that the solution set is {all real numbers}, and the equation $5x - 15 = 5(x - 3)$ is an identity. (*Note:* The first step yielded $5x - 15 = 5x - 15$, which is true for all values of x, implying an identity there.)

(c)

$$5x - 15 = 5(x - 4)$$
$$5x - 15 = 5x - 20 \qquad \text{Distributive property}$$
$$5x - 15 - 5x = 5x - 20 - 5x \qquad \text{Subtract } 5x.$$
$$-15 = -20 \qquad \text{False}$$

Because the result, $-15 = -20$, is *false*, the equation has no solution. The solution set is $\emptyset$, so the equation $5x - 15 = 5(x - 4)$ is a contradiction.   ■■■

Literal Equations and Formulas

An equation involving *variables* (or letters), such as $cx + d = e$, is called a **literal equation.** The most useful examples of literal equations are *formulas*. The solution of a problem in algebra often depends on the use of a mathematical statement or **formula** in which more than one letter is used to express a relationship.

$$d = rt, \quad I = prt, \quad \text{and} \quad P = 2L + 2W \qquad \text{Examples of formulas}$$

In some cases, a formula must be solved for one of its variables. This process is called **solving for a specified variable.** The steps used are similar to those used in solving linear equations.

When you are solving for a specified variable, the key is to treat that variable as if it were the only one. Treat all other variables like numbers (constants).

Solving for a Specified Variable

Step 1 Transform the equation so that all terms containing the specified variable are on one side of the equation and all terms without that variable are on the other side.

Step 2 If necessary, use the distributive property to combine the terms with the specified variable. The result should be the product of a sum or difference and the variable.

Step 3 Divide both sides by the factor that is multiplied by the specified variable.

▌▌ **EXAMPLE 6** Solving for a Specified Variable

Solve the formula $P = 2L + 2W$ for W.

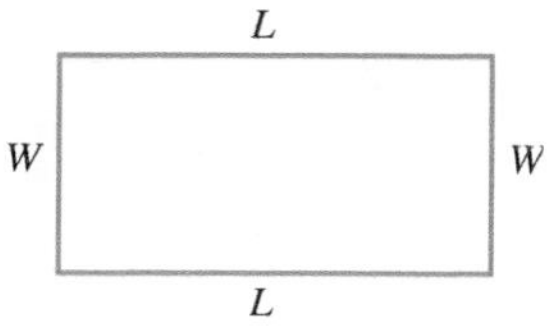

SOLUTION

Solve the formula for the perimeter (distance around) of a rectangle (**Figure 1**) for W by isolating W on one side of the equals symbol.

Perimeter, P, the sum of the lengths of the sides of the rectangle, is given by

$$P = 2L + 2W.$$

Figure 1

Step 1 $$P = 2L + 2W$$

$$P - 2L = 2L + 2W - 2L \quad \text{Subtract } 2L.$$

$$P - 2L = 2W$$

Step 2 Step 2 is not needed here.

Step 3 $$\frac{P - 2L}{2} = \frac{2W}{2} \qquad \text{Divide both sides by 2.}$$

$$\frac{P - 2L}{2} = W, \quad \text{or} \quad W = \frac{P}{2} - L \quad \frac{a-b}{c} = \frac{a}{c} - \frac{b}{c}$$

▮▮▮

Models

A **mathematical model** is an equation (or inequality) that describes the relationship between two quantities. A *linear model* is a linear equation.

▌▌ **EXAMPLE 7** Modeling the Prevention of Indoor Pollutants

If a range hood removes contaminants at a flow rate of F liters of air per second, then the percent P of contaminants that are also removed from the surrounding air can be modeled by the linear equation

$$P = 1.06F + 7.18,$$

where $10 \leq F \leq 75$. What flow rate F must a range hood have to remove 50% of the contaminants from the air? (*Source:* Rezvan, R. L., "Effectiveness of Local Ventilation in Removing Simulated Pollutants from Point Sources," 65–75. In *Proceedings of the Third International Conference on Indoor Air Quality and Climate,* 1984.)

SOLUTION

$$P = 1.06F + 7.18$$

$$50 = 1.06F + 7.18 \quad \text{Let } P = 50.$$

$$5000 = 106F + 718 \quad \text{Multiply by 100.}$$

$$4282 = 106F \quad \text{Subtract 718.}$$

$$F \approx 40.40 \quad \text{Divide by 106.}$$

The flow rate must be approximately 40.40 L of air per second. ▐▐▐

For Further Thought

The Axioms of Equality

When we solve an equation, we must make sure that it remains "balanced"—that is, any operation that is performed on one side of an equation must also be performed on the other side in order to ensure that the set of solutions remains the same.

Underlying the rules for solving equations are four axioms of equality, listed below. For all real numbers a, b, and c,

1. **Reflexive axiom** $a = a$
2. **Symmetric axiom**   If $a = b$, then $b = a$.
3. **Transitive axiom**   If $a = b$ and $b = c$, then $a = c$.
4. **Substitution axiom**   If $a = b$, then a may replace b in any statement without affecting the truth or falsity of the statement.

A relation, such as equality, which satisfies the first three of these axioms (reflexive, symmetric, and transitive), is called an equivalence relation.

For Group or Individual Investigation

1. Give an example of an everyday relation that does not satisfy the symmetric axiom.
2. Does the transitive axiom hold in sports competition, with the relation "defeats"?
3. Give an example of a relation that does not satisfy the transitive axiom.

7.1 EXERCISES

1. Which equations are linear equations in x?
   A. $2x + x - 1 = 0$ **B.** $8 = x^2$
   C. $6x + 2 = 9$ **D.** $\frac{1}{2}x - \frac{1}{x} = 0$

2. Which of the equations in **Exercise 1** are not linear equations in x? Explain why.

3. Decide whether 12 is a solution of $3(x + 4) = 4x$ by substituting 12 for x. If it is not a solution, explain why.

4. Use substitution to decide whether -2 is a solution of $5(x + 4) - 3(x + 6) = 7(x + 1)$. If it is not a solution, explain why.

5. If two equations are equivalent, they have the same _____ _____.

6. The equation $4[x + (2 - 3x)] = 2(4 - 4x)$ is an identity. Let x represent the number of letters in your last name. Is this number a solution of this equation? Check your answer.

7. Which expression is equivalent to $0.06(10 - x)(100)$?
   A. $0.06 - 0.06x$ **B.** $60 - 6x$
   C. $6 - 6x$ **D.** $6 - 0.06x$

8. Describe in your own words the steps used to solve a linear equation.

Solve each equation.

9. $7x + 8 = 1$ **10.** $5x - 4 = 21$

11. $8 - 8x = -16$ **12.** $9 - 2x = 15$

13. $7x - 5x + 15 = x + 8$

14. $2x + 4 - x = 4x - 5$

15. $12x + 15x - 9 + 5 = -3x + 5 - 9$

16. $-4x + 5x - 8 + 4 = 6x - 4$

17. $2(x + 3) = -4(x + 1)$

18. $4(x - 9) = 8(x + 3)$

19. $3(2x + 1) - 2(x - 2) = 5$

20. $4(x - 2) + 2(x + 3) = 6$

21. $2x + 3(x - 4) = 2(x - 3)$

22. $6x - 3(5x + 2) = 4(1 - x)$

23. $6x - 4(3 - 2x) = 5(x - 4) - 10$

24. $-2x - 3(4 - 2x) = 2(x - 3) + 2$

25. $-[2x - (5x + 2)] = 2 + (2x + 7)$

26. $-[6x - (4x + 8)] = 9 + (6x + 3)$

27. $-3x + 6 - 5(x - 1) = -(2x - 4) - 5x + 5$

28. $4(x + 2) - 8x - 5 = -3x + 9 - 2(x + 6)$

29. $-[3x - (2x + 5)] = -4 - [3(2x - 4) - 3x]$

30. $2[-(x - 1) + 4] = 5 + [-(6x - 7) + 9x]$

31. $-(9 - 3x) - (4 + 2x) - 4 = -(2 - 5x) - x$

32. $(2 - 4x) - (3 - 4x) + 4 = -(-3 + 6x) + x$

33. $(2x - 6) - (3x - 4) = -(-4 + x) - 4x + 6$

34. $(3x - 4) - (5x - 8) = -(x + 12) - 6x + 1$

35. To solve the linear equation

$$0.05x + 0.12(x + 5000) = 940,$$

we can multiply both sides by a power of 10 so that all coefficients are integers. What is the smallest power of 10 that will accomplish this goal?

36. Suppose that in solving the equation

$$\frac{1}{3}x + \frac{1}{2}x = \frac{1}{6}x,$$

you begin by multiplying both sides by 12, rather than the *least* common denominator, 6. Should you get the correct solution anyway? Explain.

Solve each equation.

37. $\dfrac{3x}{4} + \dfrac{5x}{2} = 13$

38. $\dfrac{8x}{3} - \dfrac{2x}{4} = -13$

39. $\dfrac{x - 8}{5} + \dfrac{8}{5} = -\dfrac{x}{3}$

40. $\dfrac{2x - 3}{7} + \dfrac{3}{7} = -\dfrac{x}{3}$

41. $\dfrac{4x + 1}{3} = \dfrac{x + 5}{6} + \dfrac{x - 3}{6}$

42. $\dfrac{2x + 5}{5} = \dfrac{3x + 1}{2} + \dfrac{-x + 7}{2}$

43. $0.05x + 0.12(x + 5000) = 940$

44. $0.09x + 0.13(x + 300) = 61$

45. $0.02(50) + 0.08x = 0.04(50 + x)$

46. $0.20(14,000) + 0.14x = 0.18(14,000 + x)$

47. $0.05x + 0.10(200 - x) = 0.45x$

48. $0.08x + 0.12(260 - x) = 0.48x$

49. The equation $x + 2 = x + 2$ is called a(n) _____, because its solution set is {all real numbers}. The equation $x + 1 = x + 2$ is called a(n) _____, because its solution set is $\emptyset$.

50. Which equation is a conditional equation?

   A. $2x + 1 = 3$ **B.** $x = 3x - 2x$

   C. $3x + 1 = 3x$ **D.** $\dfrac{1}{2}x = \dfrac{1}{2}x$

Decide whether each equation is conditional, an identity, or a contradiction. Give the solution set.

51. $-2x + 5x - 9 = 3(x - 4) - 5$

52. $-6x + 2x - 11 = -2(2x - 3) + 4$

53. $6x + 2(x - 2) = 9x + 4$

54. $-4(x + 2) = -3(x + 5) - x$

55. $-11x + 4(x - 3) + 6x = 4x - 12$

56. $3x - 5(x + 4) + 9 = -11 + 15x$

57. $7[2 - (3 + 4x)] - 2x = -9 + 2(1 - 15x)$

58. $4[6 - (1 + 2x)] + 10x = 2(10 - 3x) + 8x$

59. If we solve $\mathcal{A} = \frac{1}{2}bh$ for h, one possible correct answer is

$$h = \frac{2\mathcal{A}}{b}.$$

Which of the formulas is *not* equivalent to this?

   A. $h = 2\left(\dfrac{\mathcal{A}}{b}\right)$ **B.** $h = 2\mathcal{A}\left(\dfrac{1}{b}\right)$

   C. $h = \dfrac{\mathcal{A}}{\frac{1}{2}b}$ **D.** $h = \dfrac{\frac{1}{2}\mathcal{A}}{b}$

60. One source for geometric formulas gives the formula for the perimeter of a rectangle as

$$P = 2L + 2W,$$

while another gives it as

$$P = 2(L + W).$$

Are these equivalent? If so, what property justifies their equivalence?

Mathematical Formulas Solve each formula for the specified variable.

61. $d = rt$; for t (distance)

62. $I = prt$; for r (simple interest)

63. $\mathcal{A} = bh$; for b (area of a parallelogram)

64. $P = 2L + 2W$; for L (perimeter of a rectangle)

65. $P = a + b + c$; for a (perimeter of a triangle)

66. $V = LWH$; for W (volume of a rectangular solid)

67. $\mathcal{A} = \dfrac{1}{2}bh$; for b (area of a triangle)

68. $C = 2\pi r$; for r (circumference of a circle)

69. $S = 2\pi rh + 2\pi r^2$; for h (surface area of a right circular cylinder)

70. $\mathcal{A} = \dfrac{1}{2}h(B + b)$; for B (area of a trapezoid)

71. $C = \dfrac{5}{9}(F - 32)$; for F (Fahrenheit to Celsius)

72. $F = \dfrac{9}{5}C + 32$; for C (Celsius to Fahrenheit)

73. $V = \dfrac{1}{3}\pi r^2 h$; for h (volume of a cone)

74. $V = \dfrac{1}{3}Bh$; for h (volume of a right pyramid)

Work each problem involving a linear model.

75. *Tuition and Fees* The linear model

$$y = 226.9x - 449,700$$

describes the amount y in dollars for average tuition and fees at public colleges and universities during the years 1985 through 2008, where x is the year. (*Source:* The College Board.)

(a) Use the model to estimate tuition and fees in 2006.

(b) Use the model to determine the year in which tuition and fees reach $7150.

76. *Tuition and Fees* The linear model

$$y = 837.7x - 1,657,993$$

describes the amount y in dollars for average tuition and fees at private colleges and universities during the years 1985 through 2008, where x is the year. (*Source:* The College Board.)

(a) Use the model to estimate tuition and fees in 2005.

(b) Use the model to determine the year in which tuition and fees reach $27,000.

77. *Indoor Air Quality and Control* The excess lifetime cancer risk R is a measure of the likelihood that an individual will develop cancer from a particular pollutant. For example, if $R = 0.01$ then a person has a 1% increased chance of developing cancer during a lifetime. (This would translate into 1 case of cancer for every 100 people during an average lifetime.) The value of R for formaldehyde, a highly toxic indoor air pollutant, can be calculated using the linear model

$$R = kd,$$

where k is a constant, and d is the daily dose in parts per million. The constant k for formaldehyde can be calculated using the formula

$$k = \dfrac{0.132B}{W},$$

where B is the total number of cubic meters of air a person breathes in one day, and W is a person's weight in kilograms. (*Source:* Hines, A., T. Ghosh, S. Loyalka, and R. Warder, *Indoor Air: Quality & Control*, Prentice-Hall, 1993; Ritchie, I., and R. Lehnen, "An Analysis of Formaldehyde Concentration in Mobile and Conventional Homes," *J. Env. Health* 47: 300–305.)

(a) Find k for a person who breathes in 20 cubic meters of air per day and weighs 75 kilograms.

(b) Mobile homes in Minnesota were found to have a mean daily dose d of 0.42 part per million. Calculate R using the value of k found in part (a).

(c) For every 5000 people, how many cases of cancer could be expected each year from these levels of formaldehyde? Assume an average life expectancy of 72 years.

78. *Indoor Air Quality and Control* (See **Exercise 77.**) For nonsmokers exposed to environmental tobacco smoke (passive smokers), $R = 0.0015$.

(a) If the average life expectancy is 72 years, what is the excess lifetime cancer risk from secondhand tobacco smoke per year?

(b) Write a linear equation that will model the expected number of cancer cases C per year if there are x passive smokers.

(c) Estimate the number of cancer cases each year per 100,000 passive smokers.

▮ ▮ ▮ ▮ ▮ ▮ ▮ ▮ **7.2 APPLICATIONS OF LINEAR EQUATIONS**

Translating Words into Symbols • Guidelines for Applications • Finding Unknown Quantities • Mixture and Interest Problems • Monetary Denomination Problems • Motion Problems

Translating Words into Symbols

PROBLEM-SOLVING HINT   Usually there are key words and phrases in a verbal problem that translate into mathematical expressions involving addition, subtraction, multiplication, and division.

Translating from Words to Mathematical Expressions

Verbal Expression	Mathematical Expression (where x and y are numbers)
Addition	
The **sum** of a number and 7	$x + 7$
6 **more than** a number	$x + 6$
3 **plus** a number	$3 + x$
24 **added to** a number	$x + 24$
A number **increased by** 5	$x + 5$
The **sum** of two numbers	$x + y$
Subtraction	
2 **less than** a number	$x - 2$
12 **minus** a number	$12 - x$
A number **decreased by** 12	$x - 12$
The **difference between** two numbers	$x - y$
A number **subtracted from** 10	$10 - x$
Multiplication	
16 **times** a number	$16x$
A number **multiplied by** 6	$6x$
$\frac{2}{3}$ **of** a number (as applied to fractions and percent)	$\frac{2}{3}x$
Twice (2 times) a number	$2x$
The **product** of two numbers	xy
Division	
The **quotient** of 8 and a number	$\dfrac{8}{x}$ $(x \neq 0)$
A number **divided by** 13	$\dfrac{x}{13}$
The **ratio** of two numbers or the **quotient** of two numbers	$\dfrac{x}{y}$ $(y \neq 0)$

The symbol of equality, $=$, is often indicated by the word *is*. In fact, since equal mathematical expressions represent different names for the same number, words that indicate the idea of "sameness" translate as $=$. For example,

If the product of a number and 12 is decreased by 7, the result is 105

translates to the mathematical equation

$$12x - 7 = 105,$$

where x represents the unknown number. (Why would $7 - 12x = 105$ be incorrect?)

Guidelines for Applications

To solve applied problems, the following six steps are helpful.

George Polya's problem-solving procedure can be adapted to applications of algebra as seen in the steps in the box. Steps 1 and 2 make up the first stage of Polya's procedure (*Understand the Problem*), Step 3 forms the second stage (*Devise a Plan*), Step 4 comprises the third stage (*Carry Out the Plan*), and Steps 5 and 6 form the last stage (*Look Back*).

Solving an Applied Problem

Step 1 **Read** the problem carefully until you understand what is given and what is to be found.

Step 2 **Assign a variable** to represent the unknown value, using diagrams or tables as needed. Write down what the variable represents. If necessary, express any other unknown values in terms of the variable.

Step 3 **Write an equation** using the variable expression(s).

Step 4 **Solve** the equation.

Step 5 **State the answer.** Does it seem reasonable?

Step 6 **Check** the answer in the words of the *original* problem.

Finding Unknown Quantities

PROBLEM-SOLVING HINT A common type of problem involves finding two quantities when the sum of the quantities is known. Choose a variable to represent one of the unknowns and then represent the other quantity in terms of the same variable, using information from the problem. Then write an equation based on the words of the problem.

▌▌ **EXAMPLE 1** Finding Numbers of Strikeouts

Two outstanding major league pitchers in recent years are Randy Johnson and Johan Santana. In 2004, they combined for a total of 555 strikeouts. Johnson had 25 more strikeouts than Santana. How many strikeouts did each pitcher have? (*Source: World Almanac and Book of Facts.*)

SOLUTION

Step 1 **Read** the problem. We are asked to find the number of strikeouts each pitcher had.

Step 2 **Assign a variable** to represent the number of strikeouts for one of the men.

Let s = the number of strikeouts for Johan Santana.

We must also find the number of strikeouts for Randy Johnson. Because he had 25 more strikeouts than Santana,

$s + 25$ = the number of strikeouts for Johnson.

Johan Santana

Here is an application of linear equations, taken from the **Greek Anthology** (about 500 A.D.), a group of 46 number problems.

Demochares has lived a fourth of his life as a boy, a fifth as a youth, a third as a man, and has spent 13 years in his dotage. How old is he?

(Answer: 60 years old)

Step 3 **Write an equation.** The sum of the numbers of strikeouts is 555.

Santana's strikeouts   +   Johnson's strikeouts   =   Total
$$s \quad + \quad (s + 25) \quad = \quad 555$$

Step 4 **Solve** the equation.

$$s + (s + 25) = 555$$

$$2s + 25 = 555 \qquad \text{Combine like terms.}$$

$$2s + 25 - 25 = 555 - 25 \qquad \text{Subtract 25.}$$

$$2s = 530 \qquad \text{Combine like terms.}$$

$$\frac{2s}{2} = \frac{530}{2} \qquad \text{Divide by 2.}$$

Don't stop here.

$$s = 265$$

Step 5 **State the answer.** We let s represent the number of strikeouts for Santana, so Santana had 265. Then the number of strikeouts for Johnson is

$$s + 25 = 265 + 25 = 290. \qquad \text{Be sure to find the second answer.}$$

Step 6 **Check.** 290 is 25 more than 265, and the sum of 265 and 290 is 555. ▮▮▮

▮▮ **EXAMPLE 2** Finding Lengths of Pieces of Wood

A woodworking project calls for three pieces of wood. The longest piece must be twice the length of the middle-sized piece, and the shortest piece must be 10 inches shorter than the middle-sized piece. If the three pieces are to be cut from a board 70 inches long, how long can each piece be?

SOLUTION

Step 1 **Read** the problem. Three lengths must be found.

Step 2 **Assign a variable.** Because the middle-sized piece appears in both comparisons, let x represent the length, in inches, of the middle-sized piece.

$$x = \text{the length of the middle-sized piece,}$$
$$2x = \text{the length of the longest piece, and}$$
$$x - 10 = \text{the length of the shortest piece. See \textbf{Figure 2}.}$$

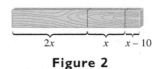

$2x \qquad x \quad x-10$

Figure 2

Step 3 **Write an equation.**

Longest plus middle-sized plus shortest is total length.

$$2x \quad + \quad x \quad + \quad (x - 10) \quad = \quad 70$$

Step 4 **Solve.**

$$4x - 10 = 70 \qquad \text{Combine like terms.}$$

$$4x - 10 + 10 = 70 + 10 \qquad \text{Add 10.}$$

$$4x = 80 \qquad \text{Combine like terms.}$$

$$\frac{4x}{4} = \frac{80}{4} \qquad \text{Divide by 4.}$$

$$x = 20$$

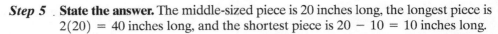

Problems involving age have been around since antiquity. The *Greek Anthology* gives the only information known about the life of the mathematician **Diophantus:**

Diophantus passed $\frac{1}{6}$ of his life in childhood, $\frac{1}{12}$ in youth, and $\frac{1}{7}$ more as a bachelor. Five years after his marriage was born a son who died 4 years before his father, at $\frac{1}{2}$ his father's final age.

Try to write an equation and solve it to show that Diophantus was 84 years old when he died.

Step 5 **State the answer.** The middle-sized piece is 20 inches long, the longest piece is $2(20) = 40$ inches long, and the shortest piece is $20 - 10 = 10$ inches long.

Step 6 **Check.** The sum of the lengths is 70 inches. All conditions of the problem are satisfied. ▮▮▮

Mixture and Interest Problems

PROBLEM-SOLVING HINT Percents often are used in problems involving mixing different concentrations of a substance or different interest rates. In each case, to get the amount of pure substance or the interest, we multiply.

Mixture Problems	Interest Problems (annual)
base × rate (%) = percentage	principal × rate (%) = interest
b × r = p	P × r = I

In an equation, the percent should be written as a decimal.

▮▮ **EXAMPLE 3** Using Percents in Applications

(a) If a chemist has 40 liters of a 35% acid solution, how much pure acid is there?

(b) If $1300 is invested for one year at 2% simple interest, how much interest is earned in one year?

SOLUTION

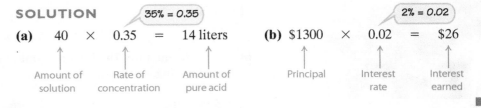

(a) 40 × 0.35 = 14 liters   (35% = 0.35)
Amount of solution / Rate of concentration / Amount of pure acid

(b) $1300 × 0.02 = $26   (2% = 0.02)
Principal / Interest rate / Interest earned

▮▮▮

PROBLEM-SOLVING HINT A table enables us to set up more easily an equation for a problem, which is usually the most difficult step.

▮▮ **EXAMPLE 4** Solving a Mixture Problem

A chemist must mix 8 liters of a 40% acid solution with some 70% solution to obtain a 50% solution. How much of the 70% solution should be used?

SOLUTION

Step 1 **Read** the problem. We must find the amount of 70% solution to be used.

Step 2 **Assign a variable.** Let $x = $ the number of liters of 70% solution to be used. The information in the problem is illustrated in **Figure 3**.

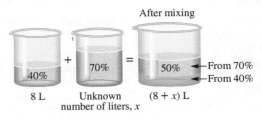

After mixing

40% + 70% = 50% ←From 70% ←From 40%
8 L   Unknown number of liters, x $(8 + x)$ L

Figure 3

In the 1941 movie *Buck Privates*, Slicker Smith (Bud Abbott) tells Herbie Brown (Lou Costello) that he is really dumb. To prove it, he challenges Herbie to answer this question:

Suppose you're 40 years old and you're in love with a little girl that's 10 years old. You're 4 times as old as that little girl. Now, you couldn't marry that little girl, could you? So you wait 5 years. Now you're 45 and she's 15. You're three times as old as the little girl. You still can't marry her, so you wait another 15 years. Now you're twice as old as that little girl. How long will you have to wait before she catches up to you?

Watch the movie to hear Herbie's clever answer.

Use the given information to complete the table.

Percent (as a decimal)	Number of Liters	Liters of Pure Acid
40% = 0.40	8	0.40(8) = 3.2
70% = 0.70	x	0.70x
50% = 0.50	8 + x	0.50(8 + x)

Sum must equal

The numbers in the right column were found by multiplying the strengths and the numbers of liters. The number of liters of pure acid in the 40% solution plus the number of liters of pure acid in the 70% solution must equal the number of liters of pure acid in the 50% solution.

Step 3 **Write an equation.**

$$3.2 + 0.70x = 0.50(8 + x)$$

Step 4 **Solve.**

$$3.2 + 0.70x = 4 + 0.50x \qquad \text{Distributive property}$$

$$0.20x = 0.8 \qquad \text{Subtract 3.2 and } 0.50x.$$

$$x = 4 \qquad \text{Divide by 0.20.}$$

Step 5 **State the answer.** The chemist should use 4 liters of the 70% solution.

Step 6 **Check.** 8 liters of 40% solution plus 4 liters of 70% solution is

$$8(0.40) + 4(0.70) = \textbf{6 liters}$$

of acid. Similarly, 8 + 4 or 12 liters of 50% solution has

$$12(0.50) = \textbf{6 liters}$$

of acid in the mixture. The total amount of pure acid is 6 liters both before and after mixing, so the answer checks. ■■■

Example 5 uses the formula for simple interest, $I = Prt$. When $t = 1$, the formula becomes $I = Pr$, as shown in the Problem-Solving Hint on the previous page.

■ EXAMPLE 5 Solving an Investment Problem

After winning the state lottery, Theo Lieber has $40,000 to invest. He will put part of the money in an account paying 4% interest and the remainder into stocks paying 6% interest. His accountant tells him that the total annual income from these investments should be $2040. How much should he invest at each rate?

SOLUTION

Step 1 **Read** the problem again. We must find the two amounts.

Step 2 **Assign a variable.**

Let x = the amount to invest at 4%.

Then 40,000 − x = the amount to invest at 6%.

The formula for interest is $I = prt$. Here the time, t, is 1 year.

Rate (as a decimal)	Principal	Interest
4% = 0.04	x	0.04x
6% = 0.06	40,000 − x	0.06(40,000 − x)
	40,000	2040

← Totals

The 1995 action thriller *Die Hard: With a Vengeance* features John McClane (Bruce Willis) and Zeus Carver (Samuel L. Jackson) matching wits with villain Simon Gruber (Jeremy Irons) who is planting bombs around New York. To keep a bomb from detonating, McClane and Carver must dial a number that requires solving the following riddle.

As I was going to St. Ives,
I met a man with seven wives,
Every wife had seven sacks,
Every sack had seven cats,
Every cat had seven kits.
Kits, cats, sacks, and wives,
How many were going to
St. Ives?

The rhyme is a derivation of an old application found in the **Rhind papyrus,** an Egyptian manuscript that dates back to about 1650 B.C. **Leonardo of Pisa (Fibonacci)** also included a similar problem in *Liber Abaci* in 1202.

The answer to the question is 1. Only "I" was *going* to St. Ives.

Step 3 **Write an equation.** The last column of the table gives the equation.

$$0.04x + 0.06(40{,}000 - x) = 2040$$

Step 4 **Solve** the equation. We do so without clearing decimals.

$0.04x + 0.06(40{,}000) - 0.06x = 2040$	Distributive property
$0.04x + 2400 - 0.06x = 2040$	Multiply.
$-0.02x + 2400 = 2040$	Combine like terms.
$-0.02x = -360$	Subtract 2400.
$x = 18{,}000$	Divide by -0.02.

Step 5 **State the answer.** Theo should invest \$18,000 at 4%. At 6%, he should invest \$40,000 − \$18,000 = \$22,000.

Step 6 **Check** by finding the annual interest at each rate.

$$0.04(\$18{,}000) = \$720 \quad \text{and} \quad 0.06(\$22{,}000) = \$1320$$

$$\$720 + \$1320 = \$2040, \quad \text{as required.} \qquad \blacksquare\blacksquare\blacksquare$$

Monetary Denomination Problems

PROBLEM-SOLVING HINT Problems that involve money are similar to mixture and investment problems.

Money Problems
Number × Value of one = Total value

For example, if a jar contains 37 quarters, the monetary value of the coins is

$$37 \quad \times \quad \$0.25 \quad = \quad \$9.25.$$

Number of coins   Denomination   Monetary value

▌▌ **EXAMPLE 6** Solving a Monetary Denomination Problem

For a bill totaling \$5.65, a cashier received 25 coins consisting of nickels and quarters. How many of each denomination did the cashier receive?

SOLUTION

Step 1 **Read** the problem. We must find the number of each denomination.

Step 2 **Assign a variable.**

Let $\quad x =$ the number of nickels.

Then $\quad 25 - x =$ the number of quarters.

Denomination	Number of Coins	Value	
\$0.05	x	$0.05x$	
\$0.25	$25 - x$	$0.25(25 - x)$	Sum must equal
	25	5.65	

Step 3   **Write an equation.** The last column of the table gives the following.

$$0.05x + 0.25(25 - x) = 5.65$$

Step 4   **Solve.** $5x + 25(25 - x) = 565$ Multiply by 100.

$$5x + 625 - 25x = 565$$ Distributive property

$$-20x = -60$$ Subtract 625. Combine like terms.

$$x = 3$$ Divide by −20.

Step 5   **State the answer.** The cashier has 3 nickels and $25 - 3 = 22$ quarters.

Step 6   **Check.** The cashier has $3 + 22 = 25$ coins, and the value of the coins is

$$\$0.05(3) + \$0.25(22) = \$5.65, \quad \text{as required.} \qquad ■■■$$

Motion Problems

If an automobile travels at an average rate of 50 miles per hour for two hours, then it travels $50 \times 2 = 100$ miles. This is an example of the basic relationship

distance = rate × time.

This is given by the formula $d = rt$. By solving, in turn, for r and t, we obtain two other equivalent forms of the formula. The three forms are given below.

Distance, Rate, Time Relationship

$$d = rt \qquad r = \frac{d}{t} \qquad t = \frac{d}{r}$$

■ EXAMPLE 7   Using the Distance, Rate, Time Relationship

(a) The speed of sound is 1088 feet per second at sea level at 32°F. In 5 seconds under these conditions, how far does sound travel?

(b) The winner of the first Indianapolis 500 race (in 1911) was Ray Harroun, driving a Marmon Wasp at an average speed of 74.59 miles per hour. How long did it take for him to complete the 500-mile course? (*Source: The Universal Almanac 1997*, John W. Wright, General Editor.)

(c) At the 2008 Olympic Games in Beijing, China, Australian swimmer Leisel Jones set an Olympic record in the women's 100-m breast stroke, swimming the event in 65.17 seconds. What was her rate? (*Source: World Almanac and Book of Facts.*)

SOLUTION

(a) $$\underset{\text{Rate}}{1088} \quad \underset{\times}{\times} \quad \underset{\text{Time}}{5} \quad \underset{=}{=} \quad \underset{\text{Distance}}{5440 \text{ feet}}$$

(b) To complete the 500 miles, it took Harroun

$$\underset{\text{Rate}}{\overset{\text{Distance}}{\frac{500}{74.59}}} = 6.70 \text{ hours} \quad \text{(rounded).} \longleftarrow \text{Time}$$

Here, we found time given rate and distance, using $t = \frac{d}{r}$. To convert 0.70 hour to minutes, multiply by 60 to get $0.70(60) = 42$ minutes. The race took him 6 hours, 42 minutes to complete.

Leisel Jones

Can we average averages? A car travels from *A* to *B* at 40 miles per hour and returns at 60 miles per hour. What is its rate for the entire trip?

The correct answer is not 50 miles per hour, as you might expect. Remembering the distance, rate, time relationship and letting *x* = the distance between *A* and *B*, we can simplify a complex fraction to find the correct answer.

$$\text{Average rate for} \atop \text{entire trip} = \frac{\text{Total distance}}{\text{Total time}}$$

$$= \frac{x + x}{\dfrac{x}{40} + \dfrac{x}{60}}$$

$$= \frac{2x}{\dfrac{3x}{120} + \dfrac{2x}{120}}$$

$$= \frac{2x}{\dfrac{5x}{120}}$$

$$= 2x \cdot \frac{120}{5x}$$

$$= 48$$

The average rate for the entire trip is 48 miles per hour.

(c) Her rate is found by dividing distance by time.

$$\text{Rate} = \frac{\text{Distance}}{\text{Time}} \longrightarrow \frac{100}{65.17} = 1.53 \text{ meters per second (rounded)} \quad ▌▌▌$$

> **PROBLEM-SOLVING HINT** Motion problems use the distance formula,
>
> $$d = rt.$$
>
> In this formula, ***when rate (or speed) is given in miles per hour, time must be given in hours.*** To solve such problems, ***draw a sketch*** to illustrate what is happening in the problem, and ***make a table*** to summarize the given information.

▌▌ **EXAMPLE 8** Solving a Motion Problem

Greg Sabo can bike from home to work in $\frac{3}{4}$ hour. By bus, the trip takes $\frac{1}{4}$ hour. If the bus travels 20 mph faster than Greg rides his bike, how far is it to his workplace?

SOLUTION

Step 1 **Read** the problem. We must find the distance between Greg's home and his workplace.

Step 2 **Assign a variable.** Although the problem asks for a distance, it is easier here to let *x* be his speed when he rides his bike to work. Then the speed of the bus is $x + 20$.

$$d = rt = x \cdot \frac{3}{4} = \frac{3}{4}x, \quad \text{Distance of trip by bike}$$

and

$$d = rt = (x + 20) \cdot \frac{1}{4} = \frac{1}{4}(x + 20) \quad \text{Distance of trip by bus}$$

We summarize this information in a table.

	Rate	Time	Distance
Bike	x	$\frac{3}{4}$	$\frac{3}{4}x$
Bus	$x + 20$	$\frac{1}{4}$	$\frac{1}{4}(x + 20)$

Same distance

Step 3 **Write an equation.** The key to setting up the correct equation is to recognize that the distance in each case is the *same*. See **Figure 4**.

Home   Workplace

Figure 4

$$\frac{3}{4}x = \frac{1}{4}(x + 20) \quad \text{The distance is the same.}$$

Step 4   **Solve.** $4\left(\dfrac{3}{4}x\right) = 4\left(\dfrac{1}{4}\right)(x + 20)$ Multiply by 4.

$3x = x + 20$ Multiply.

$2x = 20$ Subtract x.

$x = 10$ Divide by 2.

Step 5   **State the answer.** The required distance is given by $d = rt$.

$$d = \frac{3}{4}x = \frac{3}{4}(10) = \frac{30}{4} = 7.5 \text{ miles}$$ Distance by bike

Step 6   **Check** by finding the distance by bus.

$$d = \frac{1}{4}(x + 20) = \frac{1}{4}(10 + 20) = \frac{30}{4} = 7.5 \text{ miles}$$ Distance by bus

This yields the same result. It is 7.5 miles to his workplace.   ▮▮▮

PROBLEM-SOLVING HINT In motion problems such as the one in **Example 8,** once you have filled in two pieces of information in each row of the table, you should automatically fill in the third piece of information, using the appropriate form of the formula relating distance, rate, and time.

7.2 EXERCISES

Decide whether each of the following translates into an expression or an equation.

1. the product of a number and 6

2. 39% of a number

3. $\frac{2}{3}$ of a number is 36.

4. 9 is 5 more than a number.

5. the ratio of a number and 24

6. 48 divided by a number is 12.

7. Rework **Example 6,** letting the variable represent the number of quarters. Is the answer to the problem the same?

8. Explain why $19 - x$ is *not* a correct translation of "19 less than a number."

Translate each verbal phrase into a mathematical expression. Use x to represent the unknown number.

9. a number decreased by 12

10. 7 more than a number

11. the product of 6 less than a number and 4 more than the number

12. the quotient of a number and 9

13. the ratio of 25 and a nonzero number

14. $\frac{6}{7}$ of a number

15. Write a few sentences describing the six steps for problem solving.

16. Which is *not* a valid translation of "30% of a number"?

A. $0.30x$ **B.** $0.3x$ **C.** $\dfrac{3x}{10}$ **D.** 0.30

Unknown Numbers   Let x represent the number, write an equation for the sentence, and then solve.

17. If 2 is added to five times a number, the result is equal to 5 more than four times the number. Find the number.

18. If four times a number is added to 8, the result is three times the number added to 5. Find the number.

19. If 2 is subtracted from a number and this difference is tripled, the result is 6 more than the number. Find the number.

20. If 3 is added to a number and this sum is doubled, the result is 2 more than the number. Find the number.

21. The sum of three times a number and 7 more than the number is the same as the difference between −11 and twice the number. What is the number?

22. If 4 is added to twice a number and this sum is multiplied by 2, the result is the same as if the number is multiplied by 3 and 4 is added to the product. What is the number?

*Use the methods of **Examples 1 and 2** or your own method to solve each problem.*

23. ***Concert Revenues*** Bon Jovi and Bruce Springsteen had the two top-grossing North American concert tours for 2008, together generating $415.3 million in ticket sales. If Bruce Springsteen took in $6.1 million less than Bon Jovi, how much did each tour generate? (*Source:* www.billboard.com)

24. ***Automobile Sales*** The Toyota Camry was the top-selling passenger car in the United States in 2007, followed by the Honda Accord. Honda Accord sales were 81 thousand less than Toyota Camry sales, and 865 thousand of these two cars were sold. How many of each model of car were sold? (*Source: World Almanac and Book of Facts.*)

25. ***NBA Record*** In the 2008–2009 NBA regular season, the Boston Celtics won two more than three times as many games as they lost. The Celtics played 82 games. How many wins and losses did the team have? (*Source:* www.nba.com)

26. ***MLB Record*** In the 2008 Major League Baseball season, the Tampa Bay Rays won 33 fewer than twice as many games as they lost. They played 162 regular season games. How many wins and losses did the team have? (*Source:* www.mlb.com)

27. ***U.S. Senate*** During the 111th Congress (beginning in 2009), the U.S. Senate had a total of 98 Democrats and Republicans. There were 18 fewer Republicans than Democrats. How many Democrats and Republicans were there in the Senate? (*Source: World Almanac and Book of Facts.*)

28. ***U.S. House of Representatives*** The total number of Democrats and Republicans in the U.S. House of Representatives during the 111th Congress was 435. There were 31 more Democrats than Republicans. How many members of each party were there? (*Source: World Almanac and Book of Facts.*)

29. ***Submarine Sandwich*** Nagaraj Nanjappa has a party-length sandwich that is 59 inches long and is to be cut into three pieces. The middle piece will be 5 inches longer than the shortest piece, and the shortest piece will be 9 inches shorter than the longest piece. How long will the pieces be?

30. ***Office Manager Duties*** In one week, an office manager booked 55 tickets, divided among three airlines. He booked 7 more tickets on American Airlines than United Airlines. On Southwest Airlines, he booked 4 more than twice as many tickets as on United. How many tickets did he book on each airline?

31. ***U.S. Olympic Medals*** China earned a total of 100 medals at the 2008 Beijing Olympics. The number of gold medals was 23 more than the number of bronze medals. The number of bronze medals was 7 more than the number of silver medals. How many of each kind of medal did China earn? (*Source: World Almanac and Book of Facts.*)

32. ***Textbook Editor Duties*** Textbook editor Christine O'Brien spent $7\frac{1}{2}$ hours making telephone calls, writing e-mails, and attending meetings. She spent twice as much time attending meetings as making telephone calls, and $\frac{1}{2}$ hour longer writing e-mails than making telephone calls. How many hours did she spend on each task?

*Use basic formulas, as in **Example 3**, to solve each problem.*

33. *Acid Mixture* How much pure acid is in 500 milliliters of a 14% acid solution?

34. *Alcohol Mixture* How much pure alcohol is in 300 liters of a 30% alcohol solution?

35. *Interest Earned* If $10,000 is invested for one year at 2.5% simple interest, how much interest is earned?

36. *Interest Earned* If $50,000 is invested at 3% simple interest for 2 years, how much interest is earned?

37. *Monetary Value of Coins* What is the monetary amount of 497 nickels?

38. *Monetary Value of Coins* What is the monetary amount of 89 half-dollars?

*Use the method of **Example 4** or your own method to solve each problem.*

39. *Alcohol Mixture* In a chemistry class, 12 liters of a 12% alcohol solution must be mixed with a 20% solution to get a 14% solution. How many liters of the 20% solution are needed?

Strength	Liters of Solution	Liters of Alcohol
12%	12	
20%		
14%		

40. *Alcohol Mixture* How many liters of a 10% alcohol solution must be mixed with 40 liters of a 50% solution to get a 40% solution?

Strength	Liters of Solution	Liters of Alcohol
	x	
	40	
40%		

41. *Antifreeze Mixture* A car radiator needs a 40% antifreeze solution. The radiator now holds 20 liters of 20% solution. How many liters of this should be drained and replaced with 100% antifreeze to get the desired strength?

42. *Chemical Mixture* A tank holds 80 liters of a chemical solution. Currently, the solution has a strength of 30%. How much of this should be drained and replaced with a 70% solution to get a final strength of 40%?

43. *Insecticide Mixture* How much water must be added to 3 gallons of a 4% insecticide solution to reduce the concentration to 3%? (*Hint:* Water is 0% insecticide.)

44. *Alcohol Mixture in First Aid Spray* A medicated first aid spray on the market is 78% alcohol by volume. If the manufacturer has 50 liters of the spray containing 70% alcohol, how much pure alcohol should be added so that the final mixture is the required 78% alcohol? (*Hint:* Pure alcohol is 100% alcohol.)

*Use the method of **Example 5** or your own method to solve each problem. Assume all rates and amounts are annual.*

45. *Investments at Different Rates* John Allen earned $12,000 last year by giving tennis lessons. He invested part at 3% simple interest and the rest at 4%. He earned a total of $440 in interest. How much did he invest at each rate?

Rate (as a Decimal)	Principal	Interest in One Year
0.03		
0.04		
	12,000	440

46. *Investments at Different Rates* Kim Hobbs won $60,000 on a slot machine in Las Vegas. She invested part at 2% simple interest and the rest at 3%. She earned a total of $1600 in interest. How much was invested at each rate?

Rate (as a Decimal)	Principal	Interest in One Year
0.02	x	0.02x
	60,000 − x	
		1600

47. *Investments at Different Rates* Derrick Nantz invested some money at 4.5% simple interest and $1000 less than twice this amount at 3%. His total income from the interest was $1020. How much was invested at each rate?

48. *Investments at Different Rates* Dee Dee Myers invested some money at 3.5% simple interest, and $5000 more than 3 times this amount at 4%. She earned $1440 in interest. How much did she invest at each rate?

49. *Investments at Different Rates* Dave Morris has $29,000 invested in stocks paying 5%. How much additional money should he invest in certificates of deposit paying 2% so that the average return on the two investments is 3%?

50. *Investments at Different Rates* Terry McGinnis placed $15,000 in an account paying 6%. How much additional money should she deposit at 4% so that the average return on the two investments is 5.5%?

*Use the method of **Example 6** or your own method to solve each problem.*

51. Coin Mixture Mike Easley has a box of coins that he uses when playing poker with his friends. The box currently contains 44 coins, consisting of pennies, dimes, and quarters. The number of pennies is equal to the number of dimes, and the total value is $4.37. How many of each denomination of coin does he have in the box?

Denomination	Number of Coins	Value	
0.01	x	0.01x	
	x		
0.25			
	44	4.37	Totals

52. Coin Mixture Kathy Diamond found some coins while looking under her sofa pillows. There were equal numbers of nickels and quarters, and twice as many half-dollars as quarters. If she found $2.60 in all, how many of each denomination of coin did she find?

Denomination	Number of Coins	Value	
0.05	x	0.05x	
	x		
0.50	2x		
		2.60	Total

53. Attendance at a School Play For opening night of a school production of *The Mousetrap*, 410 tickets were sold. Students paid $3 each, while nonstudents paid $7 each. If a total of $1650 was collected, how many students and how many nonstudents attended?

54. Attendance at a Concert A total of 1100 people attended a James Taylor concert. Floor tickets cost $40 each, while balcony tickets cost $28 each. If a total of $41,600 was collected, how many of each type of ticket were sold?

55. Attendance at a Sporting Event At the local minor league hockey arena home games, Row 1 seats cost $35 each and Row 2 seats cost $30 each. The 105 seats in these rows were sold out for the season. The total receipts for them were $3420. How many of each type of seat were sold?

56. Coin Mixture In the nineteenth century, the United States minted two-cent and three-cent pieces. Frances Steib has three times as many three-cent pieces as two-cent pieces, and the face value of these coins is $1.76. How many of each denomination does she have?

57. Stamp Denominations In May 2009, U.S. first-class mail rates increased to 44 cents for the first ounce, plus 17 cents for each additional ounce. If Sabrina spent $17.45 for a total of 55 stamps of these two denominations, how many stamps of each denomination did she buy? (*Source:* U.S. Postal Service.)

58. Movie Ticket Prices A movie theater has two ticket prices: $9 for adults and $6 for children. If the box office took in $4716 from the sale of 600 tickets, how many tickets of each kind were sold?

Use the formula d = rt in Exercises 59–62.

59. Distance Between Cities A small plane traveled from Warsaw to Rome, averaging 164 miles per hour. The trip took two hours. What is the distance from Warsaw to Rome?

60. Distance Between Cities A driver averaged 53 miles per hour and took 10 hours to travel from Memphis to Chicago. What is the distance between Memphis and Chicago?

61. Suppose that an automobile averages 55 miles per hour, and travels for 30 minutes. Is the distance traveled $55 \cdot 30 = 1650$ miles? If not, give the correct distance.

62. Which of the following choices is the best *estimate* for the average speed of a trip of 350 miles that lasted 6.8 hours?

  A. 50 miles per hour   **B.** 30 miles per hour

  C. 60 miles per hour   **D.** 40 miles per hour

*Use the method of **Example 8** or your own method to solve each problem.*

63. Travel Times of Trains A train leaves Little Rock, Arkansas, and travels north at 85 kilometers per hour. Another train leaves at the same time and travels south at 95 kilometers per hour. How long will it take before they are 315 kilometers apart?

	Rate	Time	Distance
First train	85	t	
Second train			

64. Travel Times of Steamers Two steamers leave a port on a river at the same time, traveling in opposite directions. Each is traveling 22 miles per hour. How long will it take for them to be 110 miles apart?

	Rate	Time	Distance
First steamer		t	
Second steamer	22		

65. *Travel Times of Commuters* Nancy and Mark commute to work, traveling in opposite directions. Nancy leaves the house at 9:00 A.M. and averages 35 miles per hour. Mark leaves at 9:15 A.M. and averages 40 miles per hour. At what time will they be 140 miles apart?

66. *Travel Times of Bicyclers* Jeff leaves his house on his bicycle at 7:30 A.M. and averages 5 miles per hour. His wife, Joan, leaves at 8:00 A.M., following the same path and averaging 8 miles per hour. At what time will Joan catch up with Jeff?

67. *Time Traveled by a Pleasure Boat* A pleasure boat on the Mississippi River traveled from New Roads, LA, to New Orleans with a stop at White Castle. On the first part of the trip, the boat traveled at an average speed of 10 miles per hour. From White Castle to New Orleans the average speed was 15 miles per hour. The entire trip covered 100 miles. How long did the entire trip take if the two parts each took the same number of hours?

68. *Time Traveled on a Visit* Steve leaves Nashville to visit his cousin David in Napa, 80 miles away. He travels at an average speed of 50 miles per hour. One-half hour later David leaves to visit Steve, traveling at an average speed of 60 miles per hour. How long after David leaves will they meet?

69. *Distance Traveled to Work* When Glen Spencer drives his car to work, the trip takes 30 minutes. When he rides the bus, it takes 45 minutes. The average speed of the bus is 12 miles per hour less than his speed when driving. Find the distance he travels to work.

70. *Distance Traveled to School* Theresa Stevens can get to school in 15 minutes if she rides her bike. It takes her 45 minutes if she walks. Her speed when walking is 10 miles per hour slower than her speed when riding. How far does she travel to school?

Automobile Racing In Exercises 71–74, find the time. Use a calculator and round your answers to the nearest thousandth. (Source: The World Almanac and Book of Facts.)

	Event and Year	Participant	Distance	Rate
71.	Indianapolis 500, 2009	Helio Castroneves (Honda)	500 miles	150.318 mph
72.	Daytona 500, 2009	Matt Kenseth (Ford)	500 miles	132.816 mph
73.	Indianapolis 500, 1980	Johnny Rutherford (Hy-Gain McLaren/Goodyear)	255 miles*	148.725 mph
74.	Indianapolis 500, 1975	Bobby Unser (Jorgensen Eagle)	435 miles*	149.213 mph

*rain-shortened

Olympic Results In Exercises 75–78, find the rate. Use a calculator and round your answers to the nearest hundredth. All events were at the Beijing 2008 Olympics. (Source: World Almanac and Book of Facts.)

	Event	Participant	Distance	Time
75.	100-m hurdles, Women	Dawn Harper, USA	100 meters	12.54 seconds
76.	400-m hurdles, Women	Melanie Walker, Jamaica	400 meters	52.64 seconds
77.	400-m hurdles, Men	Angelo Taylor, USA	400 meters	47.25 seconds
78.	400-m run, Men	LaShawn Merritt, USA	400 meters	43.75 seconds

7.3 RATIO, PROPORTION, AND VARIATION

Writing Ratios • Unit Pricing • Solving Proportions • Direct Variation
• Inverse Variation • Joint and Combined Variation

Writing Ratios

One of the most frequently used mathematical concepts in everyday life is *ratio*. A baseball player's batting average is actually a ratio. The slope, or pitch, of a roof on a building may be expressed as a ratio. Ratios provide a way of comparing two numbers or quantities.

> **Ratio**
>
> A **ratio** is a quotient of two quantities. The ratio of the number *a* to the number *b* is written
>
> $$a \text{ to } b, \qquad \frac{a}{b}, \qquad \text{or} \qquad a{:}b.$$

When ratios are used in comparing units of measure, the units should be the same.

During the first season (1960) of **The Andy Griffith Show,** the episode "Opie's Charity" featured a conversation between Opie and Andy during which Andy explained to Opie that his donation of three cents to the underprivileged children's drive at school was "a piddlin' amount."

ANDY: I was reading here just the other day where there's somewhere like 400 needy boys in this county alone, or one and a half boys per square mile.
OPIE: There is?
ANDY: Sho' is.
OPIE: I've never seen one, Pa.
ANDY: Never seen one what?
OPIE: A half a boy.
ANDY: Well it's not really a half a boy. It's **a ratio.**
OPIE: Horatio who?
ANDY: Not *Horatio*, *a ratio*. It's mathematics. Arithmetic. Look now Opie, just forget that part of it. Forget the part about the half a boy.
OPIE: It's pretty hard to forget a thing like that, Pa.
ANDY: Well try.
OPIE: Poor Horatio.

EXAMPLE 1 Writing Ratios

Write a ratio for each word phrase.

(a) 5 hours to 3 hours   **(b)** 6 hours to 3 days

SOLUTION

(a) The ratio of 5 hr to 3 hr is

$$\frac{5 \text{ hr}}{3 \text{ hr}} = \frac{5}{3}. \quad \boxed{\text{The ratio is 5 to 3.}}$$

(b) To find the ratio of 6 hr to 3 days, first convert 3 days to hours.

$$3 \text{ days} = 3 \text{ days} \cdot \frac{24 \text{ hr}}{1 \text{ day}} = 72 \text{ hr}$$

The ratio of 6 hr to 3 days is found as follows.

$$\frac{6 \text{ hr}}{3 \text{ days}} = \frac{6 \text{ hr}}{72 \text{ hr}} = \frac{6}{72} = \frac{1}{12} \quad \text{The ratio is 1 to 12.}$$

Unit Pricing

Ratios can be applied in unit pricing, to see which size of an item offered in different sizes produces the best price per unit. To do this, set up the ratio of the price of the item to the number of units on the label. Then divide to obtain the price per unit.

▮▮ **EXAMPLE 2** Finding Price per Unit

A supermarket charges the following for a jar of extra crunchy peanut butter.

Peanut Butter

Size	Price
18-oz	$1.78
28-oz	$2.97
40-oz	$3.98

Which size is the best buy? That is, which size has the lowest unit price?

SOLUTION

Write ratios comparing the price for each size jar to the number of units (ounces) per jar. The results in **Table 2** are rounded to the nearest thousandth.

Table 2

Size	Unit Cost (dollars per ounce)
18-oz	$\dfrac{\$1.78}{18} = \$0.099$ ⟵———— The best buy
28-oz	$\dfrac{\$2.97}{28} = \$0.106$
40-oz	$\dfrac{\$3.98}{40} = \$0.100$

Because the 18-oz size produces the lowest unit cost, it is the best buy. Thus, buying the largest size does not always provide the best buy. ▮▮▮

Solving Proportions

Proportion

A **proportion** is a statement that says that two ratios are equal.

For example, $\dfrac{3}{4} = \dfrac{15}{20}$ Proportion

is a proportion that says that the ratios $\frac{3}{4}$ and $\frac{15}{20}$ are equal. In the proportion

$$\frac{a}{b} = \frac{c}{d} \quad (b, d \neq 0),$$

a, b, c, and d are the **terms** of the proportion. The a and d terms are called the **extremes,** and the b and c terms are called the **means.** We read the proportion $\frac{a}{b} = \frac{c}{d}$ as "a is to b as c is to d." Multiply each side of this proportion by the common denominator, bd.

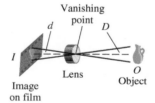

Vanishing
point

I Image on film   Lens   *O* Object

When you look a long way down a straight road or railroad track, it seems to narrow as it vanishes in the distance. The point where the sides seem to touch is called the **vanishing point.**

   The same thing occurs in the lens of a camera, as shown in the figure. Suppose *I* represents the length of the image, *O* the length of the object, *d* the distance from the lens to the film, and *D* the distance from the lens to the object.

$$\frac{\text{Image length}}{\text{Object length}} = \frac{\text{Image distance}}{\text{Object distance}}$$

or

$$\frac{I}{O} = \frac{d}{D}$$

   Given the length of the image on the film and its distance from the lens, the length of the object determines the distance the lens must be from the object.

In the 1994 movie *Little Big League*, young Billy Heywood (Luke Edwards) inherits the Minnesota Twins baseball team and becomes manager. Before the biggest game of the year, he can't keep his mind on his job, because a homework problem is giving him trouble.

If Joe can paint a house in 3 hours, and Sam can paint the same house in 5 hours, how long does it take for them to do it together?

One of his players provides a method to solve the problem, where a and b are the individual times. He claims that the expression $\frac{a \times b}{a + b}$ gives the correct answer. With $a = 5$ and $b = 3$, the answer he gives is

$$\frac{5 \times 3}{5 + 3} = \frac{15}{8} = 1\frac{7}{8} \text{ hours.}$$

The player's expression and answer are correct. Suppose a and b are the individual times. Then the hourly rates for the players are $\frac{1}{a}$ and $\frac{1}{b}$ job per hour. Multiplying rate by time worked gives the fractional part of the job performed by each player. Let x represent the time they must work together to complete one whole job.

$$\frac{1}{a}x + \frac{1}{b}x = 1$$
Linear equation

$$ab\left(\frac{1}{a}x + \frac{1}{b}x\right) = ab \cdot 1$$
Multiply by ab.

$$bx + ax = ab$$
Distributive property

$$x(a + b) = ab$$
Distributive property

$$x = \frac{ab}{a + b}$$
Divide by $a + b$.

$$bd \cdot \frac{a}{b} = bd \cdot \frac{c}{d} \qquad \text{Multiply each side by } bd.$$

$$\frac{b}{b}(d \cdot a) = \frac{d}{d}(b \cdot c) \qquad \text{Associative and commutative properties}$$

$$ad = bc \qquad \text{Commutative and identity properties}$$

We can also find the products ad and bc by multiplying diagonally.

$$\frac{a}{b} \overset{bc}{\underset{ad}{\times}} \frac{c}{d}$$

For this reason, ad and bc are called **cross products.**

> **Cross Products**
>
> If $\dfrac{a}{b} = \dfrac{c}{d}$, then the cross products ad and bc are equal.
>
> Also, if $ad = bc$, then $\dfrac{a}{b} = \dfrac{c}{d}$ (as long as $b \neq 0, d \neq 0$).

For a proportion to be true, the product of the extremes must equal the product of the means. If $\frac{a}{c} = \frac{b}{d}$, then $ad = cb$, or $ad = bc$. This means that these two corresponding proportions are equivalent:

The proportion $\dfrac{a}{b} = \dfrac{c}{d}$ *can also be written as* $\dfrac{a}{c} = \dfrac{b}{d}$ *$(c \neq 0)$.*

Sometimes one form is more convenient to work with than the other.

▌▌ **EXAMPLE 3** Solving Proportions

Solve the proportion $\dfrac{x}{63} = \dfrac{5}{9}$.

SOLUTION

$$\frac{x}{63} = \frac{5}{9}$$

$$9x = 63 \cdot 5 \qquad \text{Set the cross products equal.}$$

$$9x = 315 \qquad \text{Multiply.}$$

$$x = 35 \qquad \text{Divide by 9.}$$

The solution set is $\{35\}$. ▌▌▌

▌▌ **EXAMPLE 4** Solving an Equation Using Cross Products

Solve $\dfrac{x - 2}{5} = \dfrac{x + 1}{3}$.

SOLUTION

Find the cross products, and set them equal to each other.

$$3(x - 2) = 5(x + 1) \quad \text{Cross products}$$

Be sure to use parentheses.

$$3x - 6 = 5x + 5 \quad \text{Distributive property}$$

$$3x = 5x + 11 \quad \text{Add 6.}$$

$$-2x = 11 \quad \text{Subtract } 5x.$$

$$x = -\frac{11}{2} \quad \text{Divide by } -2.$$

The solution set is $\left\{-\frac{11}{2}\right\}$.   ▮▮▮

▮▮ **EXAMPLE 5** Using a Proportion to Predict Population

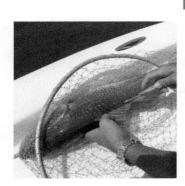

Biologists catch a sample of fish in a lake and mark each specimen with a harmless tag. Later, they catch a similar sample of fish from the same areas of the lake and determine the proportion of previously tagged fish in the new sample. The total fish population is estimated by assuming that the proportion of tagged fish in the new sample is the same as the proportion of tagged fish in the entire lake.

Suppose biologists tag 300 fish on May 1. When they return on June 1 and take a new sample of 400 fish, 5 of the 400 were previously tagged. Estimate the number of fish in the lake.

SOLUTION

Let x represent the number of fish in the lake. Set up and solve a proportion.

Tagged fish on May 1 ⟶ $\dfrac{300}{x}$ = $\dfrac{5}{400}$ ⟵ Tagged fish in the June 1 sample
Total fish in the lake ⟶   ⟵ Total number in the June 1 sample

$$5x = 120,000 \quad \text{Cross products}$$

$$x = 24,000 \quad \text{Divide by 5.}$$

Based on this sampling procedure, there are about 24,000 fish in the lake.   ▮▮▮

Direct Variation

Suppose that a carpet cleaning service charges $49.99 per room to shampoo a carpet. **Table 3** shows the relationship between the number of rooms cleaned and the cost of the total job for 1 through 5 rooms.

If we divide the cost of the job by the number of rooms, in each case we obtain the quotient, or ratio, 49.99 (dollars per room). Suppose that we let x represent the number of rooms and y represent the cost for cleaning that number of rooms. Then the relationship between x and y is given by the equation

$$\frac{y}{x} = 49.99, \quad \text{or} \quad y = 49.99x.$$

This relationship between x and y is an example of *direct variation*.

Table 3

Number of Rooms	Cost of the Job
1	$ 49.99
2	$ 99.98
3	$149.97
4	$199.96
5	$249.95

Direct Variation

y varies directly as x, or **y is directly proportional to x,** if there exists a nonzero constant k such that

$$y = kx, \quad \text{or, equivalently,} \quad \frac{y}{x} = k.$$

The constant k is a numerical value called the **constant of variation.**

▌▌ **EXAMPLE 6** Solving a Direct Variation Problem

Another Way of Thinking
In **Example 6**, because the ratio of y to x is constant, you may want to simply write the equation as

$$\frac{50}{20} = \frac{y}{14}$$

and solve for y.

Suppose y varies directly as x, and $y = 50$ when $x = 20$. Find y when $x = 14$.

SOLUTION

Since y varies directly as x, there exists a constant k such that $y = kx$. Find k by replacing y with 50 and x with 20.

$$y = kx \qquad \text{Variation equation}$$
$$50 = k \cdot 20 \qquad \text{Substitute the given values.}$$
$$\frac{5}{2} = k \qquad \text{Divide by 20. Express in lowest terms.}$$

Since $y = kx$ and $k = \frac{5}{2}$,

$$y = \frac{5}{2}x.$$

Now find y when $x = 14$.

$$y = \frac{5}{2} \cdot 14 = 35$$

The value of y is 35 when $x = 14$. ▪▪▪

▌▌ **EXAMPLE 7** Solving a Direct Variation Problem

Figure 5

Hooke's law for an elastic spring states that the distance a spring stretches is directly proportional to the force applied. If a force of 150 pounds stretches a certain spring 8 centimeters, how much will a force of 400 pounds stretch the spring? See **Figure 5**.

SOLUTION

If d is the distance the spring stretches and f is the force applied, then $d = kf$ for some constant k.

$$d = kf \qquad \text{Variation equation}$$
$$8 = k \cdot 150 \qquad \text{Let } d = 8 \text{ and } f = 150.$$
$$k = \frac{8}{150} = \frac{4}{75} \qquad \text{Find } k.$$

Thus $d = \frac{4}{75}f$.

For a force of 400 pounds,

$$d = \frac{4}{75}(400) = \frac{64}{3}. \quad \text{Let } f = 400.$$

The spring will stretch $\frac{64}{3}$ centimeters if a force of 400 pounds is applied. ▪▪▪

Solving a Variation Problem

Step 1 Write the variation equation.
Step 2 Substitute the initial values and solve for k.
Step 3 Rewrite the variation equation with the value of k from Step 2.
Step 4 Substitute the remaining values, solve for the unknown, and find the required answer.

In some cases one quantity will vary directly as a *power* of another.

$\mathcal{A} = \pi r^2$

Figure 6

Direct Variation as a Power

y **varies directly as the** *n***th power of** *x* if there exists a nonzero real number *k* such that

$$y = kx^n.$$

An example of direct variation as a power involves the area of a circle. See **Figure 6**. The formula for the area of a circle is $\mathcal{A} = \pi r^2$. Here, π is the constant of variation, and the area $\mathcal{A}$ varies directly as the square of the radius *r*.

▋▋ **EXAMPLE 8** Solving a Direct Variation Problem

The distance a body falls from rest varies directly as the square of the time it falls (here we disregard air resistance). If a skydiver falls 64 feet in 2 seconds, how far will she fall in 8 seconds?

SOLUTION

Step 1   If *d* represents the distance the skydiver falls and *t* the time it takes to fall, then *d* is a function of *t*, and, for some constant *k*, $d = kt^2$.

Step 2   To find the value of *k*, use the fact that the skydiver falls 64 feet in 2 seconds.

$$d = kt^2 \qquad \text{Formula}$$
$$64 = k(2)^2 \qquad \text{Let } d = 64 \text{ and } t = 2.$$
$$k = 16 \qquad \text{Evaluate } k.$$

Step 3   With this result, the variation equation becomes

$$d = 16t^2.$$

Step 4   Now let *t* = 8 to find the number of feet the skydiver will fall in 8 seconds.

$$d = 16t^2 = 16(8)^2 = 1024 \qquad \text{Let } t = 8.$$

$8^2 = 8 \cdot 8 = 64$

The skydiver will fall 1024 feet in 8 seconds.   ▋▋▋

Inverse Variation

In direct variation where $k > 0$, *as* *x* *increases,* *y* *increases, and similarly as* *x* *decreases,* *y* *decreases.* Another type of variation is *inverse variation*.

Inverse Variation

y **varies inversely as** *x* if there exists a nonzero real number *k* such that

$$y = \frac{k}{x}, \quad \text{or, equivalently,} \quad xy = k.$$

Also, *y* **varies inversely as the** *n***th power of** *x* if there exists a nonzero real number *k* such that

$$y = \frac{k}{x^n}.$$

▮▮ **EXAMPLE 9** Solving an Inverse Variation Problem

The weight of an object above Earth varies inversely as the square of its distance from the center of Earth. A space vehicle in an elliptical orbit has a maximum distance from the center of Earth (apogee) of 6700 miles. Its minimum distance from the center of Earth (perigee) is 4090 miles. See **Figure 7** (not to scale). If an astronaut in the vehicle weighs 57 pounds at its apogee, what does the astronaut weigh at the perigee?

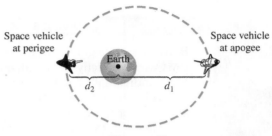

Figure 7

SOLUTION

If w is the weight and d is the distance from the center of Earth, then

$$w = \frac{k}{d^2}, \quad \text{for some constant } k.$$

At the apogee the astronaut weighs 57 pounds and the distance from the center of Earth is 6700 miles. Use these values to find k.

$$57 = \frac{k}{(6700)^2} \qquad \text{Let } w = 57 \text{ and } d = 6700.$$

$$k = 57(6700)^2 \qquad \text{Multiply by } (6700)^2. \text{ Rewrite.}$$

Then the weight at the perigee with $d = 4090$ miles is

$$w = \frac{57(6700)^2}{(4090)^2} \approx 153 \text{ pounds.} \qquad \text{Use a calculator.} \qquad ▮▮▮$$

Joint and Combined Variation

If one variable varies as the product of several other variables (perhaps raised to powers), the first variable is said to **vary jointly** as the others.

▮▮ **EXAMPLE 10** Solving a Joint Variation Problem

The strength of a rectangular beam varies jointly as its width and the square of its depth. If the strength of a beam 2 inches wide by 10 inches deep is 1000 pounds per square inch, what is the strength of a beam 4 inches wide and 8 inches deep?

SOLUTION

If S represents the strength, w the width, and d the depth, then, for some constant k, $S = kwd^2$.

$$S = kwd^2 \qquad \boxed{10^2 = 10 \cdot 10 = 100}$$

$$1000 = k(2)(10)^2 \qquad \text{Let } S = 1000, w = 2, \text{ and } d = 10.$$

$$1000 = 200k \qquad \text{Apply the exponent. Multiply.}$$

$$k = 5 \qquad \text{Divide by 200. Rewrite.}$$

Thus, $S = 5wd^2$. Find S for $w = 4$ and $d = 8$ by substitution.

$$S = 5(4)(8)^2 = 1280 \quad \text{Let } w = 4 \text{ and } d = 8.$$

The strength of the beam is 1280 pounds per square inch.   ▌▌▌

Combined variation problems involve combinations of direct and inverse variation.

▌▌ **EXAMPLE 11** Solving a Combined Variation Problem

Grady Sizemore

Body mass index, or BMI, is used by physicians to assess a person's level of fatness. BMI varies directly as an individual's weight in pounds and inversely as the square of the individual's height in inches. A person who weighs 118 lb and is 64 in. tall has a BMI of 20.25. (The BMI is usually rounded to the nearest whole number.) Grady Sizemore of the Cleveland Indians weighs 200 pounds and is 6 feet, 2 inches tall. Find his BMI. (*Source: Washington Post;* www.mlb.com)

SOLUTION

Let B represent the BMI, w the weight, and h the height. Use the given information to determine k.

$$B = \frac{kw}{h^2} \quad \begin{array}{l} \leftarrow \text{BMI varies directly as the weight.} \\ \leftarrow \text{BMI varies inversely as the square of the height.} \end{array}$$

$$20.25 = \frac{k(118)}{64^2} \quad \text{Let } B = 20.25, w = 118, \text{ and } h = 64.$$

$$k = \frac{20.25(64^2)}{118} \quad \text{Multiply by } 64^2. \text{ Divide by 118.}$$

$$k \approx 703 \quad \text{Use a calculator.}$$

For Sizemore, use $k = 703$, $w = 200$, and $h = (6 \times 12) + 2 = 74$, to find B.

$$B = \frac{703(200)}{74^2} \approx 25.68 \approx 26 \quad \text{Nearest whole number}$$

Grady's BMI is 26.   ▌▌▌

7.3 EXERCISES

Determine the ratio and write it in lowest terms.

1. 50 feet to 80 feet

2. 12 miles to 36 miles

3. 17 dollars to 68 dollars

4. 600 people to 500 people

5. 288 inches to 12 feet

6. 60 inches to 2 yards

7. 5 days to 40 hours

8. 75 minutes to 4 hours

9. Which ratio is not the same as the ratio 2 to 5?
   A. 0.4   **B.** 4 to 10   **C.** 20 to 50   **D.** 5 to 2

10. Give three ratios that are equivalent to the ratio 4 to 3.

11. Explain the distinction between *ratio* and *proportion*. Give examples.

12. Suppose that someone told you to use cross products in order to multiply fractions. How would you explain to the person what is wrong with his or her thinking?

Decide whether each proportion is true *or* false.

13. $\dfrac{5}{35} = \dfrac{8}{56}$

14. $\dfrac{4}{12} = \dfrac{7}{21}$

15. $\dfrac{120}{82} = \dfrac{7}{10}$

16. $\dfrac{27}{160} = \dfrac{18}{110}$

17. $\dfrac{\frac{1}{2}}{5} = \dfrac{1}{10}$

18. $\dfrac{\frac{1}{3}}{6} = \dfrac{1}{18}$

Solve each equation.

19. $\dfrac{x}{4} = \dfrac{175}{20}$

20. $\dfrac{49}{56} = \dfrac{x}{8}$

21. $\dfrac{3x - 2}{5} = \dfrac{6x - 5}{11}$

22. $\dfrac{5 + x}{3} = \dfrac{x + 7}{5}$

23. $\dfrac{3x + 1}{7} = \dfrac{2x - 3}{6}$

24. $\dfrac{2x + 7}{3} = \dfrac{x - 1}{4}$

Solve each problem. In Exercises 25–31, assume all items are equally priced.

25. *Price of Candy Bars* If 16 candy bars cost $20.00, how much do 24 candy bars cost?

26. *Price of Ringtones* If 12 ringtones cost $30.00, how much do 8 ringtones cost?

27. *Price of Oil* Eight quarts of oil cost $14.00. How much do 5 quarts of oil cost?

28. *Price of Tires* Four tires cost $398.00. How much do 7 tires cost?

29. *Price of Jeans* If 9 pairs of jeans cost $121.50, find the cost of 5 pairs.

30. *Price of Shirts* If 7 shirts cost $87.50, find the cost of 11 shirts.

31. *Price of Gasoline* If 6 gallons of premium unleaded gasoline cost $17.82, how much would it cost to completely fill a 15-gallon tank?

32. *Sales Tax* If sales tax on a $16.00 DVD is $1.40, how much would the sales tax be on a $120.00 Blu-ray disc player?

33. *Distance Between Cities* The distance between Kansas City, Missouri, and Denver is 600 miles. On a certain wall map, this is represented by a length of 2.4 feet. On the map, how many feet would there be between Memphis and Philadelphia, two cities that are actually 1000 miles apart?

34. *Distance Between Cities* The distance between Singapore and Tokyo is 3300 miles. On a certain wall map, this distance is represented by 11 inches. The actual distance between Mexico City and Cairo is 7700 miles. How far apart are they on the same map?

35. *Distance Between Cities* A wall map of the United States has a distance of 8.5 inches between Memphis and Denver, two cities that are actually 1040 miles apart. The actual distance between St. Louis and Des Moines is 333 miles. How far apart are St. Louis and Des Moines on the map?

36. *Distance Between Cities* A wall map of the United States has a distance of 8.0 inches between New Orleans and Chicago, two cities that are actually 912 miles apart. The actual distance between the cities of Milwaukee and Seattle is 1940 miles. How far apart are Milwaukee and Seattle on the map?

37. *Distance Between Cities* On a world globe, the distance between Capetown and Bangkok, two cities that are actually 10,080 kilometers apart, is 12.4 inches. The actual distance between Moscow and Berlin is 1610 kilometers. How far apart are Moscow and Berlin on this globe?

38. *Distance Between Cities* On a world globe, the distance between Rio de Janeiro and Hong Kong, two cities that are actually 17,615 kilometers apart, is 21.5 inches. The actual distance between Paris and Stockholm is 1605 kilometers. How far apart are Paris and Stockholm on this globe?

39. *Cleaning Mixture* According to the directions on a bottle of Armstrong® Concentrated Floor Cleaner, for routine cleaning, $\frac{1}{4}$ cup of cleaner should be mixed with 1 gallon of warm water. How much cleaner should be mixed with $10\frac{1}{2}$ gallons of water?

40. *Cleaning Mixture* The directions on the bottle mentioned in **Exercise 39** also specify that for extra-strength cleaning, $\frac{1}{2}$ cup of cleaner should be used for each gallon of water. For extra-strength cleaning, how much cleaner should be mixed with $15\frac{1}{2}$ gallons of water?

41. Exchange Rate (Dollars and Euros) The euro is the common currency used by most European countries, including Italy. On August 15, 2009, the exchange rate between euros and U.S. dollars was 1 euro to $1.4294. Ashley went to Rome and exchanged her U.S. currency for euros, receiving 300 euros. How much in U.S. dollars did she exchange? (*Source:* www.xe.com/ucc)

42. Exchange Rate (U.S. and Mexico) If 8 U.S. dollars can be exchanged for 103.0 Mexican pesos, how many pesos, to the nearest hundredth, can be obtained for $65?

43. Tagging Fish for a Population Estimate Louisiana biologists tagged 250 fish in the oxbow lake False River on October 5. On a later date they found 7 tagged fish in a sample of 350. Estimate the total number of fish in False River to the nearest hundred.

44. Tagging Fish for a Population Estimate On May 13 researchers at Spirit Lake tagged 420 fish. When they returned a few weeks later, their sample of 500 fish contained 9 that were tagged. Give an approximation of the fish population in Spirit Lake to the nearest hundred.

Merchandise Pricing *A supermarket was surveyed to find the prices charged for items in various sizes. Find the best buy (based on price per unit) for each item.*

45. Granulated Sugar

Size	Price
4-lb	$1.79
10-lb	$4.29

46. Ground Coffee

Size	Price
15-oz	$3.43
34.5-oz	$6.98

47. Salad Dressing

Size	Price
16-oz	$2.44
32-oz	$2.98
48-oz	$4.95

48. Black Pepper

Size	Price
2-oz	$2.23
4-oz	$2.49
8-oz	$6.59

49. Vegetable Oil

Size	Price
16-oz	$1.66
32-oz	$2.59
64-oz	$4.29
128-oz	$6.49

50. Mouthwash

Size	Price
8.5-oz	$0.99
16.9-oz	$1.87
33.8-oz	$2.49
50.7-oz	$2.99

51. Tomato Ketchup

Size	Price
14-oz	$1.39
24-oz	$1.55
36-oz	$1.78
64-oz	$3.99

52. Grape Jelly

Size	Price
12-oz	$1.05
18-oz	$1.73
32-oz	$1.84
48-oz	$2.88

*Two triangles are **similar** if they have the same shape (but not necessarily the same size). Similar triangles have sides that are proportional. The figure shows two similar triangles.*

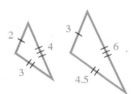

Notice that the ratios of the corresponding sides are all equal to $\frac{3}{2}$:

$$\frac{3}{2} = \frac{3}{2} \qquad \frac{4.5}{3} = \frac{3}{2} \qquad \frac{6}{4} = \frac{3}{2}.$$

If we know that two triangles are similar, we can set up a proportion to solve for the length of an unknown side. Use a proportion to find the lengths x and y given that the pair of triangles are similar.

53.

54.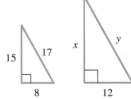

55.

56.

For the problems in Exercises 57 and 58, **(a)** *draw a sketch consisting of two right triangles, depicting the situation described, and* **(b)** *solve the problem. (Source: Guinness World Records.)*

57. **George Washington's Chair** An enlarged version of the chair used by George Washington at the Constitutional Convention casts a shadow 18 feet long at the same time a vertical pole 12 feet high casts a shadow 4 feet long. How tall is the chair?

58. **Candle at an Exhibition** One of the tallest candles ever constructed was exhibited at the 1897 Stockholm Exhibition. If it cast a shadow 5 feet long at the same time a vertical pole 32 feet high cast a shadow 2 feet long, how tall was the candle?

Consumer Price Index *The Consumer Price Index, issued by the U.S. Bureau of Labor Statistics, provides a means of determining the purchasing power of the U.S. dollar from one year to the next. Using the period from 1982 to 1984 as a measure of* 100.0, *the Consumer Price Index for selected years from 1995 to 2007 is shown here.*

Year	Consumer Price Index
1995	152.4
1997	160.5
1999	166.6
2001	177.1
2003	184.0
2005	195.3
2007	207.3

Source: Bureau of Labor Statistics.

To use the Consumer Price Index to predict a price in a particular year, we can set up a proportion and compare it with a known price in another year, as follows:

$$\frac{\text{Price in year } A}{\text{Index in year } A} = \frac{\text{Price in year } B}{\text{Index in year } B}.$$

Use the Consumer Price Index figures in the table to find the amount that would be charged for using the same amount of electricity that cost $225 in 1995. Give your answer to the nearest dollar.

59. in 1997

60. in 1999

61. in 2003

62. in 2007

Solve each problem involving variation.

63. If x varies directly as y, and $x = 27$ when $y = 6$, find x when $y = 2$.

64. If z varies directly as x, and $z = 30$ when $x = 8$, find z when $x = 4$.

65. If m varies directly as p^2, and $m = 20$ when $p = 2$, find m when $p = 5$.

66. If a varies directly as b^2, and $a = 48$ when $b = 4$, find a when $b = 7$.

67. If p varies inversely as q^2, and $p = 4$ when $q = \frac{1}{2}$, find p when $q = \frac{3}{2}$.

68. If z varies inversely as x^2, and $z = 9$ when $x = \frac{2}{3}$, find z when $x = \frac{5}{4}$.

69. **Interest on an Investment** The interest on an investment varies directly as the rate of interest. If the interest is $48 when the interest rate is 5%, find the interest when the rate is 4.2%.

70. **Area of a Triangle** For a constant base length, the area of a triangle varies directly as its height. Find the area of a triangle with a height of 6 inches, if the area is 10 square inches when the height is 4 inches.

71. **Speed of a Car** Over a specified distance, rate varies inversely with time. If a car goes a certain distance in one-half hour at 30 miles per hour, what rate is needed to go the same distance in three-fourths of an hour?

72. **Length of a Rectangle** For a constant area, the length of a rectangle varies inversely as the width. The length of a rectangle is 27 feet when the width is 10 feet. Find the length of a rectangle with the same area if the width is 18 feet.

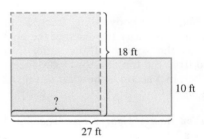

73. **Weight of a Moose** The weight of an object on the moon varies directly as the weight of the object on Earth. According to *Guinness World Records*, "Shad," a goat owned by a couple in California, weighs 352 pounds. Shad would weigh about 59 pounds on the moon. A bull moose weighing 1800 pounds was shot in Canada. How much would the moose have weighed on the moon?

74. **Voyage in a Paddleboat** According to *Guinness World Records*, the longest recorded voyage in a paddle boat is 2226 miles in 103 days by the foot power of two boaters down the Mississippi River. Assuming a constant rate, how far would they have gone if they had traveled 120 days? (Distance varies directly as time.)

75. *Pressure Exerted by a Liquid* The pressure exerted by a certain liquid at a given point varies directly as the depth of the point beneath the surface of the liquid. The pressure at a depth of 10 feet is 50 pounds per square inch. What is the pressure at a depth of 20 feet?

76. *Pressure of a Gas in a Container* If the volume is constant, the pressure of a gas in a container varies directly as the temperature. (Temperature must be measured in *Kelvin* (K), a unit of measurement used in physics.) If the pressure is 5 pounds per square inch at a temperature of 200 degrees K, what is the pressure at a temperature of 300 degrees K?

77. *Pressure of a Gas in a Container* If the temperature is constant, the pressure of a gas in a container varies inversely as the volume of the container. If the pressure is 10 pounds per square foot in a container with volume 3 cubic feet, what is the pressure in a container with volume 1.5 cubic feet?

78. *Force Required to Compress a Spring* The force required to compress a spring varies directly as the change in the length of the spring. If a force of 12 pounds is required to compress a certain spring 3 inches, how much force is required to compress the spring 5 inches?

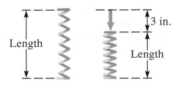

79. *Falling Body* For a body falling freely from rest (disregarding air resistance), the distance the body falls varies directly as the square of the time. If an object is dropped from the top of a tower 400 feet high and hits the ground in 5 seconds, how far did it fall in the first 3 seconds?

80. *Illumination from a Light Source* The illumination produced by a light source varies inversely as the square of the distance from the source. If the illumination produced 4 feet from a light source is 75 foot-candles, find the illumination produced 9 feet from the same source.

81. *Volume of Gas* Natural gas provides 35.8% of U.S. energy. (*Source*: U.S. Energy Department.) The volume of gas varies inversely as the pressure and directly as the temperature. If a certain gas occupies a volume of 1.3 liters at 300 K and a pressure of 18 newtons, find the volume at 340 K and a pressure of 24 newtons.

82. *Skidding Car* The force needed to keep a car from skidding on a curve varies inversely as the radius of the curve and jointly as the weight of the car and the square of the rate. If 242 pounds of force keep a 2000-pound car from skidding on a curve of radius 500 feet at 30 miles per hour, what force would keep the same car from skidding on a curve of radius 750 feet at 50 miles per hour?

83. *Load Supported by a Column* The maximum load that a cylindrical column with a circular cross section can hold varies directly as the fourth power of the diameter of the cross section and inversely as the square of the height. A 9-meter column 1 meter in diameter will support 8 metric tons. How many metric tons can be supported by a column 12 meters high and $\frac{2}{3}$ meter in diameter?

Load = 8 metric tons

Fish Weight-Estimation Girth is the distance around the body of a fish. (*Source:* Sacramento Bee, *November 9, 2000.*)

84. The weight of a bass varies jointly as its girth and the square of its length. A prize-winning bass weighed in at 22.7 pounds and measured 36 inches long with a 21-inch girth. How much would a bass 28 inches long with an 18-inch girth weigh?

85. The weight of a trout varies jointly as its length and the square of its girth. One angler caught a trout that weighed 10.5 pounds and measured 26 inches long with an 18-inch girth. Find the weight of a trout that is 22 inches long with a 15-inch girth.

86. Bill Veeck was the owner of several major league base-ball teams in the 1950s and 1960s. He was known to often sit in the stands and enjoy games with his paying customers. Here is a quote attributed to him:

> *"I have discovered in 20 years of moving around a ballpark, that the knowledge of the game is usually in inverse proportion to the price of the seats."*

Explain in your own words the meaning of this statement. (To prove his point, Veeck once allowed the fans—as shown in the photo—to vote on managerial decisions.)

7.5 PROPERTIES OF EXPONENTS AND SCIENTIFIC NOTATION

Exponents and Exponential Expressions • The Product Rule • Zero and Negative Exponents • The Quotient Rule • The Power Rules • Summary of Rules for Exponents • Scientific Notation

The term **googol**, meaning 10^{100}, was coined by Professor Edward Kasner of Columbia University. A googol is made up of a 1 with one hundred zeros following it. This number exceeds the estimated number of electrons in the universe, which is 10^{79}.

The Web search engine Google is named after a googol. Sergey Brin, president and cofounder of Google, Inc., was a mathematics major. He chose the name Google to describe the vast reach of this search engine. (*Source: The Gazette*, March 2, 2001.) The term "googling" is now part of the English language.

If a googol isn't big enough for you, try a **googolplex**:

googolplex $= 10^{\text{googol}}$.

Exponents and Exponential Expressions

Exponents are used to write products of repeated factors. For example, the product $3 \cdot 3 \cdot 3 \cdot 3$ is written

$$\underbrace{3 \cdot 3 \cdot 3 \cdot 3}_{\text{4 factors of 3}} = 3^{\underset{\text{Base}}{4}}. \longleftarrow \text{Exponent}$$

The number 4 shows that 3 appears as a factor four times. The number 4 is the **exponent** and 3 is the **base.** The quantity 3^4 is called an **exponential expression.** Read 3^4 as "3 to the fourth power," or "3 to the fourth." Multiplying out the four 3s gives 81.

$$3^4 = 3 \cdot 3 \cdot 3 \cdot 3 = 81$$

Exponential Expression

If a is a real number and n is a natural number, then the exponential expression a^n is defined as

$$a^n = \underbrace{a \cdot a \cdot a \cdot \ldots \cdot a.}_{n \text{ factors of } a}$$

The number a is the *base* and n is the *exponent.*

▮▮ **EXAMPLE 1** Evaluating Exponential Expressions

Evaluate each exponential expression.

(a) 7^2 **(b)** 5^3 **(c)** $(-2)^4$ **(d)** $(-2)^5$ **(e)** 5^1

SOLUTION $7^2 = 7 \cdot 7, \text{ not } 7 \cdot 2.$

(a) $7^2 = 7 \cdot 7 = 49$ Read 7^2 as "7 squared."

(b) $5^3 = 5 \cdot 5 \cdot 5 = 125$ Read 5^3 as "5 cubed."

(c) $(-2)^4 = (-2)(-2)(-2)(-2) = 16$

(d) $(-2)^5 = (-2)(-2)(-2)(-2)(-2) = -32$

(e) $5^1 = 5$ ▮▮▮

In the exponential expression $3z^7$, the base of the exponent 7 is z, *not* $3z$.

$$3z^7 = 3 \cdot z \cdot z \cdot z \cdot z \cdot z \cdot z \cdot z \qquad \text{Base is } z.$$

$$(3z)^7 = (3z)(3z)(3z)(3z)(3z)(3z)(3z) \qquad \text{Base is } 3z.$$

For $(-2)^6$, the parentheses around -2 indicate that the base is -2.

$$(-2)^6 = (-2)(-2)(-2)(-2)(-2)(-2) = 64 \qquad \text{Base is } -2.$$

$(\text{-}2)^6$
                                    64
$\text{-}2^6$
                                    $^\text{-}64$

This screen supports the discussion
preceding **Example 2.**

In the expression -2^6, the base is 2, *not* -2. The $-$ sign tells us to find the negative, or additive inverse, of 2^6. It acts as a symbol for the factor -1.

$$-2^6 = -(2 \cdot 2 \cdot 2 \cdot 2 \cdot 2 \cdot 2) = -64 \quad \text{Base is 2.}$$

Therefore, since $64 \neq -64$, $(-2)^6 \neq -2^6$.

▌▌ EXAMPLE 2 Evaluating Exponential Expressions

Evaluate each exponential expression.

(a) -4^2 **(b)** -8^4 **(c)** $(-8)^4$

SOLUTION

(a) $-4^2 = -(4 \cdot 4) = -16$

(b) $-8^4 = -(8 \cdot 8 \cdot 8 \cdot 8) = -4096$

(c) $(-8)^4 = (-8)(-8)(-8)(-8) = 4096$

Note how parts (b) and (c) differ.   ■■■

The Product Rule

Consider the product $2^5 \cdot 2^3$, which can be simplified as follows.

$$2^5 \cdot 2^3 = \overbrace{(2 \cdot 2 \cdot 2 \cdot 2 \cdot 2)(2 \cdot 2 \cdot 2)}^{5 + 3 = 8} = 2^8$$

This result—products of exponential expressions with the same base are found by adding exponents—is generalized as the **product rule for exponents.**

> **Product Rule for Exponents**
>
> If m and n are natural numbers and a is any real number, then
>
> $$a^m \cdot a^n = a^{m+n}.$$

▌▌ EXAMPLE 3 Applying the Product Rule

Apply the product rule for exponents in each case.

(a) $3^4 \cdot 3^7$ **(b)** $5^3 \cdot 5$ **(c)** $y^3 \cdot y^8 \cdot y^2$

(d) $(5y^2)(-3y^4)$ **(e)** $(7p^3q)(2p^5q^2)$

SOLUTION

(a) $3^4 \cdot 3^7 = 3^{4+7} = 3^{11}$ **(b)** $5^3 \cdot 5 = 5^3 \cdot 5^1 = 5^{3+1} = 5^4$

> Do not make the error of writing
> $3 \cdot 3 = 9$ as the base.

(c) $y^3 \cdot y^8 \cdot y^2 = y^{3+8+2} = y^{13}$ Product rule extended to three powers

(d) $(5y^2)(-3y^4) = 5(-3)y^2y^4$ Associative and commutative properties

$\qquad\qquad = -15y^{2+4}$ Multiply; product rule

$\qquad\qquad = -15y^6$ Add.

(e) $(7p^3q)(2p^5q^2) = 7(2)p^3p^5qq^2$

$\qquad\qquad = 14p^8q^3$ ■■■

Zero and Negative Exponents

We now consider 0 as an exponent. How can we define an expression such as 4^0 so that it is consistent with the product rule? By the product rule, we should have

$$4^2 \cdot 4^0 = 4^{2+0} = 4^2.$$

For the product rule to hold true, 4^0 must equal 1. This leads to the definition of a^0 for any nonzero real number a.

> **Zero Exponent**
>
> If a is any nonzero real number, then $\quad a^0 = 1.$

The expression 0^0 **is undefined.***

▮▮ **EXAMPLE 4** Applying the Definition of Zero Exponent

Evaluate each expression.

(a) 12^0 **(b)** $(-6)^0$ **(c)** -6^0

(d) $5^0 + 12^0$ **(e)** $(8k)^0, \quad k \neq 0$

SOLUTION

(a) $12^0 = 1$ **(b)** $(-6)^0 = 1$ Base is -6.

(c) $-6^0 = -(6^0) = -1$ Base is 6.   **(d)** $5^0 + 12^0 = 1 + 1 = 2$

(e) $(8k)^0 = 1, \quad k \neq 0$ ▮▮▮

We now define a negative exponent. Using the product rule again,

$$8^2 \cdot 8^{-2} = 8^{2+(-2)} = 8^0 = 1.$$

This indicates that 8^{-2} is the reciprocal of 8^2. But $\frac{1}{8^2}$ is the reciprocal of 8^2, and a number can have only one reciprocal. Therefore, it is reasonable to conclude that $8^{-2} = \frac{1}{8^2}$. We can generalize and make the following definition.

> **Negative Exponent**
>
> For any natural number n and any nonzero real number a,
>
> $$a^{-n} = \frac{1}{a^n}.$$

With this definition, and the ones given earlier for positive and zero exponents, the expression a^n is meaningful for any integer exponent n and any nonzero real number a.

▮▮ **EXAMPLE 5** Applying the Definition of Negative Exponents

Write the following expressions with only positive exponents. Assume that all variables represent nonzero real numbers.

(a) 2^{-3} **(b)** 3^{-2} **(c)** 6^{-1} **(d)** $(5z)^{-3}$

(e) $5z^{-3}$ **(f)** $(5z^2)^{-3}$ **(g)** $-m^{-2}$ **(h)** $(-m)^{-4}$

---

*In advanced studies, 0^0 is called an *indeterminate form.*

(-6)⁰

-6⁰   1

            -1

5⁰+12⁰

            2

This screen supports the results in parts (b), (c), and (d) of **Example 4.**

SOLUTION

(a) $2^{-3} = \dfrac{1}{2^3} = \dfrac{1}{8}$

(b) $3^{-2} = \dfrac{1}{3^2} = \dfrac{1}{9}$

(c) $6^{-1} = \dfrac{1}{6^1} = \dfrac{1}{6}$

(d) $(5z)^{-3} = \dfrac{1}{(5z)^3}$ Base is 5z.

(e) $5z^{-3} = 5\left(\dfrac{1}{z^3}\right) = \dfrac{5}{z^3}$ Base is z.

(f) $(5z^2)^{-3} = \dfrac{1}{(5z^2)^3}$

(g) $-m^{-2} = -\dfrac{1}{m^2}$

(h) $(-m)^{-4} = \dfrac{1}{(-m)^4}$ ▐▐▐

▌▌ **EXAMPLE 6** Evaluating Exponential Expressions

Evaluate each expression.

(a) $3^{-1} + 4^{-1}$ **(b)** $5^{-1} - 2^{-1}$ **(c)** $\dfrac{1}{2^{-3}}$ **(d)** $\dfrac{2^{-3}}{3^{-2}}$

SOLUTION

(a) $3^{-1} + 4^{-1} = \dfrac{1}{3} + \dfrac{1}{4} = \dfrac{4}{12} + \dfrac{3}{12} = \dfrac{7}{12}$ $3^{-1} = \frac{1}{3};\ 4^{-1} = \frac{1}{4}$

(b) $5^{-1} - 2^{-1} = \dfrac{1}{5} - \dfrac{1}{2} = \dfrac{2}{10} - \dfrac{5}{10} = -\dfrac{3}{10}$

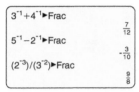

This screen supports the results in parts (a), (b), and (d) of **Example 6.**

(c) $\dfrac{1}{2^{-3}} = \dfrac{1}{\dfrac{1}{2^3}} = 1 \div \dfrac{1}{2^3} = 1 \cdot \dfrac{2^3}{1} = 2^3 = 8$

> To divide, multiply by the reciprocal of the divisor.

(d) $\dfrac{2^{-3}}{3^{-2}} = \dfrac{\dfrac{1}{2^3}}{\dfrac{1}{3^2}} = \dfrac{1}{2^3} \div \dfrac{1}{3^2} = \dfrac{1}{2^3} \cdot \dfrac{3^2}{1} = \dfrac{3^2}{2^3} = \dfrac{9}{8}$ ▐▐▐

Parts (c) and (d) of **Example 6** suggest the following generalizations.

Special Rules for Negative Exponents

If $a \neq 0$ and $b \neq 0$, then $\dfrac{1}{a^{-n}} = a^n$ and $\dfrac{a^{-n}}{b^{-m}} = \dfrac{b^m}{a^n}.$

The Quotient Rule

A quotient, such as $\dfrac{a^8}{a^3}$, can be simplified in much the same way as a product. (Assume that the denominator is not 0.) Using the definition of an exponent,

$$\frac{a^8}{a^3} = \frac{a \cdot a \cdot a \cdot a \cdot a \cdot a \cdot a \cdot a}{a \cdot a \cdot a} = a \cdot a \cdot a \cdot a \cdot a = a^5.$$

Notice that $8 - 3 = 5$. In the same way,

$$\frac{a^3}{a^8} = \frac{a \cdot a \cdot a}{a \cdot a \cdot a \cdot a \cdot a \cdot a \cdot a \cdot a} = \frac{1}{a^5} = a^{-5}.$$

Here, $3 - 8 = -5$. These examples suggest the **quotient rule for exponents.**

> ### Quotient Rule for Exponents
>
> If a is any nonzero real number and m and n are integers, then
>
> $$\frac{a^m}{a^n} = a^{m-n}.$$

▮▮ EXAMPLE 7 Applying the Quotient Rule

Apply the quotient rule for exponents in each case. Assume that all variables represent nonzero real numbers.

(a) $\dfrac{3^7}{3^2}$ **(b)** $\dfrac{p^6}{p^2}$ **(c)** $\dfrac{12^{10}}{12^9}$ **(d)** $\dfrac{7^4}{7^6}$ **(e)** $\dfrac{k^7}{k^{12}}$

SOLUTION

Numerator exponent

Denominator exponent

(a) $\dfrac{3^7}{3^2} = 3^{7-2} = 3^5$ **(b)** $\dfrac{p^6}{p^2} = p^{6-2} = p^4$

Subtract.

(c) $\dfrac{12^{10}}{12^9} = 12^{10-9} = 12^1 = 12$ **(d)** $\dfrac{7^4}{7^6} = 7^{4-6} = 7^{-2} = \dfrac{1}{7^2}$

(e) $\dfrac{k^7}{k^{12}} = k^{7-12} = k^{-5} = \dfrac{1}{k^5}$

Use the definition of negative exponent.

▮▮▮

▮▮ EXAMPLE 8 Applying the Quotient Rule

Write each quotient using only positive exponents. Assume that all variables represent nonzero real numbers.

(a) $\dfrac{2^7}{2^{-3}}$ **(b)** $\dfrac{8^{-2}}{8^5}$ **(c)** $\dfrac{6^{-5}}{6^{-2}}$ **(d)** $\dfrac{4}{4^{-1}}$ **(e)** $\dfrac{z^{-5}}{z^{-8}}$

SOLUTION

Be careful when subtracting a negative number.

(a) $\dfrac{2^7}{2^{-3}} = 2^{7-(-3)} = 2^{10}$ **(b)** $\dfrac{8^{-2}}{8^5} = 8^{-2-5} = 8^{-7} = \dfrac{1}{8^7}$

(c) $\dfrac{6^{-5}}{6^{-2}} = 6^{-5-(-2)} = 6^{-3} = \dfrac{1}{6^3}$ **(d)** $\dfrac{4}{4^{-1}} = \dfrac{4^1}{4^{-1}} = 4^{1-(-1)} = 4^2$

(e) $\dfrac{z^{-5}}{z^{-8}} = z^{-5-(-8)} = z^3$

▮▮▮

$(2^7)/(2^{-3}) = 2^{10}$

$\qquad\qquad 1$

$4/4^{-1} = 4^2$

$\qquad\qquad 1$

This screen supports the results in parts (a) and (d) of **Example 8.**

The Power Rules

The expression $(3^4)^2$ can be simplified as

$$(3^4)^2 = 3^4 \cdot 3^4 = 3^{4+4} = 3^8, \quad \text{where } 4 \cdot 2 = 8.$$

This example suggests the first of the **power rules for exponents.** The other two parts can be demonstrated with similar examples.

> **Power Rules for Exponents**
>
> If a and b are real numbers, and m and n are integers, then
>
> $$(a^m)^n = a^{mn}, \quad (ab)^m = a^m b^m, \quad \text{and} \quad \left(\frac{a}{b}\right)^m = \frac{a^m}{b^m} \quad (b \neq 0).$$

In the statements of rules for exponents, we always assume that zero never appears to a negative power or to the power zero.

▌▌ **EXAMPLE 9** Applying the Power Rules

Use one or more power rules in each case. Assume that all variables represent nonzero real numbers.

(a) $(p^8)^3$ **(b)** $\left(\frac{2}{3}\right)^4$ **(c)** $(3y)^4$ **(d)** $(6p^7)^2$ **(e)** $\left(\frac{-2m^5}{z}\right)^3$

SOLUTION

(a) $(p^8)^3 = p^{8 \cdot 3} = p^{24}$ **(b)** $\left(\frac{2}{3}\right)^4 = \frac{2^4}{3^4} = \frac{16}{81}$

(c) $(3y)^4 = 3^4 y^4 = 81y^4$ **(d)** $(6p^7)^2 = 6^2 p^{7 \cdot 2} = 6^2 p^{14} = 36p^{14}$

(e) $\left(\frac{-2m^5}{z}\right)^3 = \frac{(-2)^3 m^{5 \cdot 3}}{z^3} = \frac{(-2)^3 m^{15}}{z^3} = \frac{-8m^{15}}{z^3}$ ▮▮▮

Notice that

$$6^{-3} = \left(\frac{1}{6}\right)^3 = \frac{1}{216} \quad \text{and} \quad \left(\frac{2}{3}\right)^{-2} = \left(\frac{3}{2}\right)^2 = \frac{9}{4}.$$

These are examples of two special rules for negative exponents.

> **Special Rules for Negative Exponents**
>
> If $a \neq 0$ and $b \neq 0$ and n is an integer, then
>
> $$a^{-n} = \left(\frac{1}{a}\right)^n \quad \text{and} \quad \left(\frac{a}{b}\right)^{-n} = \left(\frac{b}{a}\right)^n.$$

▌▌ **EXAMPLE 10** Applying Special Rules for Negative Exponents

Write each expression with only positive exponents, and then evaluate.

(a) $\left(\frac{3}{7}\right)^{-2}$ **(b)** $\left(\frac{4}{5}\right)^{-3}$

SOLUTION

(a) $\left(\frac{3}{7}\right)^{-2} = \left(\frac{7}{3}\right)^2 = \frac{49}{9}$ **(b)** $\left(\frac{4}{5}\right)^{-3} = \left(\frac{5}{4}\right)^3 = \frac{125}{64}$ ▮▮▮

(3/7)⁻²▶Frac
              $\frac{49}{9}$
(4/5)⁻³▶Frac
              $\frac{125}{64}$

This screen supports the results of
Example 10.

Summary of Rules for Exponents

The definitions and rules of this section are summarized here.

Definitions and Rules for Exponents

For all integers m and n and all real numbers a and b,

Product Rule	$a^m \cdot a^n = a^{m+n}$
Quotient Rule	$\dfrac{a^m}{a^n} = a^{m-n} \quad (a \neq 0)$
Zero Exponent	$a^0 = 1 \quad (a \neq 0)$
Negative Exponent	$a^{-n} = \dfrac{1}{a^n} \quad (a \neq 0)$
Power Rules	$(a^m)^n = a^{mn} \qquad (ab)^m = a^m b^m$
	$\left(\dfrac{a}{b}\right)^m = \dfrac{a^m}{b^m} \quad (b \neq 0)$
Special Rules for Negative Exponents	$\dfrac{1}{a^{-n}} = a^n \ (a \neq 0) \quad \dfrac{a^{-n}}{b^{-m}} = \dfrac{b^m}{a^n} \quad (a, b \neq 0)$
	$a^{-n} = \left(\dfrac{1}{a}\right)^n \quad (a \neq 0)$
	$\left(\dfrac{a}{b}\right)^{-n} = \left(\dfrac{b}{a}\right)^n \quad (a, b \neq 0).$

■ **EXAMPLE 11** Writing Expressions with No Negative Exponents

Simplify each expression so that no negative exponents appear in the final result. Assume that all variables represent nonzero real numbers.

(a) $3^2 \cdot 3^{-5}$ **(b)** $x^{-3} \cdot x^{-4} \cdot x^2$ **(c)** $(4^{-2})^{-5}$

(d) $(x^{-4})^6$ **(e)** $\dfrac{x^{-4} y^2}{x^2 y^{-5}}$ **(f)** $(2^3 x^{-2})^{-2}$

SOLUTION

(a) $3^2 \cdot 3^{-5} = 3^{2+(-5)} = 3^{-3} = \dfrac{1}{3^3}, \quad \text{or} \quad \dfrac{1}{27}$

(b) $x^{-3} \cdot x^{-4} \cdot x^2 = x^{-3+(-4)+2} = x^{-5} = \dfrac{1}{x^5}$

(c) $(4^{-2})^{-5} = 4^{-2(-5)} = 4^{10}$ **(d)** $(x^{-4})^6 = x^{(-4)6} = x^{-24} = \dfrac{1}{x^{24}}$

(e) $\dfrac{x^{-4}y^2}{x^2 y^{-5}} = \dfrac{x^{-4}}{x^2} \cdot \dfrac{y^2}{y^{-5}}$ **(f)** $(2^3 x^{-2})^{-2} = (2^3)^{-2} \cdot (x^{-2})^{-2}$

$\qquad = x^{-4-2} \cdot y^{2-(-5)}$ $= 2^{-6} x^4$

$\qquad = x^{-6} y^7$ $= \dfrac{x^4}{2^6}, \quad \text{or} \quad \dfrac{x^4}{64}$

$\qquad = \dfrac{y^7}{x^6}$

■■■

Scientific Notation

Many of the numbers that occur in science are very large or very small. Writing these numbers is simplified by using *scientific notation*.

Scientific Notation

A number is written in **scientific notation** when it is expressed in the form

$$a \times 10^n, \quad \text{where } 1 \le |a| < 10, \text{ and } n \text{ is an integer.}$$

In the episode "Court-Martial" from the original *Star Trek* television series, Captain Kirk makes this statement during a scene on the bridge of the Enterprise:

Gentlemen, this computer has an auditory sensor. It can, in effect, hear sounds. By installing a booster we can increase that capability on an order of one to the fourth power. The computer should be able to bring us every sound occurring on the ship.

Can you identify the error in Kirk's statement? What do you think he might have really meant? (Think about scientific notation.)

Scientific notation requires that the number be written as a product of a number between 1 and 10 (or −1 and −10) and some integer power of 10. (1 and −1 are allowed as values of a, but 10 and −10 are not.) For example,

$$8000 = 8 \cdot 1000 = 8 \cdot 10^3, \quad \text{or} \quad 8 \times 10^3. \longleftarrow \text{Scientific notation}$$

In scientific notation, it is customary to use × instead of a multiplication dot.

The steps involved in writing a number in scientific notation follow. (If the number is negative, ignore the negative sign, go through these steps, and then attach a negative sign to the result.)

Converting a Positive Number to Scientific Notation

Step 1 **Position the decimal point.** Place a caret, ∧, to the right of the first nonzero digit, where the decimal point will be placed.

Step 2 **Determine the numeral for the exponent.** Count the number of digits from the decimal point to the caret. This number gives the absolute value of the exponent on 10.

Step 3 **Determine the sign for the exponent.** Decide whether multiplying by 10^n should make the result of Step 1 larger or smaller. The exponent should be positive to make the result larger. It should be negative to make the result smaller.

It is helpful to remember that for $n \ge 1$, $10^{-n} < 1$ and $10^n \ge 10$.

▮▮ EXAMPLE 12 Converting to Scientific Notation

Convert each number from standard notation to scientific notation.

(a) 8,200,000   **(b)** 0.000072

SOLUTION

(a) Place a caret to the right of the 8 (the first nonzero digit) to mark the new location of the decimal point.

$$8_\wedge 200,000$$

Count from the decimal point, which is understood to be after the last 0, to the caret.

$$8_\wedge 200,000. \longleftarrow \text{Decimal point}$$
$$\text{Count 6 places.}$$

Because the number 8.2 is to be made larger, the exponent on 10 is positive.

$$8,200,000 = 8.2 \times 10^6$$

8200000
          8.2E6
.000072
          7.2E⁻5

If a graphing calculator is set in scientific notation mode, it will give results as shown here. E6 means "times 10^6" and E−5 means "times 10^{-5}". Compare to the results of **Example 12.**

(b)   0.00007,2   Count from left to right.
                                          ‿‿‿‿↗
                                          5 places

Since the number 7.2 is to be made smaller, the exponent on 10 is negative.

$$0.000072 = 7.2 \times 10^{-5}$$ ▌▌▌

Converting a Positive Number from Scientific Notation to Standard Notation

Multiplying a positive number by a positive power of 10 makes the number larger, so move the decimal point to the right if n is positive in 10^n.

Multiplying a positive number by a negative power of 10 makes the number smaller, so move the decimal point to the left if n is negative.

If n is zero, do not move the decimal point.

▌▌ **EXAMPLE 13** Converting from Scientific Notation

Convert each number from scientific notation to standard notation.

(a) 6.93×10^5 **(b)** 4.7×10^{-6} **(c)** -1.083×10^0

SOLUTION

(a) $6.93 \times 10^5 = 6.93000$ Attach 0s as necessary.
                            ‿‿‿‿↗
                            5 places

The decimal point was moved 5 places to the right.

$$6.93 \times 10^5 = 693{,}000$$

(b) $4.7 \times 10^{-6} = 000004.7$ Attach 0s as necessary.
                              ↙‿‿‿‿‿
                              6 places

The decimal point was moved 6 places to the left.

$$4.7 \times 10^{-6} = 0.0000047$$

(c) $-1.083 \times 10^0 = -1.083$ ▌▌▌

▌▌ **EXAMPLE 14** Using Scientific Notation in Computation

Evaluate $\dfrac{1{,}920{,}000 \times 0.0015}{0.000032 \times 45{,}000}$ by using scientific notation.

SOLUTION

$$\frac{1{,}920{,}000 \times 0.0015}{0.000032 \times 45{,}000} = \frac{1.92 \times 10^6 \times 1.5 \times 10^{-3}}{3.2 \times 10^{-5} \times 4.5 \times 10^4}$$ Express all numbers in scientific notation.

$$= \frac{1.92 \times 1.5 \times 10^6 \times 10^{-3}}{3.2 \times 4.5 \times 10^{-5} \times 10^4}$$ Commutative and associative properties

$$= \frac{1.92 \times 1.5}{3.2 \times 4.5} \times 10^4$$ Product and quotient rules

Don't stop here. $= 0.2 \times 10^4$ Simplify.

$$= (2 \times 10^{-1}) \times 10^4$$ Write 0.2 using scientific notation.

$$= 2 \times 10^3, \text{ or } 2000$$ Associative property; product rule; multiply.   ▌▌▌

EXAMPLE 15 Using Scientific Notation in an Application

In 1990, the national health care expenditure in the United States was \$714.0 billion. By 2005, this figure had risen by a factor of 2.8; that is, it almost tripled in 15 years. (*Source:* U.S. Centers for Medicare & Medicaid Services.)

(a) Write the 1990 health care expenditure using scientific notation.

(b) What was the expenditure in 2005?

SOLUTION

(a)   714.0 billion

$$= 714.0 \times 10^9 \qquad \text{1 billion} = 10^9$$

$$= (7.140 \times 10^2) \times 10^9 \quad \text{Write 714.0 in scientific notation.}$$

$$= 7.140 \times 10^{11} \qquad \text{Product rule}$$

In 1990, the expenditure was \$7.140 × 10^{11}.

(b) Multiply the result in part (a) by 2.8.

$$(7.140 \times 10^{11}) \times 2.8$$

$$= (2.8 \times 7.140) \times 10^{11} \qquad \text{Commutative and associative properties}$$

$$= 19.992 \times 10^{11} \qquad \text{Round to three decimal places.}$$

$$= (1.9992 \times 10^1) \times 10^{11} \quad \text{Write 19.992 in scientific notation.}$$

$$= 1.9992 \times 10^{12} \qquad \text{Associative property; product rule; multiply.}$$

The 2005 expenditure was about \$1,999,200,000,000 (almost \$2 trillion).   ■■■

7.5 EXERCISES

Match the exponential expressions in Exercises 1–6 with their equivalent expressions in choices A–F below. Choices may be used once, more than once, or not at all.

1. $\left(\dfrac{5}{3}\right)^2$ **2.** $\left(\dfrac{3}{5}\right)^2$ **3.** $\left(-\dfrac{3}{5}\right)^{-2}$

4. $\left(-\dfrac{5}{3}\right)^{-2}$ **5.** $-\left(-\dfrac{3}{5}\right)^2$ **6.** $-\left(-\dfrac{5}{3}\right)^2$

A. $\dfrac{25}{9}$ **B.** $-\dfrac{25}{9}$ **C.** $\dfrac{9}{25}$

D. $-\dfrac{9}{25}$ **E.** none of these   **F.** all of these

Evaluate each exponential expression.

7. 5^4 **8.** 10^3

9. $(-2)^5$ **10.** $(-5)^4$

11. -2^3 **12.** -3^2

13. $-(-3)^4$ **14.** $-(-5)^2$

15. 7^{-2} **16.** 4^{-1}

17. -7^{-2} **18.** -4^{-1}

19. $\dfrac{2}{(-4)^{-3}}$ **20.** $\dfrac{2^{-3}}{3^{-2}}$

21. $\dfrac{5^{-1}}{4^{-2}}$ **22.** $\left(\dfrac{1}{2}\right)^{-3}$

23. $\left(\dfrac{1}{5}\right)^{-3}$ **24.** $\left(\dfrac{2}{3}\right)^{-2}$

25. $\left(\dfrac{4}{5}\right)^{-2}$ **26.** $3^{-1} + 2^{-1}$

27. $4^{-1} + 5^{-1}$ **28.** 8^0

29. 12^0 **30.** $(-23)^0$

31. $(-4)^0$ **32.** -2^0

33. $3^0 - 4^0$ **34.** $-8^0 - 7^0$

35. In order to raise a fraction to a negative power, we may change the fraction to its _____ and change the exponent to the _____ _____ of the original exponent.

36. Explain in your own words how to raise a power to a power.

37. Which one of the following is correct?

A. $-\dfrac{3}{4} = \left(\dfrac{3}{4}\right)^{-1}$ **B.** $\dfrac{3^{-1}}{4^{-1}} = \left(\dfrac{4}{3}\right)^{-1}$

C. $\dfrac{3^{-1}}{4} = \dfrac{3}{4^{-1}}$ **D.** $\dfrac{3^{-1}}{4^{-1}} = \left(\dfrac{3}{4}\right)^{-1}$

38. Which one of the following is incorrect?

A. $(3r)^{-2} = 3^{-2}r^{-2}$ **B.** $3r^{-2} = (3r)^{-2}$

C. $(3r)^{-2} = \dfrac{1}{(3r)^2}$ **D.** $(3r)^{-2} = \dfrac{r^{-2}}{9}$

Use the product, quotient, and power rules to simplify each expression. Write answers with only positive exponents. Assume that all variables represent nonzero real numbers.

39. $x^{12} \cdot x^4$ **40.** $\dfrac{x^{12}}{x^4}$

41. $\dfrac{5^{17}}{5^{16}}$ **42.** $\dfrac{3^{12}}{3^{13}}$

43. $\dfrac{3^{-5}}{3^{-2}}$ **44.** $\dfrac{2^{-4}}{2^{-3}}$

45. $\dfrac{9^{-1}}{9}$ **46.** $\dfrac{12}{12^{-1}}$

47. $t^5 t^{-12}$ **48.** $p^5 p^{-6}$

49. $(3x)^2$ **50.** $(-2x^{-2})^2$

51. $a^{-3}a^2a^{-4}$ **52.** $k^{-5}k^{-3}k^4$

53. $\dfrac{x^7}{x^{-4}}$ **54.** $\dfrac{p^{-3}}{p^5}$

55. $\dfrac{r^3 r^{-4}}{r^{-2}r^{-5}}$ **56.** $\dfrac{z^{-4}z^{-2}}{z^3 z^{-1}}$

57. $7k^2(-2k)(4k^{-5})$ **58.** $3a^2(-5a^{-6})(-2a)$

59. $(z^3)^{-2}z^2$ **60.** $(p^{-1})^3 p^{-4}$

61. $-3r^{-1}(r^{-3})^2$ **62.** $2(y^{-3})^4(y^6)$

63. $(3a^{-2})^3(a^3)^{-4}$ **64.** $(m^5)^{-2}(3m^{-2})^3$

65. $(x^{-5}y^2)^{-1}$ **66.** $(a^{-3}b^{-5})^2$

67. Which one of the following does *not* represent the reciprocal of x $(x \neq 0)$?

A. x^{-1} **B.** $\dfrac{1}{x}$ **C.** $\left(\dfrac{1}{x^{-1}}\right)^{-1}$ **D.** $-x$

68. Which one of the following is *not* in scientific notation?

A. 6.02×10^{23} **B.** 14×10^{-6}
C. 1.4×10^{-5} **D.** 3.8×10^3

Convert each number from standard notation to scientific notation.

69. 230   **70.** 46,500

71. 0.02   **72.** 0.0051

Convert each number from scientific notation to standard notation.

73. 6.5×10^3 **74.** 2.317×10^5

75. 1.52×10^{-2} **76.** 1.63×10^{-4}

Use scientific notation to perform each of the following computations. Leave the answers in scientific notation.

77. $\dfrac{0.002 \times 3900}{0.000013}$ **78.** $\dfrac{0.009 \times 600}{0.02}$

79. $\dfrac{0.0004 \times 56,000}{0.000112}$ **80.** $\dfrac{0.018 \times 20,000}{300 \times 0.0004}$

81. $\dfrac{840,000 \times 0.03}{0.00021 \times 600}$ **82.** $\dfrac{28 \times 0.0045}{140 \times 1500}$

In Exercises 83–86, write the boldface numbers in scientific notation.

83. U.S. Budget The U.S. budget first passed **$1,000,000,000** in 1917. Seventy years later in 1987 it exceeded **$1,000,000,000,000** for the first time. President George W. Bush's budget request for fiscal 2009 was **$3,100,000,000,000.** If stacked in dollar bills, this amount would stretch **210,385** mi, almost 90% of the distance to the moon. (*Source: The New York Times.*)

84. U.S. Area By area, the largest of the fifty United States is Alaska, with land area of about **365,482,000** acres, while the smallest is Rhode Island, with land area of about **677,000** acres. The total land area of the United States is about **2,271,343,000** acres. (*Source: World Almanac and Book of Facts.*)

85. NASA Budget The budget for the Operating Plan in 2010 for the National Aeronautics and Space Administration was **$18.69 billion.** Write this amount in scientific notation. (*Source*: www.nasa.gov)

86. *Motor Vehicle Registrations* In 2007, there were about **247,264,600** motor vehicle registrations in the United States. Write this number in scientific notation. (*Source: U.S. Federal Highway Administration.*)

Astronomy Data *Each of the following statements (Exercises 87–90) comes from* Astronomy! A Brief Edition *by James B. Kaler (Addison-Wesley). If the number in the statement is in scientific notation, write it in standard notation without using exponents. If the number is in standard notation, write it in scientific notation.*

87. Multiplying this view over the whole sky yields a galaxy count of more than **10 billion.** (page 496)

88. The circumference of the solar orbit is . . . about **4.7 billion** km . . . . (in reference to the orbit of Jupiter, page 395)

89. The solar luminosity requires that 2×10^9 kg of mass be converted into energy every second. (page 327)

90. At maximum, a cosmic ray particle—a mere atomic nucleus of only 10^{-13} cm across—can carry the energy of a professionally pitched baseball. (page 445)

Solve each problem.

91. *U.S. Population* In May 2008, the population of the United States was 304.1 million. (*Source: U.S. Census Bureau.*)

   (a) Write the May 2008 population using scientific notation.

   (b) Write $1 trillion, that is, $1,000,000,000,000, using scientific notation.

   (c) Using your answers from parts (a) and (b), calculate how much each person in the United States in the year 2008 would have had to contribute in order to make someone a trillionaire. Write this amount in standard notation to the nearest dollar.

92. *Powerball Lottery* In the early years of the Powerball Lottery, a player had to choose five numbers from 1 through 49 and one number from 1 through 42. It can be shown that there are about 8.009×10^7 different ways to do this. Suppose that a group of 2000 people decided to purchase tickets for all these numbers and each ticket cost $1.00. How much should each person have expected to pay? (*Source:* www.powerball.com)

93. *Distance of Uranus from the Sun* A parsec, a unit of length used in astronomy, is 1.9×10^{13} miles. The mean distance of Uranus from the sun is 1.8×10^7 miles. How many parsecs is Uranus from the sun?

94. *Number of Inches in a Mile* An inch is approximately 1.57828×10^{-5} mile. Find the reciprocal of this number to determine the number of inches in a mile.

95. *Speed of Light* The speed of light is approximately 3×10^{10} centimeters per second. How long will it take light to travel 9×10^{12} centimeters?

96. *Rocket from Earth to the Sun* The average distance from Earth to the sun is 9.3×10^7 miles. How long would it take a rocket, traveling at 2.9×10^3 miles per hour, to reach the sun?)

97. *Miles in a Light-Year* A *light-year* is the distance that light travels in one year. Find the number of miles in a light-year if light travels 1.86×10^5 miles per second.

98. *Time for Light to Travel* Use the information given in the previous two exercises to find the number of minutes necessary for light from the sun to reach Earth.

99. *Rocket from Venus to Mercury* The planet Mercury has an average distance from the sun of 3.6×10^7 miles, while the mean distance of Venus from the sun is 6.7×10^7 miles. How long would it take a spacecraft traveling at 1.55×10^3 miles per hour to travel from Venus to Mercury? Assume the trip could be timed so that its start and finish would occur when the respective planets are at their average distances from the sun and the same direction from the sun. (Give your answer in hours, without scientific notation.)

100. *Distance from an Object to the Moon* When the distance between the centers of the moon and Earth is 4.60×10^8 meters, an object on the line joining the centers of the moon and Earth exerts the same gravitational force on each when it is 4.14×10^8 meters from the center of Earth. How far is the object from the center of the moon at that point?

COUNTING METHODS 10

February 7, 2010, Miami, FL. Super Bowl XLIV pits the National Football Conference (NFC) New Orleans Saints against the American Football Conference (AFC) Indianapolis Colts. The Saints, led by quarterback Drew Brees (the game's MVP), eventually win an exciting game 31 to 17.

Before the game starts, the coin toss by Emmitt Smith, under the watchful eye of referee Scott Green, is called "heads" by the visiting Saints and comes up heads.

ANNOUNCER: "Can you believe this? (For) thirteen straight years the NFC has won the toss. The odds of any one side winning thirteen straight coin tosses is about 8100 to 1."

Was the announcer correct? The methods of this chapter enable us to count those odds exactly. The answer is on page 537.

10.1 COUNTING BY SYSTEMATIC LISTING

Counting • One-Part Tasks • Product Tables for Two-Part Tasks • Tree Diagrams for Multiple-Part Tasks • Other Systematic Listing Methods

Counting

In this chapter, "counting" means finding the number of objects, of some certain type, that exist. Among many possible reasons to ask and answer such a question, a major one is to be able to calculate the likelihood that some event may occur, that is the *probability* of the event. (Probability is the subject of **Chapter 11.**)

The methods of counting presented in this section involve listing the possible results for a given task. This approach is practical only for fairly short lists. When listing possible results, it is extremely important to use a *systematic* approach, so that no possibilities are missed.

One-Part Tasks

The results for simple, one-part tasks can often be listed easily. For the task of tossing a single fair coin, for example, the list is *heads, tails,* with two possible results. If the task is to roll a single fair die (a cube with faces numbered 1 through 6), the different results are 1, 2, 3, 4, 5, 6, a total of six possibilities.

▌▌ **EXAMPLE 1** Selecting a Club President

Consider a club N with five members:

$$N = \{\text{Alan, Bill, Cathy, David, Evelyn}\}, \quad \text{abbreviated as} \quad N = \{A, B, C, D, E\}.$$

In how many ways can this group select a president (assuming all members are eligible)?

SOLUTION

The task in this case is to select one of the five members as president. There are five possible results:

$$A, \ B, \ C, \ D, \ \text{and} \ E. \qquad \blacksquare\blacksquare\blacksquare$$

Product Tables for Two-Part Tasks

▌▌ **EXAMPLE 2** Building Numbers from a Set of Digits

Determine the number of two-digit numbers that can be written using only the digits 1, 2, and 3.

SOLUTION

This task consists of two parts:

1. Choose a first digit.   **2.** Choose a second digit.

The results for a two-part task can be pictured in a **product table** such as **Table 1**. From the table we obtain our list of possible results:

$$11, \ 12, \ 13, \ 21, \ 22, \ 23, \ 31, \ 32, \ 33.$$

There are nine possibilities. 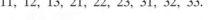 ▇▇▇

Counting methods can be used to find the number of moves required to solve a Rubik's Cube. The scrambled cube must be modified so that each face is a solid color. Rubik's royalties from sales of the cube in Western countries made him Hungary's richest man.

Although the craze over the cube of the early 1980s has waned, certain groups have remained intensely interested in not only solving the scrambled cube, but doing so as fast as possible. And the 30-year search for an exact number of moves (called face turns) that is guaranteed to suffice in all cases while no smaller number will suffice finally ended in July of 2010. That number is now known to be 20.

Even so, it is not yet known if an "efficient" algorithm exists for finding an actual solution in every case. So the cube still conceals mysteries for computer scientists to pursue.

Today, the cube's popularity is rivaled, among many people, by Sudoku puzzles.

Table 1

		Second Digit		
		1	**2**	**3**
First Digit	**1**	11	12	13
	2	21	22	23
	3	31	32	33

▮▮ **EXAMPLE 3** Rolling a Pair of Dice

Determine the number of different possible results when two ordinary dice are rolled.

SOLUTION

Assume the dice are easily distinguishable. Perhaps one is red and the other green. Then the task consists of two parts:

1. Roll the red die.   **2.** Roll the green die.

The product table in **Table 2** shows that there are thirty-six possible results.

Table 2   Rolling Two Fair Dice

		Green Die					
		1	**2**	**3**	**4**	**5**	**6**
Red Die	**1**	(1, 1)	(1, 2)	(1, 3)	(1, 4)	(1, 5)	(1, 6)
	2	(2, 1)	(2, 2)	(2, 3)	(2, 4)	(2, 5)	(2, 6)
	3	(3, 1)	(3, 2)	(3, 3)	(3, 4)	(3, 5)	(3, 6)
	4	(4, 1)	(4, 2)	(4, 3)	(4, 4)	(4, 5)	(4, 6)
	5	(5, 1)	(5, 2)	(5, 3)	(5, 4)	(5, 5)	(5, 6)
	6	(6, 1)	(6, 2)	(6, 3)	(6, 4)	(6, 5)	(6, 6)

▮▮▮

You will want to refer to **Table 2** *when various dice-rolling problems occur in the remainder of this chapter and the next.*

▮▮ **EXAMPLE 4** Electing Two Club Officers

Find the number of ways that club N of **Example 1** can elect both a president and a secretary. Assume that all members are eligible, but that no one can hold both offices.

SOLUTION

Again, the required task has two parts:

1. Determine the president.   **2.** Determine the secretary.

Constructing **Table 3** gives us the possibilities (where, for example, AB denotes president A and secretary B, while BA denotes president B and secretary A).

Table 3   Electing Two Officers

		Secretary				
		A	**B**	**C**	**D**	**E**
President	**A**		AB	AC	AD	AE
	B	BA		BC	BD	BE
	C	CA	CB		CD	CE
	D	DA	DB	DC		DE
	E	EA	EB	EC	ED	

Notice that certain entries (down the main diagonal, from upper left to lower right) are omitted from the table, since the cases AA, BB, and so on would imply one person holding both offices. Altogether, there are twenty possibilities.

▮▮▮

Bone dice were unearthed in the remains of a Roman garrison, Vindolanda, near the border between England and Scotland. Life on the Roman frontier was occupied with gaming as well as fighting. Some of the Roman dice were loaded in favor of 6 and 1.

Life on the American frontier was reflected in cattle brands that were devised to keep alive the memories of hardships, feuds, and romances. A rancher named Ellis from Paradise Valley in Arizona designed his cattle brand in the shape of a pair of dice. You can guess that the pips were 6 and 1.

▮▮ **EXAMPLE 5** Selecting Committees for a Club

Find the number of ways that club N can appoint a committee of two members to represent them at an association conference.

SOLUTION

The required task again has two parts. In fact, we can refer to **Table 3** again, but this time, the order of the two letters (people) in a given pair really makes no difference. For example, BD and DB are the same committee. (In **Example 4,** BD and DB were different results since the two people would be holding different offices.)

In the case of committees, we can eliminate not only the main diagonal entries but also all entries below the main diagonal. The resulting list contains ten possibilities:

$$AB, \quad AC, \quad AD, \quad AE, \quad BC, \quad BD, \quad BE, \quad CD, \quad CE, \quad DE.$$ ▮▮▮

Tree Diagrams for Multiple-Part Tasks

PROBLEM-SOLVING HINT A task that has more than two parts is not easy to analyze with a product table. Another helpful device is the **tree diagram.**

▮▮ **EXAMPLE 6** Building Numbers from a Set of Digits

Find the number of three-digit numbers that can be written using only the digits 1, 2, and 3, assuming that **(a)** repeated digits are allowed and **(b)** repeated digits are not allowed.

SOLUTION

(a) The task of constructing such a number has three parts:

1. Select the first digit.   **2.** Select the second digit.   **3.** Select the third digit.

As we move from left to right through the tree diagram in **Figure 1,** the tree branches at the first-stage to all possibilities for the first digit. Then each first-stage branch again branches, or splits, at the second stage, to all possibilities for the second digit. Finally, the third-stage branching shows the third-digit possibilities. The list of possible results (twenty-seven of them) is shown in **Figure 1.**

(b) For the case of nonrepeating digits, we could construct a whole new tree diagram, as in **Figure 2,** or we could simply go down the list of numbers from the first tree diagram and strike out any that contain repeated digits. In either case we obtain only six possibilities.

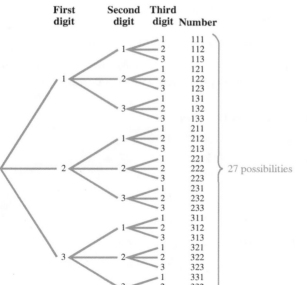

Tree diagram for three-digit numbers using digits 1, 2, and 3

Figure 1

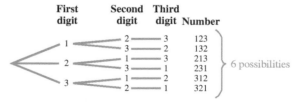

Tree diagram for nonrepeating three-digit numbers using digits 1, 2, and 3

Figure 2 ▮▮▮

Notice the distinction between parts (a) and (b) of **Example 6.** There are twenty-seven possibilities when "repetitions (of digits) are allowed," but only six possibilities when "repetitions are not allowed."

Here is another way to phrase the problem of **Example 6:**

A three-digit number is to be determined by placing three slips of paper (marked 1, 2, and 3) into a hat and drawing out three slips in succession. Find the number of possible results if the drawing is done **(a)** *with replacement* and **(b)** *without replacement.*

Drawing "with replacement" means drawing a slip, recording its digit, and replacing the slip into the hat so that it is again available for subsequent draws.

Drawing "with replacement" has the effect of "allowing repetitions," while drawing "without replacement" has the effect of "not allowing repetitions."

The words "repetitions" and "replacement" are important in the statement of a problem. In **Example 2,** since no restrictions were stated, we assumed that *repetitions* (of digits) *were allowed,* or equivalently that digits were to be selected *with replacement.*

▌▌ EXAMPLE 7 Selecting Switch Settings on a Printer

Pamela DeMar's computer printer allows for optional settings with a panel of four on-off switches in a row. How many different settings can she select if no two adjacent switches can both be off?

SOLUTION

This situation is typical of user-selectable options on various devices, including computer equipment, garage door openers, and other appliances. In **Figure 3**, we denote "on" and "off" with 1 and 0, respectively. The number of possible settings is eight.

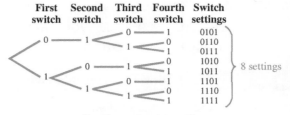

Notice that each time a switch is indicated as off (0), the next switch can only be on (1). This is to satisfy the restriction that no two adjacent switches can both be off.

Tree diagram for printer settings

Figure 3

■■■

▌▌ EXAMPLE 8 Seating Attendees at a Concert

Arne, Bobbette, Chuck, and Deirdre have tickets for four reserved seats in a row at a concert. In how many different ways can they seat themselves so that Arne and Bobbette will sit next to each other?

SOLUTION

Here we have a four-part task:

Assign people to the first, second, third, and fourth seats.

The tree diagram in **Figure 4** on the next page avoids repetitions, because no person can occupy more than one seat. Also, once *A* or *B* appears in the tree, the other one *must* occur at the next stage. (Why is this?) No splitting occurs from stage three to stage four because by that time there is only one person left unassigned. The right column in the figure shows the twelve possible seating arrangements.

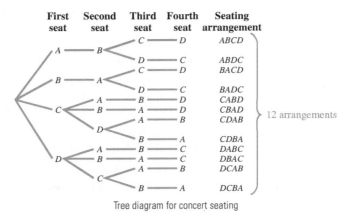

Tree diagram for concert seating

Figure 4   ■■■

Although we have applied tree diagrams only to tasks with three or more parts, they can also be used for two-part or even simple, one-part tasks. Product tables, on the other hand, are practical only for two-part tasks.

Other Systematic Listing Methods

There are additional systematic ways to produce complete listings of possible results besides product tables and tree diagrams.

In **Example 4,** where we used a product table (**Table 3**) to list all possible president-secretary pairs for the club $N = \{A, B, C, D, E\}$, we could have systematically constructed the same list using a sort of alphabetical or left-to-right approach.

First, consider the results where A is president. Any of the remaining members (B, C, D, or E) could then be secretary. That gives us the pairs AB, AC, AD, and AE. Next, assume B is president. The secretary could then be A, C, D, or E. We get the pairs BA, BC, BD, and BE. Continuing in order, we get the complete list just as in **Example 4:**

$$AB, \quad AC, \quad AD, \quad AE, \quad BA, \quad BC, \quad BD, \quad BE, \quad CA, \quad CB,$$
$$CD, \quad CE, \quad DA, \quad DB, \quad DC, \quad DE, \quad EA, \quad EB, \quad EC, \quad ED.$$

▌ EXAMPLE 9 Counting Triangles in a Figure

How many different triangles (of any size) can be traced in **Figure 5**?

SOLUTION

One systematic approach is to label points as shown, begin with A, and proceed in alphabetical order to write all three-letter combinations, then cross out the ones that are not triangles in the figure.

$$ABC, \quad ABD, \quad ABE, \quad ABF, \quad ACD, \quad ACE, \quad \cancel{ACF}, \quad \cancel{ADE}, \quad \cancel{ADF}, \quad AEF,$$
$$\cancel{BCD}, \quad BCE, \quad BCF, \quad BDE, \quad \cancel{BDF}, \quad \cancel{BEF}, \quad CDE, \quad \cancel{CDF}, \quad CEF, \quad \cancel{DEF}$$

Finally, there are twelve different triangles in the figure. Why are ACB and CBF (and many others) not included in the list?

Another method might be first to identify the triangles consisting of a single region each: DEC, ECF, AEF, BCF, ABF. Then list those consisting of two regions each: AEC, BEC, ABE, ABC; and those with three regions each: ACD, BED. There are no triangles with four regions, but there is one with five: ABD. The total is again twelve. Can you think of other systematic ways of getting the same list? ■■■

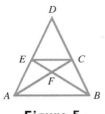

Figure 5

Notice that in the first method shown in **Example 9,** the labeled points were considered in alphabetical order. In the second method, the single-region triangles were listed by using a top-to-bottom and left-to-right order. Using a definite system helps to ensure that we get a complete list.

10.1 EXERCISES

Electing Officers of a Club Refer to **Examples 1 and 4,** involving the club

$$N = \{\text{Alan, Bill, Cathy, David, Evelyn}\}.$$

Assuming all members are eligible, but that no one can hold more than one office, list and count the different ways the club could elect each group of officers.

1. a president and a treasurer

2. a president and a treasurer if the president must be a female

3. a president and a treasurer if the two officers must be the same sex

4. a president, a secretary, and a treasurer, if the president and treasurer must be women

5. a president, a secretary, and a treasurer, if the president must be a man and the other two must be women

6. a president, a secretary, and a treasurer, if all three officers must be men

Appointing Committees List and count the ways club *N* could appoint a committee of three members under each condition.

7. There are no restrictions.

8. The committee must include more men than women.

Refer to **Table 2** *(the product table for rolling two dice). Of the 36 possibilities, determine the number for which the sum (for both dice) is the following.*

9. 2   **10.** 3   **11.** 4

12. 5   **13.** 6   **14.** 7

15. 8   **16.** 9   **17.** 10

18. 11   **19.** 12   **20.** odd

21. even

22. from 6 through 8 inclusive

23. between 6 and 10

24. less than 5

25. Construct a product table showing all possible two-digit numbers using digits from the set

$$\{2, 3, 5, 7\}.$$

Of the sixteen numbers in the product table for Exercise 25, list the ones that belong to each category.

26. even numbers

27. numbers with repeating digits

28. multiples of 3

29. prime numbers

30. Construct a tree diagram showing all possible results when three fair coins are tossed. Then list the ways of getting each result.
   (a) at least two heads
   (b) more than two heads
   (c) no more than two heads
   (d) fewer than two heads

31. Extend the tree diagram of **Exercise 30** for four fair coins. Then list the ways of getting each result.
   (a) more than three tails
   (b) fewer than three tails
   (c) at least three tails
   (d) no more than three tails

Determine the number of triangles (of any size) in each figure.

32.   **33.**

34.   **35.**

Determine the number of squares (of any size) in each figure.

36.    **37.**

38.   **39.**

Consider only the smallest individual cubes and assume solid stacks (no gaps). Determine the number of cubes in each stack that are not visible from the perspective shown.

40.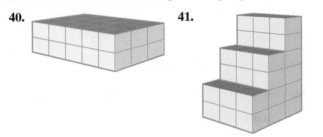

41.

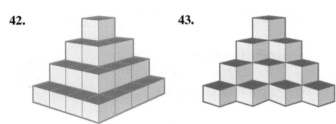

42.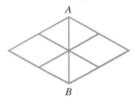

43.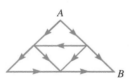

44. In the plane figure illustrated here, only movement that tends downward is allowed. Find the total number of paths from *A* to *B*.

45. Find the number of paths from *A* to *B* in the figure illustrated here if the directions on various segments are restricted as shown.

In each of Exercises 46–48, determine the number of different ways the given number can be written as the sum of two primes.

46. 30 **47.** 40 **48.** 95

49. Rolling Unusual Dice An unusual die has the numbers 2, 2, 3, 3, 5, and 8 on its six faces. Two of these dice are rolled, and the two numbers on the top faces are added. How many different sums are possible? (*Mathematics Teacher* calendar problem)

50. Shaking Hands in a Group A group of six strangers sat in a circle, and each one got acquainted only with the person to the left and the person to the right. Then all six people stood up and each one shook hands (once) with each of the others who was still a stranger. How many handshakes occurred?

51. Number of Games in a Chess Tournament Fifty people enter a single-elimination chess tournament. (If you lose one game, you're out.) Assuming no ties occur, what is the number of games required to determine the tournament champion?

52. Sums of Digits How many positive integers less than 100 have the sum of their digits equal to a perfect square?

53. Sums of Digits How many three-digit numbers have the sum of their digits equal to 22?

54. Integers Containing the Digit 2 How many integers between 100 and 400 contain the digit 2?

55. Filling an Order A customer ordered fifteen Zingers. Zingers are placed in packages of four, three, or one. In how many different ways can this order be filled? (*Mathematics Teacher* calendar problem)

56. Selecting Dinner Items Michael Bailey and friends are dining at the Clam Shell Restaurant this evening, where a complete dinner consists of three items:

(1) soup (clam chowder or minestrone) or salad (fresh spinach or shrimp),

(2) sourdough rolls or bran muffin, and

(3) entree (lasagna, lobster, or roast turkey).

Michael selects his meal subject to the following restrictions. He cannot stomach more than one kind of seafood at a sitting. Also, whenever he tastes minestrone, he cannot resist having lasagna as well. Use a tree diagram to determine the number of different choices Michael has.

*Setting Options on a Computer Printer For Exercises 57–59, refer to **Example 7**. How many different settings could Pamela choose in each case?*

57. No restrictions apply to adjacent switches.

58. No two adjacent switches can be off *and* no two adjacent switches can be on.

59. There are five switches rather than four, and no two adjacent switches can be on.

60. Building Numbers from Sets of Digits Determine the number of odd, nonrepeating three-digit numbers that can be written using only the digits 0, 1, 2, and 3.

61. Lattice Points on a Line Segment A line segment joins the points

$$(8, 12) \quad \text{and} \quad (53, 234)$$

in the Cartesian plane. Including its endpoints, how many lattice points does this line segment contain? (A *lattice point* is a point with integer coordinates.)

62. *Lengths of Segments Joining Lattice Points* In the pattern that follows, dots are one unit apart horizontally and vertically. If a segment can join any two dots, how many segments can be drawn with each length?

(a) 1   **(b)** 2   **(c)** 3   **(d)** 4   **(e)** 5

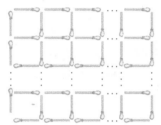

63. *Counting Matchsticks in a Grid* Uniform-length matchsticks are used to build a rectangular grid as shown here. If the grid is 12 matchsticks high and 25 matchsticks wide, how many matchsticks are used?

64. *Patterns in Floor Tiling* A square floor is to be tiled with square tiles as shown at the top of the next column, with blue tiles on the main diagonals and red tiles everywhere else. (In all cases, both blue and red tiles must be used and the two diagonals must have a common blue tile at the center of the floor.)

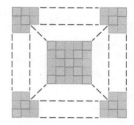

(a) If 81 blue tiles will be used, how many red tiles will be needed?

(b) For what numbers in place of 81 would this problem still be solvable?

(c) Find an expression in k giving the number of red tiles required in general.

65. *Shaking Hands in a Group* Chris Heister and his son were among four father-and-son pairs who gathered to trade baseball cards. As each person arrived, he shook hands with anyone he had not known previously. Each person ended up making a different number of new acquaintances (0–6), except Chris and his son, who each met the same number of people. How many hands did Chris shake?

In Exercises 66 and 67, restate the given counting problem in two ways, first **(a)** *using the word* repetition, *and then* **(b)** *using the word* replacement.

66. Example 2

67. Example 4

10.2   USING THE FUNDAMENTAL COUNTING PRINCIPLE

Uniformity and the Fundamental Counting Principle • Factorials • Arrangements of Objects

Uniformity and the Fundamental Counting Principle

In **Section 10.1,** we obtained complete lists of all possible results for various tasks. However, if the total number of possibilities is all we need to know, then an actual listing usually is unnecessary and often is difficult or tedious to obtain, especially when the list is long.

Figure 6 repeats **Figure 2** of **Section 10.1** (for **Example 6(b)**), which shows all possible nonrepeating three-digit numbers using only the digits 1, 2, and 3.

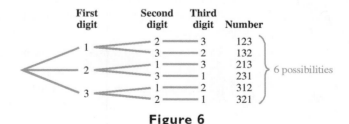

Figure 6

The tree diagram in **Figure 6** is "uniform" in the sense that a given part of the task can be done in the same number of ways no matter which choices were selected for previous parts. For example, there are always two choices for the second digit. (If the first digit is 1, the second can be 2 or 3. If the first is 2, the second can be 1 or 3. If the first is 3, the second can be 1 or 2.)

Example 6(a) of **Section 10.1** addressed the same basic situation:

Find the number of three-digit numbers that can be written using the digits 1, 2, and 3.

In that case repetitions were allowed. With repetitions allowed, there were many more possibilities (27 rather than 6—see **Figure 1** of **Section 10.1**). But the uniformity criterion mentioned above still applied. No matter what the first digit is, there are three choices for the second (1, 2, 3). And no matter what the first and second digits are, there are three choices for the third. This uniformity criterion can be stated in general as follows.

Uniformity Criterion for Multiple-Part Tasks

A multiple-part task is said to satisfy the **uniformity criterion** if the number of choices for any particular part is the same *no matter which choices were selected for previous parts.*

The uniformity criterion is not always satisfied. Refer to **Example 7** (and **Figure 3**) of **Section 10.1.** After the first switch (two possibilities), other switches had either one or two possible settings depending on how previous switches were set. (This "nonuniformity" arose, in that case, from the requirement that no two adjacent switches could both be off.)

In the many cases where uniformity does hold, we can avoid having to construct a tree diagram by using the **fundamental counting principle,** stated as follows.

Fundamental Counting Principle

When a task consists of k separate parts and satisfies the uniformity criterion, if the first part can be done in n_1 ways, the second part can then be done in n_2 ways, and so on through the kth part, which can be done in n_k ways, then the total number of ways to complete the task is given by the product

$$n_1 \cdot n_2 \cdot n_3 \cdot \ldots \cdot n_k.$$

PROBLEM-SOLVING HINT A problem-solving strategy suggested in **Chapter 1** was: "*If a formula applies, use it.*" The fundamental counting principle provides a formula that applies to a variety of problems. The trick is to visualize the "task" at hand as being accomplished in a sequence of two or more separate parts.

A helpful technique when applying the fundamental counting principle is to write out all the separate parts of the task, with a blank for each one. Reason out how many ways each part can be done, and enter these numbers in the blanks. Finally, multiply these numbers together.

▮▮ **EXAMPLE 1**   Counting the Two-Digit Numbers

How many two-digit numbers are there in our (base-ten) system of counting numbers? (**While 40 is a two-digit number, 04 is not.**)

SOLUTION

Our "task" here is to select, or construct, a two-digit number. Set up the work as follows.

Part of task	Select first digit	Select second digit
Number of ways	_____	_____

There are nine choices for the first digit (1 through 9). Since there were no stated or implied restrictions, we assume that repetition of digits is allowed. Therefore, no matter which nonzero digit is used as the first digit, all nine choices are available for the second digit. Also, unlike the first digit, the second digit may be zero, so we have ten choices for the second digit. We can now fill in the blanks and multiply.

Part of task	Select first digit	Select second digit	
Number of ways	9 ·	10	= 90

There are 90 two-digit numbers. (As a check, notice that they are the numbers from 10 through 99, a total of $99 - 10 + 1 = 90$.)   ▮▮▮

▮▮ **EXAMPLE 2**   Building Two-Digit Numbers with Restrictions

Find the number of two-digit numbers that do not contain repeated digits.

SOLUTION

The basic task is again to select a two-digit number, and there are two parts:

  1. Select the first digit.   **2.** Select the second digit.

But a new restriction applies—no repetition of digits. There are nine choices for the first digit (1 through 9). Then nine choices remain for the second digit, since one nonzero digit has been used and cannot be repeated, but zero is now available. The total number is $9 \cdot 9 = 81$.   ▮▮▮

▮▮ **EXAMPLE 3**   Electing Club Officers with Restrictions

In how many ways can Club N of the previous section elect a president and a secretary if no one may hold more than one office and the secretary must be a man?

SOLUTION

Recall that $N = \{A, B, C, D, E\} = \{$Alan, Bill, Cathy, David, Evelyn$\}$. Considering president first, there are five choices (no restrictions). But now we have a problem with finding the number of choices for secretary. If a woman was selected president (C or E), there are three choices for secretary (A, B, and D). If a man was selected president, only two choices (the other two men) remain for secretary. ***In other words, the uniformity criterion is not met and our attempt to apply the fundamental counting principle has failed.***

    All is not lost, however. To find the total number of ways, we can consider secretary first. There are three choices (A, B, and D). Now, no matter which man was chosen secretary, both of the other men, and both women, are available for president (four choices in every case). In this order, we satisfy the uniformity criterion and can use the fundamental counting principle. The total number of ways to elect a president and a secretary is $3 \cdot 4 = 12$.   ▮▮▮

Richard Dedekind (1831–1916) studied at the University of Göttingen, where he was Gauss's last student. His work was not recognized during his lifetime, but his treatment of the infinite and of what constitutes a real number are influential even today.

    While on vacation in Switzerland, Dedekind met Georg Cantor (profiled on **page 44**). Dedekind was interested in Cantor's work on infinite sets. Perhaps because both were working in new and unusual fields of mathematics, such as number theory, and because neither received the professional attention he deserved during his lifetime, the two struck up a lasting friendship.

> **PROBLEM-SOLVING HINT Example 3** suggests a useful problem-solving strategy: Whenever one or more parts of a task have special restrictions, try considering that part (or those parts) before other parts.

▌▌ **EXAMPLE 4** Counting Three-Digit Numbers with Restrictions

How many nonrepeating odd three-digit counting numbers are there?

SOLUTION

The most restricted digit is the third, since it must be odd. There are five choices (1, 3, 5, 7, and 9). Next, consider the first digit. It can be any nonzero digit except the one already chosen as the third digit. There are eight choices. Finally, the second digit can be any digit (including 0) except for the two (nonzero) digits already used. There are eight choices.

Part of task	Select third digit		Select first digit		Select second digit	
Number of ways	5	·	8	·	8	= 320

There are 320 nonrepeating odd three-digit counting numbers. ▌▌▌

▌▌ **EXAMPLE 5** Counting License Plates

In some states, auto license plates have contained three letters followed by three digits. How many such licenses are possible?

SOLUTION

The basic task is to design a license plate with three letters followed by three digits. There are six component parts to this task. Since there are no restrictions on letters or digits, the fundamental counting principle gives

$$26 \cdot 26 \cdot 26 \cdot 10 \cdot 10 \cdot 10 = 26^3 \cdot 10^3 = 17{,}576{,}000 \text{ possible licenses.}$$

(In practice, a few of the possible sequences of letters are considered undesirable and are not used.) ▌▌▌

EXAMPLE 6 Building Numbers with Specified Digits

A four-digit number is to be constructed using only the digits 1, 2, and 3.

(a) How many such numbers are possible?

(b) How many of these numbers are odd and less than 2000?

SOLUTION

(a) To construct such a number, we must select four digits, in succession, from the given set of three digits, where the selection is done with replacement (since repetition of digits is apparently allowed). The number of possibilities is

$$3 \cdot 3 \cdot 3 \cdot 3 = 3^4 = 81 \quad \text{Fundamental counting principle}$$

(b) The number is less than 2000 only if the first digit is 1 (just one choice) and is odd only if the fourth digit is 1 or 3 (two choices). The second and third digits are unrestricted (three choices for each). The answer is

$$1 \cdot 3 \cdot 3 \cdot 2 = 18.$$

As a check, can you list the eighteen possibilities? ■■■

> **PROBLEM-SOLVING HINT** Two of the problem-solving strategies of **Chapter 1** were to "*First solve a similar simpler problem*," and to "*Look for a pattern*." In fact, a counting problem may sometimes prove to be essentially the same, or at least fit the same pattern, as another problem already solved.

EXAMPLE 7 Distributing Golf Clubs

Vern has four antique wood head golf clubs that he wants to give to his three sons, Mark, Chris, and Scott.

(a) How many ways can the clubs be distributed?

(b) How many choices are there if the power driver must go to Mark and the number 3 wood must go to either Chris or Scott?

SOLUTION

(a) The task is to distribute four clubs among three sons. Consider the clubs in succession, and, for each one, ask how many sons could receive it. In effect, we must select four sons, in succession, from the list Mark, Chris, Scott, selecting with replacement. Compare this with **Example 6(a),** in which we selected four digits, in succession, from the digits 1, 2, and 3, selecting with replacement. In this case, we are selecting sons rather than digits, but the pattern is the same and the numbers are the same. Again our answer is

$$3^4 = 81.$$

(b) Just as in **Example 6(b),** one part of the task is now restricted to a single choice and another part is restricted to two choices. As in that example, the number of possibilities is

$$1 \cdot 3 \cdot 3 \cdot 2 = 18.$$ ■■■

Answer to the Chapter Opener Question The Super Bowl announcer was pretty close. Since each coin must fall in one of two ways (heads or tails), the 13 consecutive NFC wins was just one of

$$2^{13} = 8192 \text{ possibilities.}$$

▮▮ **EXAMPLE 8** Seating Attendees at a Concert

Rework **Example 8** of **Section 10.1,** this time using the fundamental counting principle.

SOLUTION

Recall that Arne, Bobbette, Chuck, and Deirdre (A, B, C, and D) are to seat themselves in four adjacent seats (say 1, 2, 3, and 4) so that A and B are side-by-side. One approach to accomplish this task is to make three successive decisions as follows.

```
1   2   3   4
X   X   _   _
_   X   X   _
_   _   X   X
```

Seats available to A and B

1. Which pair of seats should A and B occupy? There are *three* choices (1 and 2, 2 and 3, 3 and 4, as illustrated in the margin).
2. Which order should A and B take? There are *two* choices (A left of B, or B left of A).
3. Which order should C and D take? There are *two* choices (C left of D, or D left of C, not necessarily right next to each other).

(Why did we not ask which two seats C and D should occupy?) The fundamental counting principle now gives the total number of choices:

$$3 \cdot 2 \cdot 2 = 12 \quad \text{Same result as in Section 10.1}$$ ▮▮▮

Factorials

Short Table of Factorials Factorial values increase rapidly. The value of 100! is a number with 158 digits.

0!	= 1
1!	= 1
2!	= 2
3!	= 6
4!	= 24
5!	= 120
6!	= 720
7!	= 5040
8!	= 40,320
9!	= 362,880
10!	= 3,628,800

This section began with a discussion of nonrepeating three-digit numbers using digits 1, 2, and 3. The number of possibilities was

$$3 \cdot 2 \cdot 1 = 6. \quad \text{Fundamental counting principle}$$

That product can also be thought of as the total number of distinct *arrangements* of the three digits 1, 2, and 3.

Similarly, the number of distinct arrangements of four objects, say A, B, C, and D, is

$$4 \cdot 3 \cdot 2 \cdot 1 = 24. \quad \text{Fundamental counting principle}$$

Since this type of product occurs so commonly in applications, we give it a special name and symbol as follows. For any counting number n, the product of *all* counting numbers from n down through 1 is called **n factorial,** and is denoted **$n!$**.

Factorial Formula

For any counting number n, the quantity **n factorial** is given as follows.

$$n! = n(n - 1)(n - 2) \ldots 2 \cdot 1$$

The first few factorial values are easily found by simple multiplication, but they rapidly become very large. The use of a calculator is advised in most cases.

PROBLEM-SOLVING HINT Sometimes expressions involving factorials can be evaluated easily by observing that, in general, $n! = n(n - 1)!$, $n! = n(n - 1)(n - 2)!$, and so on. For example,

$$8! = 8 \cdot 7!, \quad 12! = 12 \cdot 11 \cdot 10 \cdot 9!, \quad \text{and so on.}$$

This pattern is especially helpful in evaluating quotients of factorials, such as

$$\frac{10!}{8!} = \frac{10 \cdot 9 \cdot 8!}{8!} = 10 \cdot 9 = 90.$$

▋▋ **EXAMPLE 9** Evaluating Expressions Containing Factorials

Evaluate each expression.

(a) 3!   **(b)** 6!   **(c)** $(6 - 3)!$ **(d)** $6! - 3!$

(e) $\dfrac{6!}{3!}$ **(f)** $\left(\dfrac{6}{3}\right)!$ **(g)** 15!   **(h)** 100!

The results of **Example 9(b), (d), and (g)** are illustrated in this calculator screen.

SOLUTION

(a) $3! = 3 \cdot 2 \cdot 1 = 6$

(b) $6! = 6 \cdot 5 \cdot 4 \cdot 3 \cdot 2 \cdot 1 = 720$

(c) $(6 - 3)! = 3! = 6$

(d) $6! - 3! = 720 - 6 = 714$

(e) $\dfrac{6!}{3!} = \dfrac{6 \cdot 5 \cdot 4 \cdot 3!}{3!} = 6 \cdot 5 \cdot 4 = 120$ Note application of the Problem-Solving Hint.

(f) $\left(\dfrac{6}{3}\right)! = 2! = 2 \cdot 1 = 2$

(g) $15! = 1.307674368000 \times 10^{12}$ ← Done on a calculator

(h) $100! = 9.332621544 \times 10^{157}$ ← Too large for most calculators

Notice the distinction between parts (c) and (d) and between parts (e) and (f).   ▋▋▋

So that factorials will be defined for all whole numbers, including zero, we define 0! as follows.

The definition 0! = 1 is illustrated here.

Definition of Zero Factorial

$$0! = 1$$

(We will see later that this special definition makes other results easier to state.)

Arrangements of Objects

When finding the total number of ways to *arrange* a given number of distinct objects, we can use a factorial. The fundamental counting principle would do, but factorials provide a shortcut.

Arrangements of n Distinct Objects

The total number of different ways to arrange n distinct objects is $n!$.

▋▋ **EXAMPLE 10** Arranging Essays

Michelle Cook has seven essays to include in her English 1A folder. In how many different orders can she arrange them?

SOLUTION

The number of ways to arrange seven distinct objects is $7! = 5040$.   ▋▋▋

▮▮ **EXAMPLE 11** Arranging Preschoolers

Tricia Caruso is taking thirteen preschoolers to the park. How many ways can the children line up, in single file, to board the van?

SOLUTION

Thirteen children can be arranged in $13! = 6{,}227{,}020{,}800$ different ways. ▮▮▮

D_1AD_2
D_2AD_1

D_1D_2A
D_2D_1A

AD_1D_2
AD_2D_1

   In counting arrangements of objects that contain look-alikes, the normal factorial formula must be modified to find the number of truly different arrangements. For example, the number of distinguishable arrangements of the letters of the word DAD is not $3! = 6$ but rather $\frac{3!}{2!} = 3$. The listing in the margin shows how the six total arrangements consist of just three groups of two, where the two in a given group look alike.

Arrangements of *n* Objects Containing Look-Alikes

The number of **distinguishable arrangements** of n objects, where one or more subsets consist of look-alikes (say n_1 are of one kind, n_2 are of another kind, ..., and n_k are of yet another kind), is given by

$$\frac{n!}{n_1! n_2! \dots n_k!}.$$

▮▮ **EXAMPLE 12** Counting Distinguishable Arrangements

Determine the number of distinguishable arrangements of the letters in each word.

(a) ATTRACT   **(b)** NIGGLING

SOLUTION

(a) For the letters of ATTRACT, the number of distinguishable arrangements is

7 letters total $\longrightarrow$
$$\frac{7!}{3!\,2!} = 420.$$
3 T's, 2 A's $\longrightarrow$

(b) For the letters of NIGGLING, the number of distinguishable arrangements is

8 letters total $\longrightarrow$
$$\frac{8!}{2!\,2!\,3!} = 1680.$$
2 N's, 2 I's, 3 G's $\longrightarrow$ ▮▮▮

For Further Thought

Stirling's Approximation for *n*!

Although all factorial values are counting numbers, they can be approximated using **Stirling's formula,**

$$n! \approx \sqrt{2\pi n} \cdot n^n \cdot e^{-n},$$

which involves two famous irrational numbers, π and e. For example, while the exact value of 5! is $5 \cdot 4 \cdot 3 \cdot 2 \cdot 1 = 120$, the corresponding approximation is

$$5! \approx \sqrt{2\pi \cdot 5} \cdot 5^5 \cdot e^{-5} \approx 118.019168,$$

which is off by less than 2, an error of only 1.65%.

For Group or Individual Investigation

Use a calculator to fill in all values in the table on the next page. The column values are defined as follows.

$C = n!$ (exact value, by calculator)
$S \approx n!$ (Stirling's approximation, by calculator)
$D = $ Difference $(C - S)$
$P = $ Percentage
    difference $\left(\dfrac{D}{C} \cdot 100\%\right)$

n	C	S	D	P
1				
2				
3				
4				
5				
6				
7				
8				
9				
10				

Try to obtain percentage differences accurate to two decimal places.

Based on your calculations, answer each question.

1. In general, is Stirling's approximation too low or too high?

2. Observe the values in the table as n grows larger.

 (a) Do the differences (D) get larger or smaller?

 (b) Do the percentage differences (P) get larger or smaller?

 (c) Does Stirling's formula become more accurate or less accurate?

10.2 EXERCISES

1. Explain the fundamental counting principle in your own words.

2. Describe how factorials can be used in counting problems.

For Exercises 3–6, n and m are counting numbers. Do the following: **(a)** *Tell whether the given statement is true in general, and* **(b)** *explain your answer, using specific examples.*

3. $(n + m)! = n! + m!$

4. $(n \cdot m)! = n! \cdot m!$

5. $(n - m)! = n! - m!$

6. $n! = n(n - 1)!$

Evaluate each expression without using a calculator.

7. $4!$

8. $6!$

9. $\dfrac{9!}{7!}$

10. $\dfrac{16!}{14!}$

11. $\dfrac{5!}{(5 - 2)!}$

12. $\dfrac{6!}{(6 - 3)!}$

13. $\dfrac{8!}{6!(8 - 6)!}$

14. $\dfrac{10!}{4!(10 - 4)!}$

15. $\dfrac{n!}{(n - r)!}$, where $n = 7$ and $r = 4$

16. $\dfrac{n!}{r!(n - r)!}$, where $n = 12$ and $r = 4$

Evaluate each expression using a calculator.

17. $10!$

18. $14!$

19. $\dfrac{12!}{5!}$

20. $\dfrac{13!}{(13 - 6)!}$

21. $\dfrac{20!}{10! \cdot 10!}$

22. $\dfrac{19!}{9! \cdot 10!}$

23. $\dfrac{n!}{(n - r)!}$, where $n = 17$ and $r = 8$

24. $\dfrac{n!}{r!(n - r)!}$, where $n = 24$ and $r = 18$

Arranging Letters *Find the number of distinguishable arrangements of the letters of each word.*

25. GOOGOL

26. HEEBIE-JEEBIES

Settings on a Switch Panel *A panel containing three on–off switches in a row is to be set.*

27. Assuming no restrictions on individual switches, use the fundamental counting principle to find the total number of possible panel settings.

28. Assuming no restrictions, construct a tree diagram to list all the possible panel settings of **Exercise 27.**

29. Now assume that no two adjacent switches can both be off. Explain why the fundamental counting principle does not apply.

30. Construct a tree diagram to list all possible panel settings under the restriction of **Exercise 29.**

31. Rolling Dice **Table 2** in the previous section shows that there are 36 possible outcomes when two fair dice are rolled. How many would there be if three fair dice were rolled?

32. Counting Five-Digit Numbers How many five-digit numbers are there in our system of counting numbers?

33. Bowling After rolling the first ball of a frame in a game of 10-pin bowling, how many different pin configurations can remain (assuming all configurations are physically possible)? (*Mathematics Teacher* calendar problem)

34. Bowling Answer the question of **Exercise 33** assuming that pins 1, 2, and 3 were knocked down on the first roll.

Matching Club Members with Tasks *Recall the club*

$$N = \{\text{Alan, Bill, Cathy, David, Evelyn}\}.$$

In how many ways could they do each of the following?

35. line up all five members for a photograph

36. schedule one member to work in the office on each of five different days, assuming members may work more than one day

37. select a male and a female to decorate for a party

38. select two members, one to open their next meeting and another to close it, given that Bill will not be present

Building Numbers with Specified Digits *In Exercises 39–42, counting numbers are to be formed using only the digits 3, 4, and 5. Determine the number of different possibilities for each type of number described.*

39. two-digit numbers   **40.** odd three-digit numbers

41. four-digit numbers with one pair of adjacent 4s and no other repeated digits (*Hint:* You may want to split the task of designing such a number into three parts, such as *(1)* position the pair of 4s, *(2)* position the 3, and *(3)* position the 5.)

42. five-digit numbers beginning and ending with 3 and with unlimited repetitions allowed

Selecting Dinner Items *The Gourmet de Coeur Restaurant offers five choices in the soup and salad category (two soups and three salads), two choices in the bread category, and four choices in the entree category. Find the number of dinners available in each case.*

43. One item is to be included from each of the three categories.

44. Only salad and entree are to be included.

Selecting Answers on a Test *Determine the number of possible ways to mark your answer sheet (with an answer for each question) for each test.*

45. a six-question true-or-false test

46. a ten-question multiple-choice test with five answer choices for each question

Selecting a College Class Schedule *Jessica Elbern's class schedule for next semester must consist of exactly one class from each of the four categories shown in the table at the top of the next column.*

For each situation in Exercises 47–52, use the table to determine the number of different sets of classes Jessica can take.

Category	Choices	Number of Choices
Economics	Free Markets Controlled Markets	2
Mathematics	History of Mathematics College Algebra Finite Mathematics	3
Education	Classroom Technology Group Dynamics Language Supervision Parent/Teacher Relations	4
Sociology	Social Problems Sociology of the Middle East Aging in America Minorities in America Women in American Culture	5

47. All classes shown are available.

48. She is not eligible for Free Markets or for Group Dynamics.

49. All sections of Minorities in America and Women in American Culture already are filled.

50. She does not have the prerequisites for Controlled Markets, College Algebra, or Language Supervision.

51. Funding has been withdrawn for three of the Education courses and for two of the Sociology courses.

52. She must complete Finite Mathematics and Social Problems next semester to fulfill her degree requirements.

53. Selecting Clothing Don Beville took two pairs of shoes, four pairs of pants, and six shirts on a trip. If all items are compatible, how many different outfits can he wear?

54. Selecting Music Equipment A music equipment outlet stocks ten different guitars, three guitar cases, six amplifiers, and five effects processors, with all items mutually compatible and all suitable for beginners. How many different complete setups could Lionel choose to start his musical career?

55. Counting ZIP Codes Tonya's ZIP code is 85726. How many ZIP codes altogether could be formed, each one using those same five digits?

56. Listing Phone Numbers John Cross keeps the phone numbers for his seven closest friends (three men and four women) in his digital phone memory. (Refer to **Example 8**.) How many ways can he list them if

(a) men are listed before women?

(b) men are all listed together?

(c) no two men are listed next to each other?

57. *Counting Telephone Area Codes* Until 1995, the rules for three-digit area codes in the United States were as follows:

- The first digit could not be 0 or 1.
- The second digit had to be 0 or 1.
- The third digit had no such restrictions.

In 1995, the restriction on the second digit of area codes was removed. How many area codes are currently possible? (*Mathematics Teacher* calendar problem)

Seating Arrangements at a Theater In Exercises 58–61, Arne, Bobbette, Chuck, Deirdre, Ed, and Fran have reserved six seats in a row at the theater, starting at an aisle seat. (Refer to **Example 8.**)

58. In how many ways can they arrange themselves? (*Hint:* Divide the task into the series of six parts shown below, performed in order.)

(a) If A is seated first, how many seats are available for him?

(b) Now, how many are available for B?

(c) Now, how many for C?

(d) Now, how many for D?

(e) Now, how many for E?

(f) Now, how many for F?

Now multiply together your six answers above.

59. In how many ways can they arrange themselves so that Arne and Bobbette will be next to each other?

Seats available to A and B

(*Hint:* Answer these questions, in order.)

(a) How many pairs of adjacent seats can A and B occupy?

(b) Now, given the two seats for A and B, in how many orders can they be seated?

(c) Now, how many seats are available for C?

(d) Now, how many for D?

(e) Now, how many for E?

(f) Now, how many for F?

Now multiply your six answers above.

60. In how many ways can they arrange themselves if the men and women are to alternate seats and a man must sit on the aisle? (*Hint:* Answer the questions at the top of the next column, in order.)

(a) How many choices are there for the person to occupy the first seat, next to the aisle? (It must be a man.)

(b) Now, how many choices of people may occupy the second seat from the aisle? (It must be a woman.)

(c) Now, how many for the third seat? (one of the remaining men)

(d) Now, how many for the fourth seat? (a woman)

(e) Now, how many for the fifth seat? (a man)

(f) Now, how many for the sixth seat? (a woman)

Now multiply your six answers above.

61. In how many ways can they arrange themselves if the men and women are to alternate with either a man or a woman on the aisle? (*Hint:* Answer these questions.)

(a) How many choices of people are there for the aisle seat?

(b) Now, how many are there for the second seat? (This person may not be of the same sex as the person on the aisle.)

(c) Now, how many choices are there for the third seat?

(d) Now, how many for the fourth seat?

(e) Now, how many for the fifth seat?

(f) Now, how many for the sixth seat?

Now multiply your six answers above.

62. Try working **Example 4** by considering digits in the order first, then second, then third. Explain what goes wrong.

63. Try working **Example 4** by considering digits in the order third, then second, then first. Explain what goes wrong.

64. Repeat **Example 4** but this time allow repeated digits. Does the order in which digits are considered matter in this case?

65. If all the six-digit numbers formed by using the digits 1, 2, 3, 4, 5, and 6, without repetition, are listed from least to greatest, which number will be 500th in the list? (*Mathematics Teacher* calendar problem)

66. The number $2^7 \cdot 3^4 \cdot 5 \cdot 7^2 \cdot 11^3$ is divisible by many perfect squares. How many? (*Mathematics Teacher* calendar problem)

67. How many of the anagrams [arrangements of the letters] of INDIANA are palindromes, that is arrangements that read the same forward and backward? *Hint:* One such palindrome is INADANI. (*Mathematics Teacher* calendar problem)

68. How many distinguishable rearrangements of the letters in the word CONTEST start with the two vowels? (*Mathematics Teacher* calendar problem)

10.3 USING PERMUTATIONS AND COMBINATIONS

Permutations • Combinations • Guidelines on Which Method to Use

Permutations

Again recall the club

$$N = \{\text{Alan, Bill, Cathy, David, Evelyn}\} = \{A, B, C, D, E\},$$

and consider two questions:

1. How many ways can all the club members arrange themselves in a row for a photograph?
2. How many ways can the club elect a president, a secretary, and a treasurer if no one can hold more than one office?

From **Section 10.2,** the answer to the first question above is

$$5! = 5 \cdot 4 \cdot 3 \cdot 2 \cdot 1 = 120,$$

the number of possible arrangements of 5 distinct objects. We previously answered questions like the second one by using a tree diagram, or the fundamental counting principle. The answer is

$$5 \cdot 4 \cdot 3 = 60.$$

A good way to think of this second question is:

How many arrangements are there of five things taken three at a time?

The factors begin with 5 and proceed downward, just as in a factorial product, but do not go all the way to 1. (In this example the product stops when there are three factors.)

In the context of counting problems, arrangements are called **permutations.** The number of permutations of n distinct things taken r at a time is denoted ${}_nP_r$.* Since the number of objects being arranged cannot exceed the total number available, we assume that $r \le n$. Applying the fundamental counting principle gives

$${}_nP_r = n(n - 1)(n - 2) \ldots [n - (r - 1)].$$

The first factor is $n - 0$, the second is $n - 1$, the third is $n - 2$, and so on. The rth factor, the last one in the product, will be the one with $r - 1$ subtracted from n, as shown above. We can express permutations, in general, in terms of factorials, to obtain a formula as follows.

$$
\begin{aligned}
{}_nP_r &= n(n - 1)(n - 2) \ldots [n - (r - 1)] \\
&= n(n - 1)(n - 2) \ldots (n - r + 1) &&\text{Simplify the last factor.} \\
&= \frac{n(n - 1)(n - 2) \ldots (n - r + 1)(n - r)(n - r - 1) \ldots 2 \cdot 1}{(n - r)(n - r - 1) \ldots 2 \cdot 1} &&\begin{array}{l}\text{Multiply and divide by}\\ (n - r)(n - r - 1) \ldots 2 \cdot 1.\end{array} \\
&= \frac{n!}{(n - r)!} &&\text{Definition of factorial}
\end{aligned}
$$

---

*Alternative notations are $P(n, r)$ and P_r^n.

Factorial Formula for Permutations

The number of **permutations,** or *arrangements,* of n distinct things taken r at a time, where $r \leq n$, can be calculated as follows.

$$_nP_r = \frac{n!}{(n-r)!}$$

Although we sometimes refer to a symbol such as $_4P_2$ as "a permutation"(see **Examples 1 and 2**), the symbol actually represents "the number of permutations of 4 distinct things taken 2 at a time" (or "the number of size-2 arrangements that can be selected from 4 distinct things").

▮▮ **EXAMPLE 1** Using the Factorial Formula for Permutations

Evaluate each permutation.

(a) $_4P_2$ **(b)** $_8P_5$ **(c)** $_5P_5$

SOLUTION

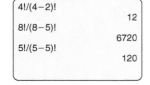

This screen uses factorials to support the results of **Example 1.**

(a) $_4P_2 = \dfrac{4!}{(4-2)!} = \dfrac{4!}{2!} = \dfrac{24}{2} = 12$

(b) $_8P_5 = \dfrac{8!}{(8-5)!} = \dfrac{8!}{3!} = \dfrac{40{,}320}{6} = 6720$

(c) $_5P_5 = \dfrac{5!}{(5-5)!} = \dfrac{5!}{0!} = \dfrac{120}{1} = 120$ ▮▮▮

Notice that $_5P_5$ is equal to 5!. The following is true for all whole numbers n.

$$_nP_n = n!$$

(This is the number of arrangements of n distinct objects taken all n at a time.)

Most graphing and scientific calculators allow direct calculation of permutations, in which case the factorial formula is not needed.

▮▮ **EXAMPLE 2** Calculating Permutations Directly

Evaluate each permutation.

(a) $_{10}P_6$ **(b)** $_{28}P_0$ **(c)** $_{18}P_{12}$

SOLUTION

(a) $_{10}P_6 = 151{,}200$ **(b)** $_{28}P_0 = 1$ **(c)** $_{18}P_{12} = 8{,}892{,}185{,}702{,}400$

Concerning part (c), many calculators will not display this many digits, so you may obtain an answer such as 8.8921857×10^{12}.   ▮▮▮

This screen uses the permutations feature to support the results of **Example 2.**

PROBLEM-SOLVING HINT Permutations can be used any time we need to know the number of arrangements of r objects that can be selected from a collection of n objects. The word *arrangement* implies an ordering, so we use permutations only in cases when

1. repetitions are not allowed,   and   **2. order is important.**

Change ringing, the English way of ringing church bells, combines mathematics and music. Bells are rung first in sequence, 1, 2, 3, ... Then the sequence is permuted ("changed"). On six bells, 720 different "changes" (different permutations of tone) can be rung:
$$_6P_6 = 6!.$$

The church bells are swung by means of ropes attached to the wheels beside them. One ringer swings each bell, listening intently and watching the other ringers closely. If one ringer gets lost and stays lost, the rhythm of the ringing cannot be maintained; all the ringers have to stop.

A ringer can spend weeks just learning to keep a bell going and months learning to make the bell ring in exactly the right place. Errors of $\frac{1}{4}$ second mean that two bells are ringing at the same time. Even errors of $\frac{1}{10}$ second can be heard.

▮▮ **EXAMPLE 3** Building Numbers from a Set of Digits

How many nonrepeating three-digit numbers can be written using only the digits 3, 4, 5, 6, 7, and 8?

SOLUTION

Repetitions are not allowed since the numbers are to be "nonrepeating." (For example, 448 is not acceptable.) Also, order is important. (For example, 476 and 746 are *distinct* cases.) So we use permutations.

$$_6P_3 = 6 \cdot 5 \cdot 4 = 120$$ ▮▮▮

▮▮ **EXAMPLE 4** Designing Account Numbers

Suppose certain account numbers are to consist of two letters followed by four digits and then three more letters, where repetitions of letters or digits are not allowed *within* any of the three groups, but the last group of letters may contain one or both of those used in the first group. How many such accounts are possible?

SOLUTION

The task of designing such a number consists of three parts:

1. Determine the first set of two letters.
2. Determine the set of four digits.
3. Determine the final set of three letters.

Each part requires an arrangement without repetitions, which is a permutation. Multiply together the results of the three parts.

$$_{26}P_2 \cdot {}_{10}P_4 \cdot {}_{26}P_3 = \underbrace{650}_{\text{Part 1}} \cdot \underbrace{5040}_{\text{Part 2}} \cdot \underbrace{15{,}600}_{\text{Part 3}}$$

$$= 51{,}105{,}600{,}000$$ ▮▮▮

Combinations

We introduced permutations to evaluate the number of arrangements of *n* things taken *r* at a time, where repetitions are not allowed. The order of the items was important. Recall that club

$$N = \{\text{Alan, Bill, Cathy, David, Evelyn}\}$$

could elect three officers in $_5P_3 = 60$ different ways. With three-member committees, on the other hand, order is not important. The committees *B, D, E* and *E, B, D* are not different. The possible number of committees is not the number of arrangements of size 3. Rather, it is the number of *subsets* of size 3.

Recall that in the study of sets (**Chapter 2**), a **set** is a collection or group of things, commonly designated using a list within braces, as we have been designating the club

$$N = \{A, B, C, D, E\}.$$

The order of listing of the members (of any set) is unimportant. For example, $\{D, B, A, E, C\}$ is the same club. A **subset** of a set is a collection of some of the members. It may be all members of the original set, or even none of them, or anywhere in between. Again, the order of listing of the members is unimportant.

In the study of counting methods, subsets are called **combinations.** The number of combinations of n things taken r at a time (that is, the number of size r subsets, given a set of size n) is written $_nC_r$.*

Since there are n things available and we are choosing r of them, we can read $_nC_r$ as "n choose r."

The size-3 committees (subsets) of the club (set) $N = \{A, B, C, D, E\}$ are:

$$\{A, B, C\}, \quad \{A, B, D\}, \quad \{A, B, E\}, \quad \{A, C, D\}, \quad \{A, C, E\},$$
$$\{A, D, E\}, \quad \{B, C, D\}, \quad \{B, C, E\}, \quad \{B, D, E\}, \quad \{C, D, E\}.$$

There are ten subsets of size 3, so ten is the number of three-member committees possible. Just as with permutations, repetitions are not allowed. For example, $\{E, E, B\}$ is not a valid three-member subset, just as EEB is not a valid three-member arrangement.

To see how to find the number of such subsets without listing them all, notice that each size-3 subset (combination) gives rise to six size-3 arrangements (permutations). For example, the single combination ADE yields these six permutations:

$$A, D, E \quad A, E, D \quad D, A, E \quad D, E, A \quad E, A, D \quad E, D, A.$$

There must be six times as many size-3 permutations as there are size-3 combinations, or, in other words, one-sixth as many combinations as permutations.

$$_5C_3 = \frac{_5P_3}{6} = \frac{60}{6} = 10$$

Again, the 6 appears in the denominator because there are six different ways to arrange a set of three things (since $3! = 3 \cdot 2 \cdot 1 = 6$). Generalizing from this example, we obtain a formula for evaluating numbers of combinations.

$$_nC_r = \frac{_nP_r}{r!} \qquad \text{r things can be arranged in $r!$ ways.}$$

$$= \frac{\dfrac{n!}{(n-r)!}}{r!} \qquad \text{Substitute the factorial formula for $_nP_r$.}$$

$$= \frac{n!}{r!(n-r)!} \qquad \text{Simplify algebraically.}$$

Factorial Formula for Combinations

The number of **combinations,** or *subsets*, of n distinct things taken r at a time, where $r \le n$, can be calculated as follows.

$$_nC_r = \frac{_nP_r}{r!} = \frac{n!}{r!(n-r)!}$$

In **Examples 5 and 6,** we refer to $_nC_r$ as "a combination" even though it actually represents "the number of combinations of n distinct things taken r at a time" (or "the number of size-r subsets that can be selected from a set of n things").

*Alternative notations are $C(n, r)$, C_r^n, and $\binom{n}{r}$.

$\mathcal{A}$ $\mathcal{B}$ C $\mathcal{D}$ E F
Aaaaa aaaab aaaba. aaabb. aabaa. aabab.
G H I K L $\mathcal{M}$
aabba aabbb abaaa. abaab. ababa. ababb.
$\mathcal{N}$ O $\mathcal{P}$ Q $\mathcal{R}$ S
abbaa. abbab. abbba. abbbb. baaaa. baaab.
T $\mathcal{V}$ W X Y Z
baaba. baabb. babaa. babab. babba. babbb.

$\{\dot{A}\dot{A}\dot{a}\dot{a}\ \dot{B}\dot{B}\dot{b}\dot{b}\ \dot{C}\dot{C}\dot{c}\dot{c}\ \dot{D}\dot{D}\dot{d}\dot{d}\ \dot{E}\dot{E}\dot{s}\dot{s}\ \dot{F}\dot{F}\dot{f}\dot{f}$
$\{\dot{G}\dot{G}\dot{g}\dot{g}\ \dot{H}\dot{H}\dot{b}\dot{h}\ \dot{J}\dot{I}\dot{i}\dot{i}\ \dot{K}\dot{K}\dot{k}\dot{k}\ \dot{L}\dot{L}\dot{l}\dot{l}\ \dot{M}\dot{M}\dot{m}\dot{m}$
$\{\dot{N}\dot{N}\dot{n}\dot{n}\ \dot{O}\dot{O}\dot{o}\dot{o}\ \dot{P}\dot{P}\dot{p}\dot{p}\ \dot{Q}\dot{Q}\dot{q}\dot{q}\ \dot{R}\dot{R}\dot{r}\dot{r}\ \dot{S}\dot{S}\dot{s}\dot{s}$
$\{\dot{T}\dot{T}\dot{t}\dot{t}\ \dot{U}\dot{V}\dot{v}\dot{v}\dot{u}\dot{u}\ \dot{W}\dot{W}\dot{w}\dot{w}\ \dot{X}\dot{X}\dot{x}\dot{x}\ \dot{Y}\dot{Y}\dot{y}\dot{y}\ \dot{Z}\dot{Z}\dot{z}\dot{z}$

"Bilateral cipher" (above) was invented by **Francis Bacon** early in the seventeenth century to code political secrets. This binary code, *a* and *b* in combinations of five, has 32 permutations. Bacon's "biformed alphabet" (bottom four rows) uses two type fonts to conceal a message in some straight text. The decoder deciphers a string of *a*s and *b*s, groups them by fives, then deciphers letters and words. This code was applied to Shakespeare's plays in efforts to prove Bacon the rightful author.

EXAMPLE 5 Using the Factorial Formula for Combinations

Evaluate each combination.

(a) $_9C_7$ **(b)** $_{24}C_{18}$

SOLUTION

$$\boxed{\begin{array}{l} 9!/(7!*2!) \\ \hspace{3cm} 36 \\ 24!/(18!*6!) \\ \hspace{2.5cm} 134596 \end{array}}$$

This screen uses factorials to support the results of **Example 5**.

(a) $_9C_7 = \dfrac{9!}{7!(9-7)!} = \dfrac{9!}{7!\,2!} = \dfrac{362{,}880}{5040 \cdot 2} = 36$

(b) $_{24}C_{18} = \dfrac{24!}{18!(24-18)!} = \dfrac{24!}{18!\,6!} = 134{,}596$ ▌▌▌

EXAMPLE 6 Calculating Combinations Directly

Evaluate each combination.

(a) $_{14}C_6$ **(b)** $_{21}C_{15}$

$$\boxed{\begin{array}{l} 14 \ \text{nCr} \ 6 \\ \hspace{3cm} 3003 \\ 21 \ \text{nCr} \ 15 \\ \hspace{2.7cm} 54264 \end{array}}$$

This screen uses the combinations feature to support the results of **Example 6**.

SOLUTION

(a) $_{14}C_6 = 3003$ **(b)** $_{21}C_{15} = 54{,}264$ Use a calculator in each case. ▌▌▌

> **PROBLEM-SOLVING HINT** Combinations have an important common property with permutations (repetitions are not allowed) and have an important distinction (order is *not* important with combinations). Combinations are applied only when
>
> **1.** repetitions are not allowed, and **2. order is *not* important.**

EXAMPLE 7 Finding the Number of Subsets

Find the number of different subsets of size 2 in the set $\{a, b, c, d\}$. List them to check the answer.

SOLUTION

A subset of size 2 must have two distinct elements, so repetitions are not allowed. And since the order in which the elements of a set are listed makes no difference, order is not important. Use the combinations formula with $n = 4$ and $r = 2$.

$$_4C_2 = \frac{4!}{2!(4-2)!} = \frac{4!}{2!\,2!} = 6$$

The six subsets of size 2 are $\{a, b\}, \{a, c\}, \{a, d\}, \{b, c\}, \{b, d\}, \{c, d\}$. ▌▌▌

EXAMPLE 8 Finding the Number of Possible Poker Hands

A common form of poker involves "hands" (sets) of five cards each, dealt from a standard deck consisting of 52 different cards. How many different 5-card hands are possible?

SOLUTION

A 5-card hand must contain five distinct cards, so repetitions are not allowed. Also, the order is not important since a given hand depends only on the cards it contains, and not on the order in which they were dealt or the order in which they are displayed or played.

Since order does not matter, use combinations (and a calculator).

$$_{52}C_5 = \frac{52!}{5!(52-5)!} = \frac{52!}{5!\,47!} = 2{,}598{,}960$$

███

EXAMPLE 9   Finding the Number of Subsets of Paintings

Keri Beers would like to buy ten different paintings but can afford only four of them. In how many ways can she make her selections?

SOLUTION

The four paintings selected must be distinct (repetitions are not allowed), and the order of the four chosen has no bearing in this case, so we use combinations.

$$_{10}C_4 = \frac{10!}{4!(10-4)!} = \frac{10!}{4!\,6!} = 210 \text{ ways}$$

███

Notice that, according to our formula for combinations,

$$_{10}C_6 = \frac{10!}{6!(10-6)!} = \frac{10!}{6!\,4!} = 210,$$

which is the same as $_{10}C_4$. In fact, **Exercise 62** asks you to prove the following fact, in general, for all whole numbers n and r, with $r \le n$.

$$_nC_r = {}_nC_{n-r}$$

Guidelines on Which Method to Use

The following table summarizes the similarities and differences between permutations and combinations, as well as the appropriate formulas for calculating their values.

The set of 52 playing cards in the standard deck has four suits.

♠ spades   ♦ diamonds
♥ hearts   ♣ clubs

Ace is the unit card. Jacks, queens, and kings are "face cards." Each suit contains thirteen denominations: ace, 2, 3, . . . , 10, jack, queen, king. (In some games, ace rates above king, instead of counting as 1.)

Permutations	**Combinations**
Number of ways of selecting r items out of n items	
Repetitions are not allowed.	
Order is important.	Order is not important.
Arrangements of n items taken r at a time	Subsets of n items taken r at a time
$_nP_r = \dfrac{n!}{(n-r)!}$	$_nC_r = \dfrac{n!}{r!(n-r)!}$
Clue words: arrangement, schedule, order	Clue words: set, group, sample, selection

In cases where r items are to be selected from n items and repetitions are allowed, it is usually best to make direct use of the fundamental counting principle.

Most, if not all, of the exercises in this section will call for permutations and/or combinations. And in the case of multiple-part tasks, the fundamental counting principle may also be required. *In all cases, decide carefully whether order is important, since that determines whether to use permutations or combinations.*

> **PROBLEM-SOLVING HINT** Many counting problems involve selecting some of the items from a given set of items. The particular conditions of the problem will determine which specific technique to use.
>
> **1. If selected items can be repeated, use the fundamental counting principle.**
>   *Example:* How many four-digit numbers are there?
>
> $$9 \cdot 10^3 = 9000$$
>
> **2. If selected items cannot be repeated, and order is important, use permutations.**
>   *Example:* How many ways can three of eight people line up at a ticket counter?
>
> $$_8P_3 = \frac{8!}{(8-3)!} = 336$$
>
> **3. If selected items cannot be repeated, and order is *not* important, use combinations.**
>   *Example:* How many ways can a committee of three be selected from a group of twelve people?
>
> $$_{12}C_3 = \frac{12!}{3!(12-3)!} = 220$$

▮▮ **EXAMPLE 10** Distributing Toys to Children

In how many ways can a mother distribute three different toys among her seven children if a child may receive anywhere from none to all three toys?

SOLUTION

Because a given child can be a repeat recipient, repetitions are allowed here, so we use the fundamental counting principle. Each of the three toys can go to any of the seven children. The number of possible distributions is $7 \cdot 7 \cdot 7 = 343$.   ▮▮▮

▮▮ **EXAMPLE 11** Selecting Committees

How many different three-member committees could club N appoint so that exactly one woman is on the committee?

SOLUTION

Recall that $N = \{$Alan, Bill, Cathy, David, Evelyn$\}$. Two members are women; three are men. Although the question mentioned only that the committee must include exactly one woman, to complete the committee two men must be selected as well. The task of selecting the committee members consists of two parts:

  1. Choose one woman.   **2.** Choose two men.

    Because order is not important for committees, use combinations for the two parts. One woman can be chosen in $_2C_1 = \frac{2!}{1!1!} = 2$ ways, and two men can be chosen in $_3C_2 = \frac{3!}{2!1!} = 3$ ways. Finally, use the fundamental counting principle to obtain $2 \cdot 3 = 6$ different committees. This small number can be checked by listing.

    $\{C, A, B\}, \quad \{C, A, D\}, \quad \{C, B, D\}, \quad \{E, A, B\}, \quad \{E, A, D\}, \quad \{E, B, D\}$ ▮▮▮

The illustration above is from the 1560s text **Logistica,** by the mathematician J. Buteo. Among other topics, the book discusses the number of possible throws of four dice and the number of arrangements of the cylinders of a combination lock. Note that "combination" is a misleading name for these locks since repetitions are allowed, and, also, order makes a difference.

▮▮ **EXAMPLE 12** Selecting Attendees for an Event

Every member of the Alpha Beta Gamma fraternity would like to attend a special event this weekend, but only ten members will be allowed to attend. How many ways could the lucky ten be selected if there are a total of forty-eight members?

SOLUTION

In this case, ten distinct men are required (repetitions are not allowed), and the order of selection makes no difference, so we use combinations.

$$_{48}C_{10} = \frac{48!}{10!\,38!} = 6{,}540{,}715{,}896 \quad \text{Use a calculator.} \quad ▮▮▮$$

▮▮ **EXAMPLE 13** Selecting Escorts

When the ten fraternity men of **Example 12** arrive at the event, four of them are selected to escort the four homecoming queen candidates. In how many ways can this selection be made?

SOLUTION

Of the ten, four distinct men are required, and order is important here because different orders will pair the men with different women. Use permutations.

$$_{10}P_4 = \frac{10!}{6!} = 5040 \text{ possible selections} \quad ▮▮▮$$

▮▮ **EXAMPLE 14** Dividing into Groups

In how many ways can the 9 members of a baseball lineup divide into groups of 4, 3, and 2 players?

SOLUTION

Order is not important within the groups. The players within a group are interchangeable in their order of listing. Use combinations.

First, 4 can be chosen from 9 in $_9C_4 = 126$ ways.

Then, 3 can be chosen from the remaining 5 in $_5C_3 = 10$ ways.

Then, 2 can be chosen from the remaining 2 in $_2C_2 = 1$ way.

The three groups also are not interchangeable. They all have different sizes. Apply the fundamental counting principle.

$$_9C_4 \cdot {_5C_3} \cdot {_2C_2} = 126 \cdot 10 \cdot 1 = 1260 \quad ▮▮▮$$

▮▮ **EXAMPLE 15** Dividing into Groups

In how many ways can the 9 players of **Example 14** divide into three groups of 3?

SOLUTION

After the pattern of **Example 14,** the answer may *seem* to be

$$_9C_3 \cdot {_6C_3} \cdot {_3C_3} = 84 \cdot 20 \cdot 1 = 1680.$$

However, this would impose an *unwanted order,* not within the groups, but *among* the groups. Ordering the three group selections was appropriate in **Example 14,** because those three groups were distinguishable. They were all different sizes. But here, all groups are size-3.

If the players are denoted A, B, C, D, E, F, G, H, and I, then the list

(1) *BIG, HEF, CAD* **(2)** *BIG, CAD, HEF* **(3)** *HEF, BIG, CAD*

(4) *HEF, CAD, BIG* **(5)** *CAD, BIG, HEF* **(6)** *CAD, HEF, BIG*

contains six orderings of the same three groups. Since the product calculated above, from the fundamental counting principle, duplicates every set of three groups in this way, we must adjust that value by dividing by $3! = 6$ to obtain the true number of *unordered* sets of three groups. The idea is the same as when we adjust the number of arrangements—orderings—of n things taken r at a time to obtain the number of unordered sets of n things taken r at a time according to the formula

$$_nC_r = \frac{_nP_r}{r!}.$$

The number of ways 9 players can divide into three groups of 3 is

$$\frac{_9C_3 \cdot {}_6C_3 \cdot {}_3C_3}{3!} = \frac{1680}{6} = 280. \qquad \blacksquare\blacksquare\blacksquare$$

For Further Thought

Poker Hands

In 5-card poker, played with a standard 52-card deck, 2,598,960 different hands are possible. (See **Example 8.**) The desirability of the various hands depends upon their relative chance of occurrence, which, in turn, depends on the number of different ways they can occur, as shown in **Table 4**. Note that an ace can generally be positioned either below 2 (as a 1) or above king (as a 14). This is important in counting straight flush hands and straight hands.

Table 4 Categories of Hands in 5-Card Poker

Event E	Description of Event E	Number of Outcomes Favorable to E
Royal flush	Ace, king, queen, jack, and 10, all of the same suit	4
Straight flush	5 cards of consecutive denominations, all in the same suit (excluding royal flush)	36
Four of a kind	4 cards of the same denomination, plus 1 additional card	_____
Full house	3 cards of one denomination, plus 2 cards of a second denomination	3744
Flush	Any 5 cards all of the same suit (excluding royal flush and straight flush)	_____
Straight	5 cards of consecutive denominations (not all the same suit)	10,200
Three of a kind	3 cards of one denomination, plus 2 cards of two additional denominations	54,912
Two pairs	2 cards of one denomination, plus 2 cards of a second denomination, plus 1 card of a third denomination	_____
One pair	2 cards of one denomination, plus 3 additional cards of three different denominations	1,098,240
No pair	No two cards of the same denomination (and excluding any sort of flush or straight)	1,302,540
Total		**2,598,960**

For Group or Individual Investigation

As the table shows, a full house is a relatively rare occurrence. (Only four of a kind, straight flush, and royal flush are less likely.) To verify that there are 3744 different full house hands possible, carry out the following steps.

1. Explain why there are $_4C_3$ different ways to select three aces from the deck.

2. Explain why there are $_4C_2$ different ways to select two 8s from the deck.

3. If "aces and 8s" (three aces and two 8s) is one kind of full house, show that there are $_{13}P_2$ different kinds of full house altogether.

4. Multiply the expressions from Steps 1, 2, and 3 together. Explain why this product should give the total number of full house hands possible.

5. Find the three missing values in the right column of **Table 4**. (Answers are on **page 581**.)

6. Verify the right column total shown in **Table 4**.

10.3 EXERCISES

Evaluate each expression.

1. $_9P_3$

2. $_{12}P_5$

3. $_{11}C_7$

4. $_{14}C_6$

Determine the number of permutations (arrangements) of each of the following.

5. 20 things taken 4 at a time

6. 15 things taken 5 at a time

Determine the number of combinations (subsets) of each of the following.

7. 9 things taken 4 at a time

8. 13 things taken 6 at a time

Use a calculator to evaluate each expression.

9. $_{22}P_9$

10. $_{32}C_{12}$

11. Is it possible to evaluate $_8P_{10}$? Explain.

12. Is it possible to evaluate $_9C_{14}$? Explain.

13. Explain how permutations and combinations differ.

14. Explain how factorials are related to permutations.

15. **Permutations or Combinations?** Decide whether each object is a permutation or a combination.

(a) a telephone number

(b) a Social Security number

(c) a hand of cards in poker

(d) a committee of politicians

(e) the "combination" on a student gym locker combination lock

(f) a lottery choice of six numbers where the order does not matter

(g) an automobile license plate number

(h) an internet password

Exercises 16–23 can be solved with permutations even though the problem statements will not always include a form of the word "permutation," or "arrangement," or "ordering."

16. **Placing in a Race** How many different ways could first-, second-, and third-place finishers occur in a race with six runners competing?

17. **Arranging New Home Models** Tyler Aunan, a contractor, builds homes of eight different models and presently has five lots to build on. In how many different ways can he arrange homes on these lots? Assume five different models will be built.

18. **ATM PIN Numbers** An automated teller machine (ATM) requires a four-digit personal identification number (PIN), using the digits 0–9. (The first digit may be 0.) How many such PINs have no repeated digits?

19. **Electing Officers of a Club** How many ways can president and vice president be determined in a club with twelve members?

20. **Counting Prize Winners** First, second, and third prizes are to be awarded to three different people. If there are ten eligible candidates, how many outcomes are possible?

21. **Counting Prize Winners** How many ways can a teacher give five different prizes to five of her 25 students?

22. **Scheduling Security Team Visits** A security team visits 12 offices each night. How many different ways can the team order its visits?

23. **Sums of Digits** How many counting numbers have four distinct nonzero digits such that the sum of the four digits is

   (a) 10?   **(b)** 11?

Exercises 24–31 can be solved with combinations even though the problem statements will not always include the word "combination" or "subset."

24. **Sampling Cell Phones** How many ways can a sample of five cell phones be selected from a shipment of twenty-four cell phones?

25. **Detecting Defective Cell Phones** If the shipment of **Exercise 24** contains six defective phones, how many of the size-five samples would not include any of the defective ones?

26. **Committees of U.S. Senators** How many different five-member committees could be formed from the 100 U.S. senators?

27. **Selecting Hands of Cards** Refer to the standard 52-card deck pictured on **page 549** and notice that the deck contains four aces, twelve face cards, thirteen hearts (all red), thirteen diamonds (all red), thirteen spades (all black), and thirteen clubs (all black). Of the 2,598,960 different five-card hands possible, decide how many would consist of the following cards.

   (a) all diamonds   **(b)** all black cards

   (c) all aces

28. **Selecting Lottery Entries** In a $\frac{7}{39}$ lottery, you select seven distinct numbers from the set 1 through 39, where order makes no difference. How many different ways can you make your selection?

29. **Arranging New Home Models** Tyler Aunan (the contractor) is to build six homes on a block in a new subdivision, using two different models, standard and deluxe. (All standard model homes are the same and all deluxe model homes are the same.)

   (a) How many different choices does Tyler have in positioning the six houses if he decides to build three standard and three deluxe models?

   (b) If Tyler builds two deluxes and four standards, how many different positionings can he use?

30. **Choosing a Monogram** Sheryl Jett wants to name her new baby so that his monogram (first, middle, and last initials) will be distinct letters in alphabetical order and he will share her last name. How many different monograms could she select?

31. **Number of Paths from Point to Point** In a certain city, there are seven streets going north–south and four streets going east–west. How many street paths start at the southwest corner of the city, end at the northeast corner of the city, and have the shortest possible length? (*Mathematics Teacher* calendar problem)

For Exercises 32–60, you may use permutations, combinations, the fundamental counting principle, or other counting methods as appropriate.

32. **Selecting Lottery Entries** In SuperLotto Plus, a California state lottery game, you select five distinct numbers from 1 to 47, and one MEGA number from 1 to 27, hoping that your selection will match a random list selected by lottery officials.

   (a) How many different sets of six numbers can you select?

   (b) Paul Burke always includes his age and his wife's age as two of the first five numbers in his SuperLotto Plus selections. How many ways can he complete his list of six numbers?

33. **Drawing Cards** How many cards must be drawn (without replacement) from a standard deck of 52 to guarantee the following?

   (a) Two of the cards will be of the same suit.

   (b) Three of the cards will be of the same suit.

34. **Flush Hands in Poker** How many different 5-card poker hands would contain only cards of a single suit?

35. **Identification Numbers in Research** Subject identification numbers in a certain scientific research project consist of three letters followed by three digits and then three more letters. Assume repetitions are not allowed within any of the three groups, but letters in the first group of three may occur also in the last group of three. How many distinct identification numbers are possible?

36. Radio Station Call Letters Radio stations in the United States have call letters that begin with K or W (for west or east of the Mississippi River, respectively). Some have three call letters, such as WBZ in Boston, WLS in Chicago, and KGO in San Francisco. Assuming no repetition of letters, how many three-letter sets of call letters are possible? (Count all possibilities even though, practically, some may be inappropriate.)

37. Radio Station Call Letters Most stations that were licensed after 1927 have four call letters starting with K or W, such as WXYZ in Detroit or KRLD in Dallas. Assuming no repetitions, how many four-letter sets are possible? (Count all possibilities even though, practically, some may be inappropriate.)

38. Scheduling Games in a Basketball League Each team in an eight-team basketball league is scheduled to play each other team three times. How many games will be played altogether?

39. Scheduling Batting Orders in Baseball The Coyotes, a youth league baseball team, have seven pitchers, who only pitch, and twelve other players, all of whom can play any position other than pitcher. For Saturday's game, the coach has not yet determined which nine players to use nor what the batting order will be, except that the pitcher will bat last. How many different batting orders may occur?

40. Ordering Performers in a Music Recital A music class of five girls and four boys is having a recital. If each member is to perform once, how many ways can the program be arranged in each of the following cases?

(a) All girls must perform first.
(b) A girl must perform first and a boy must perform last.
(c) Elisa and Doug will perform first and last, respectively.
(d) The entire program will alternate between girls and boys.
(e) The first, fifth, and ninth performers must be girls.

41. Scheduling Daily Reading Carole begins each day by reading from one of seven inspirational books. How many ways can she arrange her reading for one week if the selection is done

(a) with replacement?   (b) without replacement?

42. Counting Card Hands How many of the possible 5-card hands from a standard 52-card deck would consist of the following cards?
(a) four clubs and one non-club
(b) two face cards and three non-face cards
(c) two red cards, two clubs, and a spade

43. Dividing People into Groups In how many ways could fifteen people be divided into five groups containing, respectively, one, two, three, four, and five people?

44. Dividing People into Groups In how many ways could fifteen people be divided into five groups of three people?

45. Dividing People into Groups In how many ways could eight people be divided into two groups of three people and a group of two people?

46. Points and Lines in a Plane If any two points determine a line, how many lines are determined by seven points in a plane, no three of which are collinear?

47. Points and Triangles in a Plane How many triangles are determined by twenty points in a plane, no three of which are collinear?

48. Counting Possibilities on a Combination Lock How many different three-number "combinations" are possible on a combination lock having 40 numbers on its dial? (*Hint:* "Combination" is a misleading name for these locks since repetitions are allowed and order makes a difference.)

49. Selecting Drivers and Passengers for a Trip Natalie Graham, her husband and son, and four additional friends are driving, in two vehicles, to the seashore.

(a) If all seven people can drive, how many ways can the two drivers be selected? (Everyone wants to drive the sports car, so it is important which driver gets which car.)
(b) If the sports car must be driven by Natalie, her husband, or their son, how many ways can the drivers now be determined?
(c) If the sports car will accommodate only two people, and there are no other restrictions, how many ways can both drivers and passengers be assigned to both cars?

50. Winning the Daily Double in Horse Racing You win the "daily double" by purchasing a ticket and selecting the winners of two specific races. If there are six and eight horses running in those races, respectively, how many tickets must you buy to guarantee a win?

51. Winning the Trifecta in Horse Racing Many race tracks offer a "trifecta" race. You win by selecting the correct first-, second-, and third-place finishers. If eight horses are entered, how many tickets must you purchase to guarantee that one of them will be a trifecta winner?

52. Selecting Committees Nine people are to be distributed among three committees of two, three, and four members, and a chairperson is to be selected for each committee. How many ways can this be done? (*Hint:* Break the task into the following sequence of parts.)

(a) Select the members of the two-person committee.

(b) Select the members of the three-person committee.

(c) Select the chair of the two-person committee.

(d) Select the chair of the three-person committee.

(e) Select the chair of the four-person committee.

53. Selecting Committee Members Repeat **Exercise 52** in case the three committees are to have three members each. (*Hint:* Use the same general sequence of task parts, but remember to adjust for *unwanted ordering* of the three committees.)

54. Arranging New Home Models (See **Exercise 29.**) Because of his good work, Tyler Aunan gets a contract to build homes on three additional blocks in the subdivision, with six homes on each block. He decides to build nine deluxe homes on these three blocks: two on the first block, three on the second, and four on the third. The remaining nine homes will be standard.

(a) Altogether on the three-block stretch, how many different choices does Tyler have for positioning the eighteen homes? (*Hint:* Consider the three blocks separately and use the fundamental counting principle.)

(b) How many choices would he have if he built 2, 3, and 4 deluxe models on the three different blocks as before, but not necessarily on the first, second, and third blocks in that order?

55. Building Numbers from Sets of Digits

(a) How many six-digit counting numbers use all six digits 4, 5, 6, 7, 8, and 9?

(b) Suppose all these numbers were arranged in increasing order: 456,789; 456,798; and so on. Which number would be 364th in the list?

56. Arranging Five-letter Words The 120 permutations of AHSME are arranged in dictionary order, as if each were an ordinary five-letter word. Find the last letter of the 86th word in the list. (*Mathematics Teacher* calendar problem)

57. Arranging a Wedding Reception Line At a wedding reception, the bride and groom, and four attendants will form a reception line. How many ways can they be arranged in each of the following cases?

(a) Any order will do.

(b) The bride and groom must be the last two in line.

(c) The groom must be last in line with the bride next to him.

58. Assigning Student Grades A professor teaches a class of 60 students and another class of 40 students. Five percent of the students in each class are to receive a grade of A. How many different ways can the A grades be distributed?

59. Sums of Digits How many counting numbers consist of four distinct nonzero digits such that the sum of the four digits is

(a) 12? (b) 13?

60. Screening Computer Processors A computer company will screen a shipment of 30 processors by testing a random sample of five of them. How many different samples are possible?

61. Verify that $_{12}C_9 = _{12}C_3$.

62. Use the factorial formula for combinations to prove that in general,

$$_nC_r = _nC_{n-r}.$$

10.4 USING PASCAL'S TRIANGLE

Pascal's Triangle • Applications

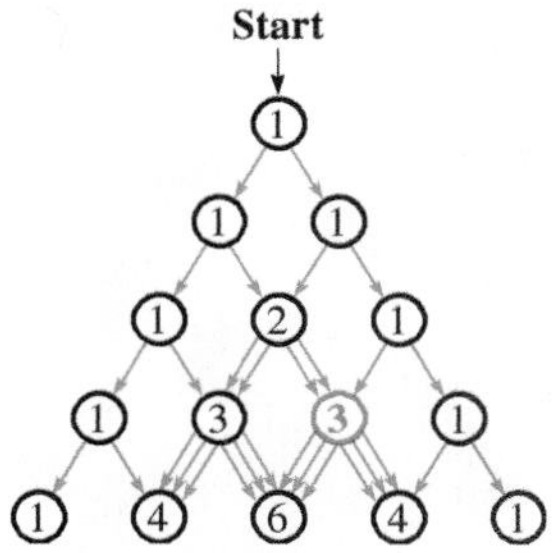

Start

Figure 7

Pascal's Triangle

The triangular array in **Figure 7** represents what we can call "random walks" that begin at START and proceed downward according to the following rule:

At each circle (branch point), a coin is tossed. If it lands heads, we go downward to the left. If it lands tails, we go downward to the right. At each point, left and right are equally likely.

In each circle we have recorded the number of different routes that could bring us to that point. For example, the colored 3 can be reached as the result of three different coin-tossing sequences:

htt, tht, and tth.

Another way to generate the same pattern of numbers is to begin with 1s down both diagonals and then fill in the interior entries by adding the two numbers just above a given position (to the left and right). For example, the colored 28 in **Table 5** is the result of adding 7 and 21 in the row above it.

Table 5	Pascal's Triangle											Row Sum
Row Number												
0						1						1
1					1		1					2
2				1		2		1				4
3			1		3		3		1			8
4		1		4		6		4		1		16
5	1		5		10		10		5		1	32
6	1	6		15		20		15		6	1	64
7	1	7	21		35		35		21	7	1	128
8	1	8	28	56		70		56	28	8	1	256
9	1	9	36	84	126		126	84	36	9	1	512
10	1	10	45	120	210	252	210	120	45	10	1	1024

By continuing to add pairs of numbers, we extend the array indefinitely downward, always beginning and ending each row with 1s. (The table shows just rows 0 through 10.) This unending "triangular" array of numbers is called **Pascal's triangle,** since Blaise Pascal wrote a treatise about it in 1653. There is evidence, though, that it was known as early as around 1100 and may have been studied in China or India still earlier.

At any rate, the "triangle" possesses many interesting properties. In counting applications, the most useful property is that, in general, entry number r in row number n is equal to $_nC_r$—the number of *combinations* of n things taken r at a time. This correspondence is shown (through row 7) in **Table 6** on the next page.

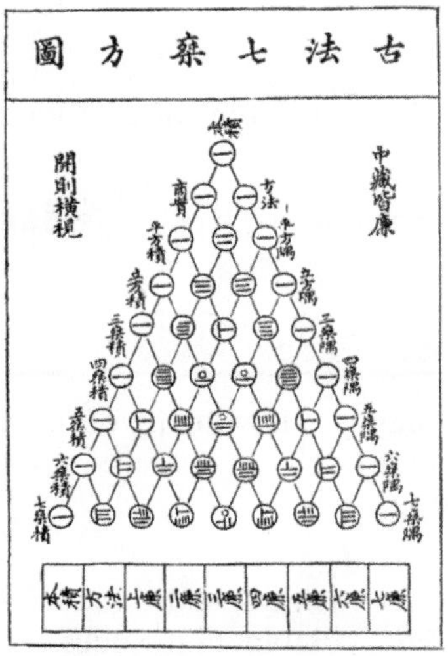

"Pascal's" triangle shown in the 1303 text **Szu-yuen Yu-chien** (*The Precious Mirror of the Four Elements*) by the Chinese mathematician Chu Shih-chieh.

Table 6   Combination Values in Pascal's Triangle

Row Number								
0				$_0C_0$				
1			$_1C_0$		$_1C_1$			
2			$_2C_0$	$_2C_1$	$_2C_2$			
3		$_3C_0$	$_3C_1$	$_3C_2$	$_3C_3$			
4		$_4C_0$	$_4C_1$	$_4C_2$	$_4C_3$	$_4C_4$		
5	$_5C_0$	$_5C_1$	$_5C_2$	$_5C_3$	$_5C_4$	$_5C_5$		
6	$_6C_0$	$_6C_1$	$_6C_2$	$_6C_3$	$_6C_4$	$_6C_5$	$_6C_6$	
7	$_7C_0$	$_7C_1$	$_7C_2$	$_7C_3$	$_7C_4$	$_7C_5$	$_7C_6$	$_7C_7$

and so on

Having a copy of Pascal's triangle handy gives us another option for evaluating combinations. Any time we need to know the number of combinations of *n* things taken *r* at a time (that is, the number of subsets of size *r* in a set of size *n*), we can simply read entry number *r* of row number *n*. ***Keep in mind that the first row shown is row number 0.*** Also, the first entry of each row can be called entry number 0. This entry gives the number of subsets of size 0 (which is always 1 since there is only one empty set).

Applications

▮▮ **EXAMPLE 1** Applying Pascal's Triangle to Counting People

A group of ten people includes six women and four men. If five of these people are randomly selected to fill out a questionnaire, how many different samples of five people are possible?

SOLUTION

This is simply a matter of selecting a subset of five from a set of ten (or combinations of ten things taken five at a time).

$$_{10}C_5 = 252 \quad \text{See row 10 of Pascal's triangle in } \textbf{Table 5.} \qquad ▮▮▮$$

▮▮ **EXAMPLE 2** Applying Pascal's Triangle to Counting People

Among the 252 possible samples of five people in **Example 1,** how many of them would consist of exactly two women and three men?

SOLUTION

Two women can be selected from six women in $_6C_2$ different ways, and three men can be selected from four men in $_4C_3$ different ways. These combination values can be read from Pascal's triangle. Then, since the task of obtaining two women and three men requires both individual parts, the fundamental counting principle tells us to multiply the two values.

$$_6C_2 \cdot {}_4C_3 = 15 \cdot 4 = 60 \quad \text{Rows 6 and 4 of Pascal's triangle} \qquad ▮▮▮$$

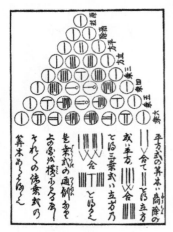

This **Japanese version** of the triangle dates from the eighteenth century. The "stick numerals" evolved from bamboo counting pieces used on a ruled board. Possibly Omar Khayyam, twelfth-century Persian mathematician and poet, may also have divined its patterns in pursuit of algebraic solutions. (The triangle lists the coefficients of the binomial expansion, explained in **For Further Thought** on **pages 559 and 560**.)

▐▐ **EXAMPLE 3** Applying Pascal's Triangle to Coin Tossing

If five fair coins are tossed, in how many different ways could exactly three heads be obtained?

SOLUTION

There are various "ways" of obtaining exactly three heads because the three heads can occur on different subsets of the coins. For example, hhtht and thtth are just two of many possibilities. When such a possibility is written down, exactly three positions are occupied by an h, the other two by a t. Each distinct way of choosing three positions from a set of five positions gives a different possibility. (Once the three positions for h are determined, each of the other two positions automatically receives a t.)

So our answer is just the number of size-three subsets of a size-five set, that is, the number of combinations of five things taken three at a time.

$$_5C_3 = 10 \quad \text{Row 5 of Pascal's triangle}$$ ▐▐▐

Notice that row 5 of Pascal's triangle also provides answers to several other questions about tossing five fair coins. They are summarized in **Table 7**.

Table 7   Tossing Five Fair Coins

Number of Heads n	Ways of Obtaining Exactly n Heads	Listing
0	$_5C_0 = 1$	ttttt
1	$_5C_1 = 5$	htttt, thttt, tthtt, tttht, tttth
2	$_5C_2 = 10$	hhttt, hthtt, htthht, httth, thhtt, ththt, thtth, tthht, tthth, ttthh
3	$_5C_3 = 10$	hhhtt, hhtht, hhtth, hthht, hthth, htthh, thhht, thhth, ththh, tthhh
4	$_5C_4 = 5$	hhhht, hhhth, hhthh, hthhh, thhhh
5	$_5C_5 = 1$	hhhhh

To analyze the tossing of a different number of fair coins, we can simply take the pertinent numbers from a different row of Pascal's triangle. Repeated coin tossing is an example of a "binomial" experiment (because each toss has *two* possible outcomes, heads and tails).

For Further Thought

The Binomial Theorem

The combination values that comprise Pascal's triangle also arise in a totally different mathematical context. In algebra, "binomial" refers to a two-term expression such as

$$x + y, \quad \text{or} \quad a + 2b, \quad \text{or} \quad w^3 - 4.$$

The first few powers of the binomial $x + y$ are shown here.

$$(x + y)^0 = 1$$
$$(x + y)^1 = x + y$$
$$(x + y)^2 = x^2 + 2xy + y^2$$
$$(x + y)^3 = x^3 + 3x^2y + 3xy^2 + y^3$$
$$(x + y)^4 = x^4 + 4x^3y + 6x^2y^2 + 4xy^3 + y^4$$
$$(x + y)^5 = x^5 + 5x^4y + 10x^3y^2 + 10x^2y^3$$
$$+ 5xy^4 + y^5$$

(continued)

For Further Thought (cont.)

The numerical coefficients of these expansions form the first six rows of Pascal's triangle. In our study of counting, we have called these numbers combinations, but in the study of algebra, they are called **binomial coefficients** and are usually denoted

$$\binom{n}{r} \quad \text{rather than} \quad {}_nC_r.$$

Generalizing the pattern of the powers shown on the preceding page yields the important result known as the **binomial theorem.**

Binomial Theorem

For any whole number n,

$$(x + y)^n = \binom{n}{0} \cdot x^n + \binom{n}{1} \cdot x^{n-1}y$$

$$+ \binom{n}{2} \cdot x^{n-2}y^2 + \binom{n}{3} \cdot x^{n-3}y^3 +$$

$$\cdots + \binom{n}{n-1} \cdot xy^{n-1} + \binom{n}{n} \cdot y^n,$$

where each binomial coefficient can be calculated by the formula

$$\binom{n}{r} = \frac{n!}{r!(n-r)!}.$$

Notice that, if $n = 0$, then the first term shown in the expansion is, at the same time, the last term, for

$$\binom{n}{0} \cdot x^n = \binom{0}{0} \cdot x^0 = \frac{0!}{0!0!} \cdot 1 = 1,$$

and $\binom{n}{n} \cdot y^n = \binom{0}{0} \cdot y^0 = \frac{0!}{0!0!} \cdot 1 = 1.$

EXAMPLE   Applying the Binomial Theorem

Write out the binomial expansion for $(2a + 5)^4$.

SOLUTION

We take the initial coefficients from row 4 of Pascal's triangle and then simplify algebraically.

$(2a + 5)^4$ *Recall that $(xy)^n = x^n \cdot y^n$.*

$$= \binom{4}{0} \cdot (2a)^4 + \binom{4}{1} \cdot (2a)^3 \cdot 5$$

$$+ \binom{4}{2} \cdot (2a)^2 \cdot 5^2 + \binom{4}{3} \cdot (2a) \cdot 5^3$$

$$+ \binom{4}{4} \cdot 5^4$$

$$= 1 \cdot 2^4 \cdot a^4 + 4 \cdot 2^3 \cdot a^3 \cdot 5 + 6 \cdot 2^2 \cdot a^2 \cdot 5^2$$

$$+ 4 \cdot 2 \cdot a \cdot 5^3 + 1 \cdot 5^4$$

$$= 16a^4 + 160a^3 + 600a^2 + 1000a + 625 \quad ▌▌▌$$

For Group or Individual Investigation

Write out the binomial expansion for each of the following powers.

1. $(x + y)^6$ **2.** $(x + y)^7$

3. $(w + 4)^5$ **4.** $(4x + 2y)^4$

5. $(u - v)^6$ (*Hint:* First change $u - v$ to $u + (-v)$.)

6. $(5m - 2n)^3$

7. How many terms are in the binomial expansion for $(x + y)^n$?

8. Identify the 15th term only of the expansion for $(a + b)^{18}$.

10.4 EXERCISES

Read each combination value directly from Pascal's triangle.

1. ${}_4C_2$ **2.** ${}_5C_3$ **3.** ${}_6C_3$ **4.** ${}_7C_5$

5. ${}_8C_5$ **6.** ${}_9C_6$ **7.** ${}_9C_2$ **8.** ${}_{10}C_7$

Selecting Committees of Congressmen *A committee of four Congressmen will be selected from a group of seven Democrats and three Republicans. Find the number of ways of obtaining each result.*

9. exactly one Democrat

10. exactly two Democrats

11. exactly three Democrats

12. exactly four Democrats

Tossing Coins *Suppose eight fair coins are tossed. Find the number of ways of obtaining each result.*

13. exactly three heads

14. exactly four heads

15. exactly five heads

16. exactly six heads

Selecting Classrooms Diana Baniak, searching for an Ecology class, knows that it must be in one of nine classrooms. Since the professor does not allow people to enter after the class has begun, and there is very little time left, she decides to try just four of the rooms at random.

17. How many different selections of four rooms are possible?

18. How many of the selections of **Exercise 17** will fail to locate the class?

19. How many of the selections of **Exercise 17** will succeed in locating the class?

20. What fraction of the possible selections will lead to "success"? (Give three decimal places.)

For a set of five objects, find the number of different subsets of each size. (Use row 5 of Pascal's triangle to find the answers.)

21. 0   **22.** 1

23. 2   **24.** 3

25. 4   **26.** 5

27. How many subsets (of any size) are there for a set of five elements?

28. For a given row in Pascal's triangle, let *n* be the row number and let *s* be the row sum.

   (a) Write an equation relating *s* and *n*.

   (b) Explain the relationship in part (a).

29. Which rows of Pascal's triangle have a single greatest entry?

30. What is the least four-digit number in Pascal's triangle? (*Mathematics Teacher* calendar problem)

Over the years, many interesting patterns have been discovered in Pascal's triangle.* We explore a few of them in Exercises 31–37.

31. Refer to **Table 5**.

   (a) Choose a row whose row number is prime. Except for the 1s in this row, what is true of all the other entries?

   (b) Choose a second prime row number and see if the same pattern holds.

   (c) Use the usual method to construct row 11 in **Table 5**, and verify that the same pattern holds in that row.

32. Name the next five numbers of the diagonal sequence in the figure. What are these numbers called? (See **Section 1.2**.)

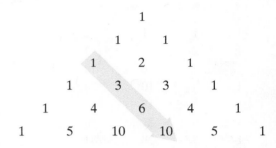

33. Complete the sequence of sums on the diagonals shown in the figure. What pattern do these sums make? What is the name of this important sequence of numbers? The presence of this sequence in the triangle apparently was not recognized by Pascal.

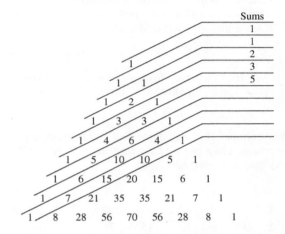

34. Construct another "triangle" by replacing every number in Pascal's triangle (rows **0** through **5**) by its remainder when divided by 2. What special property is shared by rows **2** and **4** of this new triangle?

35. What is the next row that would have the same property as rows **2** and **4** in **Exercise 34**?

36. How many even numbers are there in row **256** of Pascal's triangle? (Work **Exercises 34 and 35** first.)

37. The figure shows a portion of Pascal's triangle with several inverted triangular regions outlined. For any one of these regions, what can be said of the sum of the squares of the entries across its top row?

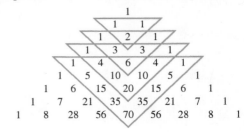

---

*For example, see the article "Serendipitous Discovery of Pascal's Triangle" by Francis W. Stanley in *The Mathematics Teacher*, February 1975.

38. More than a century before Pascal's treatise on the "triangle" appeared, another work by the Italian mathematician Niccolo Tartaglia (1506–1559) came out and included the table of numbers shown here.

1	1	1	1	1	1
1	2	3	4	5	6
1	3	6	10	15	21
1	4	10	20	35	56
1	5	15	35	70	126
1	6	21	56	126	252
1	7	28	84	210	462
1	8	36	120	330	792

Explain the connection between Pascal's triangle and Tartaglia's "rectangle."

39. It was stated in the text that each interior entry in Pascal's triangle can be obtained by adding the two numbers just above it (to the left and right). This fact, known as the "Pascal identity," can be written as

$$_nC_r = {}_{n-1}C_{r-1} + {}_{n-1}C_r.$$

Use the factorial formula for combinations (along with some algebra) to prove the Pascal identity.

The "triangle" that Pascal studied and published in his treatise was actually more like a truncated corner of Tartaglia's rectangle, as shown here.

1	1	1	1	1	1	1	1	1	1
1	2	3	4	5	6	7	8	9	
1	3	6	10	15	21	28	36		
1	4	10	20	35	56	84			
1	5	15	35	70	126				
1	6	21	56	126					
1	7	28	84						
1	8	36							
1	9								
1									

Each number in the truncated corner of Tartaglia's rectangle can be calculated in various ways. In each of Exercises 40–43, consider the number N to be located anywhere in the array. By checking several locations in the given array, determine how N is related to the sum of all entries in the shaded cells. Describe the relationship in words.

40.

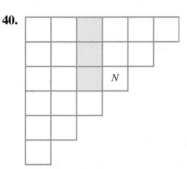

41.

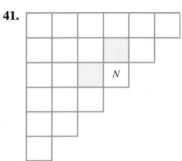

42.

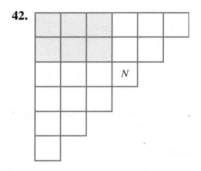

43.

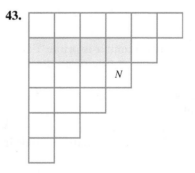

EXTENSION Magic Squares

Magic Square • Magic Sum Formula

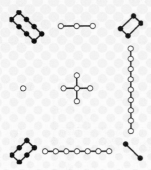

Figure 8

8	3	4
1	5	9
6	7	2

Figure 9

Magic Square The array of numbers known as Pascal's triangle has so many interesting patterns that we could almost think of it as a "magic" triangle. This **Extension** concerns another class of number arrays known as *magic squares*.

Legend has it that in about 2200 B.C. the Chinese Emperor Yu discovered on the bank of the Yellow River a tortoise whose shell bore the diagram in **Figure 8**. This so-called *lo-shu* is an early example of a **magic square.** If the numbers of dots are counted and arranged in a square fashion, the array in **Figure 9** is obtained. A magic square is a square array of numbers with the property that the sum along each row, column, and diagonal is the same. This common value is called the "magic sum." The **order** of a magic square is simply the number of rows (and columns) in the square. The magic square of **Figure 9** is an order 3 magic square.

Magic Sum Formula By using the formula for the sum of the first n terms of an arithmetic sequence, it can be shown that if a magic square of order n has entries $1, 2, 3, \ldots, n^2$, then the sum of *all entries* in the square is

$$\frac{n^2(n^2 + 1)}{2}.$$

Because there are n rows (and columns), the magic sum of the square may be found by dividing the above expression by n. This results in the following formula.

> **Magic Sum Formula**
>
> If a magic square of order n has entries $1, 2, 3, \ldots, n^2$, then the magic sum MS is given by the following formula.
>
> $$\mathbf{MS = \frac{n(n^2 + 1)}{2}}$$

The magic sum of the square in **Figure 9** is

$$MS = \frac{3(3^2 + 1)}{2} = 15. \quad \text{Let } n = 3 \text{ in the formula.}$$

We can construct an odd-order magic square using the "staircase method," attributed to an early French envoy, *de la Loubere*. The method is described below for an order 5 square, with entries $1, 2, 3, \ldots, 25$.

Begin by sketching a square divided into 25 cells into which the numbers 1–25 are to be entered. Proceed as described below, referring to **Figures 10 and 11**.

Consider blocked

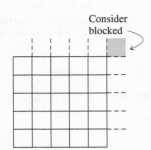

Figure 10

18	25	2	9	16
17	24	1	8	15	17
23	5	7	14	16	23
4	6	13	20	22	4
10	12	19	21	3	10
11	18	25	2	9

Figure 11

Step 1 Write 1 in the middle cell of the top row.

Step 2 Always try to enter numbers in sequence in the cells by moving diagonally from lower left to upper right. There are two exceptions to this:

    (a) If you go outside of the magic square, move all the way across the row or down the column to enter the number. Then proceed to move diagonally.

    (b) If you run into a cell that is already occupied (that is, you are "blocked"), drop down one cell from the last entry written and enter the next number there. Then proceed to move diagonally.

Step 3 Your last entry, 25, will be in the middle cell of the bottom row.

Figure 11 shows the completed magic square. Its magic sum is 65.

If magic squares catch your interest, a good source for further exploration is the website

http://mathforum.org/alejandre/magic.square.html.

Benjamin Franklin admitted that he would amuse himself while in the Pennsylvania Assembly with magic squares or circles "or any thing to avoid Weariness." He wrote about the usefulness of mathematics in the *Gazette* in 1735, saying that no employment can be managed without arithmetic, no mechanical invention without geometry. He also thought that mathematical demonstrations are better than academic logic for training the mind to reason with exactness and distinguish truth from falsity even outside of mathematics.

The square shown here is one developed by Franklin. It has a sum of 2056 in each row and diagonal, and, in Franklin's words, has the additional property "that a four-square hole being cut in a piece of paper of such size as to take in and show through it just 16 of the little squares, when laid on the greater square, the sum of the 16 numbers so appearing through the hole, wherever it was placed on the greater square should likewise make 2056." He claimed that it was "the most magically magic square ever made by any magician."

You might wish to verify the following property of this magic square: The sum of any four numbers that are opposite each other and at equal distances from the center is 514 (which is one-fourth of the magic sum).

EXTENSION EXERCISES

Given a magic square, other magic squares may be obtained by rotating the given one. For example, starting with the magic square in **Figure 9**, *a 90° rotation in a clockwise direction gives the magic square shown here.*

6	1	8
7	5	3
2	9	4

Start with **Figure 9** *and give the magic square obtained by each rotation described.*

1. 180° in a clockwise direction

2. 90° in a counterclockwise direction

Start with **Figure 11** *and give the magic square obtained by each rotation described.*

3. 90° in a clockwise direction

4. 180° in a clockwise direction

5. 90° in a counterclockwise direction

6. Try to construct an order-2 magic square containing the entries 1, 2, 3, 4. What happens?

Given a magic square, other magic squares may be obtained by adding or subtracting a constant value to or from each entry, multiplying each entry by a constant value, or dividing each entry by a nonzero constant value. In Exercises 7–10, start with the magic square whose figure number is indicated, and perform the operation described to find a new magic square. Give the new magic sum.

7. Figure 9, multiply by 3   **8. Figure 9**, add 7

9. Figure 11, divide by 2   **10. Figure 11**, subtract 10

According to a fanciful story by Charles Trigg in Mathematics Maga- zine *(September 1976, page 212), the Emperor Charlemagne (742–814) ordered a five-sided fort to be built at an important point in his kingdom. As good-luck charms, he had magic squares placed on all five sides of the fort. He had one restriction for these magic squares: all the numbers in them must be prime.*

Charlemagne's magic squares are given in Exercises 11–15, with one missing entry. Find the missing entry in each square.

11.

	71	257
47	269	491
281	467	59

12.

389		227
107	269	431
311	347	149

13.

389	227	191
71	269	
347	311	149

14.

401	227	179
47	269	491
359		137

15.

401	257	149
17		521
389	281	137

16. Compare the magic sums in **Exercises 11–15.** Charlemagne had stipulated that each magic sum should be the year in which the fort was built. What was that year?

Find the missing entries in each magic square.

17.

75	68	(a)
(b)	72	(c)
71	76	(d)

18.

1	8	13	(a)
(b)	14	7	2
16	9	4	(c)
(d)	(e)	(f)	15

19.

3	20	(a)	24	11
(b)	14	1	18	10
9	21	13	(c)	17
16	8	25	12	(d)
(e)	2	(f)	(g)	(h)

20.

3	36	2	35	31	4
10	12	(a)	26	7	27
21	13	17	14	(b)	22
16	(c)	23	(d)	18	15
28	30	8	(e)	25	9
(f)	1	32	5	6	34

21. Use the "staircase method" to construct a magic square of order 7, containing the entries 1, 2, 3, . . . , 49.

The magic square shown in the photograph is from a woodcut by Albrecht Dürer entitled Melancholia.

The two bottom center numbers give 1514, the date of the *woodcut. Refer to this magic square for Exercises 22–30.*

16	3	2	13
5	10	11	8
9	6	7	12
4	15	14	1

Dürer's Magic Square

22. What is the magic sum?

23. Verify: The sum of the entries in the four corners is equal to the magic sum.

24. Verify: The sum of the entries in any 2 by 2 square at a corner of the given magic square is equal to the magic sum.

25. Verify: The sum of the entries in the diagonals is equal to the sum of the entries not in the diagonals.

26. Verify: The sum of the squares of the entries in the diagonals is equal to the sum of the squares of the entries not in the diagonals.

27. Verify: The sum of the cubes of the entries in the diagonals is equal to the sum of the cubes of the entries not in the diagonals.

28. Verify: The sum of the squares of the entries in the top two rows is equal to the sum of the squares of the entries in the bottom two rows.

29. Verify: The sum of the squares of the entries in the first and third rows is equal to the sum of the squares of the entries in the second and fourth rows.

30. Find another interesting property of Dürer's magic square and state it.

31. A magic square of order 4 may be constructed as follows.
   (1) Lightly sketch in the diagonals of the blank magic square.

(2) Beginning at the upper left, move across each row from left to right, counting the cells as you go along. If the cell is on a diagonal, count it but do not enter its number. If it is not on a diagonal, enter its number.

(3) When this is completed, reverse the procedure, beginning at the bottom right and moving across from right to left. As you count the cells, enter the number if the cell is not occupied. If it is already occupied, count it but do not enter its number.

You should obtain a magic square similar to the one given for **Exercises 22–30.** How do they differ?

With chosen values for a, b, and c, an order-3 magic square can be constructed by substituting these values in the generalized form shown here.

$a+b$	$a-b-c$	$a+c$
$a-b+c$	a	$a+b-c$
$a-c$	$a+b+c$	$a-b$

Use the given values of a, b, and c to construct an order-3 magic square, using this generalized form.

32. $a = 5, \quad b = 1, \quad c = -3$

33. $a = 16, \quad b = 2, \quad c = -6$

34. $a = 5, \quad b = 4, \quad c = -8$

35. It can be shown that if an order-n magic square has least entry k, and its entries are consecutive counting numbers, then its magic sum is given by the formula

$$MS = \frac{n(2k + n^2 - 1)}{2}.$$

Construct an order-7 magic square with least entry 10 using the staircase method. Find its magic sum.

36. Use the formula of **Exercise 35** to find the missing entries in the following order-4 magic square whose least entry is 24.

(a)	38	37	27
35	**(b)**	30	32
31	33	**(c)**	28
(d)	26	25	**(e)**

In a 1769 letter from Benjamin Franklin to a Mr. Peter Collinson, Franklin exhibited the following semimagic square of order 8. (Note: A square is semimagic if it is magic except that one or both diagonals fail to give the magic sum.)

52	61	4	13	20	29	36	45
14	3	62	51	46	35	30	19
53	60	5	12	21	28	37	44
11	6	59	54	43	38	27	22
55	58	7	10	23	26	39	42
9	8	57	56	41	40	25	24
50	63	2	15	18	31	34	47
16	1	64	49	48	33	32	17

37. What is the magic sum?

Verify the following properties of this semimagic square.

38. The sums in the first half of each row and the second half of each row are both equal to half the magic sum.

39. The four corner entries added to the four center entries is equal to the magic sum.

40. The "bent diagonals" consisting of eight entries, going up four entries from left to right and down four entries from left to right, give the magic sum. (For example, starting with 16, one bent diagonal sum is $16 + 63 + 57 + 10 + 23 + 40 + 34 + 17$.)

If we use a "knight's move" (up two, right one) from chess, a variation of the staircase method gives the magic square shown here. (When blocked, we move to the cell just below the previous entry.)

10	18	1	14	22
11	24	7	20	3
17	5	13	21	9
23	6	19	2	15
4	12	25	8	16

Use a similar process to construct an order-5 magic square, starting with 1 in the cell described.

41. fourth row, second column (up two, right one; when blocked, move to the cell just below the previous entry)

42. third row, third column (up one, right two; when blocked, move to the cell just to the left of the previous entry)

43. The integers from 1 through 27 are placed in the cells of a 3 × 3 cube so that the sum in all nine rows and in all nine columns is the same. Finish the solution. (*Mathematics Teacher* calendar problem)

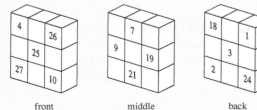

front   middle   back

44. Consider the "magic cube" of **Exercise 43.**

(a) What is the magic sum?

(b) How many three-cell "diagonals" does the cube contain?

(c) Do the entries in all the diagonals also add to the magic sum?

(d) How many rows does the cube *really* have?

(e) Do all the additional rows also have the magic sum?

10.5   COUNTING PROBLEMS INVOLVING "NOT" AND "OR"

Problems Involving "Not" • Problems Involving "Or"

The counting techniques in this section, which can be thought of as *indirect techniques*, are based on some useful correspondences (from **Chapters 2 and 3**) between set theory, logic, and arithmetic, as shown in **Table 8**.

Table 8   Set Theory/Logic/Arithmetic Correspondences

	Set Theory	Logic	Arithmetic
Operation or Connective (Symbol)	Complement $(')$	Not $(\sim)$	Subtraction $(-)$
Operation or Connective (Symbol)	Union $(\cup)$	Or $(\vee)$	Addition $(+)$

Problems Involving "Not"

Suppose U is the set of all possible results of some type. (The "universal set U," comprises all possibilities as discussed in **Chapter 2**.) Let A be the set of all those results that satisfy a given condition. For any set S, its cardinal number is written $n(S)$, and its complement is written S'. **Figure 12** suggests that

$$n(A) + n(A') = n(U).$$

Also, $n(A) = n(U) - n(A')$ and $n(A') = n(U) - n(A).$

We focus here on the form that expresses the following indirect counting principle (based on the complement/not/subtraction correspondence from **Table 8**).

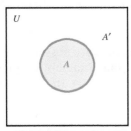

The complement of a set

Figure 12

Complements Principle of Counting

The number of ways a certain condition can be satisfied is the total number of possible results minus the number of ways the condition would **not** be satisfied. Symbolically, if A is any set within the universal set U, then

$$n(A) = n(U) - n(A').$$

▮▮ **EXAMPLE 1** Counting the Proper Subsets of a Set

For the set $S = \{a, b, c, d, e, f\}$, find the number of proper subsets.

SOLUTION

A proper subset of S is any subset with fewer than all six elements. Subsets of several different sizes would satisfy this condition. But, it is easier to consider the one subset that is not proper, namely S itself. From set theory, we know that set S has a total of

$$2^6 = 64 \text{ subsets.}$$

Thus, from the complements principle, the number of proper subsets is

$$64 - 1 = 63.$$

In words, the number of subsets that *are* proper is the total number of subsets minus the number of subsets that are *not* proper. ▮▮▮

Consider the tossing of three fair coins. Since each coin will land either heads (h) or tails (t), the possible results can be listed as follows.

hhh, hht, hth, thh, htt, tht, tth, ttt   Results of tossing three fair coins

(Even without the listing, we could have concluded that there would be eight possibilities. There are two possible outcomes for each coin, so the fundamental counting principle gives $2 \cdot 2 \cdot 2 = 2^3 = 8$.)

Suppose we wanted the number of ways of obtaining *at least* one head. In this case, "at least one" means one or two or three. Rather than dealing with all three cases, we can note that "at least one" is the opposite (or complement) of "fewer than one" (which is zero). Because there is only one way to get zero heads (ttt), and there are a total of eight possibilities, the complements principle gives the number of ways of getting at least one head:

$$8 - 1 = 7.$$

Indirect counting methods can often be applied to problems involving "at least," or "at most," or "less than," or "more than."

▮▮ **EXAMPLE 2** Counting Coin-Tossing Results

If four fair coins are tossed, in how many ways can at least one tail be obtained?

SOLUTION

By the fundamental counting principle, $2^4 = 16$ different results are possible. Exactly one of these fails to satisfy the condition of "at least one tail" (namely, no tails, or hhhh). So the answer (from the complements principle) is $16 - 1 = 15$. ▮▮▮

▮▮ **EXAMPLE 3** Counting Selections of Airliner Seats

Carol Britz and three friends are boarding an airliner just before departure time. There are only ten seats left, three of which are aisle seats. How many ways can the four people arrange themselves in available seats so that at least one of them sits on the aisle?

SOLUTION

The word "arrange" implies that order is important, so we shall use permutations. "At least one aisle seat" is the opposite (complement) of "no aisle seats." The total number of ways to arrange four people among ten seats is

$$_{10}P_4 = 5040.$$

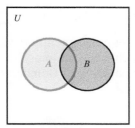

Nondisjoint sets

Figure 13

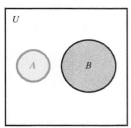

Disjoint sets

Figure 14

The number of ways to arrange four people among seven (non-aisle) seats is

$$_7P_4 = 840.$$

Therefore, by the complements principle, the number of arrangements with at least one aisle seat is

$$\underset{\downarrow}{_{10}P_4} \quad \underset{\downarrow}{_7P_4}$$
$$5040 - 840 = 4200.$$ ■■■

Problems Involving "Or"

The complements principle is one way of counting indirectly. Another technique is to count the elements of a set by breaking that set into simpler component parts. If

$$S = A \cup B,$$

the cardinal number formula (from **Section 2.4**) says to find the number of elements in S by adding the number in A to the number in B. We must then subtract the number in the intersection $A \cap B$ if A and B are not disjoint, as in **Figure 13**. But if A and B are disjoint, as in **Figure 14**, the subtraction is not necessary.

The following principle reflects the union/or/addition correspondence from **Table 8**.

Additive Principle of Counting

The number of ways that one **or** the other of two conditions could be satisfied is the number of ways one of them could be satisfied plus the number of ways the other could be satisfied minus the number of ways they could both be satisfied together.

If A and B are any two sets, then

$$n(A \cup B) = n(A) + n(B) - n(A \cap B).$$

If sets A and B are disjoint, then

$$n(A \cup B) = n(A) + n(B).$$

┃┃ EXAMPLE 4 Counting Card Hands

How many five-card poker hands consist of either all clubs or all red cards?

SOLUTION

No hand that satisfies one of these conditions could also satisfy the other, so the two sets of possibilities (all clubs, all red cards) are disjoint. Therefore the second formula of the additive principle applies.

$n(\text{all clubs or all red cards}) = n(\text{all clubs}) + n(\text{all red cards})$ Additive counting principle

$$= {_{13}C_5} + {_{26}C_5}$$ 13 clubs, 26 red cards

$$= 1287 + 65{,}780$$ Substitute values.

$$= 67{,}067$$ Add.   ■■■

(10 nPr 4)−(7 nPr 4)
         4200
(13 nCr 5)+(26 nCr 5)
        67067

Results in **Examples 3 and 4** are supported in this screen.

■■ **EXAMPLE 5** Counting Selections from a Diplomatic Delegation

Table 9 categorizes a diplomatic delegation of 18 congressional members as to political party and gender. If one of the members is chosen randomly to be spokesperson for the group, in how many ways could that person be a Democrat or a woman?

Table 9

	Men (M)	Women (W)	Totals
Republican (R)	5	3	8
Democrat (D)	4	6	10
Totals	9	9	18

SOLUTION

Since D and W are not disjoint (6 delegates are both Democrats and women), the first formula of the additive principle is required.

$$n(D \text{ or } W) = n(D \cup W) \qquad \text{Union/or correspondence}$$
$$= n(D) + n(W) - n(D \cap W) \qquad \text{Additive principle}$$
$$= 10 + 9 - 6 \qquad \text{Substitute values.}$$
$$= 13 \qquad \text{Add and subtract.} \qquad ■■■$$

■■ **EXAMPLE 6** Counting Course Selections for a Degree Program

Chrissy Jenkins needs to take twelve more specific courses for a bachelors degree, including four in math, three in physics, three in computer science, and two in business. If five courses are randomly chosen from these twelve for next semester's program, how many of the possible selections would include at least two math courses?

SOLUTION

Of all the information given here, what is important is that there are four math courses and eight other courses to choose from, and that five of them are being selected for next semester. If T denotes the set of selections that include at least two math courses, then we can write

$$T = A \cup B \cup C$$

where A = the set of selections with exactly two math courses,

    B = the set of selections with exactly three math courses,

and C = the set of selections with exactly four math courses.

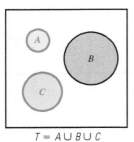

$T = A \cup B \cup C$

Figure 15

(In this case, *at least two* means exactly two **or** exactly three **or** exactly four.) The situation is illustrated in **Figure 15**. By previous methods, we know that

$$n(A) = {}_4C_2 \cdot {}_8C_3 = 6 \cdot 56 = 336,$$
$$n(B) = {}_4C_3 \cdot {}_8C_2 = 4 \cdot 28 = 112,$$

and $$n(C) = {}_4C_4 \cdot {}_8C_1 = 1 \cdot 8 = 8,$$

so that, by the additive principle,

$$n(T) = 336 + 112 + 8 = 456. \qquad ■■■$$

▌▌ **EXAMPLE 7** Counting Three-Digit Numbers with Conditions

How many three-digit counting numbers are multiples of 2 or multiples of 5?

SOLUTION

A multiple of 2 must end in an even digit (0, 2, 4, 6, or 8), so there are $9 \cdot 10 \cdot 5 = 450$ three-digit multiples of 2. A multiple of 5 must end in either 0 or 5, so there are $9 \cdot 10 \cdot 2 = 180$ of those. A multiple of both 2 and 5 is a multiple of 10 and must end in 0. There are $9 \cdot 10 \cdot 1 = 90$ of those. By the additive principle there are

$$450 + 180 - 90 = 540$$

possible three-digit numbers that are multiples of 2 or multiples of 5. ▌▌▌

▌▌ **EXAMPLE 8** Counting Card-Drawing Results

A single card is drawn from a standard 52-card deck.

(a) In how many ways could it be a heart or a king?

(b) In how many ways could it be a club or a face card?

SOLUTION

(a) A single card can be both a heart and a king (the king of hearts), so use the first additive formula. There are thirteen hearts, four kings, and one card that is both a heart and a king.

$$13 + 4 - 1 = 16$$

(b) There are 13 clubs, 12 face cards, and 3 cards that are both clubs and face cards.

$$13 + 12 - 3 = 22$$ ▌▌▌

▌▌ **EXAMPLE 9** Counting Subsets of a Set with Conditions

How many subsets of a 25-element set have more than three elements?

SOLUTION

It would be a real job to count directly all subsets of size 4, 5, 6, ..., 25. It is much easier to count those with three or fewer elements and apply the complements principle.

There is	$_{25}C_0 = 1$	size-0 subset.
There are	$_{25}C_1 = 25$	size-1 subsets.
There are	$_{25}C_2 = 300$	size-2 subsets.
There are	$_{25}C_3 = 2300$	size-3 subsets.

The total number of subsets (of all sizes, 0 through 25) is $2^{25} = 33{,}554{,}432$ (use a calculator). So the number with more than three elements must be

$$33{,}554{,}432 - (1 + 25 + 300 + 2300) = 33{,}554{,}432 - 2626$$

$$= 33{,}551{,}806.$$ ▌▌▌

In **Example 9,** we used both the additive principle (to get the number of subsets with no more than three elements) and the complements principle.

How many proper subsets are there of each set?

1. {A, B, C, D}

2. {u, v, w, x, y, z}

Tossing Coins *If you toss seven fair coins, in how many ways can you obtain each result?*

3. at least one head ("At least one" is the complement of "none.")

4. at least two heads ("At least two" is the complement of "zero or one.")

5. at least two tails

6. at least one of each (a head and a tail)

Rolling Dice *If you roll two fair dice (say red and green), in how many ways can you obtain each result? (Refer to* **Table 2** *in* **Section 10.1.***)*

7. at least 2 on the green die

8. a sum of at least 3

9. a 4 on at least one of the dice

10. a different number on each die

Drawing Cards *If you draw a single card from a standard 52-card deck, in how many ways can you obtain each result?*

11. a card other than the ace of spades

12. a nonface card

Identifying Properties of Counting Numbers *How many two-digit counting numbers meet each requirement?*

13. not a multiple of 10

14. greater than 70 or a multiple of 10

15. ***Choosing Country Music Albums*** Jeanne Bronson's collection of ten country music albums includes *Southern Voice* by Tim McGraw. Jeanne will choose three of her albums to play on a drive to Nashville. (Assume order is not important.)

    (a) How many different sets of three albums could she choose?

    (b) How many of these sets would not include *Southern Voice*?

    (c) How many of them would include *Southern Voice*?

16. ***Choosing Broadway Hits*** The ten longest Broadway runs include *The Phantom of the Opera* and *Les Misérables*. Four of the ten are chosen randomly. (Assume order is not important.)

    (a) How many ways can the four be chosen?

    (b) How many of those groups of four would include neither of the two productions mentioned?

    (c) How many of them would include at least one of the two productions mentioned?

17. ***Choosing Days of the Week*** How many different ways could three distinct days of the week be chosen so that at least one of them begins with the letter S? (Assume order of selection is not important.)

18. ***Choosing School Assignments for Completion*** Diona Brown has nine major assignments to complete for school this week. Two of them involve writing essays. Diona decides to work on two of the nine assignments tonight. How many different choices of two would include at least one essay assignment? (Assume order is not important.)

Selecting Restaurants *Jason Ignacio wants to dine at four different restaurants during a summer getaway. If three of eight available restaurants serve seafood, find the number of ways that at least one of the selected restaurants will serve seafood given the following conditions.*

19. The order of selection is important.

20. The order of selection is not important.

21. ***Seating Arrangements on an Airliner*** Refer to **Example 3.** If one of the group decided at the last minute not to fly, then how many ways could the remaining three arrange themselves among the ten available seats so that at least one of them will sit on the aisle?

22. ***Identifying Properties of Counting Numbers*** Find the number of four-digit counting numbers containing at least one zero, under each of the following conditions.

    (a) Repeated digits are allowed.

    (b) Repeated digits are not allowed.

23. ***Counting Radio Call Letters*** Radio stations in the United States have call letters that begin with either K or W. Some have a total of three letters, and others have four letters. How many different call letter combinations are possible? Count all possibilities even though, practically, some may be inappropriate. (*Mathematics Teacher* calendar problem) (*Hint:* Do *not* apply combinations.)

24. ***Selecting Faculty Committees*** A committee of four faculty members will be selected from a department of twenty-five which includes professors Fontana and Spradley. In how many ways could the committee include at least one of these two professors?

25. ***Selecting Search and Rescue Teams*** A Civil Air Patrol unit of twelve members includes four officers. In how many ways can four members be selected for a search and rescue mission such that at least one officer is included?

26. Choosing Team Members Three students from a class of 12 will form a math contest team that must include at least 1 boy and at least 1 girl. If 160 different teams can be formed from the 12 students, which of the following can be the difference between the number of boys and the number of girls in the class?

A. 0   **B.** 2   **C.** 4   **D.** 6   **E.** 8

(*Mathematics Teacher* calendar problem)

Drawing Cards *If a single card is drawn from a standard 52-card deck, in how many ways could it be the following? (Use the additive principle.)*

27. a club or a jack

28. a face card or a black card

Counting Students Who Enjoy Music and Cinema *Of a group of 30 students, 25 enjoy music, 22 enjoy cinema, and 18 enjoy both music and cinema. How many of them enjoy the following?*

29. at least one of the two (Use the additive principle.)

30. neither of the two (complement of "at least one")

Counting Card Hands *Among the 2,598,960 possible 5-card poker hands from a standard 52-card deck, how many contain the following cards?*

31. at least one card that is not a heart (complement of "all hearts")

32. cards of more than one suit (complement of "all the same suit")

33. at least one face card (complement of "no face cards")

34. at least one club, but not all clubs (complement of "no clubs or all clubs")

35. Selecting Doughnuts A doughnut shop has a special on its Mix-n-Match selection, which allows customers to select three doughnuts from among the following varieties: plain, maple, frosted, chocolate, glazed, and jelly. How many different Mix-n-Match selections are possible? (*Mathematics Teacher* calendar problem)

36. Rolling Three Dice Three fair, standard six-faced dice of different colors are rolled. In how many ways can the dice be rolled such that the sum of the numbers rolled is 10? (*Mathematics Teacher* calendar problem)

The Size of Subsets of a Set *If a given set has ten elements, how many of its subsets have the given numbers of elements?*

37. at most two elements   **38.** at least eight elements

39. more than two elements

40. from three through seven elements

41. Counting License Numbers If license numbers consist of two letters followed by three digits, how many different licenses could be created having at least one letter or digit repeated? (*Hint:* Use the complements principle of counting.)

42. Drawing Cards If two cards are drawn from a 52-card deck without replacement (that is, the first card is not replaced in the deck before the second card is drawn), in how many different ways is it possible to obtain a king on the first draw and a heart on the second? (*Hint:* Split this event into the two disjoint components "king of hearts and then another heart" and "non-heart king and then heart." Use the fundamental counting principle on each component, then apply the additive principle.)

43. Extend the additive counting principle to three overlapping sets (as in the figure) to show that

$$n(A \cup B \cup C) = n(A) + n(B) + n(C)$$
$$- n(A \cap B) - n(A \cap C)$$
$$- n(B \cap C) + n(A \cap B \cap C).$$

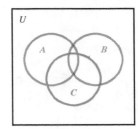

44. How many of the counting numbers 1 through 300 are *not* divisible by 2, 3, or 5? (*Hint:* Use the complements principle and the result of **Exercise 43.**)

Selecting National Monuments to Visit *Megan Lozano is planning a driving tour. While she is interested in seeing the twelve national monuments listed here, she will have to settle for seeing just three of them.*

New Mexico	Arizona	California
Gila Cliff Dwellings	Canyon de Chelly	Devils Postpile
Petroglyph	Organ Pipe Cactus	Joshua Tree
White Sands	Saguaro	Lava Beds
Aztec Ruins		Muir Woods
		Pinnacles

In how many ways could the three monuments chosen include the following? (Assume that order of selection is not important.)

45. sites in only one state

46. at least one site not in California

47. sites in fewer than all three states

48. sites in exactly two of the three states

Counting Categories of Poker Hands **Table 4** *in this chapter (**For Further Thought** in Section 10.3) described the various kinds of hands in 5-card poker. Verify each statement in Exercises 49–52. (Explain all steps of your argument.)*

49. There are four ways to get a royal flush.

50. There are 36 ways to get a straight flush.

51. There are 10,200 ways to get a straight.

52. There are 54,912 ways to get three of a kind.

53. Explain why the complements principle of counting is called an "indirect" method.

54. Explain the difference between the two formulas of the additive principle of counting.

COLLABORATIVE INVESTIGATION

Solving a Traveling Salesman Problem

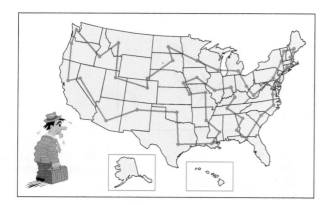

In 1985, Shen Lin came up with the route shown above for a salesman wanting to visit all capital cities in the forty-eight contiguous states, starting and ending at the same capital and traveling the shortest possible total distance. He could not prove that his 10,628-mile route was the shortest possible, but he offered $100 to anyone who could find a shorter one.

This is an example of a classic problem, the so-called **traveling salesman problem** (or **TSP**), which has many practical applications in business and industry but has baffled mathematicians for years. In the case above, there are 47! possible routes, although many of them can be quickly eliminated, leaving $\frac{24!}{3}$ possibilities to consider. This is still a 24-digit number, far too large for even state-of-the-art computers to analyze directly.

Although computer scientists have so far failed to find an "efficient algorithm" to solve the general traveling salesman problem, successes are periodically achieved for particular cases. In 2005, an optimal route was computed for a 33,810-city instance, which arose from a microchip layout problem.

A much smaller set (of seven cities, A through G), which can be completely analyzed using a calculator, is shown here.

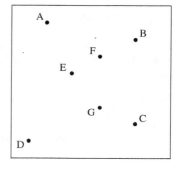

Notice that certain routes clearly are *not* the shortest. For example, it is apparent that the route ACEDFGBA involves too much jumping back and forth across the diagram to result in the least possible total distance. (In fact, the total distance for this route is 360 miles, considerably more than necessary.) The fifteen distances given here (in miles) between pairs of cities should be sufficient data for computing the shortest possible route.

AB = 51	AF = 36	BF = 22	CG = 22	EF = 22
AD = 71	BC = 50	BG = 45	DE = 45	EG = 28
AE = 32	BE = 45	CD = 61	DG = 45	FG = 30

Topics for Discussion

Divide the class into groups of 3 or 4 students each. Each group is to do the following.

1. Study the drawing, and make a list of all routes that you think may be the shortest.

2. For each candidate route, add the appropriate seven terms to get a total distance.

3. Arrive at a group consensus as to which route is shortest.

Now bring the whole class back together, and do the following.

1. Make a list of routes, with total distances, that the various groups thought were shortest.

2. Observe whether the different groups all agreed on which route was shortest.

3. As a class, try to achieve a consensus on the shortest route. Do you think that someone else may be able to find a shorter one?

Optimal routes joining points, computed by traveling salesman theories (see the **Collaborative Investigation**), have been used to produce a variety of art. For example, the likeness shown at the right, based on the work of Andy Warhol, consists of a route that, if printed on $8\frac{1}{2}$-by-11-inch paper, would be 45.5 feet long.

Reproduced with permission from Robert Bosch.

CHAPTER 10 TEST

Counting Three-digit Numbers If only digits 0, 1, 2, 3, 4, 5, *and* 6 *may be used, find the number of possibilities in each category.*

1. three-digit numbers

2. odd three-digit numbers

3. three-digit numbers without repeated digits

4. three-digit multiples of five without repeated digits

5. *Counting Triangles in a Figure* Determine the number of triangles (of any size) in the figure shown here.

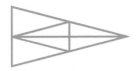

6. *Tossing Coins* Construct a tree diagram showing all possible results when a fair coin is tossed four times, if no two consecutive tosses can both be heads.

7. *Sums of Digits* How many nonrepeating four-digit numbers have the sum of their digits equal to 30?

8. *Arranging People* Tia, Jo, and four friends sit at a round table. How many ways can they be arranged if Tia and Jo refuse to sit next to each other? Assume that any rotation of a given arrangement, that is, when everyone moves the same number of seats in either clockwise or counterclockwise direction, is the same as the original arrangement. (*Mathematics Teacher* calendar problem)

Evaluate each expression.

9. 6!

10. $\dfrac{8!}{6!}$

11. $_{12}P_3$

12. $_8C_5$

13. *Building Words from Sets of Letters* How many five-letter "words" without repeated letters are possible using the English alphabet? (Assume that any five letters make a "word.")

14. *Building Words from Sets of Letters* Using the Russian alphabet (which has 32 letters), and allowing repeated letters, how many five-letter "words" are possible?

Scheduling Assignments Eileen Burke has seven homework assignments to complete. She wants to do two of them on Thursday and the other five on Saturday.

15. In how many ways can she order Thursday's work?

16. Assuming she finishes Thursday's work successfully, in how many ways can she order Saturday's work?

17. *Arranging Letters* Find the number of distinguishable arrangements of the letters of the word GOOGOL.

Selecting Groups of Basketball Players If there are ten players on a basketball team, find the number of choices the coach has in selecting each of the following.

18. four players to carry the team equipment

19. two players for guard positions and two for forward positions

20. five starters and five subs

21. two groups of four

22. a group of three or more of the players

Choosing Switch Settings *Determine the number of possible settings for a row of five on–off switches under each condition.*

23. There are no restrictions.

24. The first and fifth switches must be on.

25. The first and fifth switches must be set the same.

26. No two adjacent switches can both be off.

27. No two adjacent switches can be set the same.

28. At least two switches must be on.

Choosing Subsets of Letters *Three distinct letters are to be chosen from the set*

$$\{A, B, C, D, E, F, G\}.$$

Determine the number of ways to obtain a subset that includes each of the following.

29. the letter B

30. both A and E

31. either A or E, but not both

32. letters to spell the word AD

33. more consonants than vowels

34. **Number of Paths from Point to Point** A transit bus can travel in only two directions, north and east. From its starting point on the map shown, determine how many paths exist to reach the garage. (*Mathematics Teacher* calendar problem)

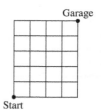

35. State the fundamental counting principle in your own words.

36. If $_nC_r = 495$ and $_nC_{r+1} = 220$, find the value of $_{n+1}C_{r+1}$.

37. If you write down the second entry of each row of Pascal's triangle (starting with row 1), what sequence of numbers do you obtain?

38. Explain why there are $r!$ permutations of n things taken r at a time corresponding to each combination of n things taken r at a time.

PROBABILITY

11

*S*uppose you're on a game show, and you're given the choice of three doors: Behind one of the doors is a car, and behind the other doors, goats. Of course, you want to win the car. You pick one of the doors, say Door 1, and the host, who knows what's behind the other doors, opens another door, say Door 3, to reveal a goat. He then says to you, "Do you want to change your choice?" Is it to your advantage to switch to Door 2?

This question appeared in *Parade* magazine in a column written by Marilyn vos Savant in the early 1990s. This probability problem, known as the Monty Hall Problem, was named after the host of the popular game show *Let's Make a Deal*. Marilyn's answer caused an incredible amount of discussion and argument among the general public at that time.

The answer and its justification can also be found at the interactive Web site www.math.ucsd.edu/~crypto/Monty/monty .html. *Would YOU switch doors?* (See page 613 for the answer.)

11.1 BASIC CONCEPTS

Historical Background • Probability • The Law of Large Numbers
• Probability in Genetics • Odds

If the **Pascal–Fermat correspondence** of 1654 marks the birth of probability theory, it wasn't an easy birth. In his 2010 book, *The Unfinished Game: Pascal, Fermat, and the Seventeenth-Century Letter that Made the World Modern* (see the photo above), Keith Devlin describes how the two "struggled for several weeks" to solve the unfinished game problem. In fact, this is no exception, but rather the rule, even for the greatest mathematicians. The reams of scratch work behind the elegant results are seldom seen and rarely published.

Historical Background

The modern mathematical theory of probability came mainly from the Russian scholars P. L. Chebyshev (1821–1922), A. A. Markov (1856–1922), and Andrei Nikolaevich Kolmogorov (1903–1987). But the basic ideas arose much earlier, mostly in questions of games and gambling. In 1654, two French mathematicians, Pierre de Fermat (about 1601–1665) and Blaise Pascal (1623–1662), corresponded with each other regarding a problem posed by the Chevalier de Méré, a gambler and member of the aristocracy.

> *If the two players of a game are forced to quit before the game is finished, how should the pot be divided?*

Pascal and Fermat solved the problem by developing basic methods of determining each player's chance, or probability, of winning.

The Dutch mathematician and scientist Christiaan Huygens (1629–1695) wrote a formal treatise on probability. It appeared in 1657 and was based on the Pascal–Fermat correspondence.

One of the first to apply probability to matters other than gambling was the French mathematician Pierre Simon de Laplace (1749–1827), who is usually credited with being the "father" of probability theory.

Probability

If you go to a supermarket and select five pounds of peaches at 89¢ per pound, you can easily predict the amount you will be charged at the checkout counter.

$$5 \cdot \$0.89 = \$4.45.$$

This is an example of a **deterministic phenomenon.** It can be predicted exactly on the basis of obtainable information, namely, in this case, number of pounds and cost per pound.

On the other hand, consider the problem faced by the produce manager of the market, who must order peaches to have on hand each day without knowing exactly how many pounds customers will buy during the day. Customer demand is an example of a **random phenomenon.** It fluctuates in such a way that its value (on a given day) cannot be predicted exactly with obtainable information.

The study of probability is concerned with such random phenomena. Even though we cannot be certain whether a given result will occur, we often can obtain a good measure of its *likelihood,* or **probability.** This chapter discusses various ways of finding and using probabilities.

Any observation, or measurement, of a random phenomenon is an **experiment.** The possible results of the experiment are **outcomes,** and the set of all possible outcomes is the **sample space.**

Usually we are interested in some particular collection of the possible outcomes. Any such subset of the sample space is an **event.** Outcomes that belong to the event are "favorable outcomes," or "successes." Any time a success is observed, we say that the event has "occurred." The probability of an event, being a numerical measure of the event's likelihood, is determined in one of two ways, either *theoretically* (mathematically) or *empirically* (experimentally).

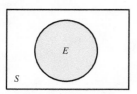

Every event is a subset of the sample space.

▌▌ EXAMPLE 1 Finding Probability When Tossing a Coin

If a single coin is tossed, find the probability that it will land heads up.

SOLUTION

There is no apparent reason for one side of a coin to land up any more often than the other (in the long run), so we assume that heads and tails are equally likely.

The experiment here is the tossing of a single fair coin, the sample space is $S = \{h, t\}$, and the event whose probability we seek is $E = \{h\}$. Since one of the two equally likely outcomes is a head, the probability of heads is the quotient of 1 and 2.

$$\text{Probability (heads)} = \frac{1}{2}, \quad \text{written} \quad P(h) = \frac{1}{2} \quad \text{or} \quad P(E) = \frac{1}{2}. \quad ▋▋▋$$

▌▌ EXAMPLE 2 Finding Probability When Tossing a Cup

If a Styrofoam cup is tossed, find the probability that it will land on its top.

SOLUTION

Intuitively, it seems that such a cup will land on its side much more often than on its top or its bottom. But just how much more often is not clear. To get an idea, we performed the experiment of tossing such a cup 50 times. It landed on its side 44 times, on its top 5 times, and on its bottom just 1 time. By the frequency of "success" in this experiment, we concluded for the cup we used that

$$P(\text{top}) \approx \frac{5}{50} = \frac{1}{10}. \quad \text{Write in lowest terms.} \quad ▋▋▋$$

In **Example 1** involving the tossing of a fair coin, the number of possible outcomes was obviously two, both were equally likely, and one of the outcomes was a head. No actual experiment was required. The desired probability was obtained *theoretically.* Theoretical probabilities apply to dice rolling, card games, roulette, lotteries, and so on, and apparently to many phenomena in nature.

Laplace, in his famous *Analytic Theory of Probability,* published in 1812, gave a formula that applies to any such theoretical probability, as long as the sample space S is finite and all outcomes are equally likely. (It is sometimes referred to as the *classical definition of probability.*)

Theoretical Probability Formula

If all outcomes in a sample space S are equally likely, and E is an event within that sample space, then the **theoretical probability** of event E is given by the following formula.

$$P(E) = \frac{\textbf{number of favorable outcomes}}{\textbf{total number of outcomes}} = \frac{n(E)}{n(S)}$$

On the other hand, **Example 2** involved the tossing of a cup, where the likelihoods of the various outcomes were not intuitively clear. It took an actual experiment to arrive at a probability value of $\frac{1}{10}$, and that value, based on a portion of all possible tosses of the cup, should be regarded as an approximation of the true theoretical probability. The value was found according to the *experimental,* or *empirical,* probability formula.

Empirical Probability Formula

If E is an event that may happen when an experiment is performed, then an **empirical probability** of event E is given by the following formula.

$$P(E) = \frac{\text{number of times event } E \text{ occurred}}{\text{number of times the experiment was performed}}$$

Usually it is clear in applications which probability formula should be used.

▌▌ **EXAMPLE 3**   Finding the Probability of Having Daughters

Kathy Campbell wants to have exactly two daughters. Assuming that boy and girl babies are equally likely, find her probability of success if

(a) she has a total of two children.   **(b)** she has a total of three children.

SOLUTION

(a) The equal likelihood assumption allows the use of theoretical probability. But how can we determine the number of favorable outcomes and the total number of possible outcomes?

One way is to use a tree diagram (see **Section 10.1**) to enumerate the possibilities, as shown in **Figure 1**. From the outcome column we obtain the sample space $S = \{gg, gb, bg, bb\}$. Only one outcome, marked with an arrow, is favorable to the event of exactly two daughters: $E = \{gg\}$.

$$P(E) = \frac{n(E)}{n(S)} = \frac{1}{4} \quad \text{Theoretical probability formula}$$

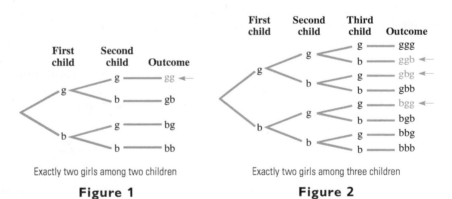

Exactly two girls among two children   Exactly two girls among three children

Figure 1   **Figure 2**

(b) For three children altogether, we construct another tree diagram, as shown in **Figure 2**. In this case, we see that

$$S = \{ggg, ggb, gbg, gbb, bgg, bgb, bbg, bbb\} \quad \text{and} \quad E = \{ggb, gbg, bgg\},$$

so $P(E) = \frac{3}{8}$.   ▌▌▌

When dealing (or drawing) cards, as in the next example, the dealing is generally done "without replacement." Once dealt, a card is *not* replaced in the deck. So all cards in a hand are distinct. (Repetitions are *not* allowed.) In many cases, such as building three-digit numbers, repetition of digits *is* allowed. For example, 255 is a legitimate three-digit number. So digit selection is done "with replacement."

▮▮ EXAMPLE 4 Finding Probability When Dealing Cards

Find the probability of being dealt each of the following hands in five-card poker. Use a calculator to obtain answers to eight decimal places.

(a) a full house (three of one denomination and two of another)

(b) a royal flush (the five highest cards—ace, king, queen, jack, ten—of a single suit)

SOLUTION

(a) Table 1 summarizes the various possible kinds of five-card hands. (For more on card hands, see **Section 10.3.**) Since the 2,598,960 possible individual hands all are equally likely, we can enter the appropriate numbers from the table into the theoretical probability formula.

$$P(\text{full house}) = \frac{3744}{2,598,960} = \frac{6}{4165} \approx 0.00144058$$

(b) The table shows that there are four royal flushes, one for each suit.

$$P(\text{royal flush}) = \frac{4}{2,598,960} = \frac{1}{649,740} \approx 0.00000154$$ ▮▮▮

Examples 3 and 4 both utilized the theoretical probability formula because we were able to enumerate all possible outcomes and all were equally likely. In **Example 3,** however, the equal likelihood of girl and boy babies was *assumed.* In fact, male births typically occur a little more frequently. (At the same time, there usually are more females living at any given time, due to higher infant mortality rates among males and longer female life expectancy in general.) **Example 5** shows a way of incorporating such empirical information.

Table 1	Number of Poker Hands in 5-Card Poker; Nothing Wild	
Event E	**Number of Outcomes Favorable to E**
Royal flush	4
Straight flush	36
Four of a kind	624
Full house	3744
Flush	5108
Straight	10,200
Three of a kind	54,912
Two pairs	123,552
One pair	1,098,240
No pair	1,302,540
Total	**2,598,960**

▮▮ EXAMPLE 5 Finding the Probability of the Gender of a Resident

According to *Pocket World in Figures,* 2009 edition, published by *The Economist,* the U.S. population at the end of 2006 included 148.2 million males and 152.8 million females. If a person were selected randomly from the population in that year, what is the probability that the person would be a male?

SOLUTION

In this case, we calculate the empirical probability from the given experimental data.

$$P(\text{male}) = \frac{\text{number of males}}{\text{total number of persons}}$$

$$= \frac{148.2 \text{ million}}{148.2 \text{ million} + 152.8 \text{ million}}$$

$$\approx 0.492$$ ▮▮▮

The Law of Large Numbers

Recall the cup of **Example 2.** If we tossed it 50 more times, we would have 100 total tosses upon which to base an empirical probability of the cup landing on its top. The new value would likely be (at least slightly) different from what we obtained before. It would still be an empirical probability, but it would be "better" in the sense that it is based upon a larger set of outcomes.

The **law of large numbers** also can be stated as follows.

A theoretical probability really says nothing about one, or even a few, repetitions of an experiment, but only about the proportion of successes we would expect over the long run.

If, as we increase the number of tosses, the resulting empirical probability values approach some particular number, that number can be defined as the theoretical probability of that particular cup landing on its top. We could determine this "limiting" value only as the actual number of observed tosses approaches the total number of possible tosses of the cup. Since there are potentially an infinite number of possible tosses, we could never actually find the theoretical probability. But we can still assume such a number exists. And as the number of actual observed tosses increases, the resulting empirical probabilities should tend ever closer to the theoretical value.

This very important principle is known as the **law of large numbers** (or sometimes as the "law of averages").

Law of Large Numbers

As an experiment is repeated more and more times, the proportion of outcomes favorable to any particular event will tend to come closer and closer to the theoretical probability of that event.

▌▌ EXAMPLE 6 Graphing a Sequence of Proportions

A fair coin was tossed 35 times, producing the following sequence of outcomes.

tthhh, ttthh, hthtt, hhthh, ttthh, thttt, hhthh

Calculate the ratio of heads to total tosses after the first toss, the second toss, and so on through all 35 tosses, and plot these ratios on a graph.

SOLUTION

After the first toss, we have 0 heads out of 1 toss, for a ratio of $\frac{0}{1} = 0.00$. After two tosses, we have $\frac{0}{2} = 0.00$. After three tosses, we have $\frac{1}{3} \approx 0.33$. Verify that the first six ratios are

0.00, 0.00, 0.33, 0.50, 0.60, 0.50.

The thirty-five ratios are plotted as points in **Figure 3**. The fluctuations away from 0.50 become smaller as the number of tosses increases, and the ratios appear to approach 0.50 toward the right side of the graph, in keeping with the law of large numbers.

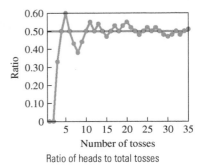

Ratio of heads to total tosses

Figure 3

▌▌▌

Comparing Empirical and Theoretical Probabilities

A series of repeated experiments provides an *empirical probability* for an event, which, by *inductive reasoning,* is an *estimate* of the event's *theoretical probability.* (Increasing the number of repetitions increases the reliability of the estimate.)

Likewise, an established *theoretical probability* for an event enables us, by *deductive reasoning,* to *predict* the proportion of times the event will occur in a series of repeated experiments. (The prediction should be more accurate for larger numbers of repetitions.)

Probability in Genetics

Probabilities, both empirical and theoretical, have been valuable tools in many areas of science. An important early example was the work of the Austrian monk Gregor Mendel, who used the idea of randomness to help establish the study of genetics.

In an effort to understand the mechanism of character transmittal from one generation to the next in plants, Mendel counted the number of occurrences of various characteristics. He found that the flower color in certain pea plants obeyed this scheme:

Pure red crossed with pure white produces red.

Mendel theorized that red is "dominant" (symbolized with the capital letter R), while white is "recessive" (symbolized with the lowercase letter r). The pure red parent carried only genes for red (R), and the pure white parent carried only genes for white (r). The offspring would receive one gene from each parent, hence one of the four combinations shown in the body of **Table 2**. Because every offspring receives one gene for red, that characteristic dominates and the offspring exhibits the color red.

Gregor Johann Mendel (1822–1884) came from a peasant family who managed to send him to school. By 1847 he had been ordained and was teaching at the Abbey of St. Thomas. He finished his education at the University of Vienna and returned to the abbey to teach mathematics and natural science.

Mendel began to carry out experiments on plants in the abbey garden, notably pea plants, whose distinct traits (unit characters) he had puzzled over. In 1865 he published his results. His work was not appreciated at the time even though he had laid the foundation of **classical genetics.**

Table 2 **First to Second Generation**

		Second Parent	
		r	**r**
First	**R**	Rr	Rr
Parent	**R**	Rr	Rr

Table 3 **Second to Third Generation**

		Second Parent	
		R	**r**
First	**R**	RR	Rr
Parent	**r**	rR	rr

Now each of these second-generation offspring, though exhibiting the color red, still carries one of each gene. So when two of them are crossed, each third-generation offspring will receive one of the gene combinations shown in **Table 3**. Mendel theorized that each of these four possibilities would be equally likely and produced experimental counts that were close enough to support this hypothesis.

▌▌ **EXAMPLE 7** Finding Probabilities of Flower Colors

Referring to **Table 3**, determine the probability that a third-generation offspring will exhibit each flower color. Base the probabilities on the sample space of equally likely outcomes: $S = \{RR, Rr, rR, rr\}$.

(a) red   **(b)** white

SOLUTION

(a) Since red dominates white, any combination with at least one gene for red (R) will result in red flowers. Since three of the four possibilities meet this criterion, $P(\text{red}) = \frac{3}{4}$.

(b) Only the combination rr has no gene for red, so $P(\text{white}) = \frac{1}{4}$.   ▌▌▌

Odds

Whereas probability compares the number of favorable outcomes to the total number of outcomes, **odds** compare the number of favorable outcomes to the number of unfavorable outcomes. Odds are commonly quoted, rather than probabilities, in horse racing, lotteries, and most other gambling situations. And the odds quoted normally are odds "against" rather than odds "in favor."

Smoking 1.4 cigarettes
Spending 1 hour in a coal mine
Living 2 days in New York or Boston
Eating 40 teaspoons of peanut butter
Living 2 months with a cigarette smoker
Flying 1000 miles in a jet
Traveling 300 miles in a car
Riding 10 miles on a bicycle

Risk is the probability that a harmful event will occur. Almost every action or substance exposes a person to some risk, and the assessment and reduction of risk accounts for a great deal of study and effort in our world. The list above, from *Calculated Risk*, by J. Rodricks, contains activities that carry an annual increased risk of death by one chance in a million.

Odds

If all outcomes in a sample space are equally likely, a of them are favorable to the event E, and the remaining b outcomes are unfavorable to E, then the **odds in favor** of E are a to b, and the **odds against** E are b to a.

▐▐ **EXAMPLE 8** Finding the Odds of Getting an Intern Position

Theresa Cortesini has been promised one of six jobs, three of which would be intern positions at the state capitol. If she has equal chances for all six jobs, find the odds that she will get one of the intern positions.

SOLUTION

Since three possibilities are favorable and three are not, the odds of becoming an intern at the capitol are 3 to 3 (or 1 to 1 in reduced terms). Odds of 1 to 1 are often termed "even odds," or a "50–50 chance." ▓▓▓

▐▐ **EXAMPLE 9** Finding the Odds of Winning a Raffle

Bob Barickman has purchased 12 tickets for an office raffle in which the winner will receive an iPad. If 104 tickets were sold altogether and each has an equal chance of winning, what are the odds against Bob's winning the iPad?

SOLUTION

Bob has 12 chances to win and $104 - 12 = 92$ chances to lose, so the odds against winning are 92 to 12, or 23 to 3. (Divide both 92 and 12 by 4.) ▓▓▓

Converting between Probability and Odds

Let E be an event.

1. If $P(E) = \frac{a}{b}$, then the odds in favor of E are a to $(b - a)$.

2. If the odds in favor of E are a to b, then $P(E) = \frac{a}{a + b}$.

▐▐ **EXAMPLE 10** Converting from Probability to Odds

There is a 30% chance of rain tomorrow. Give this information in terms of odds.

SOLUTION

$$P(\text{rain}) = 0.30 = \frac{30}{100} = \frac{3}{10}$$

> Convert the decimal fraction to a quotient of integers and reduce.

By conversion formula 1 above, the odds in favor of rain are 3 to $10 - 3$, or 3 to 7. Or, we can say the odds are 7 to 3 against rain tomorrow. ▓▓▓

▐▐ **EXAMPLE 11** Converting from Odds to Probability

In a certain sweepstakes, your odds of winning are 1 to 99,999. What is the probability that you will win?

SOLUTION

$$P(\text{win}) = \frac{1}{1 + 99,999} = \frac{1}{100,000} = 0.00001 \quad \text{Conversion formula 2}$$ ▓▓▓

11.1 EXERCISES

In Exercises 1–4, give the probability that the spinner shown would land on **(a)** *red,* **(b)** *yellow,* **(c)** *blue.*

1.   **2.**

3. **4.**

Solve each probability problem.

5. Using Spinners to Generate Numbers Suppose the spinner shown here is spun once, to determine a single-digit number, and we are interested in the event E that the resulting number is odd. Give each of the following.

 (a) the sample space

 (b) the number of favorable outcomes

 (c) the number of unfavorable outcomes

 (d) the total number of possible outcomes

 (e) the probability of an odd number

 (f) the odds in favor of an odd number

6. Lining Up Preschool Children Kim Lenaghan's group of preschool children includes nine girls and seven boys. If Kim randomly selects one child to be first in line, with E being the event that the one selected is a girl, give each of the following.

 (a) the total number of possible outcomes

 (b) the number of favorable outcomes

 (c) the number of unfavorable outcomes

 (d) the probability of event E

 (e) the odds in favor of event E

7. Using Spinners to Generate Numbers The spinner of **Exercise 5** is spun twice in succession to determine a two-digit number. Give each of the following.

 (a) the sample space

 (b) the probability of an odd number

 (c) the probability of a number with repeated digits

 (d) the probability of a number greater than 30

 (e) the probability of a prime number

8. Probabilities in Coin Tossing Two fair coins are tossed (say a dime and a quarter). Give each of the following.

 (a) the sample space

 (b) the probability of heads on the dime

 (c) the probability of heads on the quarter

 (d) the probability of getting both heads

 (e) the probability of getting the same outcome on both coins

9. Drawing Balls from an Urn Anne Kelly randomly chooses a single ball from the urn shown here. Find the odds against each event.

 (a) red   (b) yellow   (c) blue

10. Random Selection of Club Officers Five people (Alan, Bill, Cathy, David, and Evelyn) form a club $N = \{A, B, C, D, E\}$. If they choose a president randomly, find the odds against each result.

 (a) Cathy   (b) a woman

 (c) a person whose name begins with a consonant

11. Random Selection of Fifties Music Butch LeBeau has fifty hit singles from the fifties, including exactly one by Smiley Lewis, two by The Drifters, three by Bobby Darin, four by The Coasters, and five by Fats Domino. If Butch randomly selects one hit from his collection of fifty, find the probability it will be by each of the following.

 (a) Smiley Lewis   (b) The Drifters

 (c) Bobby Darin   (d) The Coasters

 (e) Fats Domino

12. Probabilities in Coin Tossing Three fair coins are tossed.

 (a) Write out the sample space.

 Determine the probability of each event.

 (b) no heads   (c) exactly one head

 (d) exactly two heads   (e) three heads

13. Number Sums for Rolling Two Dice The sample space for the rolling of two fair dice appeared in **Table 2** of **Section 10.1**. Reproduce that table, but replace each of the 36 equally likely ordered pairs with its corresponding sum (for the two dice). Then find the probability of rolling each sum.

 (a) 2   (b) 3   (c) 4

 (d) 5   (e) 6   (f) 7

 (g) 8   (h) 9   (i) 10

 (j) 11   (k) 12

In Exercises 14 and 15, give answers to three decimal places.

14. Probability of Seed Germination In a hybrid corn research project, 200 seeds were planted, and 175 of them germinated. Find the empirical probability that any particular seed of this type will germinate.

11.2 EVENTS INVOLVING "NOT" AND "OR"

Properties of Probability • Events Involving "Not" • Events Involving "Or"

Properties of Probability

Recall that an empirical probability, based upon experimental observation, may be the best value available but still is only an approximation to the ("true") theoretical probability. For example, no human has ever been known to jump higher than 8.5 feet vertically, so the empirical probability of such an event is zero. Observing the rate at which high jump records have been broken, we suspect that the event is, in fact, possible and may one day occur. Hence it must have some nonzero theoretical probability, even though we have no way of assessing its exact value.

Selecting Class Reports *Assuming that Ben, Jill, and Pam are three of the 26 members of the class, and that three of the class members will be chosen randomly to deliver their reports during the next class meeting, find the probability (to six decimal places) of each event.*

61. Ben, Jill, and Pam are selected, in that order.

62. Ben, Jill, and Pam are selected, in any order.

63. Random Selection of Prime Numbers If two distinct prime numbers are randomly selected from among the first eight prime numbers, what is the probability that their sum will be 24?

64. Building Numbers from Sets of Digits The digits 1, 2, 3, 4, and 5 are randomly arranged to form a five-digit number. Find the probability of each event.

 (a) The number is even.

 (b) The first and last digits of the number both are even.

68. Building Fractions with Dice Lisa has one red die and one green die, which she rolls to make up fractions. The green die is the numerator, and the red die is the denominator. Some of the fractions have terminating decimal representations. How many different terminating decimal results can these two dice represent? What is the probability of rolling a fraction with a terminating decimal representation? (*Mathematics Teacher* calendar problem)

Finding Palindromic Numbers *Numbers that are palindromes read the same forward and backward. For example, 30203 is a five-digit palindrome. If a single number is chosen randomly from each of the following sets, find the probability that it will be palindromic.*

69. the set of all two-digit numbers

70. the set of all three-digit numbers

Six people, call them A, B, C, D, E, and F, are randomly divided into three groups of two. Find the probability of each event. (Do not impose unwanted ordering among groups.)

71. A and B are in the same group, as are C and D.

72. E and F are in the same group.

15. **Probability of Forest Land in California** According to *The World Almanac and Book of Facts 2010,* California has 155,959 square miles of land area, 51,250 square miles of which are forested. Find the probability that a randomly selected location in California will be forested.

16. **Probabilities of Two Daughters Among Four Children** In **Example 3,** what would be Kathy's probability of having exactly two daughters if she were to have four children altogether? (You may want to use a tree diagram to construct the sample space.)

17. **Rolling Altered Dice** A six-sided die has been altered so that the side that had been a single dot is now a blank face. Another die has a blank face instead of the face with four dots. What is the probability that a sum of 7 is rolled when the two dice are thrown? (*Mathematics Teacher* calendar problem)

18. **Probability of Location in a Tunnel** Mr. Davis is driving through a tunnel that is eight miles long. At this instant, what is the probability that he is at least six miles from one end of the tunnel? (*Mathematics Teacher* calendar problem)

Genetics in Snapdragons Mendel found no dominance in snapdragons (in contrast to peas) with respect to red and white flower color. When pure red and pure white parents are crossed (see **Table 2**), the resulting Rr combination (one of each gene) produces second-generation offspring with pink flowers. These second-generation pinks, however, still carry one red and one white gene, so when they are crossed the third generation is still governed by **Table 3**.
Find each probability for third-generation snapdragons.

19. $P(\text{red})$ 20. $P(\text{pink})$ 21. $P(\text{white})$

Genetics in Pea Plants   Mendel also investigated various characteristics besides flower color. For example, round peas are dominant over recessive wrinkled peas. First, second, and third generations can again be analyzed using **Tables 2 and 3**, where R represents round and r represents wrinkled.

22. Explain why crossing pure round and pure wrinkled first-generation parents will always produce round peas in the second-generation offspring.

23. When second-generation round pea plants (each of which carries both R and r genes) are crossed, find the probability that a third-generation offspring will have
    (a) round peas,   (b) wrinkled peas.

Genetics of Cystic Fibrosis Cystic fibrosis *is one of the most common inherited diseases in North America (including the United States), occurring in about* 1 *of every* 2000 *Caucasian births and about* 1 *of every* 250,000 *non-Caucasian births. Even with modern treatment, victims usually die from lung damage by their early twenties.*
    If we denote a cystic fibrosis gene with a c and a disease-free gene with a C (since the disease is recessive), then only a

cc *person will actually have the disease. Such persons would ordinarily die before parenting children, but a child can also inherit the disease from two Cc parents (who themselves are healthy, that is, have no symptoms but are "carriers" of the disease). This is like a pea plant inheriting white flowers from two red-flowered parents that both carry genes for white.*

24. Find the empirical probability (to four decimal places) that cystic fibrosis will occur in a randomly selected infant birth among U.S. Caucasians.

25. Find the empirical probability (to six decimal places) that cystic fibrosis will occur in a randomly selected infant birth among U.S. non-Caucasians.

26. Among 150,000 North American Caucasian births, about how many occurrences of cystic fibrosis would you expect?

Suppose that both partners in a marriage are cystic fibrosis carriers (a rare occurrence). Construct a chart similar to **Table 3** *and determine the probability of each of the following events.*

27. Their first child will have the disease.

28. Their first child will be a carrier.

29. Their first child will neither have nor carry the disease.

Suppose a child is born to one cystic fibrosis carrier parent and one non-carrier parent. Find the probability of each of the following events.

30. The child will have cystic fibrosis.

31. The child will be a healthy cystic fibrosis carrier.

32. The child will neither have nor carry the disease.

Genetics of Sickle-Cell Anemia Sickle-cell anemia *occurs in about* 1 *of every* 500 *black baby births and about* 1 *of every* 160,000 *non-black baby births. It is ordinarily fatal in early childhood. There is a test to identify carriers. Unlike cystic fibrosis, which is recessive, sickle-cell anemia is* **codominant.** *This means that inheriting two sickle-cell genes causes the disease, while inheriting just one sickle-cell gene causes a mild (non-fatal) version (which is called* **sickle-cell trait***). This is similar to a snapdragon plant manifesting pink flowers by inheriting one red gene and one white gene.*
    In Exercises 33 and 34, find the empirical probabilities of the given events.

33. A randomly selected black baby will have sickle-cell anemia. (Give your answer to three decimal places.)

34. A randomly selected non-black baby will have sickle-cell anemia. (Give your answer to six decimal places.)

35. Among 80,000 births of black babies, about how many occurrences of sickle-cell anemia would you expect?

(c) Is it possible that the event of part (a) will occur?

40. Is there any way a coin could fail to be "fair"? Explain.

41. On page 27 of their book *Descartes' Dream,* Philip Davis and Reuben Hersh ask the question, "Is probability real or is it just a cover-up for ignorance?" What do you think? Are some things truly random, or is everything potentially deterministic?

42. If $P(E) = 0.37$, find
    (a) the odds in favor of E.   (b) the odds against E.

43. If the odds in favor of event E are 12 to 19, find $P(E)$.

44. If the odds against event E are 10 to 3, find $P(E)$.

Probabilities of Poker Hands *In* 5-*card poker, find the probability of being dealt each of the following. Give each answer to eight decimal places. (Refer to* **Table 1.**)

45. a straight flush   46. two pairs

47. four of a kind   48. four queens

49. a hearts flush (*not* a royal flush or a straight flush)

50. **Probabilities in Dart Throwing** If a dart hits the square target shown here at random, what is the probability that it will hit in a colored region? (*Hint:* Compare the area of the colored regions to the total area of the target.

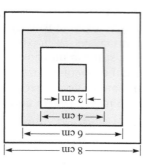

51. *The remaining exercises require careful thought to determine* n(E) *and* n(S). *(In some cases, you may want to employ counting methods from* **Chapter 10,** *such as the fundamental counting principle, permutations, or combinations.)*

52. **Drawing Cards** When drawing cards without replacement from a standard 52-card deck, find the maximum number of cards you could possibly draw and still get
    (a) fewer than three black cards,
    (b) fewer than six spades,
    (c) fewer than four face cards,
    (d) fewer than two kings.

53. Each man will sit immediately to the left of his wife.

54. Each man will sit immediately to the left of a woman.

55. The women will be in three adjacent seats.

56. The women will be in three adjacent seats, as will the men.

57. **Selecting Slopes** If two distinct numbers are chosen randomly from the set $\{-2, -\frac{2}{3}, -\frac{1}{2}, 0, \frac{2}{3}, \frac{3}{4}, 3\}$, find the probability that they will be the slopes of two perpendicular lines. (See **Section 8.2.**)

58. **Racing Bets** At most horse-racing tracks, the "trifecta" is a particular race in which you win if you correctly pick the "win," "place," and "show" horses (the first-, second-, and third-place winners), in their proper order. If five horses of equal ability are entered in today's trifecta race, and Tracy Light selects an entry, what is the probability that she will be a winner?

Probabilities of Seating Arrangements   Six people (three married couples) arrange themselves randomly in six consecutive seats in a row. Find the probability of each of the events in Exercises 53–56. (*Hint:* In each case the denominator of the probability fraction will be 6! = 720, *the total number of ways to arrange six items.*)

Pierre Simon de Laplace (1749–1827) began in 1773 to solve the problem of why Jupiter's orbit seems to shrink and Saturn's orbit seems to expand. Eventually Laplace worked out a complete theory of the solar system. *Celestial Mechanics* resulted from almost a lifetime of work. In five volumes, it was published between 1799 and 1825 and gained for Laplace the reputation "Newton of France."

Laplace's work on probability was actually an adjunct to his celestial mechanics. He needed to demonstrate that probability is useful in interpreting scientific data.

Recall also that the theoretical probability formula,

$$P(E) = \frac{n(E)}{n(S)},$$

is valid only when all outcomes in the sample space S are equally likely. For the experiment of tossing two fair coins, we can write $S = \{hh, ht, th, tt\}$ and compute

$$P(\text{both heads}) = \frac{1}{4}, \quad \text{which is } correct,$$

whereas if we define the sample space with non-equally likely outcomes as $S = \{\text{both heads, both tails, one of each}\}$, we are led to

$$P(\text{both heads}) = \frac{1}{3}, \quad \text{which is } incorrect.$$

(To convince yourself that $\frac{1}{4}$ is a better value than $\frac{1}{3}$, toss two fair coins 100 times or so to see what the empirical fraction seems to approach.)

For any event E within a sample space S, we know that $0 \leq n(E) \leq n(S)$. Dividing all members of this inequality by $n(S)$ gives

$$\frac{0}{n(S)} \leq \frac{n(E)}{n(S)} \leq \frac{n(S)}{n(S)}, \quad \text{or} \quad \mathbf{0 \leq P(E) \leq 1.}$$

In words, the probability of any event is a number from 0 through 1, inclusive.

If event E is *impossible* (cannot happen), then $n(E)$ must be 0 (E is the empty set), so $P(E) = 0$. If event E is *certain* (cannot help but happen), then $n(E) = n(S)$, so

$$P(E) = \frac{n(E)}{n(S)} = \frac{n(S)}{n(S)} = 1.$$

Properties of Probability

Let E be an event within the sample space S. That is, E is a subset of S. Then the following properties hold.

1. **$0 \leq P(E) \leq 1$** (The probability of an event is a number from 0 through 1, inclusive.)

2. **$P(\emptyset) = 0$** (The probability of an impossible event is 0.)

3. **$P(S) = 1$** (The probability of a certain event is 1.)

▌▌ EXAMPLE 1 Finding Probability When Rolling a Die

When a single fair die is rolled, find the probability of each event.

(a) the number 2 is rolled   **(b)** a number other than 2 is rolled

(c) the number 7 is rolled   **(d)** a number less than 7 is rolled

SOLUTION

(a) Since one of the six possibilities is a 2, $P(2) = \frac{1}{6}$.

(b) There are five such numbers, 1, 3, 4, 5, and 6, so $P(\text{a number other than 2}) = \frac{5}{6}$.

(c) None of the possible outcomes is 7. Thus, $P(7) = \frac{0}{6} = 0$.

(d) Since all six of the possible outcomes are less than 7,

$$P(\text{a number less than 7}) = \frac{6}{6} = 1.$$

■■■

No probability in **Example 1** was less than 0 or greater than 1, which illustrates probability property 1. The "impossible" event of part (c) had probability 0, illustrating property 2. The "certain" event of part (d) had probability 1, illustrating property 3.

Events Involving "Not"

Table 4 repeats the information of **Table 8** of **Section 10.5,** with a third correspondence added in row 3. These correspondences are the basis for the probability rules. For example, the probability of an event *not* happening involves the *complement* and *subtraction,* according to row 1 of the table.

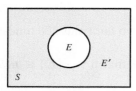

The logical connective "not" corresponds to "complement" in set theory.

$$P(not\ E) = P(S) - P(E)$$
$$= 1 - P(E)$$

Figure 4

Table 4   Set Theory/Logic/Arithmetic Correspondences

	Set Theory	Logic	Arithmetic
1. Operation or Connective (Symbol)	Complement $(')$	Not $(\sim)$	Subtraction $(-)$
2. Operation or Connective (Symbol)	Union $(\cup)$	Or $(\vee)$	Addition $(+)$
3. Operation or Connective (Symbol)	Intersection $(\cap)$	And $(\wedge)$	Multiplication $(\cdot)$

The rule for the probability of a complement follows and is illustrated in **Figure 4.**

Probability of a Complement (for Not E)

The probability that an event E will *not* occur is equal to one minus the probability that it *will* occur.

$$P(\text{not } E) = 1 - P(E)$$

Notice that the events of **Examples 1(a) and (b),** namely "2" and "not 2," are complements of one another, and that their probabilities add up to 1. This illustrates the above probability rule. The equation

$$P(E) + P(E') = 1$$

is a rearrangement of the formula for the probability of a complement. Another form of the equation that is also useful at times follows.

$$P(E) = 1 - P(E')$$

■■ **EXAMPLE 2**   Finding the Probability of a Complement

When a single card is drawn from a standard 52-card deck, what is the probability that it will not be a king?

SOLUTION

$$P(\text{not a king}) = 1 - P(\text{king}) = 1 - \frac{4}{52} = \frac{48}{52} = \frac{12}{13}$$

Remember to write in lowest terms.

■■■

Mary Somerville (1780–1872) is associated with Laplace because of her brilliant exposition of his *Celestial Mechanics*.

Somerville studied Euclid thoroughly and perfected her Latin so she could read Newton's *Principia*. In about 1816 she went to London and soon became part of its literary and scientific circles.

Somerville's book on Laplace's theories came out in 1831 with great acclaim. Then followed a panoramic book, *Connection of the Physical Sciences* (1834). A statement in one of its editions suggested that irregularities in the orbit of Uranus might indicate that a more remote planet, not yet seen, existed. This caught the eye of the scientists who worked out the calculations for Neptune's orbit.

▌▌ EXAMPLE 3 Finding the Probability of a Complement

If five fair coins are tossed, find the probability of obtaining at least two heads.

SOLUTION

There are $2^5 = 32$ possible outcomes for the experiment of tossing five fair coins. Most include at least two heads. In fact, only the outcomes

$$tttt, \quad htttt, \quad thttt, \quad tthtt, \quad ttht, \quad ttth$$

do *not* include at least two heads. If E denotes the event "at least two heads," then E' is the event "not at least two heads,"

$$P(E) = 1 - P(E') = 1 - \frac{6}{32} = \frac{26}{32} = \frac{13}{16} \qquad ■■■$$

Events Involving "Or"

Examples 2 and 3 showed how the probability of an event can be approached *indirectly,* by first considering the complement of the event. Another indirect approach is to break the event into simpler component events. Row 2 of **Table 4** indicates that the probability of one event *or* another should involve the *union* and *addition.*

▌▌ EXAMPLE 4 Selecting From a Set of Numbers

If one number is selected randomly from the set $\{1, 2, 3, 4, 5, 6, 7, 8, 9, 10\}$, find the probability that it will be

(a) odd or a multiple of 4 **(b)** odd or a multiple of 3.

SOLUTION

Define the following events:

$$
\begin{aligned}
S &= \{1, 2, 3, 4, 5, 6, 7, 8, 9, 10\} && \text{Sample space}\\
A &= \{1, 3, 5, 7, 9\} && \text{Odd outcomes}\\
B &= \{4, 8\} && \text{Multiples of 4}\\
C &= \{3, 6, 9\} && \text{Multiples of 3}
\end{aligned}
$$

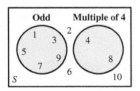

Figure 5

(a) **Figure 5** shows the positioning of the 10 integers within the sample space and within the pertinent sets A and B. The composite event "A or B" corresponds to the set $A \cup B = \{1, 3, 4, 5, 7, 8, 9\}$. By the theoretical probability formula,

$$P(A \text{ or } B) = \frac{7}{10}. \qquad \text{Of 10 total outcomes, 7 are favorable.}$$

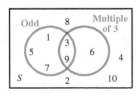

Figure 6

(b) **Figure 6** shows the situation.

$$P(A \text{ or } C) = \frac{6}{10} = \frac{3}{5} \qquad \text{Of 10 total outcomes, 6 are favorable.} \qquad ■■■$$

Would an addition formula have worked in **Example 4**? Let's check.

Part (a): $P(A \text{ or } B) = P(A) + P(B) = \dfrac{5}{10} + \dfrac{2}{10} = \dfrac{7}{10}$ Correct

Part (b): $P(A \text{ or } C) = P(A) + P(C) = \dfrac{5}{10} + \dfrac{3}{10} = \dfrac{8}{10} = \dfrac{4}{5}$ Incorrect

The trouble in part (b) is that A and C are not disjoint sets. They have outcomes in common. Just as with the additive counting principle in **Chapter 10,** an adjustment must be made here to compensate for counting the common outcomes twice.

$$P(A \text{ or } C) = P(A) + P(C) - P(A \text{ and } C)$$
$$= \frac{5}{10} + \frac{3}{10} - \frac{2}{10} = \frac{6}{10} = \frac{3}{5} \qquad \text{Correct}$$

In probability theory, events that are disjoint sets are called *mutually exclusive events.*

> **Mutually Exclusive Events**
>
> Two events A and B are **mutually exclusive events** if they have no outcomes in common. (Mutually exclusive events cannot occur simultaneously.)

The results observed in **Example 4** are generalized as follows. The two possibilities are illustrated in **Figures 7 and 8.**

> **Addition Rule of Probability (for A or B)**
>
> If A and B are any two events, then
>
> $$P(A \text{ or } B) = P(A) + P(B) - P(A \text{ and } B).$$
>
> If A and B are mutually exclusive, then
>
> $$P(A \text{ or } B) = P(A) + P(B).$$

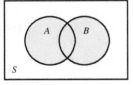

The logical connective "or" corresponds to "union" in set theory.

$P(A \text{ or } B)$
$\quad = P(A) + P(B) - P(A \text{ and } B)$

Figure 7

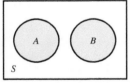

When A and B are mutually exclusive,

$P(A \text{ or } B) = P(A) + P(B).$

Figure 8

Actually, the first formula in the addition rule applies in all cases. (The third term on the right drops out when A and B are mutually exclusive, because $P(A \text{ and } B) = 0$.) Still it is good to remember the second formula in the preceding box for the many cases where the component events are mutually exclusive. In this section, we consider only cases where the event "A and B" is simple. We deal with more involved composites involving "and" in the next section.

▌▌ **EXAMPLE 5** Finding the Probability of an Event Involving "Or"

If a single card is drawn from a standard 52-card deck, what is the probability that it will be a spade or a red card?

SOLUTION

First note that "spade" and "red" cannot both occur, because there are no red spades. (All spades are black.) Therefore, we can use the formula for mutually exclusive events. There are 13 spades and 26 red cards in the deck.

$$P(\text{spade or red}) = P(\text{spade}) + P(\text{red}) = \frac{13}{52} + \frac{26}{52} = \frac{39}{52} = \frac{3}{4} \qquad ▮▮▮$$

We often need to consider composites of more than two events. When each event involved is mutually exclusive of all the others, we extend the addition rule to the appropriate number of components.

| **EXAMPLE 6** | Treating Unions of Several Components |

Amy Hogan plans to spend from 1 to 6 hours on her homework. If x represents the number of hours to be spent, then the probabilities of the various values of x, rounded to the nearest hour, are shown in **Table 5**. Find the probabilities that Amy will spend

Table 5

x	$P(x)$
1	0.05
2	0.10
3	0.20
4	0.40
5	0.10
6	0.15

(a) fewer than 3 hours

(b) more than 2 hours

(c) more than 1 but no more than 5 hours

(d) fewer than 5 hours.

SOLUTION

Because the time periods in **Table 5** are mutually exclusive of one another, we can simply add the appropriate component probabilities.

(a) $P(\text{fewer than } 3) = P(1 \text{ or } 2)$ Fewer than 3 means 1 or 2.

$= P(1) + P(2)$ Addition rule

$= 0.05 + 0.10$ Substitute values from **Table 5**.

$= 0.15$

(b) $P(\text{more than } 2) = P(3 \text{ or } 4 \text{ or } 5 \text{ or } 6)$ More than 2 means 3, 4, 5, or 6.

$= P(3) + P(4) + P(5) + P(6)$ Addition rule

$= 0.20 + 0.40 + 0.10 + 0.15$ Substitute values from **Table 5**.

$= 0.85$

(c) $P(\text{more than } 1 \text{ but no more than } 5)$

$= P(2 \text{ or } 3 \text{ or } 4 \text{ or } 5)$ 2, 3, 4, and 5 are more than 1 and no more than 5.

$= P(2) + P(3) + P(4) + P(5)$ Addition rule

$= 0.10 + 0.20 + 0.40 + 0.10$ Substitute values from **Table 5**.

$= 0.80$

(d) Although we could take a direct approach here, as in parts (a), (b), and (c), we will combine the complement rule with the addition rule.

$P(\text{fewer than } 5) = 1 - P(\text{not fewer than } 5)$ Complement rule

$= 1 - P(5 \text{ or more})$ 5 or more is equivalent to not fewer than 5.

$= 1 - P(5 \text{ or } 6)$ 5 or more means 5 or 6.

$= 1 - [P(5) + P(6)]$ Addition rule

$= 1 - (0.10 + 0.15)$ Substitute values from **Table 5**.

$= 1 - 0.25$ Add inside the parentheses first.

$= 0.75$ ▮▮▮

Table 5 in **Example 6** lists all possible time intervals so the corresponding probabilities add up to 1, a necessary condition for the way part (d) was done. The time spent on homework here is an example of a **random variable.** (It is "random" since we cannot predict which of its possible values will occur.)

A listing like **Table 5**, which shows all possible values of a random variable, along with the probabilities that those values will occur, is called a **probability distribution** for that random variable. Since *all* possible values are listed, they make up the entire sample space, and so the listed probabilities must add up to 1 (by probability property 3). Probability distributions will occur in **Exercises 32 and 33** of this section and will be discussed further in later sections.

▮▮ **EXAMPLE 7** Finding the Probability of an Event Involving "Or"

Find the probability that a single card drawn from a standard 52-card deck will be a diamond or a face card.

SOLUTION

The component events "diamond" and "face card" can occur simultaneously. (The jack, queen, and king of diamonds belong to both events.) So, we must use the first formula of the addition rule. We let D denote "diamond" and F denote "face card."

$$P(D \text{ or } F) = P(D) + P(F) - P(D \text{ and } F) \quad \text{Addition rule}$$

$$= \frac{13}{52} + \frac{12}{52} - \frac{3}{52} \quad \begin{array}{l}\text{There are 13 diamonds, 12 face cards,} \\ \text{and 3 that are both.}\end{array}$$

$$= \frac{22}{52} \quad \text{Add and subtract.}$$

$$= \frac{11}{26} \quad \text{Write in lowest terms.} \quad ▮▮▮$$

▮▮ **EXAMPLE 8** Finding the Probability of an Event Involving "Or"

Of 20 elective courses, Emily Horowitz plans to enroll in one, which she will choose by throwing a dart at the schedule of courses. If 8 of the courses are recreational, 9 are interesting, and 3 are both recreational and interesting, find the probability that the course Emily chooses will have at least one of these two attributes.

SOLUTION

If R denotes "recreational" and I denotes "interesting," then $P(R) = \frac{8}{20}$, $P(I) = \frac{9}{20}$, and $P(R \text{ and } I) = \frac{3}{20}$. R and I are not mutually exclusive.

$$P(R \text{ or } I) = \frac{8}{20} + \frac{9}{20} - \frac{3}{20} = \frac{14}{20} = \frac{7}{10} \quad \text{Addition rule; lowest terms} \quad ▮▮▮$$

11.2 EXERCISES

1. **Determining Whether Events Are Mutually Exclusive** Amanda Crotts has three office assistants. If A is the event that at least two of them are men and B is the event that at least two of them are women, are A and B mutually exclusive?

2. **Determining Whether Events Are Mutually Exclusive** Jeanne Jalufka earned her college degree several years ago. Consider the following four events.

   Her alma mater is in the East.
   Her alma mater is a private college.
   Her alma mater is in the Northwest.
   Her alma mater is in the South.

   Are these events all mutually exclusive of one another?

3. Explain the difference between the two formulas in the addition rule of probability on **page 592**, illustrating each one with an appropriate example.

Probabilities for Rolling a Die For the experiment of rolling a single fair die, find the probability of each event.

4. not less than 2

5. not prime

6. odd or less than 5

7. even or prime

8. odd or even

9. less than 3 or greater than 4

Probability and Odds for Drawing a Card For the experiment of drawing a single card from a standard 52-card deck, find (a) the probability, and (b) the odds in favor, of each event.

10. not an ace

11. king or queen

12. club or heart

13. spade or face card

14. not a heart, or a 7

15. neither a heart nor a 7

Number Sums for Rolling a Pair of Dice *For the experiment of rolling an ordinary pair of dice, find the probability that the sum will be each of the following. (You may want to use a table showing the sum for each of the 36 equally likely outcomes.)*

16. 11 or 12

17. even or a multiple of 3

18. odd or greater than 9

19. less than 3 or greater than 9

20. Find the probability of getting a prime number in each case.

(a) A number is chosen randomly from the set $\{1, 2, 3, 4, \ldots, 12\}$.

(b) Two dice are rolled and the sum is observed.

21. Suppose, for a given experiment, A, B, C, and D are events, all mutually exclusive of one another, such that $A \cup B \cup C \cup D = S$ (the sample space). By extending the addition rule of probability on **page 592** to this case, and utilizing probability property 3, what statement can you make?

Probabilities of Poker Hands *If you are dealt a 5-card hand (this implies without replacement) from a standard 52-card deck, find the probability of getting each of the following. Refer to* **Table 1** *of* **Section 11.1**, *and give answers to six decimal places.*

22. a flush or three of a kind

23. a full house or a straight

24. a black flush or two pairs

25. nothing any better than two pairs

Probabilities in Golf Scoring *The table gives golfer Brian Donahue's probabilities of scoring in various ranges on a par-70 course. In a given round, find the probability of each event in Exercises 26–30.*

26. 95 or higher

27. par or above

28. in the 80s

29. less than 90

30. not in the 70s, 80s, or 90s

31. What are the odds of Brian's scoring below par?

x	$P(x)$
Below 60	0.04
60–64	0.06
65–69	0.14
70–74	0.30
75–79	0.23
80–84	0.09
85–89	0.06
90–94	0.04
95–99	0.03
100 or above	0.01

32. ***Drawing Balls from an Urn*** Anne Kelly randomly chooses a single ball from the urn shown here, and x represents the color of the ball chosen. Construct a complete probability distribution for the random variable x.

33. Let x denote the sum of two distinct numbers selected randomly from the set $\{1, 2, 3, 4, 5\}$. Construct the probability distribution for the random variable x.

34. ***Comparing Empirical and Theoretical Probabilities for Rolling Dice*** Roll a pair of dice 50 times, keeping track of the number of times the sum is "less than 3 or greater than 9" (that is 2, 10, 11, or 12).

(a) From your results, calculate an empirical probability for the event "less than 3 or greater than 9."

(b) By how much does your answer differ from the *theoretical* probability of **Exercise 19?**

For Exercises 35–38, let A be an event within the sample space S, and let $n(A) = a$ and $n(S) = s$.

35. Use the complements principle of counting to find an expression for $n(A')$.

36. Use the theoretical probability formula to express $P(A)$ and $P(A')$.

37. Evaluate, and simplify, $P(A) + P(A')$.

38. What rule have you proved?

The remaining exercises require careful thought for the determination of $n(E)$ and $n(S)$. (In some cases, you may want to employ counting methods from Chapter 10, such as the fundamental counting principle, permutations, or combinations.)

Building Numbers from Sets of Digits *Suppose we want to form three-digit numbers using the set of digits*

$$\{0, 1, 2, 3, 4, 5\}.$$

For example, 501 and 224 are such numbers but 035 is not.

39. How many such numbers are possible?

40. How many of these numbers are multiples of 5?

41. If one three-digit number is chosen at random from all those that can be made from the above set of digits, find the probability that the one chosen is not a multiple of 5.

42. *Multiplying Numbers Generated by Spinners* An experiment consists of spinning both spinners shown here and multiplying the resulting numbers together. Find the probability that the resulting product will be even.

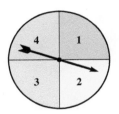 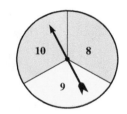

43. *Drawing Colored Marbles from Boxes* A bag contains fifty blue and fifty green marbles. Two marbles at a time are randomly selected. If both are green, they are placed in box A; if both are blue, in box B; if one is green and the other is blue, in box C. After all marbles are drawn, what is the probability that the numbers of marbles in box A and box B are the same? (*Mathematics Teacher* calendar problem)

44. *Random Births on the Same Day of the Week* What is the probability that, of three people selected at random, at least two were born on the same day of the week? (*Mathematics Teacher* calendar problem)

11.3 CONDITIONAL PROBABILITY; EVENTS INVOLVING "AND"

Conditional Probability • Events Involving "And"

Conditional Probability

Sometimes the probability of an event must be computed using the knowledge that some other event has happened (or is happening, or will happen—the timing is not important). This type of probability is called *conditional probability*.

> **Conditional Probability**
>
> The probability of event B, computed on the assumption that event A has happened, is called the **conditional probability of B given A**, and is denoted
>
> $$P(B|A).$$

Even **a rare occurrence** can sometimes cause widespread controversy. When Mattel Toys marketed a new talking Barbie doll a few years ago, some of the Barbies were programmed to say "Math class is tough." The National Council of Teachers of Mathematics (NCTM), the American Association of University Women (AAUW), and numerous consumers voiced complaints about the damage such a message could do to the self-confidence of children and to their attitudes toward school and mathematics. Mattel subsequently agreed to erase the phrase from the microchip to be used in future doll production.

Each Barbie was programmed to say four different statements, randomly selected from a pool of 270 prerecorded statements. Therefore, the probability of getting one that said "Math class is tough" was only

$$\frac{1 \cdot {}_{269}C_3}{{}_{270}C_4} \approx 0.015.$$

Other messages included in the pool were "I love school, don't you?," "I'm studying to be a doctor," and "Let's study for the quiz."

▮▮ **EXAMPLE 1** Selecting from a Set of Numbers

From the sample space $S = \{1, 2, 3, 4, 5, 6, 7, 8, 9, 10\}$, a single number is to be selected randomly. Find each probability given the events

A: The selected number is odd, and B: The selected number is a multiple of 3.

(a) $P(B)$ **(b)** $P(A \text{ and } B)$ **(c)** $P(B|A)$

SOLUTION

(a) $B = \{3, 6, 9\}$, so $P(B) = \frac{n(B)}{n(S)} = \frac{3}{10}$.

(b) A and B is the set $A \cap B = \{1, 3, 5, 7, 9\} \cap \{3, 6, 9\} = \{3, 9\}$.

$$P(A \text{ and } B) = \frac{n(A \cap B)}{n(S)} = \frac{2}{10} = \frac{1}{5}$$

(c) The given condition, that A occurs, effectively reduces the sample space from S to A, and the elements of the new sample space A that are also in B are the elements of $A \cap B$.

$$P(B|A) = \frac{n(A \cap B)}{n(A)} = \frac{2}{5}$$

▮▮▮

Example 1 illustrates some important points. First, because

$$\frac{n(A \cap B)}{n(A)} = \frac{\frac{n(A \cap B)}{n(S)}}{\frac{n(A)}{n(S)}} \qquad \text{Multiply numerator and denominator by } \frac{1}{n(S)}.$$

$$= \frac{P(A \cap B)}{P(A)}, \qquad \text{Theoretical probability formula}$$

the final line of the example gives the following convenient formula.

> **Conditional Probability Formula**
>
> The **conditional probability of B given A** is calculated as follows.
>
> $$P(B|A) = \frac{P(A \cap B)}{P(A)} = \frac{P(A \text{ and } B)}{P(A)}$$

A second observation from **Example 1** is that the conditional probability of B, given A, was $\frac{2}{5}$, whereas the "unconditional" probability of B (with no condition given) was $\frac{3}{10}$, so the condition did make a difference.

▮▮ **EXAMPLE 2** Finding Probabilities of Boys and Girls in a Family

Given a family with two children, find the probabilities that

(a) both are girls, given that at least one is a girl, and

(b) both are girls, given that the older child is a girl.

(Assume boys and girls are equally likely.)

SOLUTION

We define the following events.

$$S = \{gg, gb, bg, bb\} \qquad \text{Sample space}$$
$$A = \{gg\} \qquad \text{Both are girls.}$$
$$B = \{gg, gb, bg\} \qquad \text{At least one is a girl.}$$
$$C = \{gg, gb\} \qquad \text{The older one is a girl.}$$

Note that $A \cap B = \{gg\}$.

(a) $P(A|B) = \dfrac{P(A \text{ and } B)}{P(B)} = \dfrac{\frac{1}{4}}{\frac{3}{4}} = \dfrac{1}{4} \div \dfrac{3}{4} = \dfrac{1}{4} \cdot \dfrac{4}{3} = \dfrac{1}{3}$

(b) $P(A|C) = \dfrac{P(A \text{ and } C)}{P(C)} = \dfrac{\frac{1}{4}}{\frac{2}{4}} = \dfrac{1}{4} \div \dfrac{2}{4} = \dfrac{1}{4} \cdot \dfrac{4}{2} = \dfrac{1}{2}$ ▮▮▮

Sometimes a conditional probability is no different than the corresponding unconditional probability, in which case we call the two events *independent*.

> **Independent Events**
>
> Two events A and B are called **independent events** if knowledge about the occurrence of one of them has no effect on the probability of the other one, that is, if
>
> $$P(B|A) = P(B), \quad \text{or, equivalently,} \quad P(A|B) = P(A).$$

A **cosmic impact**, the collision of a meteor, comet, or asteroid with Earth, could be as catastrophic as full-scale nuclear war, killing a billion or more people. The Web site www.impact.arc.nasa.gov reports that a large enough object (1 kilometer or more in diameter) could even put the human species at risk of annihilation by causing drastic climate changes and destroying food crops.

The Spaceguard Survey has discovered more than half of the estimated number of near-Earth asteroids (NEAs) in this size range and hopes to locate 90% of them in the next decade. Although the risk of finding one on a collision course with the Earth is slight, it is anticipated that, if we did, we would be able to deflect it before impact.

The photo above shows a crater in Arizona, 4000 feet in diameter and 570 feet deep, thought to have been formed 20,000 to 50,000 years ago by a meteorite about 50 meters across, hitting the ground at several kilometers per second. (See http://en.wikipedia.org/wiki/Meteor_Crater.)

▎▎ **EXAMPLE 3** Checking Events for Independence

A single card is to be drawn from a standard 52-card deck. (The sample space S has 52 elements.) Given the events

A: The selected card is a face card,   and B: The selected card is black,

(a) Find $P(B)$.

(b) Find $P(B|A)$.

(c) Determine whether events A and B are independent.

SOLUTION

(a) There are 26 black cards in the 52-card deck.

$$P(B) = \frac{26}{52} = \frac{1}{2} \quad \text{Theoretical probability formula}$$

(b) $P(B|A) = \dfrac{P(B \text{ and } A)}{P(A)}$ Conditional probability formula

$= \dfrac{\frac{6}{52}}{\frac{12}{52}}$ Of 52 cards, 12 are face cards and 6 are black face cards.

$= \dfrac{6}{52} \cdot \dfrac{52}{12}$ To divide, multiply by the reciprocal.

$= \dfrac{1}{2}$ Calculate and write in lowest terms.

(c) Because $P(B|A) = P(B)$, events A and B are independent.   ▮▮▮

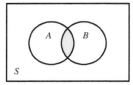

The logical connective "and" corresponds to "intersection" in set theory.

$P(A \text{ and } B) = P(A) \cdot P(B|A)$

Figure 9

Events Involving "And"

If we multiply both sides of the conditional probability formula by $P(A)$, we obtain an expression for $P(A \cap B)$, which applies to events of the form "A and B." The resulting formula is related to the fundamental counting principle of **Chapter 10.** It is illustrated in **Figure 9.**

Just as the calculation of $P(A \text{ or } B)$ is simpler when A and B are mutually exclusive, the calculation of $P(A \text{ and } B)$ is simpler when A and B are independent.

Multiplication Rule of Probability (for A and B)

If A and B are any two events, then

$$P(A \text{ and } B) = P(A) \cdot P(B|A).$$

If A and B are independent, then

$$P(A \text{ and } B) = P(A) \cdot P(B).$$

The first formula in the multiplication rule actually applies in all cases. ($P(B|A) = P(B)$ when A and B are independent.) Still, the independence of the component events is clear in many cases, so it is good to remember the second formula as well.

EXAMPLE 4 Selecting from a Set of Books

Each year, Jacqui Carper adds to her book collection a number of new publications that she believes will be of lasting value and interest. She has categorized each of her twenty acquisitions for 2011 as hardcover or paperback and as fiction or nonfiction. The numbers of books in the various categories are shown in **Table 6**.

Table 6 Year 2011 Books	Fiction (F)	Nonfiction (N)	Totals
Hardcover (H)	3	5	8
Paperback (P)	8	4	12
Totals	11	9	20

If Jacqui randomly chooses one of these 20 books, find the probability it will be

(a) hardcover,   **(b)** fiction, given it is hardcover,   **(c)** hardcover and fiction.

SOLUTION

(a) Eight of the 20 books are hardcover, so $P(H) = \frac{8}{20} = \frac{2}{5}$.

(b) The given condition that the book is hardcover reduces the sample space to eight books. Of those eight, just three are fiction, so $P(F|H) = \frac{3}{8}$.

(c) $P(H \text{ and } F) = P(H) \cdot P(F|H) = \frac{2}{5} \cdot \frac{3}{8} = \frac{3}{20}$ Multiplication rule

It is easier here if we simply notice, directly from **Table 6**, that 3 of the 20 books are "hardcover and fiction." This verifies that the general multiplication rule of probability did give us the correct answer.   ■■■

EXAMPLE 5 Selecting from a Set of Planets

Table 7 lists the eight planets of our solar system together with their mean distances from the sun, in millions of kilometers. (Data is from *The World Almanac and Book of Facts 2010*.) Carrie Ayers must choose two distinct planets to cover in her astronomy report. If she selects randomly, find the probability that the first one selected is closer to the sun than Mars and the second is closer than Saturn.

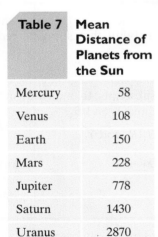

Table 7	Mean Distance of Planets from the Sun
Mercury	58
Venus	108
Earth	150
Mars	228
Jupiter	778
Saturn	1430
Uranus	2870
Neptune	4500

SOLUTION

We define the events

   A: The first is closer than Mars,   and B: The second is closer than Saturn.

Then $P(A) = \frac{3}{8}$. (Three of the original eight choices are favorable.) If the planet selected first is closer than Mars, it is also closer than Saturn, and since that planet is no longer available, $P(B|A) = \frac{4}{7}$. (Four of the remaining seven are favorable.)

$$P(A \text{ and } B) = P(A) \cdot P(B|A) = \frac{3}{8} \cdot \frac{4}{7} = \frac{3}{14} \approx 0.214 \quad \text{Multiplication rule} \quad ■■■$$

In **Example 5,** the condition that A had occurred changed the probability of B, since the selection was done, in effect, without replacement. (Repetitions were not allowed.) Events A and B were not independent. On the other hand, in the next example, the same events, A and B, will be independent.

■■ **EXAMPLE 6** Selecting from a Set of Planets

Carrie must again select two planets, but this time one is for an oral report, the other is for a written report, and they need not be distinct. (The same planet may be selected for both reports.) Again find the probability that, if she selects randomly, the first is closer than Mars and the second is closer than Saturn.

SOLUTION

Defining events A and B as in **Example 5,** we have $P(A) = \frac{3}{8}$, just as before. But the selection is now done *with* replacement. (Repetitions *are* allowed.) Event B is independent of event A, so we can use the second form of the multiplication rule.

$$P(A \text{ and } B) = P(A) \cdot P(B) = \frac{3}{8} \cdot \frac{5}{8} = \frac{15}{64} \approx 0.234 \quad \text{\small Answer is different than in \textbf{Example 5.}}$$ ■■■

■■ **EXAMPLE 7** Selecting from a Deck of Cards

A single card is drawn from a standard 52-card deck. Let B denote the event that the card is black, and let D denote the event that it is a diamond. Are events B and D

(a) independent?   **(b)** mutually exclusive?

SOLUTION

(a) For the unconditional probability of D, we get $P(D) = \frac{13}{52} = \frac{1}{4}$. (Thirteen of the 52 cards are diamonds.) But for the conditional probability of D, given B, we have $P(D|B) = \frac{0}{26} = 0$. (None of the 26 black cards are diamonds.) Since the conditional probability $P(D|B)$ is different than the unconditional probability $P(D)$, B and D are not independent.

(b) Mutually exclusive events are events that cannot both occur for a given performance of an experiment. Since no card in the deck is both black and a diamond, B and D are mutually exclusive. ■■■

■■ **EXAMPLE 8** Selecting from an Urn of Balls

Anne is still drawing balls from the same urn (shown at the side). This time she draws three balls, without replacement. Find the probability that she gets red, yellow, and blue balls, in that order.

SOLUTION

Using appropriate letters to denote the colors, and subscripts to indicate first, second, and third draws, the event can be symbolized R_1 and Y_2 and B_3.

$$P(R_1 \text{ and } Y_2 \text{ and } B_3) = P(R_1) \cdot P(Y_2|R_1) \cdot P(B_3|R_1 \text{ and } Y_2)$$
$$= \frac{4}{11} \cdot \frac{5}{10} \cdot \frac{2}{9} = \frac{4}{99} \approx 0.0404$$ ■■■

■■ **EXAMPLE 9** Selecting from a Deck of Cards

If five cards are drawn without replacement from a standard 52-card deck, find the probability that they all are hearts.

SOLUTION

Each time a heart is drawn, the number of available cards decreases by one and the number of hearts decreases by one.

$$P(\text{all hearts}) = \frac{13}{52} \cdot \frac{12}{51} \cdot \frac{11}{50} \cdot \frac{10}{49} \cdot \frac{9}{48} = \frac{33}{66,640} \approx 0.000495$$ ■■■

The search for extraterrestrial intelligence (SETI) may have begun in earnest as early as 1961 when Dr. Frank Drake presented an equation for estimating the number of possible civilizations in the Milky Way galaxy whose communications we might detect. Over the years, the effort has been advanced by many scientists, including the late astronomer and exobiologist Carl Sagan, who popularized the issue in TV appearances and in his book *The Cosmic Connection: An Extraterrestrial Perspective* (Dell Paperback). "There must be other starfolk," said Sagan. In fact, some astronomers have estimated the odds against life on Earth being the only life in the universe at one hundred billion billion to one.

Other experts disagree. Freeman Dyson, a noted mathematical physicist and astronomer, says in his book *Disturbing the Universe* that after considering the same evidence and arguments, he believes it is just as likely as not (even odds) that there never was any other intelligent life out there.

If you studied counting methods (**Chapter 10**), you may prefer to solve the problem of **Example 9** by using the theoretical probability formula and combinations. The total possible number of 5-card hands, drawn without replacement, is $_{52}C_5$, and the number of those containing only hearts is $_{13}C_5$.

$$P(\text{all hearts}) = \frac{_{13}C_5}{_{52}C_5} = \frac{\dfrac{13!}{5!8!}}{\dfrac{52!}{5!47!}} \approx 0.000495 \quad \text{Use a calculator.}$$

■ EXAMPLE 10 Using Both Addition and Multiplication Rules

The local garage employs two mechanics, Arnie and Burt. Your consumer club has found that Arnie does twice as many jobs as Burt, Arnie does a good job three out of four times, and Burt does a good job only two out of five times. If you plan to take your car in for repairs, find the probability that a good job will be done.

SOLUTION

We define the events

    A: work done by Arnie; B: work done by Burt; G: good job done.

Since Arnie does twice as many jobs as Burt, the (unconditional) probabilities of events A and B are, respectively, $\frac{2}{3}$ and $\frac{1}{3}$. Since Arnie does a good job three out of four times, the probability of a good job, given that Arnie did the work, is $\frac{3}{4}$. And since Burt does well two out of five times, the probability of a good job, given that Burt did the work, is $\frac{2}{5}$. (These last two probabilities are conditional.) These four values can be summarized.

$$P(A) = \frac{2}{3}, \quad P(B) = \frac{1}{3}, \quad P(G|A) = \frac{3}{4}, \quad \text{and} \quad P(G|B) = \frac{2}{5}.$$

Event G can occur in two mutually exclusive ways: Arnie could do the work and do a good job $(A \cap G)$, or Burt could do the work and do a good job $(B \cap G)$.

$$
\begin{aligned}
P(G) &= P(A \cap G) + P(B \cap G) &&\text{Addition rule}\\
&= P(A) \cdot P(G|A) + P(B) \cdot P(G|B) &&\text{Multiplication rule}\\
&= \frac{2}{3} \cdot \frac{3}{4} + \frac{1}{3} \cdot \frac{2}{5} &&\text{Substitute the values.}\\
&= \frac{1}{2} + \frac{2}{15} = \frac{19}{30} \approx 0.633 &&■■■
\end{aligned}
$$

Multiply first, then add.

The tree diagram in **Figure 10** shows a graphical way to organize the work of **Example 10.** Use the given information to draw the tree diagram, then find the probability of a good job by adding the probabilities from the indicated branches of the tree.

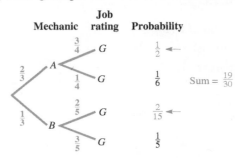

Garage mechanics experiment

Figure 10

▮▮ **EXAMPLE 11** Selecting Door Prizes

The **search for extraterrestrial intelligence (SETI)** has been mainly accomplished over the last decade through **SETI@HOME,** the largest distributed computing program on Earth. Most of the data are collected by the world's largest radio telescope, built into a 20-acre natural bowl in Aricebo, Puerto Rico (pictured above), and processed by millions of personal computers around the world.

To learn more, or for a chance to be the first to "contact" an extraterrestrial civilization, check out www.setiathome.ssl.berkeley.edu.

Rob Brown is among five door prize winners at a Christmas party. The five winners are asked to choose, without looking, from a bag which, they are told, contains five tokens, four of them redeemable for candy canes and one specific token redeemable for a $100 gift certificate. Can Rob improve his chance of getting the gift certificate by drawing first among the five people?

SOLUTION

We denote candy cane by C, gift certificate by G, and first draw, second draw, and so on by subscripts $1, 2, \ldots$. Then if Rob draws first, his probability of getting the gift certificate is

$$P(G_1) = \frac{1}{5}.$$

If he draws second, his probability of getting the gift certificate is

$$\begin{aligned} P(G_2) &= P(C_1 \text{ and } G_2) \\ &= P(C_1) \cdot P(G_2|C_1) \\ &= \frac{4}{5} \cdot \frac{1}{4} = \frac{1}{5}. \quad \text{Same result as above} \end{aligned}$$

For the third draw,

$$\begin{aligned} P(G_3) &= P(C_1 \text{ and } C_2 \text{ and } G_3) \\ &= P(C_1) \cdot P(C_2|C_1) \cdot P(G_3|C_1 \text{ and } C_2) \\ &= \frac{4}{5} \cdot \frac{3}{4} \cdot \frac{1}{3} = \frac{1}{5}. \quad \text{Same result as above} \end{aligned}$$

The probability of getting the gift certificate is $\frac{1}{5}$ when drawing fourth or fifth. The order in which the five winners draw does not affect Rob's chances. ▮▮▮

For Further Thought

The Birthday Problem

A classic problem (with a surprising result) involves the probability that a given group of people will include at least one pair of people with the same birthday (the same day of the year, not necessarily the same year). This problem can be analyzed using the probability of a complement formula (**Section 11.2**) and the multiplication rule of probability from this section. Suppose there are three people in the group.

P(at least one duplication of birthdays)

$= 1 - P(\text{no duplications})$ Complement formula

$= 1 - P(\text{2nd is different than 1st and 3rd is different than 1st and 2nd})$

$= 1 - \dfrac{364}{365} \cdot \dfrac{363}{365}$ Multiplication rule

$\approx 1 - 0.992$

$= 0.008$

(To simplify the calculations, we have assumed 365 possible birth dates, ignoring February 29.)

By doing more calculations like the one above, we find that the smaller the group, the smaller the probability of a duplication. The larger the group, the larger the probability of a duplication. The table on the next page shows the probability of at least one duplication for numbers of people from 2 through 52.

For Group or Individual Investigation

1. Based on the data shown in the table, what are the odds in favor of a duplication in a group of 30 people?

2. Estimate from the table the least number of people for which the probability of duplication is at least $\frac{1}{2}$.

3. How small a group is required for the probability of a duplication to be *exactly* 0?

4. How large a group is required for the probability of a duplication to be *exactly* 1?

Number of People	Probability of at Least One Duplication	Number of People	Probability of at Least One Duplication	Number of People	Probability of at Least One Duplication
2	0.003	19	0.379	36	0.832
3	0.008	20	0.411	37	0.849
4	0.016	21	0.444	38	0.864
5	0.027	22	0.476	39	0.878
6	0.040	23	0.507	40	0.891
7	0.056	24	0.538	41	0.903
8	0.074	25	0.569	42	0.914
9	0.095	26	0.598	43	0.924
10	0.117	27	0.627	44	0.933
11	0.141	28	0.654	45	0.941
12	0.167	29	0.681	46	0.948
13	0.194	30	0.706	47	0.955
14	0.223	31	0.730	48	0.961
15	0.253	32	0.753	49	0.966
16	0.284	33	0.775	50	0.970
17	0.315	34	0.795	51	0.974
18	0.347	35	0.814	52	0.978

11.3   EXERCISES

For each experiment, determine whether the two given events are independent.

1. **Tossing Coins** A fair coin is tossed twice. The events are "head on the first" and "head on the second."

2. **Rolling Dice** A pair of dice are rolled. The events are "even on the first" and "odd on the second."

3. **Comparing Planets' Mean Distances from the Sun** Two planets are selected, without replacement, from the list in **Table 7**. The events are "the first selected planet is closer than Jupiter" and "the second selected planet is farther than Mars."

4. **Comparing Mean Distances from the Sun** Two celestial bodies are selected, with replacement, from the list in **Table 7**. The events are "the first selected body is closer than Earth" and "the second selected body is farther than Uranus."

5. **Guessing Answers on a Multiple-choice Test** The answers are all guessed on a twenty-question multiple-choice test. The events are "the first answer is correct" and "the last answer is correct."

6. **Selecting Committees of U.S. Senators** A committee of five is randomly selected from the 100 U.S. Senators. The events are "the first member selected is a Republican" and "the second member selected is a Republican." (Assume that there are both Republicans and non-Republicans in the Senate.)

Comparing Gender and Career Motivation of College Students *One hundred college seniors attending a career fair at a university were categorized according to gender and according to primary career motivation, as summarized here.*

	Primary Career Motivation			
	Money	Allowed to be Creative	Sense of Giving to Society	Total
Male	19	15	14	48
Female	12	23	17	52
Total	31	38	31	100

If one of these students is to be selected at random, find the probability that the student selected will satisfy each condition in Exercises 7–12.

7. female

8. motivated primarily by creativity

9. not motivated primarily by money

10. male and motivated primarily by money

11. male, given that primary motivation is a sense of giving to society

12. motivated primarily by money or creativity, given that the student is female

Selecting Pets *A pet store has seven puppies, including four poodles, two terriers, and one retriever. If Rebecka and Aaron, in that order, each select one puppy at random,* with replacement *(they may both select the same one), find the probability of each event in Exercises 13–16.*

13. both select a poodle

14. Rebecka selects a retriever, Aaron selects a terrier

15. Rebecka selects a terrier, Aaron selects a retriever

16. both select a retriever

Selecting Pets *Suppose two puppies are selected as earlier, but this time* without replacement *(Rebecka and Aaron cannot both select the same puppy). Find the probability of each event in Exercises 17–22.*

17. both select a poodle

18. Aaron selects a terrier, given Rebecka selects a poodle

19. Aaron selects a retriever, given Rebecka selects a poodle

20. Rebecka selects a retriever

21. Aaron selects a retriever, given Rebecka selects a retriever

22. both select a retriever

Dealing Cards *Let two cards be dealt successively,* without replacement, *from a standard 52-card deck. Find the probability of each event in Exercises 23–27.*

23. spade second, given spade first

24. club second, given diamond first

25. two face cards

26. no face cards

27. The first card is a jack and the second is a face card.

28. Given events A and B within the sample space S, the following sequence of steps establishes formulas that can be used to compute conditional probabilities. Justify each statement.

(a) $P(A \text{ and } B) = P(A) \cdot P(B \mid A)$

(b) Therefore, $P(B \mid A) = \dfrac{P(A \text{ and } B)}{P(A)}$.

(c) Therefore, $P(B \mid A) = \dfrac{n(A \text{ and } B)/n(S)}{n(A)/n(S)}$.

(d) Therefore, $P(B \mid A) = \dfrac{n(A \text{ and } B)}{n(A)}$.

Considering Conditions in Card Drawing *Use the results of* **Exercise 28** *to find each probability when a single card is drawn from a standard 52-card deck.*

29. $P(\text{queen} \mid \text{face card})$

30. $P(\text{face card} \mid \text{queen})$

31. $P(\text{red} \mid \text{diamond})$

32. $P(\text{diamond} \mid \text{red})$

Investigating P(A and B) *Complete Exercises 33 and 34 to discover a general property of the probability of an event of the form A and B.*

33. If one number is chosen randomly from the integers 1 through 10, the probability of getting a number that is *odd and prime*, by the multiplication rule, is

$$P(\text{odd}) \cdot P(\text{prime} \mid \text{odd}) = \frac{5}{10} \cdot \frac{3}{5} = \frac{3}{10}.$$

Compute the product $P(\text{prime}) \cdot P(\text{odd} \mid \text{prime})$, and compare to the product above.

34. What does **Exercise 33** imply, in general, about the probability of an event of the form A and B?

35. **Gender in Sequences of Babies** Two authors of this book each have three sons and no daughters. Assuming boy and girl babies are equally likely, what is the probability of this event?

36. **Rolling Dice** Three dice are tossed. What is the probability that the numbers shown will all be different? (*Mathematics Teacher* calendar problem)

The remaining exercises, and groups of exercises, may require concepts from earlier sections, such as the complements principle of counting and addition rules, as well as the multiplication rule of this section.

Probabilities in Warehouse Grocery Shopping *Therese Felser manages a grocery warehouse which encourages volume shopping on the part of its customers. Therese has discovered that, on any given weekday,* 70 percent *of the customer sales amount to more than $100. That is, any given sale on such a day has a probability of* 0.70 *of being for more than $100. (Actually, the conditional probabilities throughout the day would change slightly, depending on earlier sales, but this effect would be negligible for the first several sales of the day, so we can treat them as independent.)*

Find the probability of each event in Exercises 37–40. (Give answers to three decimal places.)

37. The first two sales on Wednesday are both for more than $100.

38. The first three sales on Wednesday are all for more than $100.

39. None of the first three sales on Wednesday is for more than $100.

40. Exactly one of the first three sales on Wednesday is for more than $100.

Pollution from the Space Shuttle Launch Site One problem encountered by developers of the space shuttle program is air pollution in the area surrounding the launch site. A certain direction from the launch site is considered critical in terms of hydrogen chloride pollution from the exhaust cloud. It has been determined that weather conditions would cause emission cloud movement in the critical direction only 5% of the time.

In Exercises 41–44, find the probability for each event. Assume that probabilities for a particular launch in no way depend on the probabilities for other launches. (Give answers to two decimal places.)

41. A given launch will not result in cloud movement in the critical direction.

42. No cloud movement in the critical direction will occur during any of 5 launches.

43. Any 5 launches will result in at least one cloud movement in the critical direction.

44. Any 10 launches will result in at least one cloud movement in the critical direction.

Ordering Job Interviews Three men and three women are waiting to be interviewed for jobs. If they are all selected in random order, find the probability of each event in Exercises 45–47.

45. All the women will be interviewed first.

46. The first three interviewees will all be the same sex.

47. No man will be interviewed until at least two women have been interviewed.

48. *Cutting Up a Cube* A $4'' \times 4'' \times 4''$ cube is painted and then cut into sixty-four $1'' \times 1'' \times 1''$ cubes. A unit cube is then randomly selected and rolled. What is the probability that the top face of the rolled cube is painted? Express your answer as a common fraction. (*Mathematics Teacher* calendar problem)

49. *Tossing a Two-Headed Coin?* A gambler has two coins in his pocket—one fair coin and one two-headed coin. He selects a coin at random and flips it twice. If he gets two heads, what is the probability that he selected the fair coin? (*Mathematics Teacher* calendar problem)

50. In **Example 8,** where Anne draws three balls without replacement, what would be her probability of getting one of each color, where the order does not matter?

51. *Gender in Sequences of Babies* Assuming boy and girl babies are equally likely, find the probability that it would take

(a) at least three births to obtain two girls,

(b) at least four births to obtain two girls,

(c) at least five births to obtain two girls.

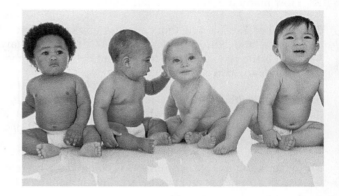

52. *Drawing Cards* Cards are drawn, without replacement, from an ordinary 52-card deck.

(a) How many must be drawn before the probability of obtaining at least one face card is greater than $\frac{1}{2}$?

(b) How many must be drawn before the probability of obtaining at least one king is greater than $\frac{1}{2}$?

Fair Decisions from Biased Coins Many everyday decisions, like who will drive to lunch, or who will pay for the coffee, are made by the toss of a (presumably fair) coin and using the criterion "heads, you will; tails, I will." This criterion is not quite fair, however, if the coin is biased (perhaps due to slightly irregular construction or wear). John von Neumann suggested a way to make perfectly fair decisions even with a possibly biased coin. If a coin, biased so that

$$P(h) = 0.5200 \quad \text{and} \quad P(t) = 0.4800,$$

is tossed twice, find each probability. (Give answers to four decimal places.)

53. $P(hh)$ **54.** $P(ht)$

55. $P(th)$ **56.** $P(tt)$

57. Having completed **Exercises 53–56,** can you suggest what von Neumann's scheme may have been?

Programming a Garage Door Opener *Kevin Frye installed a certain brand of automatic garage door opener that utilizes a transmitter control with six independent switches, each one set on or off. The receiver (wired to the door) must be set with the same pattern as the transmitter. (Exercises 58–61 are based on ideas similar to those of the "birthday problem" in the **For Further Thought** feature in this section.)*

58. How many different ways can Kevin set the switches?

59. If one of Kevin's neighbors also has this same brand of opener, and both of them set the switches randomly, what is the probability, to four decimal places, that they are able to open each other's garage doors?

60. If five neighbors with the same type of opener set their switches independently, what is the probability of at least one pair of neighbors using the same settings? (Give your answer to four decimal places.)

61. What is the minimum number of neighbors who must use this brand of opener before the probability of at least one duplication of settings is greater than $\frac{1}{2}$?

62. ***Choosing Cards*** There are three cards, one that is green on both sides, one that is red on both sides, and one that is green on one side and red on the other. One of the three cards is selected randomly and laid on the table. If it happens that the card on the table has a red side up, what is the probability that it is also red on the other side?

Weather Conditions on Successive Days *In November, the rain in a certain valley tends to fall in storms of several days' duration. The unconditional probability of rain on any given day of the month is 0.500. But the probability of rain on a day that follows a rainy day is 0.800, and the probability of rain on a day following a nonrainy day is 0.300. Find the probability of each event in Exercises 63–66. Give answers to three decimal places.*

63. rain on two randomly selected consecutive days in November

64. rain on three randomly selected consecutive days in November

65. rain on November 1 and 2, but not on November 3

66. rain on the first four days of November, given that October 31 was clear all day

Engine Failures in a Vintage Aircraft *In a certain four-engine vintage aircraft, now quite unreliable, each engine has a 10% chance of failure on any flight, as long as it is carrying its one-fourth share of the load. But if one engine fails, then the chance of failure increases to 20% for each of the other three engines. And if a second engine fails, each of the remaining two has a 30% chance of failure.*

Assuming that no two engines ever fail simultaneously, and that the aircraft can continue flying with as few as two operating engines, find each probability for a given flight of this aircraft. (Give answers to four decimal places.)

67. no engine failures

68. exactly one engine failure (any one of four engines)

69. exactly two engine failures (any two of four engines)

70. a failed flight

One-and-one Free Throw Shooting in Basketball *In basketball, "one-and-one" free throw shooting (commonly called foul shooting) is done as follows: if the player makes the first shot (1 point), he is given a second shot. If he misses the first shot, he is not given a second shot (see the tree diagram).*

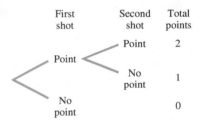

Christine Ellington, a basketball player, has a 70% foul shot record. (She makes 70% of her foul shots.) Find the probability that, on a given one-and-one foul shooting opportunity, Christine will score each number of points.

71. no points   **72.** one point

73. two points

74. ***Comparing Empirical and Theoretical Probabilities in Dice Rolling*** Roll a pair of dice until a sum of seven appears, keeping track of how many rolls it took. Repeat the process a total of 50 times, each time recording the number of rolls it took to get a sum of seven.

  (a) Use your experimental data to compute an empirical probability (to two decimal places) that it would take at least three rolls to get a sum of seven.

  (b) Find the theoretical probability (to two decimal places) that it would take at least three rolls to obtain a sum of seven.

75. Go to the Web site mentioned in the *cosmic impact* margin note in this section and write a report on the threat to humanity of cosmic impacts. Include an explanation of the abbreviation *NEO*.

11.4   BINOMIAL PROBABILITY

Binomial Probability Distribution   •   Binomial Probability Formula

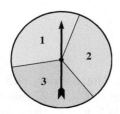

Binomial Probability Distribution

Suppose the spinner in the margin is spun twice. We are interested in the number of times a 2 is obtained. (Assume that 1, 2, and 3 all are equally likely on a given spin.) We can think of the outcome 2 as a "success," while a 1 or a 3 would be a "failure."

When the outcomes of an experiment are divided into just two categories, success and failure, the associated probabilities are called "binomial" (the prefix *bi* meaning *two*). Repeated performances of such an experiment, where the probability of success remains constant throughout all repetitions, are also known as repeated **Bernoulli trials** (after James Bernoulli). If we use an ordered pair to represent the result of each pair of spins, then the sample space for this experiment is

$$S = \{(1,1), (1,2), (1,3), (2,1), (2,2), (2,3), (3,1), (3,2), (3,3)\}.$$

The nine outcomes in S are all equally likely. (This follows from the numbers 1, 2, and 3 being equally likely on a particular spin.)

If x denotes the number of 2s occurring on each pair of spins, then x is an example of a *random variable*. Although we cannot predict the result of any particular pair of spins, we can find the probabilities of various events from the sample space listing. In S, the number of 2s is 0 in four cases, 1 in four cases, and 2 in one case, as reflected in **Table 8**. Because the table includes all possible values of x, together with their probabilities, it is an example of a *probability distribution*. In this case, we have a **binomial probability distribution.** Notice that the probability column in **Table 8** has a sum of 1, in agreement with property 3 of probability (**Section 11.2**).

In order to develop a general formula for binomial probabilities, we can consider another way to obtain the probability values in **Table 8**. The various spins of the spinner are independent of one another, and on each spin the probability of success (S) is $\frac{1}{3}$ and the probability of failure (F) is $\frac{2}{3}$. We will denote success on the first spin by S_1, failure on the second by F_2, and so on.

Table 8	Probability Distribution for the Number of 2s in Two Spins
x	$P(x)$
0	$\frac{4}{9}$
1	$\frac{4}{9}$
2	$\frac{1}{9}$
	Sum = $\frac{9}{9}$ = 1

$$
\begin{aligned}
P(x = 0) &= P(F_1 \text{ and } F_2) \\
&= P(F_1) \cdot P(F_2) \quad &\text{Multiplication rule} \\
&= \frac{2}{3} \cdot \frac{2}{3} \quad &\text{Substitute values.} \\
&= \frac{4}{9} \quad &\text{Multiply.}
\end{aligned}
$$

$$
\begin{aligned}
P(x = 1) &= P[(S_1 \text{ and } F_2) \text{ or } (F_1 \text{ and } S_2)] \quad &\text{2 ways to get } x = 1 \\
&= P(S_1 \text{ and } F_2) + P(F_1 \text{ and } S_2) \quad &\text{Addition rule} \\
&= P(S_1) \cdot P(F_2) + P(F_1) \cdot P(S_2) \quad &\text{Multiplication rule} \\
&= \frac{1}{3} \cdot \frac{2}{3} + \frac{2}{3} \cdot \frac{1}{3} \quad &\text{Substitute values.} \\
&= \frac{2}{9} + \frac{2}{9} \quad &\text{Multiply.} \\
&= \frac{4}{9} \quad &\text{Add.}
\end{aligned}
$$

James Bernoulli (1654–1705) is also known as Jacob or Jacques. He was charmed away from theology by the writings of Leibniz, became his pupil, and later headed the mathematics faculty at the University of Basel. His results in probability are contained in the *Art of Conjecture*, which was published in 1713, after his death, and which also included a reprint of the earlier Huygens paper. Bernoulli also made many contributions to calculus and analytic geometry.

$$P(x = 2) = P(S_1 \text{ and } S_2)$$
$$= P(S_1) \cdot P(S_2) \qquad \text{Multiplication rule}$$
$$= \frac{1}{3} \cdot \frac{1}{3} \qquad \text{Substitute values.}$$
$$= \frac{1}{9} \qquad \text{Multiply.}$$

Notice the following pattern in the above calculations. There is only one way to get $x = 0$ (namely, F_1 and F_2). And there is only one way to get $x = 2$ (namely, S_1 and S_2). But there are two ways to get $x = 1$. One way is S_1 and F_2; the other is F_1 and S_2. There are two ways because the one success required can occur on the first spin or on the second spin. How many ways can exactly one success occur in two repeated trials? This question is equivalent to:

How many size-one subsets are there of the set of two trials?

The answer is $_2C_1 = 2$. (The expression $_2C_1$ denotes "combinations of 2 things taken 1 at a time." Combinations were discussed in **Section 10.3**.) Each of the two ways to get exactly one success has a probability equal to $\frac{1}{3} \cdot \frac{2}{3}$, the probability of success times the probability of failure.

If the same spinner is spun three times rather than two, then x, the number of successes (2s) could have values of 0, 1, 2, or 3. Then the number of ways to get exactly 1 success is $_3C_1 = 3$. They are: S_1 and F_2 and F_3, F_1 and S_2 and F_3, F_1 and F_2 and S_3. The probability of each of these three ways is $\frac{1}{3} \cdot \frac{2}{3} \cdot \frac{2}{3} = \frac{4}{27}$.

$$P(x = 1) = 3 \cdot \frac{4}{27} = \frac{12}{27} = \frac{4}{9}$$

Figure 11 shows all possibilities for three spins, and **Table 9** gives the associated probability distribution. In the tree diagram, the number of ways of getting two successes in three trials is 3, in agreement with the fact that $_3C_2 = 3$. Also the sum of the $P(x)$ column in **Table 9** is again 1.

Table 9	Probability Distribution for the Number of 2s in Three Spins	
x		$P(x)$
0		$\frac{8}{27}$
1		$\frac{12}{27}$
2		$\frac{6}{27}$
3		$\frac{1}{27}$
	Sum $= \frac{27}{27} = 1$	

First spin	Second spin	Third spin	Number of successes	Probability
		S	3	$\frac{1}{3} \cdot \frac{1}{3} \cdot \frac{1}{3} = \frac{1}{27}$
		F	2	$\frac{1}{3} \cdot \frac{1}{3} \cdot \frac{2}{3} = \frac{2}{27}$
		S	2	$\frac{1}{3} \cdot \frac{2}{3} \cdot \frac{1}{3} = \frac{2}{27}$
		F	1	$\frac{1}{3} \cdot \frac{2}{3} \cdot \frac{2}{3} = \frac{4}{27}$
		S	2	$\frac{2}{3} \cdot \frac{1}{3} \cdot \frac{1}{3} = \frac{2}{27}$
		F	1	$\frac{2}{3} \cdot \frac{1}{3} \cdot \frac{2}{3} = \frac{4}{27}$
		S	1	$\frac{2}{3} \cdot \frac{2}{3} \cdot \frac{1}{3} = \frac{4}{27}$
		F	0	$\frac{2}{3} \cdot \frac{2}{3} \cdot \frac{2}{3} = \frac{8}{27}$

Tree diagram for three spins

Figure 11

PROBLEM-SOLVING HINT One of the problem-solving strategies from **Chapter 1** was "Look for a pattern." Having constructed complete probability distributions for binomial experiments with 2 and 3 repeated trials (and probability of success $\frac{1}{3}$), we can now generalize the observed pattern to any binomial experiment, as shown next.

Binomial Probability Formula

Define the following quantities.

n = the number of repeated trials

p = the probability of success on any given trial

$q = 1 - p$ = the probability of failure on any given trial

x = the number of successes that occur

Note that p remains fixed throughout all n trials. This means that all trials are independent of one another. The random variable x (number of successes) can have any integer value from 0 through n. In general, x successes can be assigned among n repeated trials in $_nC_x$ different ways, since this is the number of different subsets of x positions among a set of n positions. Also, regardless of which x of the trials result in successes, there will always be x successes and $n - x$ failures, so we multiply x factors of p and $n - x$ factors of q together.

Binomial Probability Formula

When n independent repeated trials occur, where

p = probability of success   and q = probability of failure

with p and q (where $q = 1 - p$) remaining constant throughout all n trials, the probability of exactly x successes is calculated as follows.

$$P(x) = {}_nC_x p^x q^{n-x} = \frac{n!}{x!(n-x)!} p^x q^{n-x}$$

Binomial probabilities for particular values of n, p, and x can be found directly using tables, statistical software, and some handheld calculators. In the following examples, we use the formula derived above.

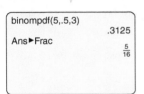

From the DISTR menu

binompdf(5,.5,3)
.3125
Ans▶Frac
$\frac{5}{16}$

The TI-83/84 Plus calculator will find the probability discussed in **Example 1.**

▮▮ **EXAMPLE 1** Finding Probability in Coin Tossing

Find the probability of obtaining exactly three heads in five tosses of a fair coin.

SOLUTION

Let heads be "success." Then this is a binomial experiment with $n = 5, p = \frac{1}{2}, q = \frac{1}{2}$, and $x = 3$.

$$P(3) = {}_5C_3\left(\frac{1}{2}\right)^3\left(\frac{1}{2}\right)^2 = 10 \cdot \frac{1}{8} \cdot \frac{1}{4} = \frac{5}{16} \quad \text{Binomial probability formula} \quad ▮▮▮$$

▮▮ **EXAMPLE 2** Finding Probability in Dice Rolling

Find the probability of obtaining exactly two 5s in six rolls of a fair die.

SOLUTION

Let 5 be "success." Then $n = 6, p = \frac{1}{6}, q = \frac{5}{6}$, and $x = 2$.

$$P(2) = {}_6C_2\left(\frac{1}{6}\right)^2\left(\frac{5}{6}\right)^4 = 15 \cdot \frac{1}{36} \cdot \frac{625}{1296} = \frac{3125}{15{,}552} \approx 0.201 \quad ▮▮▮$$

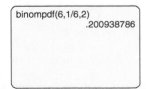

binompdf(6,1/6,2)
.200938786

This screen supports the answer in **Example 2.**

In the case of repeated independent trials, when an event involves more than one specific number of successes, we can employ the binomial probability formula along with the complement or addition rules.

▮▮ **EXAMPLE 3** Finding Probability of Female Children

A couple plans to have 5 children. Find the probability they will have more than 3 girls. (Assume girl and boy babies are equally likely.)

SOLUTION

Let a girl be "success." Then $n = 5$, $p = q = \frac{1}{2}$, and $x > 3$.

$$P(x > 3) = P(x = 4 \text{ or } 5) \qquad \text{More than 3 means 4 or 5.}$$
$$= P(4) + P(5) \qquad \text{Addition rule}$$
$$= {}_5C_4\left(\frac{1}{2}\right)^4\left(\frac{1}{2}\right)^1 + {}_5C_5\left(\frac{1}{2}\right)^5\left(\frac{1}{2}\right)^0 \qquad \text{Binomial probability formula}$$
$$= 5 \cdot \frac{1}{16} \cdot \frac{1}{2} + 1 \cdot \frac{1}{32} \cdot 1 \qquad \text{Simplify.}$$
$$= \frac{5}{32} + \frac{1}{32} = \frac{6}{32} = \frac{3}{16} = 0.1875$$

▮▮▮

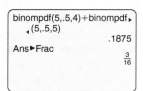

This screen supports the answer in
Example 3.

▮▮ **EXAMPLE 4** Finding Probability of Hits in Baseball

Andrew Crowley, a baseball player, has a well-established career batting average of .300. In a brief series with a rival team, Andrew will bat 10 times. Find the probability that he will get more than two hits in the series.

SOLUTION

This "experiment" involves $n = 10$ repeated Bernoulli trials, with probability of success (a hit) given by $p = 0.3$ (which implies $q = 1 - 0.3 = 0.7$). Since, in this case, "more than 2" means

"3 or 4 or 5 or 6 or 7 or 8 or 9 or 10"   (eight different possibilities),

it will be less work to apply the complement rule.

$$P(x > 2) = 1 - P(x \le 2) \qquad \text{Complement rule}$$
$$= 1 - P(x = 0 \text{ or } 1 \text{ or } 2) \qquad \text{Only three different possibilities}$$
$$= 1 - [P(0) + P(1) + P(2)] \qquad \text{Addition rule}$$
$$= 1 - [{}_{10}C_0(0.3)^0(0.7)^{10} \qquad \text{Binomial probability formula}$$
$$\quad + {}_{10}C_1(0.3)^1(0.7)^9 + {}_{10}C_2(0.3)^2(0.7)^8]$$
$$\approx 1 - [0.0282 + 0.1211 + 0.2335] \qquad \text{Simplify.}$$
$$= 1 - 0.3828$$
$$= 0.6172$$

▮▮▮

Scrolled Equation

1−(binompdf(10,.3,0)+bin▸
  ◂ompdf(10,.3,1)+binompdf▸
  ◂(10,.3,2))
                .6172172136

This screen supports the answer in
Example 4.

11.4 EXERCISES

For Exercises 1–24, give all numerical answers as common fractions reduced to lowest terms. For Exercises 25–54, give all numerical answers to three decimal places.

Coin Tossing *If three fair coins are tossed, find the probability of each number of heads.*

1. 0

2. 1

3. 2

4. 3

5. 1 or 2

6. at least 1

7. no more than 1

8. fewer than 3

9. Gender in Sequences of Babies Assuming boy and girl babies are equally likely, find the probability that a family with three children will have exactly two boys.

10. Relating Pascal's Triangle to Coin Tossing Pascal's triangle was shown in **Table 5** of **Section 10.4.** Explain how the probabilities in **Exercises 1–4** here relate to row 3 of the "triangle." (Recall that we referred to the topmost row of the triangle as "row number 0" and to the leftmost entry of each row as "entry number 0.")

11. Generalize the pattern in **Exercise 10** to complete the following statement. If n fair coins are tossed, the probability of exactly x heads is the fraction whose numerator is entry number _____ of row number _____ in Pascal's triangle, and whose denominator is the sum of the entries in row number _____.

Binomial Probability Applied to Tossing Coins Use the pattern noted in **Exercises 10 and 11** to find the probabilities of each number of heads when seven fair coins are tossed.

12. 0 **13.** 1 **14.** 2 **15.** 3

16. 4 **17.** 5 **18.** 6 **19.** 7

Binomial Probability Applied to Rolling Dice A fair die is rolled three times. A 4 is considered "success," while all other outcomes are "failures." Find the probability of each number of successes.

20. 0 **21.** 1 **22.** 2 **23.** 3

24. Exercises 10 and 11 established a way of using Pascal's triangle rather than the binomial probability formula to find probabilities of different numbers of successes in coin-tossing experiments. Explain why the same process would not work for **Exercises 20–23.**

For n repeated independent trials, with constant probability of success p for all trials, find the probability of exactly x successes in each of Exercises 25–28.

25. $n = 5$, $p = \frac{1}{3}$, $x = 4$

26. $n = 10$, $p = 0.7$, $x = 5$

27. $n = 20$, $p = \frac{1}{8}$, $x = 2$

28. $n = 30$, $p = 0.6$, $x = 22$

For Exercises 29–31, refer to **Example 4.**

29. Batting Averages in Baseball Does Andrew's probability of a hit really remain constant at exactly 0.300 through all ten times at bat? Explain your reasoning.

30. Batting Averages in Baseball If Andrew's batting average is exactly .300 going into the series, and that value is based on exactly 1200 career hits out of 4000 previous times at bat, what is the greatest his average could possibly be (to three decimal places) when he goes up to bat the tenth time of the series? What is the least his average could possibly be when he goes up to bat the tenth time of the series?

31. Do you think the use of the binomial probability formula was justified in **Example 4,** even though p is not strictly constant? Explain your reasoning.

Random Selection of Answers on a Multiple-choice Test Beth Dahlke is taking a ten-question multiple-choice test for which each question has three answer choices, only one of which is correct. Beth decides on answers by rolling a fair die and marking the first answer choice if the die shows 1 or 2, the second if it shows 3 or 4, and the third if it shows 5 or 6. Find the probability of each event in Exercises 32–35.

32. exactly four correct answers

33. exactly seven correct answers

34. fewer than three correct answers

35. at least seven correct answers

Side Effects of Prescription Drugs It is known that a certain prescription drug produces undesirable side effects in 35% of all patients who use it. Among a random sample of eight patients using the drug, find the probability of each event.

36. None have undesirable side effects.

37. Exactly one has undesirable side effects.

38. Exactly two have undesirable side effects.

39. More than two have undesirable side effects.

Likelihood of Capable Students Attending College In a certain state, it has been shown that only 60% of the high school graduates who are capable of college work actually enroll in colleges. Find the probability that, among nine capable high school graduates in this state, each number will enroll in college.

40. exactly 4 **41.** from 4 through 6

42. all 9 **43.** at least 3

44. Student Ownership of Personal Computers At a large midwestern university, 90% of all students have their own personal computers. If five students at that university are selected at random, find the probability that exactly three of them have their own computers.

45. *Frost Survival Among Orange Trees* If it is known that 65% of all orange trees will survive a hard frost, then what is the probability that at least half of a group of six trees will survive such a frost?

46. *Rate of Favorable Media Coverage of an Incumbent President* During a presidential campaign, 64% of the political columns in a certain group of major newspapers were favorable to the incumbent president. If a sample of fifteen of these columns is selected at random, what is the probability that exactly ten of them will be favorable?

Selecting Balls From a Bag A bag contains only white balls and black balls. Let p be the probability that a ball selected at random is black. Each time a ball is selected, it is placed back in the bag before the next ball is selected. Four balls are selected at random.

47. What is the probability that two of the four balls are black and two are white? (*Mathematics Teacher* calendar problem) (*Hint:* Use the binomial probability formula to express the probability in terms of *p*.)

48. Evaluate the probability of **Exercise 47** in case the bag actually contains 15 black balls and 25 white balls. Give your answer to four decimal places.

Taking a Random Walk Abby Gartland is parked at a mile marker on an east-west country road. She decides to toss a fair coin 10 *times, each time driving* 1 *mile east if it lands heads up and* 1 *mile west if it lands tails up. The term "random walk" applies to this process, even though Abby drives rather than walks. It is a simplified model of Brownian motion, mentioned on* **page 580.** *(See also* **Exercises 9–12** *in the* **Extension** *at the end of this chapter.)*

In each of Exercises 49–56, find the probability that Abby's "walk" will end as described.

49. 10 miles east of the start

50. 6 miles east of the start

51. 6 miles west of the start

52. 5 miles west of the start

53. 2 miles east of the start

54. at least 2 miles east of the start

55. at least 2 miles from the start

56. exactly at the start

11.5 EXPECTED VALUE

Expected Value • Games and Gambling • Investments • Business and Insurance

Expected Value

The probability distribution in **Table 10**, from **Example 6** of **Section 11.2,** shows the probabilities assigned by Amy to the various lengths of time her homework may take on a given night. If Amy's friend Tara asks her how many hours her studies will take, what would be her best guess? Six different time values are possible, with some more likely than others. One thing Amy could do is calculate a "weighted average" by multiplying each possible time value by its probability and then adding the six products.

$$1(0.05) + 2(0.10) + 3(0.20) + 4(0.40) + 5(0.10) + 6(0.15)$$
$$= 0.05 + 0.20 + 0.60 + 1.60 + 0.50 + 0.90 = 3.85$$

Thus 3.85 hours is the **expected value** (or the **mathematical expectation**) of the quantity of time to be spent. Since the original time values in the table were rounded to the nearest hour, the expected value also should be rounded, to 4 hours.

Table 10

x	P(x)
1	0.05
2	0.10
3	0.20
4	0.40
5	0.10
6	0.15

Expected Value

If a random variable x can have any of the values $x_1, x_2, x_3, \ldots, x_n$, and the corresponding probabilities of these values occurring are $P(x_1)$, $P(x_2)$, $P(x_3), \ldots,$ $P(x_n)$, then the **expected value of** x is calculated as follows.

$$E(x) = x_1 \cdot P(x_1) + x_2 \cdot P(x_2) + x_3 \cdot P(x_3) + \cdots + x_n \cdot P(x_n)$$

EXAMPLE 1 Finding the Expected Number of Boys

Find the expected number of boys for a three-child family (that is, the expected value of the number of boys). Assume girls and boys are equally likely.

SOLUTION

The sample space for this experiment is

$$S = \{ggg, ggb, gbg, bgg, gbb, bgb, bbg, bbb\}.$$

The probability distribution is shown in **Table 11**, along with the products and their sum, which gives the expected value.

Table 11

Number of Boys x	Probability $P(x)$	Product $x \cdot P(x)$
0	$\frac{1}{8}$	0
1	$\frac{3}{8}$	$\frac{3}{8}$
2	$\frac{3}{8}$	$\frac{6}{8}$
3	$\frac{1}{8}$	$\frac{3}{8}$
		Expected value: $E(x) = \frac{12}{8} = \frac{3}{2}$

The expected number of boys is $\frac{3}{2}$, or 1.5. This result seems reasonable. Since boys and girls are equally likely, "half" the children are expected to be boys.

Solution to the Chapter Opener Problem One way to look at the problem, given that the car is *not* behind Door 3, is that Doors 1 and 2 are now equally likely to contain the car. Thus, switching doors will neither help nor hurt your chances of winning the car.

However, there is another way to look at the problem. When you picked Door 1, the probability was $\frac{1}{3}$ that it contained the car. Being shown the goat behind Door 3 doesn't really give you any new information; after all, you knew that there was a goat behind at least one of the other doors. So seeing the goat behind Door 3 does nothing to change your assessment of the probability that Door 1 has the car. It remains $\frac{1}{3}$. But because Door 3 has been ruled out, the probability that Door 2 has the car is now $\frac{2}{3}$. Thus, you should switch.

Analysis of this problem depends on the psychology of the host. If we suppose that the host must *always* show you a losing door and then give you an option to switch, then you should switch. This was not specifically stated in the problem as posed above but was pointed out by many mathematicians who became involved in the discussion.

(The authors wish to thank David Berman of the University of New Orleans for his assistance with this explanation.)

For a convincing simulation of the Monty Hall problem, see http://www.grand-illusions.com/simulator/montysim.htm

The expected value for the number of boys in the family could never actually occur. It is only a kind of long run average of the various values that *could* occur. (For more information on "averages," see **Section 12.2.**) If we record the number of boys in many different three-child families, then by the law of large numbers, as the number of observed families increases, the observed average number of boys should approach the expected value.

Games and Gambling

EXAMPLE 2 Finding Expected Winnings

A player pays \$3 to play the following game: He tosses three fair coins and receives back "payoffs" of \$1 if he tosses no heads, \$2 for one head, \$3 for two heads, and \$4 for three heads. Find the player's expected net winnings for this game.

SOLUTION

Display the information as in **Table 12** on the next page. (Notice that, for each possible event, "net winnings" are "gross winnings" (payoff) minus cost to play.) Probabilities are derived from the sample space.

$$S = \{ttt, htt, tht, tth, hht, hth, thh, hhh\}$$

The expected net loss of 50 cents is a long-run average only. On any particular play of this game, the player would lose \$2 or lose \$1 or break even or win \$1. Over a long series of plays, say 100, there would be some wins and some losses, but the total net result would likely be around a $100 \cdot (\$0.50) = \$50$ *loss*.

Table 12

Number of Heads	Payoff	Net Winnings x	Probability $P(x)$	Product $x \cdot P(x)$
0	$1	$-\$2$	$\frac{1}{8}$	$-\$\frac{2}{8}$
1	2	-1	$\frac{3}{8}$	$-\frac{3}{8}$
2	3	0	$\frac{3}{8}$	0
3	4	1	$\frac{1}{8}$	$\frac{1}{8}$

Expected value: $E(x) = -\$\frac{1}{2} = -\$0.50$

■■■

A game in which the expected net winnings are zero is called a **fair game.** The game in **Example 2** has negative expected net winnings, so it is unfair against the player. A game with positive expected net winnings is unfair in favor of the player.

■■ **EXAMPLE 3** Finding the Fair Cost to Play a Game

The $3 cost to play the game of **Example 2** makes the game unfair against the player (since the player's expected net winnings are negative). What cost would make this a fair game?

SOLUTION

We already computed, in **Example 2,** that the $3 cost to play resulted in an expected net loss of $0.50. Therefore we can conclude that the $3 cost was 50 cents too high. A fair cost to play the game would then be $3 − $0.50 = $2.50.   ■■■

The result in **Example 3** can be verified. Disregard the cost to play and find the expected *gross* winnings (by summing the products of payoff times probability).

$$E(\text{gross winnings}) = \$1 \cdot \frac{1}{8} + \$2 \cdot \frac{3}{8} + \$3 \cdot \frac{3}{8} + \$4 \cdot \frac{1}{8} = \frac{\$20}{8} = \$2.50$$

Expected gross winnings (payoff) are $2.50, so this amount is a fair cost to play.

■■ **EXAMPLE 4** Finding the Fair Cost to Play a Game

In a certain state lottery, a player chooses three digits, in a specific order. (Leading digits may be 0, so numbers such as 028 and 003 are legitimate entries.) The lottery operators randomly select a three-digit sequence, and any player matching their selection receives a payoff of $600. What is a fair cost to play this game?

SOLUTION

In this case, no cost has been proposed, so we have no choice but to compute expected *gross* winnings. The probability of selecting all three digits correctly is $\frac{1}{10} \cdot \frac{1}{10} \cdot \frac{1}{10} = \frac{1}{1000}$, and the probability of not selecting all three correctly is $1 - \frac{1}{1000} = \frac{999}{1000}$. The expected gross winnings are

$$E(\text{gross winnings}) = \$600 \cdot \frac{1}{1000} + \$0 \cdot \frac{999}{1000} = \$0.60.$$

Thus the fair cost to play this game is 60 cents. (In fact, the lottery charges $1 to play, so players should expect to lose 40 cents per play *on the average.*)   ■■■

Roulette ("little wheel") was invented in France in the seventeenth or early eighteenth century. It has been a featured game of chance in the gambling casino of Monte Carlo.

The disk is divided into red and black alternating compartments, numbered 1 to 36 (but not in that order). There is a compartment also for 0 (and for 00 in the United States). In roulette, the wheel is set in motion, and an ivory ball is thrown into the bowl opposite to the direction of the wheel. When the wheel stops, the ball comes to rest in one of the compartments—the number and color determine who wins.

The players bet against the banker (person in charge of the pool of money) by placing money or equivalent chips in spaces on the roulette table corresponding to the wheel's colors or numbers. Bets can be made on one number or several, on odd or even, on red or black, or on combinations. The banker pays off according to the odds against the particular bet(s). For example, the classic payoff for a winning single number is $36 for each $1 bet.

State lotteries must be unfair against players because they are designed to help fund benefits (such as the state's school system) as well as to cover administrative costs and certain other expenses. Among people's reasons for playing may be a willingness to support such causes, but most people undoubtedly play for the chance to "beat the odds" and be one of the few net winners.

Gaming casinos are major business enterprises, by no means designed to break even; the games they offer are always unfair in favor of the house. The bias does not need to be great, however, since even relatively small average losses per player multiplied by large numbers of players can result in huge profits for the house.

▮▮ **EXAMPLE 5**   Finding Expected Winnings in Roulette

One simple type of *roulette* is played with an ivory ball and a wheel set in motion. The wheel contains thirty-eight compartments. Eighteen of the compartments are black, eighteen are red, one is labeled "zero," and one is labeled "double zero." (These last two are neither black nor red.) In this case, assume the player places $1 on either red or black. If the player picks the correct color of the compartment in which the ball finally lands, the payoff is $2; otherwise the payoff is zero. Find the expected net winnings.

SOLUTION

By the expected value formula, expected net winnings are

$$E(\text{net winnings}) = (\$1)\frac{18}{38} + (-\$1)\frac{20}{38} = -\$\frac{1}{19}.$$

The expected net *loss* here is $\$\frac{1}{19}$, or about 5.3¢, per play.   ▮▮▮

Investments

▮▮ **EXAMPLE 6**   Finding Expected Investment Profits

Nick Jovanovich has $5000 to invest and will commit the whole amount, for six months, to one of three technology stocks. A number of uncertainties could affect the prices of these stocks, but Nick is confident, based on his research, that one of only several possible profit scenarios will prove true of each one at the end of the six-month period. His complete analysis is shown in **Table 13**. (For example, stock *ABC* could lose $400, gain $800, or gain $1500.)

Table 13					
Company *ABC*		**Company *RST***		**Company *XYZ***	
Profit or Loss x	**Probability** $P(x)$	**Profit or Loss** x	**Probability** $P(x)$	**Profit or Loss** x	**Probability** $P(x)$
−$400	0.2	$500	0.8	$0	0.4
800	0.5	1000	0.2	700	0.3
1500	0.3			1200	0.1
				2000	0.2

Find the expected profit (or loss) for each of the three stocks and select Nick's optimum choice based on these calculations. (The solution is on the next page.)

The first **Silver Dollar Slot Machine** was fashioned in 1929 by the Fey Manufacturing Company, San Francisco, inventors of the 3-reel, automatic payout machine (1895).

SOLUTION

Apply the expected value formula.

ABC: $-\$400 \cdot (0.2) + \$800 \cdot (0.5) + \$1500 \cdot (0.3) = \$770$

RST: $\$500 \cdot (0.8) + \$1000 \cdot (0.2) = \$600$

XYZ: $\$0 \cdot (0.4) + \$700 \cdot (0.3) + \$1200 \cdot (0.1) + \$2000 \cdot (0.2) = \$730$

The largest expected profit is $770. By this analysis, Nick should invest the money in stock ABC. ▮▮▮

Of course, by investing in stock ABC, Nick may in fact *lose* $400 over the six months. The "expected" return of $770 is only a long-run average over many identical situations. Since this particular investment situation may never occur again, you may argue that using expected values is not the best approach for Nick to use.

An optimist would ignore most possibilities and focus on the *best* that each investment could do, while a pessimist would focus on the *worst* possibility for each investment.

▮▮ **EXAMPLE 7** Choosing Stock Investments

Decide which stock of **Example 6** Nick would pick in each case.

(a) He is an optimist.   **(b)** He is a pessimist.

SOLUTION

(a) Disregarding the probabilities, he would focus on the best case for each stock. Since ABC could return as much as $1500, RST as much as $1000, and XYZ as much as $2000, the optimum is $2000. He would buy stock XYZ (the best of the three *best* cases).

(b) In this situation, he would focus on the worst possible cases. Since ABC might return as little as −$400 (a $400 loss), RST as little as $500, and XYZ as little as $0, he would buy stock RST (the best of the three *worst* cases). ▮▮▮

Business and Insurance

▮▮ **EXAMPLE 8** Finding Expected Lumber Revenue

Mike Crenshaw, a lumber wholesaler, is considering the purchase of a (railroad) carload of varied dimensional lumber. Mike calculates that the probabilities of reselling the load for $10,000, $9000, or $8000 are 0.22, 0.33, and 0.45, respectively. In order to ensure an *expected* profit of at least $3000, how much can Mike afford to pay for the load?

SOLUTION

The expected revenue (or income) from resales can be found in **Table 14**.

Table 14	Expected Lumber Revenue	
Income x	Probability $P(x)$	Product $x \cdot P(x)$
$10,000	0.22	$2200
9000	0.33	2970
8000	0.45	3600
	Expected revenue:	$8770

In general, we have the relationship

$$\text{profit} = \text{revenue} - \text{cost}.$$

Therefore, in terms of expectations,

$$\text{expected profit} = \text{expected revenue} - \text{cost}.$$

So $3000 = $8770 − cost, or equivalently, cost = $8770 − $3000 = $5770. Mike can pay up to $5770 and still maintain an expected profit of at least $3000. ■■■

EXAMPLE 9 Analyzing an Insurance Decision

Jeff Marsalis, a farmer, will realize a profit of $150,000 on his wheat crop, unless there is rain before harvest, in which case he will realize only $40,000. The long-term weather forecast assigns rain a probability of 0.16. (The probability of no rain is 1 − 0.16 = 0.84.) An insurance company offers crop insurance of $150,000 against rain for a premium of $20,000. Should Jeff buy the insurance?

SOLUTION

In order to make a wise decision, Jeff computes his expected profit under both options: to insure and not to insure. The complete calculations are summarized in the two "expectation" **Tables 15 and 16**.

For example, if insurance is purchased and it rains, Jeff's net profit is

$$\begin{bmatrix} \text{Insurance} \\ \text{proceeds} \end{bmatrix} + \begin{bmatrix} \text{Reduced} \\ \text{crop profit} \end{bmatrix} - \begin{bmatrix} \text{Insurance} \\ \text{premium} \end{bmatrix} \qquad \text{Net profit}$$

$$\$150,000 + \$40,000 - \$20,000 = \$170,000.$$

Table 15   Expectation when Insuring

	Net Profit x	Probability $P(x)$	Product $x \cdot P(x)$
Rain	$170,000	0.16	$27,200
No rain	130,000	0.84	109,200
			Expected profit: $136,400

Table 16   Expectation when Not Insuring

	Net Profit x	Probability $P(x)$	Product $x \cdot P(x)$
Rain	$40,000	0.16	$6400
No rain	150,000	0.84	126,000
			Expected profit: $132,400

By comparing expected profits (136,400 > 132,400), we conclude that Jeff is better off buying the insurance. ■■■

For Further Thought

Expected Value of Games of Chance

Slot machines are a popular game for those who want to lose their money with very little mental effort. We cannot calculate an expected value applicable to all slot machines since payoffs vary from machine to machine. But we can calculate the "typical expected value."

A player operates a slot machine by pulling a handle after inserting a coin or coins. Reels inside the machine then rotate, and come to rest in some random order. Assume that three reels show the pictures listed in **Table 17**. For example, of the 20 pictures on the first reel, 2 are cherries, 5 are oranges, 5 are plums, 2 are bells, 2 are melons, 3 are bars, and 1 is the number 7.

A picture of cherries on the first reel, but not on the second, leads to a payoff of 3 coins (*net* winnings: 2 coins); a picture of cherries on the first two reels, but not the third, leads to a payoff of 5 coins (*net* winnings: 4 coins). These and all other winning combinations are listed in **Table 18**.

Since, according to **Table 17**, there are 2 ways of getting cherries on the first reel, 15 ways of *not* getting cherries on the second reel, and 20 ways of getting anything on the third reel, we have a total of $2 \cdot 15 \cdot 20 = 600$ ways of getting a net payoff of 2. Since there are 20 pictures per reel, there are a total of $20 \cdot 20 \cdot 20 = 8000$ possible outcomes. Hence, the probability of receiving a net payoff of 2 coins is 600/8000.

This Cleveland Indians fan hit four 7s in a row on a progressive nickel slot machine at the Sands Casino in Las Vegas in 1988.

Table 17   Pictures on Reels

Pictures	Reels		
	1	2	3
Cherries	2	5	4
Oranges	5	4	5
Plums	5	3	3
Bells	2	4	4
Melons	2	1	2
Bars	3	2	1
7s	1	1	1
Totals	20	20	20

Table 18   Calculating Expected Loss on a Three-Reel Slot Machine

Winning Combinations	Number of Ways	Probability	Number of Coins Received	Net Winnings (in coins)	Probability Times Net Winnings
1 cherry (on first reel)	$2 \cdot 15 \cdot 20 = 600$	600/8000	3	2	1200/8000
2 cherries (on first two reels)	$2 \cdot 5 \cdot 16 = 160$	160/8000	5	4	640/8000
3 cherries	$2 \cdot 5 \cdot 4 = 40$	40/8000	10	9	360/8000
3 oranges	$5 \cdot 4 \cdot 5 = 100$	100/8000	10	9	900/8000
3 plums	$5 \cdot 3 \cdot 3 = 45$	45/8000	14	13	585/8000
3 bells	$\_ \cdot \_ \cdot \_ = \_\_$	___/8000	18	___	___/8000
3 melons (jackpot)	$\_ \cdot \_ \cdot \_ = \_\_$	___/8000	100	___	___/8000
3 bars (jackpot)	$\_ \cdot \_ \cdot \_ = \_\_$	___/8000	200	___	___/8000
3 7s (jackpot)	$\_ \cdot \_ \cdot \_ = \_\_$	___/8000	500	___	___/8000
Totals	___				6318/8000

Table 18 takes into account all *winning* outcomes, with the necessary products for finding expectation added in the last column. However, since a *nonwinning* outcome can occur in

$$8000 - 988 = 7012 \text{ ways (with winnings of } -1 \text{ coin)},$$

the product $(-1) \cdot 7012/8000$ must also be included. Hence, the expected value of this particular slot machine is

$$\frac{6318}{8000} + (-1) \cdot \frac{7012}{8000} \approx -0.087 \text{ coin.}$$

On a machine costing one dollar per play, the expected *loss* (per play) is about

$$(0.087)(1 \text{ dollar}) = 8.7 \text{ cents.}$$

Actual slot machines vary in expected loss per dollar of play. But author Hornsby was able to beat a Las Vegas slot machine in 1988. (See the photo on **page 618**.)

Table 19 comes from an article by Andrew Sterrett in *The Mathematics Teacher* (March 1967), in which he discusses rules for various games of chance and calculates their expected values. He uses expected values to find expected times it would take to lose $1000 if you played continually at the rate of $1 per play and one play per minute.

For Group or Individual Investigation

1. Explain why the entries of the "Net Winnings" column of **Table 18** are all one fewer than the corresponding entries of the "Number of Coins Received" column.

2. Find the 29 missing values in **Table 18**. (Refer to **Table 17** for the values in the "Number of Ways" column.)

3. In order to make your money last as long as possible in a casino, which game should you play?

Table 19   Expected Time to Lose $1000

Game	Expected Value	Days	Hours	Minutes
Roulette (with one 0)	−$0.027	25	16	40
Roulette (with 0 and 00)	−$0.053	13	4	40
Chuck-a-luck	−$0.079	8	19	46
Keno (one number)	−$0.200	3	11	20
Numbers	−$0.300	2	7	33
Football pool (4 winners)	−$0.375	1	20	27
Football pool (10 winners)	−$0.658	1	1	19

11.5 EXERCISES

1. Explain in words what is meant by "expected value of a random variable."

2. Explain what a couple means by the statement, "We expect to have 1.5 sons."

3. *Tossing Coins*   Five fair coins are tossed. Find the expected number of heads.

4. *Drawing Cards*   Two cards are drawn, with replacement, from a standard 52-card deck. Find the expected number of diamonds.

Expected Winnings in a Die-rolling Game   For Exercises 5 and 6, a game consists of rolling a single fair die and pays off as follows: $3 for a 6, $2 for a 5, $1 for a 4, and no payoff otherwise.

5. Find the expected winnings for this game.

6. What is a fair price to pay to play this game?

Expected Winnings in a Die-rolling Game   For Exercises 7 and 8, consider a game consisting of rolling a single fair die, with payoffs as follows. If an even number of spots turns up, you receive as many dollars as there are spots up. But if an odd number of spots turns up, you must pay as many dollars as there are spots up.

7. Find the expected net winnings of this game.

8. Is this game fair, or unfair against the player, or unfair in favor of the player?

9. *Expected Winnings in a Coin-tossing Game*   A certain game involves tossing 3 fair coins, and it pays 10¢ for 3 heads, 5¢ for 2 heads, and 3¢ for 1 head. Is 5¢ a fair price to pay to play this game? (That is, does the 5¢ cost to play make the game fair?)

10. *Expected Winnings in Roulette* In a form of roulette slightly different from that in **Example 5,** a more generous management supplies a wheel having only thirty-seven compartments, with eighteen red, eighteen black, and one zero. Find the expected net winnings if you bet on red in this game.

11. *Expected Number of Absences in a Math Class* In a certain mathematics class, the probabilities have been empirically determined for various numbers of absentees on any given day. These values are shown in the table below. Find the expected number of absentees on a given day. (Give the answer to two decimal places.)

Number absent	0	1	2	3	4
Probability	0.18	0.26	0.29	0.23	0.04

12. *Expected Profit of an Insurance Company* An insurance company will insure a $200,000 home for its total value for an annual premium of $650. If the company spends $25 per year to service such a policy, the probability of total loss for such a home in a given year is 0.002, and you assume that either total loss or no loss will occur, what is the company's expected annual gain (or profit) on each such policy?

Profits from a College Foundation Raffle A college foundation raises funds by selling raffle tickets for a new car worth $36,000.

13. If 600 tickets are sold for $120 each, determine

    (a) the expected *net* winnings of a person buying one of the tickets,

    (b) the total profit for the foundation, assuming they had to purchase the car,

    (c) the total profit for the foundation, assuming the car was donated.

14. For the raffle described in **Exercise 13,** if 720 tickets are sold for $120 each, determine

    (a) the expected *net* winnings of a person buying one of the tickets,

    (b) the total profit for the foundation, assuming they had to purchase the car,

    (c) the total profit for the foundation, assuming the car was donated.

Winnings and Profits of a Raffle Five thousand raffle tickets are sold. One first prize of $1000, two second prizes of $500 each, and three third prizes of $100 each will be awarded, with all winners selected randomly.

15. If you purchased one ticket, what are your expected gross winnings?

16. If you purchased ten tickets, what are your expected gross winnings?

17. If the tickets were sold for $1 each, how much profit goes to the raffle sponsor?

18. *Expected Sales at a Theater Snack Bar* A children's theater found in a random survey that 58 customers bought one snack bar item, 49 bought two items, 31 bought three items, 4 bought four items, and 8 avoided the snack bar altogether. Use this information to find the expected number of snack bar items per customer. (Round your answer to the nearest tenth.)

19. *Expected Number of Children to Attend an Amusement Park* An amusement park, considering adding some new attractions, conducted a study over several typical days and found that, of 10,000 families entering the park, 1020 brought just one child (defined as younger than age twelve), 3370 brought two children, 3510 brought three children, 1340 brought four children, 510 brought five children, 80 brought six children, and 170 brought no children at all. Find the expected number of children per family attending this park. (Round your answer to the nearest tenth.)

20. *Expected Sums of Randomly Selected Numbers* Four cards are numbered 1 through 4. Two of these cards are chosen randomly (without replacement), and the numbers on them are added. Find the expected value of this sum.

21. *Prospects for Electronics Jobs in a City* In a certain California city, projections for the next year are that there is a 20% chance that electronics jobs will increase by 200, a 50% chance that they will increase by 300, and a 30% chance that they will decrease by 800. What is the expected change in the number of electronics jobs in that city in the next year?

22. *Expected Winnings in Keno* In one version of the game *keno,* the house has a pot containing 80 balls, numbered 1 through 80. A player buys a ticket for $1 and marks one number on it (from 1 to 80). The house then selects 20 of the 80 numbers at random. If the number selected by the player is among the 20 selected by the management, the player is paid $3.20. Find the expected net winnings for this game.

23. Refer to **Examples 6 and 7.** Considering the three different approaches (expected values, optimist, and pessimist), which one seems most reasonable to you, and why?

Contractor Decisions Based on Expected Profits *Lori Hales, a commercial building contractor, will commit her company to one of three projects depending on her analysis of potential profits or losses as shown here.*

Project A		Project B		Project C	
Profit or Loss *x*	**Probability** *P(x)*	**Profit or Loss** *x*	**Probability** *P(x)*	**Profit or Loss** *x*	**Probability** *P(x)*
$60,000	0.10	$0	0.20	$40,000	0.65
180,000	0.60	210,000	0.35	340,000	0.35
250,000	0.30	290,000	0.45		

Determine which project Lori should choose according to each approach.

24. expected values   **25.** the optimist viewpoint

26. the pessimist viewpoint

Expected Winnings in a Game Show *A game show contestant is offered the option of receiving a computer system worth $2300 or accepting a chance to win either a luxury vacation worth $5000 or a boat worth $8000. If the second option is chosen the contestant's probabilities of winning the vacation or the boat are 0.20 and 0.15, respectively.*

27. If the contestant were to turn down the computer system and go for one of the other prizes, what would be the expected winnings?

28. Purely in terms of monetary value, what is the contestant's wiser choice?

Evaluating an Insurance Purchase *David Glenn, the promoter of an outdoor concert, expects a gate profit of $100,000, unless it rains, which would reduce the gate profit to $30,000. The probability of rain is 0.20. For a premium of $25,000 David can purchase insurance coverage that would pay him $100,000 in case of rain.*

Use this information for Exercises 29–32.

29. Find the expected net profit when the insurance is purchased.

30. Find the expected net profit when the insurance is not purchased.

31. Based on expected values, which is David's wiser choice in this situation?

32. If you were the promoter, would you base your decision on expected values? Explain your reasoning.

Expected Values in Book Sales *Jessica Lasda, an educational publisher representative, presently has five accounts, and her manager is considering assigning her three more accounts. The new accounts would bring potential volume to her business, and some of her present accounts have potential for growth as well. See the following table and continue on the next page.*

1	2	3	4	5	6
Account Number	**Existing Volume**	**Potential Additional Volume**	**Probability of Getting Additional Volume**	**Expected Value of Additional Volume**	**Existing Volume plus Expected Value of Additional Volume**
1	$10,000	$10,000	0.40	$4000	$14,000
2	30,000	0	—	—	30,000
3	25,000	15,000	0.20	3000	
4	35,000	0	—	—	
5	15,000	5,000	0.30		
6	0	30,000	0.10		
7	0	25,000	0.70		
8	0	45,000	0.60		

Use the previous table to work Exercises 33–37.

33. Compute the four missing expected values in column 5.

34. Compute the six missing amounts in column 6.

35. What is Jessica's total "expected" additional volume?

36. If Jessica achieved her expected additional volume in all accounts, what would be the total volume of all her accounts?

37. If Jessica achieved her expected additional volume in all accounts, by what percentage (to the nearest tenth of a percent) would she increase her total volume?

38. *Expected Winnings in Keno* Recall that in the game keno of **Exercise 22,** the house randomly selects 20 numbers from the counting numbers 1–80. In the variation called 6-spot keno, the player pays 60¢ for his ticket and marks 6 numbers of his choice. If the 20 numbers selected by the house contain at least 3 of those chosen by the player, he gets a payoff according to this scheme.

3 of the player's numbers among the 20	$0.35
4 of the player's numbers among the 20	2.00
5 of the player's numbers among the 20	60.00
6 of the player's numbers among the 20	1250.00

Find the player's expected net winnings in this game. [*Hint:* The four probabilities required here can be found using combinations (**Section 10.3**), the fundamental counting principle (**Section 10.2**), and the theoretical probability formula (**Section 11.1**).]

EXTENSION   Estimating Probabilities by Simulation

Simulating Genetic Traits • Simulating Human Births

	Second Parent	
	R	**r**
First Parent **R**	RR	Rr
r	rR	rr

Simulation methods, also called **"Monte Carlo" methods,** require huge numbers of random digits, so computers are used to produce them. A computer, however, cannot toss coins. It must use an algorithmic process, programmed into the computer, which is called a **random number generator.** It is very difficult to avoid all nonrandom patterns in the results, so the digits produced are called "pseudorandom" numbers. They must pass a battery of tests of randomness before being "approved for use."

Computer scientists and physicists have been encountering unexpected difficulties with even the most sophisticated random number generators. Therefore, they must be carefully checked along with each new simulation application proposed.

Simulating Genetic Traits An important area within probability theory is the process called **simulation.** It is possible to study a complicated, or unclear, phenomenon by *simulating,* or imitating, it with a simpler phenomenon involving the same basic probabilities.

For example, recall from **Section 11.1** Mendel's discovery that when two Rr pea plants (red-flowered but carrying both red and white genes) are crossed, the offspring will have red flowers if an R gene is received from either parent or from both. This is because red is dominant and white is recessive. **Table 3**, reproduced here in the margin, shows that three of the four equally likely possibilities result in red-flowered offspring.

Now suppose we want to estimate the probability that three offspring in a row will have red flowers. It is much easier (and quicker) to toss coins than to cross pea plants. And the equally likely outcomes, heads and tails, can be used to simulate the transfer of the equally likely genes, R and r. If we toss two coins, say a nickel and a penny, then we can interpret the results as follows.

hh $\Rightarrow$ RR $\Rightarrow$ red gene from first parent and red gene from second parent
$\Rightarrow$ red flowers

ht $\Rightarrow$ Rr $\Rightarrow$ red gene from first parent and white gene from second parent
$\Rightarrow$ red flowers

th $\Rightarrow$ rR $\Rightarrow$ white gene from first parent and red gene from second parent
$\Rightarrow$ red flowers

tt $\Rightarrow$ rr $\Rightarrow$ white gene from first parent and white gene from second parent
$\Rightarrow$ white flowers

Although nothing is certain for a few tosses, the law of large numbers indicates that larger and larger numbers of tosses should become better and better indicators of general trends in the genetic process.

▐▌ **EXAMPLE 1** Simulating Genetic Processes

Toss two coins 50 times and use the results to approximate the probability that the crossing of Rr pea plants will produce three successive red-flowered offspring.

SOLUTION

We actually tossed two coins 50 times and got the following sequence.

> th, hh, th, tt, th, hh, ht, th, ht, th, hh, hh, tt, th, hh,
> ht, ht, ht, ht, th, hh, hh, hh, tt, ht, tt, hh, ht, ht, hh, tt,
> tt, tt, th, tt, tt, hh, ht, ht, ht, hh, tt, th, hh, tt, hh, ht,
> tt, tt, tt

By the color interpretation described on the previous page, this gives the following sequence of flower colors in the offspring.

> red–red–red–white–red–red–red–red–red–red–red–red–white–

Only "both tails" gives white.

> red–red–red–red–red–red–red–red–red–red–white–red–white–
> red–red–red–red–white–white–white–red–white–white–red–red–
> red–red–red–white–red–red–white–red–red–white–white–white

We now have an experimental list of 48 sets of three successive plants, the 1st, 2nd, and 3rd entries, then the 2nd, 3rd, and 4th entries, and so on. Do you see why there are 48 in all?

Now we just count up the number of these sets of three that are "red-red-red." Since there are 20 of those, our empirical probability of three successive red offspring, obtained through simulation, is $\frac{20}{48} = \frac{5}{12}$, or about 0.417. By applying the multiplication rule of probability (with all outcomes independent of one another), we find that the theoretical value is $\left(\frac{3}{4}\right)^3 = \frac{27}{64}$, or about 0.422, so our approximation obtained by simulation is very close. ▐▐▐

Simulating Human Births In human births boys and girls are (essentially) equally likely. Therefore, an individual birth can be simulated by tossing a fair coin, letting a head correspond to a girl and a tail to a boy.

▐▌ **EXAMPLE 2** Simulating Births with Coin Tossing

Pilots, astronauts, race car drivers, and others train in **simulators.** Some of these devices, which may be viewed as very technical, high-cost versions of video games, imitate conditions to be encountered later in the "real world." A simulator session allows estimation of the likelihood, or probability, of different responses that the learner would display under actual conditions. Repeated sessions help the learner to develop more successful responses before actual equipment and lives are put at risk.

A sequence of 40 actual coin tosses produced the results below.

> bbggb, gbbbg, gbgbb, bggbg, bbbbg, gbbgg, gbbgg, bgbbg

(For every head we have written g, for girl. For every tail, b, for boy.)

(a) How many pairs of two successive births are represented by the sequence?

(b) How many of those pairs consist of both boys?

(c) Find the empirical probability, based on this simulation, that two successive births both will be boys. Give your answer to three decimal places.

SOLUTION

(a) Beginning with the 1st–2nd pair and ending with the 39th–40th pair, there are 39 pairs.

(b) Observing the sequence of boys and girls, we count 11 pairs of two consecutive boys.

(c) Utilizing parts (a) and (b), we have $\frac{11}{39} \approx 0.282$. ▐▐▐

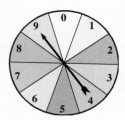

Figure 12

Table 20

→51592
77876
36500
40571
04822
→53033
92080
01587
36006
63698
→17297
22841
→91979
96480
74949
76896
47588
45521
02472
55184
40177
84861
86937
20931
22454
→73219
→55707
48007
→65191
06772
94928
→15709
39922
96365
14655
65587
76905
12369
54219
89329
90060
06975
05050
69774
→78351
11464
84086
→51497
12307
68009

Another way to simulate births, and other phenomena, is with random numbers. The spinner in **Figure 12** can be used to obtain a table of random digits, like in **Table 20**. The 250 random digits generated have been grouped conveniently so that we can easily follow down a column or across a row to carry out a simulation.

▮▮ **EXAMPLE 3** Simulating Births with Random Numbers

A couple plans to have five children. Use random number simulation to estimate the probability they will have more than three boys.

SOLUTION

Let each sequence of five digits, as they appear in **Table 20,** represent a family with five children, and (arbitrarily) associate odd digits with boys, even digits with girls. (Recall that 0 is even.) Verify that, of the fifty families simulated, only the ten marked with arrows have more than 3 boys (4 boys or 5 boys). Therefore, the estimated (empirical) probability is

$$P(\text{more than 3 boys}) = \frac{10}{50} = 0.20.$$ ▮▮▮

The theoretical value for the probability in **Example 3** above would be the same as that obtained in **Example 3** of **Section 11.4.** It was 0.1875. Our estimate above was fairly close. In light of the law of large numbers, a larger sampling of random digits (more than 50 simulated families) would likely yield a closer approximation.

▮▮ **EXAMPLE 4** Simulating Card Drawing with Random Numbers

Use random number simulation to estimate the probability that two cards drawn from a standard deck with replacement both will be of the same suit.

SOLUTION

Use this correspondence: 0 and 1 mean clubs, 2 and 3 mean diamonds, 4 and 5 mean hearts, 6 and 7 mean spades, 8 and 9 are disregarded. Now refer to **Table 20**. If we (arbitrarily) use the first digit of each five-digit group, omitting 8s and 9s, we obtain the sequence

5–7–3–4–0–5–0–3–6–1–2–7–7–4–4–0–5–4–2–2–

7–5–4–6–0–1–3–1–6–7–1–5–0–0–6–7–1–5–1–6.

First digits of all groups

This 40-digit sequence of digits yields the sequence of suits shown next.

5 gives hearts, 7 gives spades, 3 gives diamonds, and so on.

hearts–spades–diamonds–hearts–clubs–hearts–clubs–diamonds–spades–

clubs–diamonds–spades–spades–hearts–hearts–clubs–hearts–hearts–

diamonds–diamonds–spades–hearts–hearts–spades–clubs–clubs–

diamonds–clubs–spades–spades–clubs–hearts–clubs–clubs–spades–

spades–clubs–hearts–clubs–spades

Verify that, of the 39 successive pairs of suits (hearts–spades, spades–diamonds, diamonds–hearts, etc.), 9 of them are pairs of the same suit. This makes the estimated probability $\frac{9}{39} \approx 0.23$. (For comparison, the theoretical value is 0.25.) ▮▮▮

EXTENSION EXERCISES

1. *Simulating Pea Plant Reproduction with Coin Tossing*
Explain why, in **Example 1,** fifty tosses of the coins produced only 48 sets of three successive offspring.

2. *Simulating Pea Plant Reproduction with Coin Tossing* Use the sequence of flower colors of **Example 1** to approximate the probability that *four* successive offspring all will have red flowers.

3. *Comparing the Likelihoods of Girl and Boy Births* Should the probability of two successive girl births be any different from that of two successive boy births?

4. *Finding Empirical Probability* Simulate 40 births by tossing coins yourself, and obtain an empirical probability for two successive girls.

5. *Simulating Boy and Girl Children with Random Numbers* Use **Table 20** to simulate fifty families with three children. Let 0–4 correspond to boys and 5–9 to girls, and use the middle three digits of the 5-digit groupings (159, 787, 650, and so on). Estimate the probability of exactly two boys in a family of three children. Compare with the theoretical probability, which is $\frac{3}{8} = 0.375$.

Simulating One-and-One Foul Shooting with Random Numbers
In **Exercises 71–73** *of* **Section 11.3**, *Christine, who had a 70% foul-shooting record, had probabilities of scoring 0, 1, or 2 points of* 0.30, 0.21, *and* 0.49, *respectively.*

Use **Table 20** *(with digits 0–6 representing hit and 7–9 representing miss) to simulate 50 one-and-one shooting opportunities for Christine. Begin at the top left (5, 7, 3, etc., to the bottom), then move to the second column (1, 7, 6, etc.), going until 50 one-and-one opportunities are obtained. (Some "opportunities" involve one shot and one random digit, while others involve two shots and two random digits.) Keep a tally of the numbers of times 0, 1, and 2 points are scored.*

Number of Points	Tally
0	
1	
2	

From the tally, find the empirical probability (to two decimal places) of each event.

6. no points   **7.** 1 point   **8.** 2 points

Determining the Path of a Random Walk Using a Die and a Coin
Exercises 49–56 *of* **Section 11.4** *illustrated a simple version of the idea of a "random walk." Atomic particles released in nuclear fission also move in a random fashion. During World War II, John von Neumann and Stanislaw Ulam used simulation with random numbers to study particle motion in nuclear reactions. Von Neumann coined the name "Monte Carlo" for the methods used.*

The figure suggests a model for random motion in two dimensions. Assume that a particle moves in a series of 1-unit "jumps," each one in a random direction, any one of 12 equally likely possibilities. One way to choose directions is to roll a fair die and toss a fair coin. The die determines one of the directions 1–6, coupled with heads on the coin. Tails on the coin reverses the direction of the die, so that the die coupled with tails gives directions 7–12. So 3h (meaning 3 with the die and heads with the coin) gives direction 3; 3t gives direction 9 (opposite to 3); and so on.

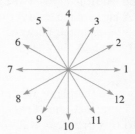

9. Simulate the motion described above with 10 rolls of a die (and tosses of a coin). Draw the 10-jump path you get. Make your drawing accurate enough so you can estimate (by measuring) how far from its starting point the particle ends up.

10. Repeat the experiment of **Exercise 9** four more times. Measure distance from start to finish for each of the 5 "random trips." Add these 5 distances and divide the sum by 5, to arrive at an "expected net distance" for such a trip.

For Exercises 11 and 12, consider another two-dimensional random walk governed by the following conditions.

- *Start out from a given street corner, and travel one block north. At each intersection:*
- *Turn left with probability $\frac{1}{6}$.*
- *Go straight with probability $\frac{2}{6} \left(= \frac{1}{3}\right)$.*
- *Turn right with probability $\frac{3}{6} \left(= \frac{1}{2}\right)$.*

(Never turn around.)

11. *A Random Walk Using a Fair Die* Explain how a fair die could be used to simulate this random walk.

12. *A Random Walk Using a Random Number Table* Use **Table 20** to simulate this random walk. For every 1 encountered in the table, turn left and proceed for another block. For every 2 or 3, go straight and proceed for another block. For every 4, 5, or 6, turn right and proceed for another block. Disregard all other digits, that is, 0s, 7s, 8s, and 9s. (Do you see how this scheme satisfies the probabilities given before **Exercise 11**?) This time begin at the upper right corner of the table, running down the column 2, 6, 0, and so on, to the bottom. When this column of digits is used up, stop the "walk." Describe, in terms of distance and direction, where you have ended up relative to your starting point.

COLLABORATIVE INVESTIGATION

Finding Empirical Values of π

The information in this investigation was obtained from Burton's History of Mathematics: An Introduction, *Third Edition, by David M. Burton, published by Wm. C. Brown, 1995, page 440.*

The following problem was posed by Georges Louis Leclerc, Comte de Buffon (1707–1788) in his *Histoire Naturelle* in 1777. A large plane area is ruled with equidistant parallel lines, the distance between two consecutive lines of the series being *a*. A thin needle of length

$$\ell < a$$

is tossed randomly onto the plane. What is the probability that the needle will intersect one of these lines?

The answer to this problem is found using integral calculus, and the probability *p* is shown to be $p = \frac{2\ell}{\pi a}$. Solving for π gives us the formula

$$\pi = \frac{2\ell}{pa}, \qquad \textbf{(1)}$$

which can be used to approximate the value of π experimentally. This was first observed by Pierre Simon de Laplace, and such an experiment was carried out by Johann Wolf, a professor of astronomy at Bern, in about 1850. In this investigation, we will perform a similar experiment.

See http://webspace.ship.edu/deensley/mathdl/stats/Buffon.html for a dynamic illustration of this Buffon Needle Problem.

Topics for Discussion

Divide the class into groups of 3 or 4 students each. Each group will need the materials listed in the next column.

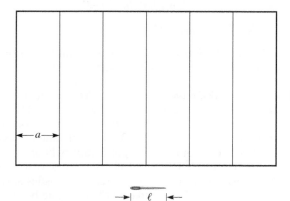

1. a sheet of paper with a series of parallel lines evenly spaced across it

2. a thin needle, or needlelike object, with a length less than the distance between adjacent parallel lines on the paper

Each group should carry out these steps:

1. Measure and record the distance between lines (*a*) and the length of the needle (ℓ), using the same units for both.

2. Assign one member to drop the needle onto the paper, another to determine whether the needle "hits" a line or not, and another to keep a tally of hits and misses.

3. Discuss ways to minimize bias so that the position and orientation of the dropped needle will be as random as possible.

4. Drop the needle 100 times, and record the number of hits.

5. Calculate the probability *p* = (number of hits)/100. Is this probability value theoretical or empirical?

6. Enter the calculated value of *p* and the measured values of *a* and ℓ into formula (1) to obtain a value of π. Round this value to four decimal places.

Now come back together as a class and record the various values obtained for π. Discuss the following questions.

1. The correct value of π, to four decimal places, is 3.1416. Which value of π, reported by the various groups, is most accurate? How far off is it?

2. Was it necessary to drop the needle 100 times, or could more or fewer tosses have been used?

3. Wolf tossed his needle 5000 times and it hit a line 2532 times, leading to an experimental value of π equal to 3.1596. How far off was Wolf's value?

4. How could the experiment be modified to produce "better" values for π?

5. Why could different groups use different ℓ to *a* ratios and still all obtain legitimate approximations for π?

6. Does the simulation method investigated here seem like a reasonable way to approximate π? Why, or why not?

CHAPTER 11 TEST

1. Explain the difference between *empirical* and *theoretical* probabilities.

2. State the *law of large numbers,* and use coin tossing to illustrate it.

Drawing Cards *A single card is chosen at random from a standard 52-card deck. Find the odds against its being each of the following.*

3. a heart

4. a red queen

5. a king or a black face card

Genetics of Cystic Fibrosis *The chart represents genetic transmission of cystic fibrosis.* C *denotes a normal gene while* c *denotes a cystic fibrosis gene. (Normal is dominant.) Both parents in this case are Cc, which means that they inherited one of each gene, and are, therefore, carriers but do not have the disease.*

		Second Parent	
		C	**c**
First Parent	**C**		Cc
	c		

6. Complete the chart, showing all four equally likely gene arrangements.

7. Find the probability that a child of these parents will also be a carrier without the disease.

8. What are the odds that a child of these parents actually will have cystic fibrosis?

Days Off for Pizza Parlor Workers *The manager of a pizza parlor (which operates seven days a week) allows each of three employees to select one day off next week. Assuming the selection is done randomly and independently, find the probability of each event.*

9. All three select different days.

10. All three select the same day, given that all three select a day beginning with the same letter.

11. Exactly two of them select the same day.

Building Numbers from Sets of Digits *Two numbers are randomly selected without replacement from the set* $\{1, 2, 3, 4, 5\}$. *Find the probability of each event.*

12. Both numbers are even.

13. Both numbers are prime.

14. The sum of the two numbers is odd.

15. The product of the two numbers is odd.

Selecting Committees *A three-member committee is selected randomly from a group consisting of three men and two women.*

16. Let *x* denote the number of men on the committee, and complete the probability distribution table.

x	*P(x)*
0	0
1	
2	
3	

17. Find the probability that the committee members are not all men.

18. Find the expected number of men on the committee.

Rolling Dice *A pair of dice are rolled. Find the following.*

19. the probability of "doubles" (the same number on both dice)

20. the odds in favor of a sum greater than 2

21. the odds against a sum of "7 or 11"

22. the probability of a sum that is even and less than 5

Making Par in Golf *Ted Krischak has a 0.78 chance of making par on each hole of golf that he plays. Today he plans to play just three holes. Find the probability of each event. Round answers to three decimal places.*

23. He makes par on all three holes.

24. He makes par on exactly two of the three holes.

25. He makes par on at least one of the three holes.

26. He makes par on the first and third holes but not on the second.

Drawing Cards *Two cards are drawn, without replacement, from a standard 52-card deck. Find the probability of each event.*

27. Both cards are red.

28. Both cards are the same color.

29. The second card is a queen, given that the first card is an ace

30. The first card is a face card and the second is black.

STATISTICS

12

T he CBS television series, NUMB3RS, focused on how mathematics is used in solving crimes. In the December 5, 2008 episode Conspiracy Theory, agent Charlie Eppes wants to prove a point to one of his colleagues: "Go with what you know, not what you don't." He cites a case of Simpson's paradox, a puzzling statistical oddity.

In both these years, David Justice had a higher batting average than Derek Jeter. But if you factor in their uneven number of at-bats, Jeter beats him.

What we know is that for the two-year period, Jeter is the better hitter, despite the fact that for both individual years, Justice had higher averages. To verify the paradox for yourself, see For Further Thought on page 649.

12.1 VISUAL DISPLAYS OF DATA

Basic Concepts • Frequency Distributions • Grouped Frequency Distributions
• Stem-and-Leaf Displays • Bar Graphs, Circle Graphs, and Line Graphs

Basic Concepts

Governments collect and analyze an amazing quantity of "statistics". The word itself comes from the Latin *statisticus,* meaning "of the state."

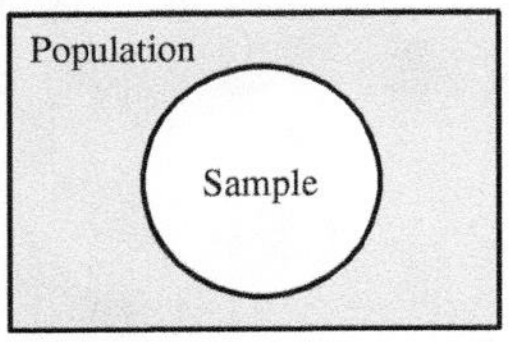

In statistical work, a **population** includes *all* items of interest, and a **sample** includes *some* (but ordinarily not all) of the items in the population. See the Venn diagram in the margin.

To predict the outcome of an approaching presidential election, we may be interested in a population of many millions of voter preferences (those of all potential voters in the country). As a practical matter, however, even national polling organizations with considerable resources will obtain only a relatively small sample, say 2000, of those preferences.

The study of statistics is divided into two main areas. **Descriptive statistics** has to do with collecting, organizing, summarizing, and presenting data (information). **Inferential statistics,** has to do with drawing inferences or conclusions (making conjectures) about populations based on information from samples.

The photos below show two random samples drawn from a large bowl of 10,000 colored beads. The 25-bead sample contains 9 green beads, from which we infer, by inductive reasoning, that the bowl (the population) must contain about $\frac{9}{25}$, or 36%, that is, about 3600 green beads.

A population of 10,000

A random sample of 25

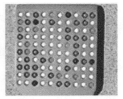
A random sample of 100

The 100-bead sample contains 28 green beads, leading to the inference that the population must contain about $\frac{28}{100}$, or 28%, that is, about 2800 green beads. This estimate, based on a larger sample, should be more accurate. In fact it is, since the bowl actually contains 30%, or 3000 green beads, and 2800 is closer to 3000 than 3600 is. (The "error" is one-third as much.)

Summarizing, if we know what a population is like, then probability theory enables us to predict what is likely to happen in a sample (deductive reasoning). If we know what a sample is like, then inferential statistics enables us to infer estimates about the population (inductive reasoning).

Information that has been collected but not yet organized or processed is called **raw data.** It is often **quantitative** (or **numerical**) but can also be **qualitative** (or **nonnumerical**), as illustrated in **Table 1**.

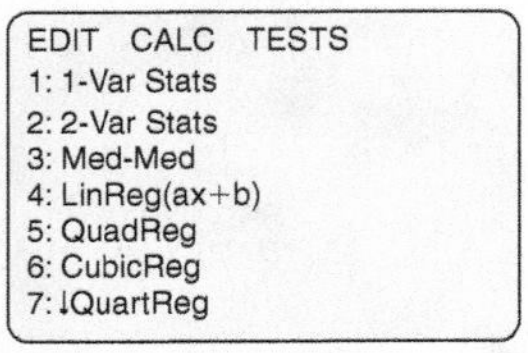

Table 1	Examples of Raw Data

Quantitative data: The number of siblings in ten different families: 3, 1, 2, 1, 5, 4, 3, 3, 8, 2

Qualitative data: The makes of six different automobiles: Toyota, Ford, Nissan, Toyota, Chevrolet, Honda

---

(margin, top left)

Population

Sample

(margin, bottom left)

EDIT CALC TESTS
1: 1-Var Stats
2: 2-Var Stats
3: Med-Med
4: LinReg(ax+b)
5: QuadReg
6: CubicReg
7: ↓QuartReg

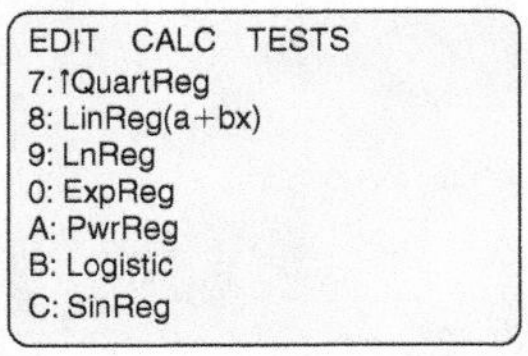

EDIT CALC TESTS
7: ↑QuartReg
8: LinReg(a+bx)
9: LnReg
0: ExpReg
A: PwrReg
B: Logistic
C: SinReg

Various statistical options on the TI-83/84 Plus.

Quantitative data are generally more useful when they are **sorted,** or arranged in numerical order. In sorted form, the first list in **Table 1** appears as follows.

$$1, 1, 2, 2, 3, 3, 3, 4, 5, 8$$

Frequency Distributions

When a data set includes many repeated items, it can be organized into a **frequency distribution,** which lists the distinct data values (x) along with their frequencies (f). The frequency designates the number of times the corresponding item occurred in the data set.

It is also helpful to show the **relative frequency** of each distinct item. This is the fraction, or percentage, of the data set represented by the item. If n denotes the total number of items, and a given item, x, occurred f times, then the relative frequency of x is $\frac{f}{n}$. **Example 1** illustrates these ideas.

▌▌ **EXAMPLE 1**   Constructing Frequency and Relative Frequency Distributions

The 25 members of a psychology class were polled as to the number of siblings in their individual families. Construct a frequency distribution and a relative frequency distribution for their responses, which are shown here.

$$2, 3, 1, 3, 3, 5, 2, 3, 3, 1, 1, 4, 2, 4, 2, 5, 4, 3, 6, 5, 1, 6, 2, 2, 2$$

SOLUTION

The data range from a low of 1 to a high of 6. The frequencies (obtained by inspection) and relative frequencies are shown in **Table 2**.

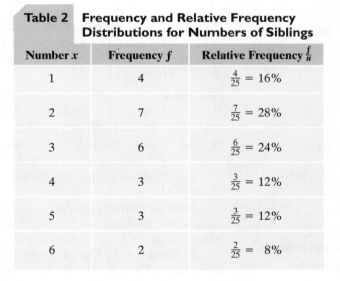

Table 2	Frequency and Relative Frequency Distributions for Numbers of Siblings	
Number x	**Frequency f**	**Relative Frequency $\frac{f}{n}$**
1	4	$\frac{4}{25} = 16\%$
2	7	$\frac{7}{25} = 28\%$
3	6	$\frac{6}{25} = 24\%$
4	3	$\frac{3}{25} = 12\%$
5	3	$\frac{3}{25} = 12\%$
6	2	$\frac{2}{25} = 8\%$

▮▮▮

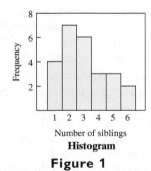

Histogram
Figure 1

The numerical data of **Table 2** can more easily be interpreted with the aid of a **histogram.** A series of rectangles, whose lengths represent the frequencies, are placed next to one another as shown in **Figure 1**. On each axis, horizontal and vertical, a label and the numerical scale should be shown.

The information shown in the histogram in **Figure 1** can also be conveyed by a **frequency polygon,** as in **Figure 2**. Simply plot a single point at the appropriate height for each frequency, connect the points with a series of connected line segments, and complete the polygon with segments that trail down to the axis beyond 1 and 6.

The frequency polygon is an instance of the more general *line graph*, used for many kinds of data, not just frequencies. Line graphs were first introduced in **Chapter 1.**

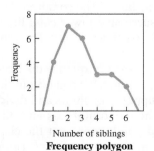

Frequency polygon
Figure 2

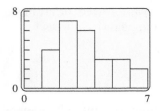

This histogram was generated with a graphing calculator using the data in **Table 2**. Compare with **Figure 1** on **page 631**.

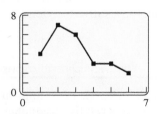

This line graph resembles the frequency polygon in **Figure 2** on **page 631**. It was generated with a graphing calculator using the data in **Table 2**.

Grouped Frequency Distributions

Data sets containing large numbers of items are often arranged into groups, or *classes*. All data items are assigned to their appropriate classes, and then a **grouped frequency distribution** can be set up and a graph displayed. Although there are no fixed rules for establishing the classes, most statisticians agree on a few general guidelines.

Guidelines for the Classes of a Grouped Frequency Distribution

1. Make sure each data item will fit into one, and only one, class.
2. Try to make all classes the same width.
3. Make sure the classes do not overlap.
4. Use from 5 to 12 classes. (Too few or too many classes can obscure the tendencies in the data.)

■■ **EXAMPLE 2** Constructing a Histogram and a Frequency Polygon

Forty students, selected randomly in the school cafeteria one morning, were asked to estimate the number of hours they had spent studying in the past week (including both in-class and out-of-class time). Their responses are recorded here.

18	60	72	58	20	15	12	26	16	29
26	41	45	25	32	24	22	55	30	31
55	39	29	44	29	14	40	31	45	62
36	52	47	38	36	23	33	44	17	24

Tabulate a grouped frequency distribution and a grouped relative frequency distribution and construct a histogram and a frequency polygon for the given data.

SOLUTION

The data range from a low of 12 to a high of 72 (that is, over a range of $72 - 12 = 60$ units.). The widths of the classes should be uniform (by Guideline 2), and there should be from 5 to 12 classes (by Guideline 4). Five classes would imply a class width of about $\frac{60}{5} = 12$, while twelve classes would imply a class width of about $\frac{60}{12} = 5$. A class width of 10 will be convenient. We let our classes run from 10 through 19, from 20 through 29, and so on up to 70 through 79, for a total of seven classes. All four guidelines are met.

Next go through the data set, tallying each item into the appropriate class. The tally totals produce class frequencies, which in turn produce relative frequencies, as shown in **Table 3** on the next page. The histogram is displayed in **Figure 3**.

In **Table 3** (and **Figure 3**) the numbers 10, 20, 30, and so on are called the **lower class limits.** They are the smallest possible data values within the respective classes. The numbers 19, 29, 39, and so on are called the **upper class limits.** The common **class width** for the distribution is the difference of any two successive lower class limits (such as 30–20), or of any two successive upper class limits (such as 59–49). The class width for this distribution is 10, as noted earlier.

To construct a frequency polygon, notice that, in a *grouped* frequency distribution, the data items in a given class are generally not all the same. We can obtain the "middle" value, or **class mark,** by adding the lower and upper class limits and dividing this sum by 2. We locate all the class marks along the horizontal axis and plot points above the class marks. The heights of the plotted points represent the class frequencies. The resulting points are connected just as for an ordinary (non-grouped) frequency distribution. The result is shown in **Figure 4**.

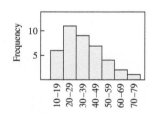

Weekly study times (in hours)
Grouped frequency histogram
Figure 3

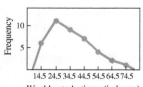

Weekly study times (in hours)
Grouped frequency polygon
Figure 4

Table 3 **Grouped Frequency and Relative Frequency Distributions for Weekly Study Times**

Class Limits	Tally	Frequency f	Relative Frequency $\frac{f}{n}$
10–19	|||||		6	$\frac{6}{40} = 15.0\%$
20–29	||||| |||||		11	$\frac{11}{40} = 27.5\%$
30–39	||||| ||||	9	$\frac{9}{40} = 22.5\%$
40–49	||||| ||	7	$\frac{7}{40} = 17.5\%$
50–59	||||	4	$\frac{4}{40} = 10.0\%$
60–69	||	2	$\frac{2}{40} = 5.0\%$
70–79			1	$\frac{1}{40} = 2.5\%$
Total:		$n = 40$	

Stem-and-Leaf Displays

In **Table 3**, the tally marks give a good visual impression of how the data are distributed. In fact, the tally marks are almost like a histogram turned on its side. Nevertheless, once the tallying is done, the tally marks are usually dropped, and the grouped frequency distribution is presented as in **Table 4**.

The pictorial advantage of the tally marks is now lost. Furthermore, we cannot tell, from the grouped frequency distribution itself (or from the tally marks either, for that matter), what any of the original items were. We only know, for example, that there were seven items in the class 40–49. We do not know specifically what any of them were.

One way to avoid these shortcoming is to employ a tool of exploratory data analysis, the **stem-and-leaf display,** as shown in **Example 3**.

Table 4 **Grouped Frequency Distribution for Weekly Study Times**

Class Limits	Frequency
10–19	6
20–29	11
30–39	9
40–49	7
50–59	4
60–69	2
70–79	1

▮▮ **EXAMPLE 3** Constructing a Stem-and-Leaf Display

Present the study times data of **Example 2** in a stem-and-leaf display.

SOLUTION

See **Example 2** for the original raw data. We arrange the numbers in **Table 5**. The tens digits, to the left of the vertical line, are the "stems," while the corresponding ones digits are the "leaves." We have entered all items from the first row of the original data, from left to right, then the items from the second row through the fourth row.

Table 5 **Stem-and-Leaf Display for Weekly Study Times**

1	8	5	2	6	4	7				
2	0	6	9	6	5	4	2	9	9	3	4
3	2	0	1	9	1	6	8	6	3		
4	1	5	4	0	5	7	4				
5	8	5	5	2							
6	0	2									
7	2										

Notice that the stem-and-leaf display of **Example 3** conveys at a glance the same pictorial impressions that a histogram would convey without the need for constructing the drawing. It also preserves the exact data values.

Bar Graphs, Circle Graphs, and Line Graphs

A frequency distribution of nonnumerical observations can be presented in the form of a **bar graph,** which is similar to a histogram except that the rectangles (bars) usually are not touching one another and sometimes are arranged horizontally rather than vertically. The bar graph of **Figure 5** shows the frequencies of occurrence of the vowels A, E, I, O, and U in this paragraph.

A graphical alternative to the bar graph is the **circle graph,** or **pie chart,** which uses a circle to represent the total of all the categories and divides the circle into sectors, or wedges (like pieces of pie), whose sizes show the relative magnitudes of the categories. The angle around the entire circle measures 360°. For example, a category representing 20% of the whole should correspond to a sector whose central angle is 20% of 360°, that is,

$$0.20(360°) = 72°.$$

A circle graph shows, at a glance, the relative magnitudes of various categories.

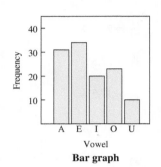

Figure 5

▮▮ **EXAMPLE 4**   Constructing a Circle Graph

Cheri Goldberg found that, during her first semester of college, her expenses fell into categories as shown in **Table 6** below. Present this information in a circle graph.

SOLUTION

The central angle of the food sector is $0.30(360°) = 108°$. Rent is $0.25(360°) = 90°$. Calculate the other four angles similarly. Then draw a circle and mark off the angles with a protractor. The completed circle graph appears in **Figure 6.**

Table 6	Student Expenses
Expense	**Percent of Total**
Food	30%
Rent	25%
Entertainment	15%
Clothing	10%
Books	10%
Other	10%

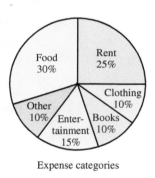

Expense categories

Figure 6

▮▮▮

To demonstrate how a quantity *changes,* say with respect to time, use a **line graph.** Connect a series of line segments that rise and fall with time, according to the magnitude of the quantity being illustrated. To compare the patterns of change for two or more quantities, we can even plot multiple line graphs together in a "comparison line graph." (A line graph looks somewhat like a frequency polygon, but the quantities graphed are not necessarily frequencies.)

EXAMPLE 5 Constructing and Interpreting a Line Graph

Suppose Cheri, from **Example 4,** wanted to keep track of her major expenses, food and rent, over the course of four years of college (eight semesters), in order to see how each one's budget percentage changed with time and how the two compared. Use the data she collected (**Table 7**) to show this information in a line graph, and state any significant conclusions that are apparent from the graph.

Table 7	Food and Rent Expense Percentages	
Semester	**Food**	**Rent**
First	30%	25%
Second	31	26
Third	30	28
Fourth	29	29
Fifth	28	34
Sixth	31	34
Seventh	30	37
Eighth	29	38

SOLUTION

A comparison line graph for the given data (**Figure 7**) shows that the food percentage stayed fairly constant over the four years (at close to 30%), while the rent percentage, starting several points below food, rose steadily, surpassing food after the fourth semester and finishing significantly higher than food.

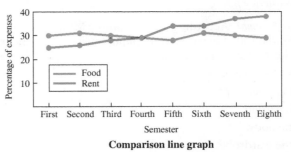

Comparison line graph

Figure 7

▮▮▮

For Further Thought

Expected and Observed Frequencies

When fair coins are tossed, the results on particular tosses cannot be reliably predicted. As more and more coins are tossed, however, the proportions of heads and tails become more predictable. This is a consequence of the "law of large numbers."

For example, if five coins are tossed, then the resulting number of heads, denoted x, is a "random variable," whose possible values are

$$0, 1, 2, 3, 4, \text{ and } 5.$$

If the five coins are tossed repeatedly, say 64 separate times, then the binomial probability formula can be used to get **expected frequencies** (or **theoretical frequencies**), as shown in the table on the next page. The first two columns of the table comprise the **expected frequency distribution** for 64 tosses of five fair coins.

(continued)

For Further Thought (*cont.*)

In an actual experiment, we could obtain **observed frequencies** (or **empirical frequencies**), which would most likely differ somewhat from the expected frequencies. But 64 repetitions of the experiment should be enough to provide fair consistency between expected and observed values.

For Group or Individual Investigation

Toss five coins a total of 64 times, keeping a record of the results.

1. Enter your experimental results in the third column of the table at the right, producing an **observed frequency distribution.**

2. Compare the second and third column entries.

3. Construct two histograms, one from the expected frequency distribution and one from your observed frequency distribution.

4. Compare the two histograms.

Number of Heads x	Expected Frequency e	Observed Frequency o
0	2	
1	10	
2	20	
3	20	
4	10	
5	2	

12.1 EXERCISES

In Exercises 1 and 2, use the given data to do the following:

(a) *Construct frequency and relative frequency distributions, in a table similar to* **Table 2**.

(b) *Construct a histogram.*

(c) *Construct a frequency polygon.*

1. **Preparation for Summer** According to *Newsmax* (May, 2010, page 76), the following are five popular "maintenance" activities performed as summer approaches.

   1. Prep the car for road trips.
   2. Clean up the house or apartment.
   3. Groom the garden.
   4. Exercise the body.
   5. Organize the wardrobe.

   The following data are the responses of 30 people who were asked, on June 1st, how many of the five they had accomplished.

   ```
   1  1  3  1  0  3  0  0  2  1
   2  2  0  0  5  3  4  0  1  0
   4  2  0  2  0  1  0  1  2  3
   ```

2. **Responses to "Pick a Number"** The following data are the responses of 28 people asked to "pick a number from 1 to 10."

   ```
   4   7  2  7  6  3   1
   7   4  9  8  5  6  10
   4  10  8  9  5  4   5
   9   2  6  6  6  8   7
   ```

In Exercises 3–6, use the given data to do the following:

(a) *Construct grouped frequency and relative frequency distributions, in a table similar to* **Table 3**. *(Follow the suggested guidelines for class limits and class width.)*

(b) *Construct a histogram.*

(c) *Construct a frequency polygon.*

3. **Exam Scores** The scores of the 54 members of a sociology lecture class on a 70-point exam were as follows.

   ```
   60  63  64  52  60  58  63  53  56
   64  48  54  64  57  51  67  60  49
   59  54  49  52  53  60  58  60  64
   52  56  56  58  66  59  62  50  58
   53  51  65  62  61  55  59  52  62
   58  61  65  56  55  50  61  55  54
   ```

   Use five classes with a uniform class width of 5 points, and use a lower limit of 45 points for the first class.

4. **Charge Card Account Balances** The following raw data represent the monthly account balances (to the nearest dollar) for a sample of 50 brand-new charge card users.

   ```
    78  175   46  138   79  118  90  163   88  107
   126  154   85   60   42   54  62  128  114   73
    67  119  116  145  129  130  81  105   96   71
   100  145  117   60  125  130  94   88  136  112
    85  165  118   84   74   62  81  110  108   71
   ```

   Use seven classes with a uniform width of 20 dollars, where the lower limit of the first class is 40 dollars.

5. **Daily High Temperatures**   The following data represent the daily high temperatures (in degrees Fahrenheit) for the month of June in a southwestern U.S. city.

79	84	88	96	102	104	99	97	92	94
85	92	100	99	101	104	110	108	106	106
90	82	74	72	83	107	111	102	97	94

Use nine classes with a uniform width of 5 degrees, where the lower limit of the first class is 70 degrees.

6. **IQ Scores of College Freshmen**   The following data represent IQ scores of a group of 50 college freshmen.

113	109	118	92	130	112	114	117	122	115
127	107	108	113	124	112	111	106	116	118
121	107	118	118	110	124	115	103	100	114
104	124	116	123	104	135	121	126	116	111
96	134	98	129	102	103	107	113	117	112

Use nine classes with a uniform width of 5, where the lower limit of the first class is 91.

In each of Exercises 7–10, construct a stem-and-leaf display for the given data. In each case, treat the ones digits as the leaves. For any single-digit data, use a stem of 0.

7. **Games Won in the National Basketball Association**   Approaching midseason, the teams in the National Basketball Association had won the following numbers of games.

27	20	29	11	26	11	12	7	26	18
22	19	14	13	22	9	25	11	10	15
38	10	22	23	31	8	24	15	24	15

8. **Accumulated College Units**   The students in a biology class were asked how many college units they had accumulated to date. Their responses are shown below.

12	4	13	12	21	22	15	17	33	24
32	42	26	11	53	62	42	25	13	8
54	18	21	14	19	17	38	17	20	10

9. **Distances to School**   The following data are the daily round-trip distances to school (in miles) for 30 randomly chosen students attending a community college in California.

16	30	10	11	18	26	34	18	8	12
21	14	5	22	4	25	9	10	6	21
12	18	9	16	44	23	4	13	36	8

10. **Yards Gained in the National Football League**   The following data represent net yards gained per game by National Football League running backs who played during a given week of the season.

25	19	36	73	37	88	67	33	54	123	79
19	39	45	22	58	7	73	30	43	24	36
65	43	33	55	40	29	112	60	94	86	62
52	29	18	25	41	3	49	102	16	32	46

Federal Government Receipts *The graph shows U.S. government receipts and outlays (both on-budget and off-budget) for 2001–2011. Refer to the graph for Exercises 11–15.*

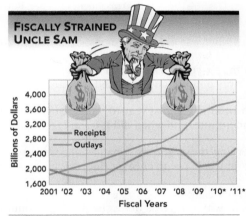

Source: Department of the Treasury, Office of Management and Budget.
*Data are estimates.

11. Of the period 2001–2011, list all years when receipts exceeded outlays.

12. Identify each of the following amounts and when it occurred.

    (a) the greatest one-year drop in receipts

    (b) the greatest one-year rise in outlays

13. In what years did receipts appear to climb faster than outlays?

14. About what was the greatest federal deficit, and in what year did it occur?

15. Plot a point for each year and draw a line graph showing the federal surplus (+) or deficit (−) over the years 2001–2011.

Reading Bar Graphs of Economic Indicators *The bar graphs here show trends in several economic indicators over the period 2004–2009. Refer to these graphs for Exercises 16–20.*

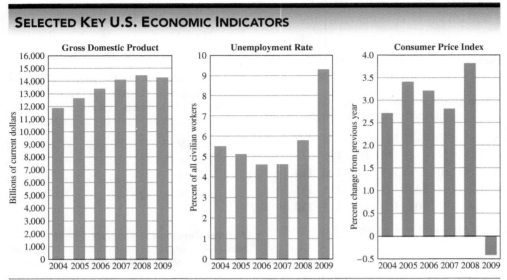

SELECTED KEY U.S. ECONOMIC INDICATORS

Sources: U.S. Department of Commerce, Bureau of Economic Analysis.
U.S. Department of Labor, Bureau of Labor Statistics.

16. About what was the gross domestic product in 2008?

17. Over the six-year period, about what was the highest consumer price index, and when did it occur?

18. What was the greatest year-to-year change in the unemployment rate, and when did it occur?

19. Observing these graphs, what would you say was the most unusual occurrence during the six years represented?

20. Explain why the gross domestic product would generally increase when the unemployment rate decreases.

Reading a Circle Graph of Government Spending *The circle graph below shows categories of planned federal spending from 2011 to 2020. Use the graph for Exercises 21 and 22.*

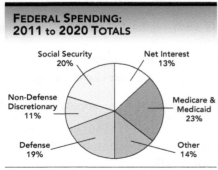

**FEDERAL SPENDING:
2011 to 2020 TOTALS**

Social Security 20%
Net Interest 13%
Non-Defense Discretionary 11%
Medicare & Medicaid 23%
Defense 19%
Other 14%

Source: Office of Management and Budget, January 2010.

21. What is the greatest single expense category? To the nearest degree, what is the central angle of that category's sector?

22. If federal spending over the decade leading up to 2020 increased by about 7.5% per year (as it did over the preceding decade), total spending for the decade would be about $54,200 billion. Of that total, what amount would go to Social Security, Medicare, and Medicaid benefits (combined)?

23. *Sources of Job Training* A survey asked American workers how they were trained for their jobs. The percentages who responded in various categories are shown in the table below. Use the information in the table to draw a circle graph.

Principal Source of Training	Approximate Percentage of Workers
Trained in school	33%
Informal on-the-job training	25
Formal training from employers	12
Trained in military, or correspondence or other courses	10
No particular training, or could not identify any	20

Source: Bureau of Labor Statistics.

24. Correspondence Between Education and Earnings Data for 2008 showed that the average annual earnings of American workers corresponded to educational level as shown in the table below. Draw a bar graph that shows this information.

Educational Level	Median Weekly Earnings
Less than a high school diploma	$453
High school graduate	618
Some college, no degree	699
Associate degree	757
Bachelor's degree	1012
Master's degree	1233
Professional degree	1531
Doctoral degree	1561

Source: Bureau of Labor Statistics.

Net Worth of Retirement Savings *Claire Kozar, wishing to retire at age 60, is studying the comparison line graph here, which shows (under certain assumptions) how the net worth of her retirement savings (initially $400,000 at age 60) will change as she gets older and as she withdraws living expenses from savings. Refer to the graph for Exercises 25–28.*

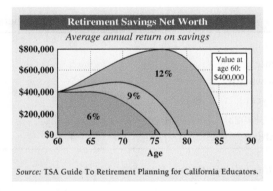

Retirement Savings Net Worth
Average annual return on savings

Value at age 60: $400,000

Source: TSA Guide To Retirement Planning for California Educators.

25. Assuming Claire can maintain an average annual return of 9%, how old will she be when her money runs out?

26. If she could earn an average of 12% annually, what maximum net worth would Claire achieve? At about what age would the maximum occur?

27. Suppose Claire reaches age 70, in good health, and the average annual return has proved to be 6%.

(a) About how much longer can she expect her money to last?

(b) What options might she consider in order to extend that time?

28. At age 77, about how many times more will Claire's net worth be if she averages a 12% return than if she averages a 9% return?

Sample Masses in a Geology Laboratory *Stem-and-leaf displays can be modified in various ways in order to obtain a reasonable number of stems. The following data, representing the measured masses (in grams) of thirty mineral samples in a geology lab, are shown in a* **double-stem** *display in* **Table 8.**

60.7	41.4	50.6	39.5	46.4
58.1	49.7	38.8	61.6	55.2
47.3	52.7	62.4	59.0	44.9
35.6	36.2	40.6	56.9	42.6
34.7	48.3	55.8	54.2	33.8
51.3	50.1	57.0	42.8	43.7

Table 8   Stem-and-Leaf Display for Mineral Sample Masses

(30–34)	3	4.7	3.8			
(35–39)	3	9.5	8.8	5.6	6.2	
(40–44)	4	1.4	4.9	0.6	2.6	2.8	3.7
(45–49)	4	6.4	9.7	7.3	8.3	
(50–54)	5	0.6	2.7	4.2	1.3	0.1
(55–59)	5	8.1	5.2	9.0	6.9	5.8	7.0
(60–64)	6	0.7	1.6	2.4		

29. Describe how the stem-and-leaf display of **Table 8** was constructed.

30. Explain why **Table 8** is called a "double-stem" display.

31. In general, how many stems (total) are appropriate for a stem-and-leaf display? Explain your reasoning.

32. Record Temperatures According to the National Climatic Data Center, the highest temperatures (in degrees Fahrenheit) ever recorded in the 50 states (as of August, 2006) were as follows.

```
112  100  128  120  134  118  106  110  109  112
100  118  117  116  118  121  114  114  105  109
107  112  114  115  118  117  118  125  106  110
122  108  110  121  113  120  119  111  104  111
120  113  120  117  105  110  118  112  114  115
```

Present these data in a double-stem display.

33. *Letter Occurrence Frequencies in the English Language*
The table below shows commonly accepted percentages of occurrence for the various letters in English language usage. (Code breakers have carefully analyzed these percentages as an aid in deciphering secret codes.)

For example, notice that E is the most commonly occurring letter, followed by T, A, O, N, and so on. The letters Q and Z occur least often. Referring to **Figure 5** in the text, would you say that the relative frequencies of occurrence of the vowels in the associated paragraph were typical or unusual? Explain your reasoning.

Letter	Percent	Letter	Percent
E	13	L	$3\frac{1}{2}$
T	9	C, M, U	3
A, O	8	F, P, Y	2
N	7	W, G, B	$1\frac{1}{2}$
I, R	$6\frac{1}{2}$	V	1
S, H	6	K, X, J	$\frac{1}{2}$
D	4	Q, Z	$\frac{1}{5}$

*Frequencies and Probabilities of Letter Occurrence The percentages shown in **Exercise 33** are based on a very large sampling of English language text. Since they are based upon experiment, they are "empirical" rather than "theoretical." By converting each percent in that table to a decimal fraction, you can produce an **empirical probability distribution.***

For example, if a single letter is randomly selected from a randomly selected passage of text, the probability that it will be an E is 0.13. The probability that a randomly selected letter would be a vowel (A, E, I, O, or U) is

$$(0.08 + 0.13 + 0.065 + 0.08 + 0.03) = 0.385.$$

34. Rewrite the distribution shown in **Exercise 33** as an empirical probability distribution. Give values to three decimal places. Note that the 26 probabilities in this distribution—one for each letter of the alphabet—should add up to 1 (except for, perhaps, a slight round-off error).

35. (a) From your distribution of **Exercise 34,** construct an empirical probability distribution just for the vowels A, E, I, O, and U. (*Hint:* Divide each vowel's probability, from **Exercise 34,** by 0.385 to obtain a distribution whose five values add up to 1.) Give values to three decimal places.

(b) Construct an appropriately labeled bar chart from your distribution of part (a).

36. Based on the occurrences of vowels in the paragraph represented by **Figure 5**, construct a probability distribution for the vowels. Give probabilities to three decimal places. The frequencies are:

$$A-31, \quad E-34, \quad I-20, \quad O-23, \quad U-10.$$

37. Is the probability distribution of **Exercise 36** theoretical or empirical? Is it different from the distribution of **Exercise 35**? Which one is more accurate? Explain your reasoning.

38. *Frequencies and Probabilities of Study Times* Convert the grouped frequency distribution of **Table 3** to an empirical probability distribution, using the same classes and giving probability values to three decimal places.

39. *Probabilities of Study Times* Recall that the distribution of **Exercise 38** was based on weekly study times for a sample of 40 students. Suppose one of those students was chosen randomly. Using your distribution, find the probability that the study time in the past week for the student selected would have been in each of the following ranges.

(a) 30–39 hours   **(b)** 40–59 hours

(c) fewer than 30 hours   **(d)** at least 50 hours

Favorite Sports Among Recreation Students The 40 members of a recreation class were asked to name their favorite sports. The table shows the numbers who responded in various ways.

Sport	Number of Class Members
Sailing	9
Hang gliding	5
Snowboarding	7
Bicycling	3
Canoeing	12
Rafting	4

Use this information in Exercises 40– 42.

40. If a member of this class is selected at random, what is the probability that the favorite sport of the person selected is snowboarding?

41. (a) Based on the data in the table, construct a probability distribution, giving probabilities to three decimal places.

(b) Is the distribution of part (a) theoretical or is it empirical?

(c) Explain your answer to part (b).

42. Explain why a frequency polygon trails down to the axis at both ends while a line graph ordinarily does not.

12.2 MEASURES OF CENTRAL TENDENCY

Mean • Median • Mode • Central Tendency from Stem-and-Leaf Displays • Symmetry in Data Sets • Summary

A small video recycling business had the following daily sales over a six-day period.

$305, $285, $240, $376, $198, $264

A single number that is, in some sense representative of this whole set of numbers, a kind of "middle" value, would be a **measure of central tendency.**

Mean

Many calculators find the **mean** (as well as other statistical measures) automatically when a set of data items are entered. To recognize these calculators, look for a key marked $\boxed{\bar{x}}$, or perhaps $\boxed{\mu}$, or look in a menu such as "LIST" for a listing of mathematical measures.

The most common measure of central tendency is the **mean** (or **arithmetic mean**). The mean of a sample is denoted $\bar{x}$ (read "x bar"), while the mean of a complete population is denoted μ (the lower case Greek letter *mu*). For our purposes here, data sets are considered to be samples, so we use $\bar{x}$.

The mean of a set of data items is found by adding up all the items and then dividing the sum by the number of items. (The mean is what most people associate with the word "average.") Since adding up, or summing, a list of items is a common procedure in statistics, we use the symbol for "summation," Σ (the capital Greek letter *sigma*). Therefore, the sum of n items, say $x_1, x_2, \ldots, x_n$, can be denoted

$$\Sigma x = x_1 + x_2 + \cdots + x_n.$$

> **Mean**
>
> The **mean** of n data items $x_1, x_2, \ldots, x_n$, is calculated as follows.
>
> $$\bar{x} = \frac{\Sigma x}{n}$$

mean({305,285,240,376,198, 264})
                            278

A calculator can find the mean of items in a list. This screen supports the text discussion of daily sales figures.

We use this formula to find the central tendency of the daily sales figures above.

$$\text{Mean} = \bar{x} = \frac{\Sigma x}{n}$$
$$= \frac{305 + 285 + 240 + 376 + 198 + 264}{6} \quad \text{Add the daily sales.}$$
$$\qquad\qquad\qquad\qquad\qquad \text{Divide by the number of days.}$$
$$= \frac{1668}{6}, \quad \text{or} \quad 278$$

The mean value (the "average daily sales") for the week is $278.

EXAMPLE 1 Finding the Mean of a List of Sales Figures

Last year's annual sales for eight different flower shops were as follows.

$374,910 $321,872 $242,943 $351,147
$382,740 $412,111 $334,089 $262,900

Scrolled Equation

mean({374910,321872,242▸ ◂943,351147,382740,412111,▸ ◂334089,262900})
                            335339

This screen supports the result in **Example 1.**

Find the mean annual sales for the eight shops.

SOLUTION

$$\bar{x} = \frac{\Sigma x}{n} = \frac{2,682,712}{8} = 335,339 \quad \begin{array}{l}\text{Add the sales.}\\ \text{Divide by the number of shops.}\end{array}$$

The mean annual sales amount is $335,339. ▪▪▪

The following table shows the units and grades earned by one student last term.

Course	Grade	Units
Mathematics	A	3
History	C	3
Chemistry	B	5
Art	B	2
PE	A	1

In one common method of defining **grade-point average,** an A grade is assigned 4 points, with 3 points for B, 2 for C, and 1 for D. Compute grade-point average as follows.

Step 1 Multiply the number of units for a course and the number assigned to each grade.

Step 2 Add these products.

Step 3 Divide by the total number of units.

Course	Grade	Grade Points	Units	(Grade Points) · (Units)
Mathematics	A	4	3	12
History	C	2	3	6
Chemistry	B	3	5	15
Art	B	3	2	6
PE	A	4	1	4
			Totals: 14	43

$$\text{Grade-point average} = \frac{43}{14} = 3.07 \ (\text{rounded})$$

The calculation of a grade-point average is an example of a **weighted mean,** because the grade points for each course grade must be weighted according to the number of units of the course. (For example, five units of A is better than two units of A.) The number of units is called the **weighting factor.**

Weighted Mean

The **weighted mean** of n numbers, $x_1, x_2, \ldots, x_n$, that are weighted by the respective factors $f_1, f_2, \ldots, f_n$ is calculated as follows.

$$\overline{w} = \frac{\Sigma(x \cdot f)}{\Sigma f}$$

In words, the weighted mean of a group of (weighted) items is the sum of all products of items times weighting factors, divided by the sum of all weighting factors.

The weighted mean formula is commonly used to find the mean for a frequency distribution. In this case, the weighting factors are the frequencies.

Salary x	Number of Employees f
$12,000	8
$16,000	11
$18,500	14
$21,000	9
$34,000	2
$50,000	1

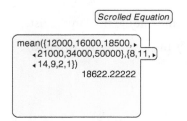

In this screen supporting **Example 2**, the first list contains the salaries and the second list contains their frequencies.

EXAMPLE 2 Finding the Mean of a Frequency Distribution of Salaries

Find the mean salary for a small company that pays annual salaries to its employees as shown in the frequency distribution in the margin.

SOLUTION

According to the weighted mean formula, we can set up the work as follows.

Salary x	Number of Employees f	Salary · Number x · f
$12,000	8	$ 96,000
$16,000	11	$176,000
$18,500	14	$259,000
$21,000	9	$189,000
$34,000	2	$ 68,000
$50,000	1	$ 50,000
Totals:	45	$838,000

$$\text{Mean salary} = \frac{\$838,000}{45} = \$18,622 \quad \text{(rounded)}$$ ▮▮▮

For some data sets the mean can be a misleading indicator of average. Consider Barry Matlock who runs a small business that employs five workers at the following annual salaries.

$$\$16,500, \quad \$16,950, \quad \$17,800, \quad \$19,750, \quad \$20,000$$

The employees, knowing that Barry accrues vast profits to himself, decide to go on strike and demand a raise. To get public support, they go on television and tell about their miserable salaries, pointing out the mean salary in the company.

$$\bar{x} = \frac{\$16,500 + \$16,950 + \$17,800 + \$19,750 + \$20,000}{5}$$

$$= \frac{\$91,000}{5}, \quad \text{or} \quad \$18,200 \quad \text{Mean salary (employees)}$$

The local television station schedules an interview with Barry to investigate. In preparation, Barry calculates the mean salary of *all* workers (including his own salary of $188,000).

$$\bar{x} = \frac{\$16,500 + \$16,950 + \$17,800 + \$19,750 + \$20,000 + \$188,000}{6}$$

$$= \frac{\$279,000}{6}, \quad \text{or} \quad \$46,500 \quad \text{Mean salary (including Barry's)}$$

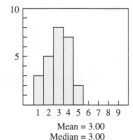

Mean = 3.00
Median = 3.00

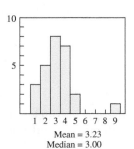

Mean = 3.23
Median = 3.00

The introduction of a single "outlier" above increased the mean by 8 percent but left the median unaffected.

Outliers should usually be considered as *possible* errors in the data.

When the TV crew arrives, Barry calmly assures them that there is no reason for his employees to complain since the company pays a generous mean salary of $46,500.

The employees, of course, would argue that when Barry included his own salary in the calculation, it caused the mean to be a misleading indicator of average. This was so because Barry's salary is not typical. It lies a good distance away from the general grouping of the items (salaries). An extreme value like this is referred to as an **outlier.** Since a single outlier can have a significant effect on the value of the mean, we say that the mean is "highly sensitive to extreme values."

Median

Another measure of central tendency, which is not so sensitive to extreme values, is the **median.** This measure divides a group of numbers into two parts, with half the numbers below the median and half above it.

Median

Find the **median** of a group of items as follows.

Step 1 Rank the items (that is, arrange them in numerical order from least to greatest).

Step 2 If the number of items is *odd,* the median is the middle item in the list.

Step 3 If the number of items is *even,* the median is the mean of the two middle items.

For Barry Matlock's business, all salaries (including Barry's), arranged in numerical order, are shown here.

$$\$16,500, \quad \$16,950, \quad \$17,800, \quad \$19,750, \quad \$20,000, \quad \$188,000$$

Thus, $$\text{median} = \frac{\$17,800 + \$19,750}{2} = \frac{\$37,550}{2} = \$18,775.$$

This figure is a representative average, based on all six salaries, that the employees would probably agree is reasonable.

▌▌ EXAMPLE 3 Finding Medians of Lists of Numbers

Find the median of each list of numbers.

(a) 6, 7, 12, 13, 18, 23, 24   **(b)** 17, 15, 9, 13, 21, 32, 41, 7, 12

(c) 147, 159, 132, 181, 174, 253

SOLUTION

(a) This list is already in numerical order. The number of values in the list, 7, is odd, so the median is the middle value, or 13.

(b) First, place the numbers in numerical order from least to greatest.

$$7, 9, 12, 13, 15, 17, 21, 32, 41$$
$$\uparrow$$
$$\text{Median}$$

The middle number can now be picked out. The median is 15.

(c) First write the numbers in numerical order.

$$132, 147, 159, 174, 181, 253$$

Since the list contains an even number of items, namely 6, there is no single middle item. Find the median by taking the mean of the two middle items, 159 and 174.

$$\frac{159 + 174}{2} = \frac{333}{2} = 166.5 \quad \leftarrow \text{Median}$$ ▐▐▐

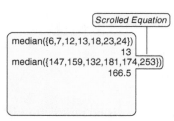

The calculator can find the median of the entries in a list. This screen supports the results in **Examples 3(a) and (c).**

Locating the middle item (the median) of a frequency distribution, is a bit different. First find the total number of items in the set by adding the frequencies ($n = \Sigma f$). Then the median is the item whose *position* is given by the following formula.

Position of the Median in a Frequency Distribution

$$\text{Position of median} = \frac{n + 1}{2} = \frac{\Sigma f + 1}{2}$$

This formula gives only the position, and not the actual value, of the median.

▮▮ **EXAMPLE 4** Finding Medians for Frequency Distributions

Find the medians for the following distributions.

(a)

Value	1	2	3	4	5	6
Frequency	1	3	2	4	8	2

(b)

Value	2	4	6	8	10
Frequency	5	8	10	6	6

SOLUTION

(a) Arrange the work as follows. Tabulate the values and frequencies, and the **cumulative frequencies,** which tell, for each different value, how many items have that value or a lesser value.

Value	Frequency	Cumulative Frequency	
1	1	1	1 item 1 or less
2	3	4	1 + 3 = 4 items 2 or less
3	2	6	4 + 2 = 6 items 3 or less
4	4	10	6 + 4 = 10 items 4 or less
5	8	18	10 + 8 = 18 items 5 or less
6	2	20	18 + 2 = 20 items 6 or less

Total: 20

Adding the frequencies shows that there are 20 items total.

$$\text{position of median} = \frac{20 + 1}{2} = \frac{21}{2} = 10.5$$

The median, then, is the average of the tenth and eleventh items. To find these items, make use of the cumulative frequencies. Since the value 4 has a cumulative frequency of 10, the tenth item is 4 and the eleventh item is 5, making the median

$$\frac{4 + 5}{2} = \frac{9}{2} = 4.5.$$

median({1,2,3,4,5,6},{1,3,2, ▸
  ◂4,8,2})
                                4.5

(b)

Value	Frequency	Cumulative Frequency
2	5	5
4	8	13
6	10	23
8	6	29
10	6	35

Total: 35

median({2,4,6,8,10},{5,8,10, ▸
  ◂6,6})
                                6

There are 35 items total.

$$\text{position of median} = \frac{35 + 1}{2} = \frac{36}{2} = 18$$

These two screens support the results in
Example 4.

From the cumulative frequency column, the fourteenth through the twenty-third items are all 6s. This means the eighteenth item is a 6, so the median is 6. ▮▮▮

Mode

The third important measure of central tendency is the **mode.** Suppose ten students earned the following scores on a business law examination.

74, 81, 39, **74**, 82, 80, 100, 92, **74**, 85

Notice that more students earned the score 74 than any other score.

Mode

The **mode** of a data set is the value that occurs most often.

▮▮ **EXAMPLE 5** Finding Modes for Sets of Data

Find the mode for each set of data.

(a) 51, 32, 49, 49, 74, 81, 92   **(b)** 482, 485, 483, 485, 487, 487, 489

(c) 10,708,   11,519,   10,972,   17,546,   13,905,   12,182

(d)

Value	19	20	22	25	26	28
Frequency	1	3	8	7	4	2

SOLUTION

(a) 51, 32, **49**, **49**, 74, 81, 92
The number 49 occurs more often than any other. Therefore, 49 is the mode. *The numbers do not need to be in numerical order when looking for the mode.*

(b) 482, **485**, 483, **485**, **487**, **487**, 489
Both 485 and 487 occur twice. This list is said to have *two* modes, or to be **bimodal.**

(c) No number here occurs more than once. This list has no mode.

(d)

Value	Frequency	
19	1	
20	3	
22	**8**	← Greatest frequency
25	7	
26	4	
28	2	

The frequency distribution shows that the most frequently occurring value (and, thus, the mode) is 22.

▮▮▮

It is traditional to include the mode as a measure of *central tendency*, because many important kinds of data sets do have their most frequently occurring values "centrally" located. However, there is no reason the mode cannot be one of the least values in the set or one of the greatest. In such a case, the mode really is not a good measure of "central tendency."

When the data items being studied are nonnumeric, the mode may be the only usable measure of central tendency. For example, the bar graph of **Figure 5** in **Section 12.1** showed frequencies of occurrence of vowels in a sample paragraph. Since A, E, I, O, and U are not numbers, they cannot be added, nor can they be numerically ordered. Thus, neither their mean nor their median exists. The mode, however, does exist. As the bar graph shows, the mode is the letter E.

Sometimes, a distribution is **bimodal** (literally, "two modes"), as in **Example 5(b).** In a large distribution, this term is commonly applied even when the two modes do not have exactly the same frequency. Three or more different items sharing the highest frequency of occurrence is not often useful information. We say that such a distribution has *no* mode.

Central Tendency from Stem-and-Leaf Displays

As shown in **Section 12.1,** data are sometimes presented in a stem-and-leaf display in order to give a graphical impression of their distribution. We can also calculate measures of central tendency from a stem-and-leaf display. The median and mode are more easily identified when the "leaves" are **ranked** (arranged in numerical order) on their "stems."

In **Table 9**, we have rearranged the leaves of **Table 5** in **Section 12.1** (which showed the weekly study times from **Example 2** of that section).

Table 9	Stem-and-Leaf Display for Weekly Study Times, with Leaves Ranked									
1	2	4	5	6	7	8				
2	0	2	3	4	4	5	6	6	9	9	9
3	0	1	1	2	3	6	6	8	9	
4	0	1	4	4	5	5	7			
5	2	5	5	8						
6	0	2								
7	2									

EXAMPLE 6 Finding the Mean, Median, and Mode from a Stem-and-Leaf Display

For the data in **Table 9**, find the following.

(a) the mean

(b) the median

(c) the mode

SOLUTION

(a) A calculator with statistical capabilities will automatically compute the mean. Otherwise, add all items (reading from the stem-and-leaf display) and divide by $n = 40$.

$$\text{mean} = \frac{12 + 14 + 15 + \cdots + 60 + 62 + 72}{40} = \frac{1395}{40} = 34.875$$

(b) In this case, $n = 40$ (an even number), so the median is the average of the twentieth and twenty-first items, in order. Counting leaves, we see that these will be the third and fourth items on the stem 3.

$$\text{median} = \frac{31 + 32}{2} = 31.5$$

(c) By inspection, we see that 29 occurred three times and no other value occurred that often.

$$\text{mode} = 29$$

▮▮▮

Symmetry in Data Sets

The most useful way to analyze a data set often depends on whether the distribution is **symmetric** or **nonsymmetric.** In a "symmetric" distribution, as we move out from the central point, the pattern of frequencies is the same (or nearly so) to the left and to the right. In a "nonsymmetric" distribution, the patterns to the left and right are different.

Figure 8 shows several types of symmetric distributions, while **Figure 9** shows some nonsymmetric distributions. A nonsymmetric distribution with a tail extending out to the left, shaped like a J, is called **skewed to the left.** If the tail extends out to the right, the distribution is **skewed to the right.** Notice that a bimodal distribution may be either symmetric or nonsymmetric.

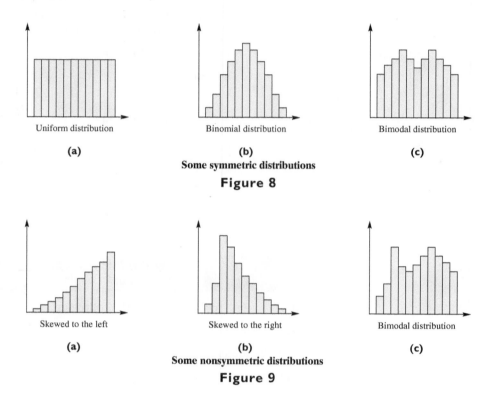

Summary

We conclude this section with a summary of the measures presented and a brief discussion of their relative advantages and disadvantages.

Summary of the Common Measures of Central Tendency

The **mean** of a set of numbers is found by adding all the values in the set and dividing by the number of values.

The **median** is a kind of "middle" number. To find the median, first arrange the values in numerical order. For an *odd* number of values, the median is the middle value in the list. For an *even* number of values, the median is the mean of the two middle values.

The **mode** is the value that occurs most often. Some sets of numbers have two most frequently occurring values and are **bimodal.** Other sets have no mode at all (if no value occurs more often than the others or if more than two values occur most often).

Some helpful points of comparison follow.

1. For distributions of numeric data, the mean and median will always exist, while the mode may not exist. On the other hand, for nonnumeric data, it may be that none of the three measures exists, or that only the mode exists.

2. Because even a single change in the data may cause the mean to change, while the median and mode may not be affected at all, *the mean is the most "sensitive" measure*.

3. In a symmetric distribution, the mean, median, and mode (if a single mode exists) will all be equal. In a nonsymmetric distribution, the mean is often unduly affected by relatively few extreme values and, therefore, may not be a good representative measure of central tendency. For example, distributions of salaries, family incomes, or home prices often include a few values that are much higher than the bulk of the items. In such cases, the median is a more useful measure.

4. *The mode is the only measure covered here that must always be equal to one of the data items of the distribution.* In fact, more of the data items are equal to the mode than to any other number. A fashion shop planning to stock only one hat size for next season would want to know the mode (the most common) of all hat sizes among their potential customers. Likewise, a designer of family automobiles would be interested in the most common family size. In examples like these, designing for the mean or the median might not be right for anyone.

For Further Thought

Simpson's Paradox

In baseball statistics, a player's "batting average" gives the average number of hits per time at bat. For example, a player who has gotten 84 hits in 250 times at bat has a batting average of $\frac{84}{250} = .336$. This "average" can be interpreted as the empirical probability of that player's getting a hit the next time at bat.

The following are actual comparisons of hits and at-bats for two major league players in the 1995, 1996, and 1997 seasons. The numbers illustrate a puzzling statistical occurrence known as **Simpson's paradox.** The example below, involving Dave Justice and Derek Jeter, was referred to in the "Conspiracy Theory" episode of the television series NUMB3RS. (*Source:* www.wikipedia.org)

For Group or Individual Investigation

1. Fill in the twelve blanks in the table, giving batting averages to three decimal places.

2. Which player had a better average in 1995?

3. Which player had a better average in 1996?

4. Which player had a better average in 1997?

5. Which player had a better average in 1995, 1996, and 1997 combined?

6. Did the results above surprise you? How can it be that one player's batting average leads another's for each of three years, and yet trails the other's for the combined years?

	Dave Justice				Derek Jeter		
	Hits	At-bats	Batting Average		Hits	At-bats	Batting Average
1995	104	411	_____		12	48	_____
1996	45	140	_____		183	582	_____
1997	163	495	_____		190	654	_____
Combined (1995–1997)	_____	_____	_____		_____	_____	_____

12.2 EXERCISES

For each list of data, calculate **(a)** *the mean,* **(b)** *the median, and* **(c)** *the mode or modes (if any). Round mean values to the nearest tenth.*

1. 7, 9, 12, 14, 34

2. 20, 27, 42, 45, 53, 62, 62, 64

3. 218, 230, 196, 224, 196, 233

4. 26, 31, 46, 31, 26, 29, 31

5. 3.1, 4.5, 6.2, 7.1, 4.5, 3.8, 6.2, 6.3

6. 14,320, 16,950, 17,330, 15,470

7. 0.78, 0.93, 0.66, 0.94, 0.87, 0.62, 0.74, 0.81

8. 0.53, 0.03, 0.28, 0.18, 0.39, 0.28, 0.14, 0.22, 0.04

9. 128, 131, 136, 125, 132, 128, 125, 127

10. 8.97, 5.64, 2.31, 1.02, 4.35, 7.68

Airline Fatalities in the United States *The table pertains to scheduled commercial carriers. Fatalities data include those on the ground except for the September 11, 2001, terrorist attacks. Use this information for Exercises 11–16.*

U.S. Airline Safety, 1999–2008

Year	Departures (millions)	Fatal Accidents	Fatalities
1999	10.9	2	12
2000	11.1	2	89
2001	10.6	6	531
2002	10.3	0	0
2003	10.2	2	22
2004	10.8	1	13
2005	10.9	3	22
2006	10.6	2	50
2007	10.7	0	0
2008	10.6	0	0

Source: The World Almanac and Book of Facts 2010.

For each category in Exercises 11–16, find **(a)** *the mean,* **(b)** *the median, and* **(c)** *the mode (if any).*

11. departures

12. fatal accidents

13. fatalities

The year 2001 was clearly an anomaly. If the data for that year are reduced by 4 fatal accidents and 265 fatalities, which of the three measures change and what are their new values for each of the following?

14. Exercise 12

15. Exercise 13

16. Following 2001, in what year did airline departures start to increase again?

Spending by U.S. Travelers *The table shows the top five U.S. states for domestic traveler spending in 2007.*

State	Spending (billions of dollars)
California	$96.2
Florida	68.9
New York	51.3
Texas	47.4
Nevada	34.5

Source: The World Almanac and Book of Facts 2010.

Find each of the following quantities for these five states.

17. the mean spending

18. the median spending

Measuring Elapsed Times *While doing an experiment, a physics student recorded the following sequence of elapsed times (in seconds) in a lab notebook.*

2.16, 22.2, 2.96, 2.20, 2.73, 2.28, 2.39

19. Find the mean.

20. Find the median.

The student from **Exercises 19 and 20,** *when reviewing the calculations later, decided that the entry 22.2 should have been recorded as 2.22, and made that change in the listing.*

21. Find the mean for the new list.

22. Find the median for the new list.

23. Which measure, the mean or the median, was affected more by correcting the error?

24. In general, which measure, mean or median, is affected less by the presence of an extreme value in the data?

Scores on Management Examinations *Rob Bates earned the following scores on his six management exams last semester.*

79, 81, 44, 89, 79, 90

25. Find the mean, the median, and the mode for Rob's scores.

26. Which of the three averages probably is the best indicator of Rob's ability?

27. If Rob's instructor gives him a chance to replace his score of 44 by taking a "make-up" exam, what must he score on the make-up to get an overall average (mean) of 85?

Exercises 28 and 29 give frequency distributions for sets of data values. For each set find the **(a)** *mean (to the nearest tenth),* **(b)** *median, and* **(c)** *mode or modes (if any).*

28.

Value	Frequency
12	3
14	1
16	8
18	4

29.

Value	Frequency
615	17
590	7
605	9
579	14
586	6
600	5

30. ***Average Employee Salaries*** A company has

5 employees with a salary of $19,500,
11 employees with a salary of $23,000,
7 employees with a salary of $28,300,
2 employees with a salary of $31,500,
4 employees with a salary of $38,900,
1 employee with a salary of $147,500.

Find the mean salary for the employees (to the nearest hundred dollars).

Grade-point Averages *Find the grade-point average for each of the following students. Assume A = 4, B = 3, C = 2, D = 1, and F = 0. Round to the nearest hundredth.*

31.

Units	Grade
4	C
7	B
3	A
3	F

32.

Units	Grade
2	A
6	B
5	C

Most Populous Countries *The table gives population (2009) and land area for the world's five most populous countries.*

Country	Population (millions)	Area (Thousands of square miles)
China	1339	3601
India	1157	1148
United States	307	3537
Indonesia	240	741
Brazil	199	3265

Source: World Almanac and Book of Facts 2010.

Use this information for Exercises 33–36.

33. Find the mean population (to the nearest million) for these 5 countries.

34. Find the mean area (to the nearest thousand square miles) for these 5 countries.

35. For each country, find the population density (to the nearest whole number of persons per square mile).

36. For the 5 countries combined, find the mean population density.

Personal Computer Use *Just six countries account for over half of all personal computers in use worldwide. The table shows figures for 2008. Use this information for Exercises 37 and 38.*

Country	PCs in use (millions)	Population (millions)
U.S.	303.8	264.10
China	1330.0	98.67
Japan	127.3	86.22
Germany	82.4	61.96
UK	60.9	47.04
France	64.7	43.11

Source: The World Almanac and Book of Facts 2010.

37. Estimate the mean number of PCs in use in 2008 for these six countries.

38. U.S. use was 22.19% of the worldwide total. How many PCs were in use in the world in 2008?

Crew, Passengers, and Hijackers on 9/11 Airliners *The table shows, for each hijacked flight on September 11, 2001, the numbers of crew members, passengers, and hijackers (not included as passengers). For each quantity in Exercises 39 – 41, find*

(a) *the mean, and* (b) *the median.*

Flight	Crew	Passengers	Hijackers
American #11	11	76	5
United #175	9	51	5
American #77	6	53	5
United #93	7	33	4

Source: www.911research.wtc7.net

39. number of crew members per plane

40. number of passengers per plane

41. total number of persons per plane

Olympic Medal Standings *The top ten medal-winning nations in the 2010 Winter Olympics at Vancouver, Canada, are shown in the table. Use the given information for Exercises 42–45.*

Medal Standings for the 2010 Winter Olympics

Nation	Gold	Silver	Bronze	Total
United States	9	15	13	37
Germany	10	13	7	30
Canada	14	7	5	26
Norway	9	8	6	23
Austria	4	6	6	16
Russia	3	5	7	15
South Korea	6	6	2	14
Sweden	5	2	4	11
China	5	2	4	11
France	2	3	6	11

Source: www.nbcolympics.com

Calculate the following for all nations shown.

42. the mean number of gold medals

43. the median number of silver medals

44. the mode, or modes, for the number of bronze medals

45. each of the following for the total number of medals
   (a) mean
   (b) median
   (c) mode or modes

In Exercises 46 and 47, use the given stem-and-leaf display to identify

(a) *the mean,* (b) *the median, and* (c) *the mode (if any) for the data represented.*

46. *Auto Repair Charges* The display here represents prices (to the nearest dollar) charged by 23 different auto repair shops for a new alternator (installed). Give answers to the nearest cent.

```
 9 | 7
10 | 2  4
10 | 5  7  9
11 | 1  3  4  4
11 | 5  5  8  8  9
12 | 0  4  4
12 | 5  7  7  9
13 | 8
```

47. *Scores on a Biology Exam* The display here represents scores achieved on a 100-point biology exam by the 34 members of the class.

```
4 | 7
5 | 1  3  6
6 | 2  5  5  6  7  8  8
7 | 0  4  5  6  7  7  8  8  8  8  9
8 | 0  1  1  3  4  5  5
9 | 0  0  0  1  6
```

48. *Calculating a Missing Test Score* Katie Campbell's Business professor lost his grade book, which contained Katie's five test scores for the course. A summary of the scores (each of which was an integer from 0 to 100) indicates the following:

The mean was 88.

The median was 87.

The mode was 92.

(The data set was not bimodal.) What is the least possible number among the missing scores?

49. Explain what an "outlier" is and how it affects measures of central tendency.

50. *Consumer Preferences in Food Packaging* A food processing company that packages individual cups of instant soup wishes to find out the best number of cups to include in a package. In a survey of 22 consumers, they found that five prefer a package of 1, five prefer a package of 2, three prefer a package of 3, six prefer a package of 4, and three prefer a package of 6.

   (a) Calculate the mean, median, and mode values for preferred package size.

   (b) Which measure in part (a) should the food processing company use?

   (c) Explain your answer to part (b).

51. *Scores on a Math Quiz* The following are scores earned by 15 college students on a 20-point math quiz.

0, 1, 3, 14, 14, 15, 16, 16, 17, 17, 18, 18, 18, 19, 20

(a) Calculate the mean, median, and mode values.

(b) Which measure in part (a) is most representative of the data?

In Exercises 52–55, begin a list of the given numbers, in order, starting with the least one. Continue the list only until the median of the listed numbers is a multiple of 4. Stop at that point and find (a) the number of numbers listed, and (b) the mean of the listed numbers (to two decimal places).

52. counting numbers

53. prime numbers

54. Fibonacci numbers (see **page 212**)

55. triangular numbers (see **pages 13–14**)

56. Seven consecutive whole numbers add up to 147. What is the result when their mean is subtracted from their median?

57. If the mean, median, and mode are all equal for the set {70, 110, 80, 60, x}, find the value of x.

58. Mike Coons wants to include a fifth counting number, n, along with the numbers 2, 5, 8, and 9 so that the mean and median of the five numbers will be equal. How many choices does Mike have for the number n, and what are those choices?

For Exercises 59–61, refer to the grouped frequency distribution shown here.

Class Limits	Frequency f
21–25	5
26–30	3
31–35	8
36–40	12
41–45	21
46–50	38
51–55	35
56–60	20

59. Is it possible to identify, based on the data shown in the table, any specific data items that occurred in this sample?

60. Is it possible to compute the actual mean for this sample?

61. Describe how you might approximate the mean for this sample. Justify your procedure.

62. *Average Employee Salaries* Refer to the salary data of **Example 2,** specifically the dollar amounts given in the salary column of the table. Explain what is wrong with simply calculating the mean salary by adding those six numbers and dividing the result by 6.

12.3 MEASURES OF DISPERSION

Range • Standard Deviation • Interpreting Measures of Dispersion • Coefficient of Variation

Table 10		
	A	**B**
	5	1
	6	2
	7	7
	8	12
	9	13
Mean	7	7
Median	7	7

The mean is a good indicator of the central tendency of a set of data values, but it does not completely describe the data. Compare distribution A with distribution B in **Table 10**.

Both distributions have the same mean and the same median, but they are quite different. In the first, 7 is a fairly typical value, but in the second, most of the values differ considerably from 7. What is needed here is some measure of the **dispersion,** or *spread,* of the data. Two of the most common measures of dispersion, the *range* and the *standard deviation,* are discussed in this section.

Range

The **range** of a data set is a straightforward measure of dispersion.

Range

For any set of data, the **range** of the set is defined as follows.

Range = (greatest value in the set) − (least value in the set)

For a short list of data, calculation of the range is simple. For a more extensive list, it is more difficult to be sure you have accurately identified the greatest and least values.

▮▮ **EXAMPLE 1** Finding and Comparing Range Values

Find the ranges for distributions A and B in **Table 10**, and describe what they imply.

SOLUTION

In distribution A, the greatest value is 9 and the least is 5.

$$\text{Range} = \text{greatest} - \text{least} = 9 - 5 = 4$$

Distribution B is handled similarly.

$$\text{Range} = 13 - 1 = 12$$

We can say that even though the two distributions have identical averages, distribution B exhibits three times more dispersion, or *spread*, than distribution A. ▮▮▮

The range can be misleading if it is interpreted unwisely. For example, look at the points scored by Max and Molly on five different quizzes, as shown in **Table 11**. The ranges for the two students make it tempting to conclude that Max is more consistent than Molly. However, Molly is actually more consistent, with the exception of one very poor score. That score, 6, is an outlier which, if not actually recorded in error, must surely be due to some special circumstance. (Notice that the outlier does not seriously affect Molly's median score, which is more typical of her overall performance than is her mean score.)

Standard Deviation

One of the most useful measures of dispersion, the *standard deviation*, is based on *deviations from the mean* of the data values.

▮▮ **EXAMPLE 2** Finding Deviations from the Mean

Find the deviations from the mean for all data values in the following sample.

$$32, 41, 47, 53, 57$$

SOLUTION

Add these values and divide by the total number of values, 5. The mean is 46. To find the deviations from the mean, subtract 46 from each data value.

Data value	32	41	47	53	57
Deviation	−14	−5	1	7	11

$$32 - 46 = -14 \qquad\qquad 57 - 46 = 11$$

To check your work, add the deviations. ***The sum of the deviations for a set of data is always 0.*** ▮▮▮

We cannot obtain a measure of dispersion by finding the mean of the deviations, because this number is always 0, since the positive deviations just cancel out the negative ones. To avoid this problem of positive and negative numbers canceling each other, we *square* each deviation.

Once the data are entered, a calculator with statistical functions may actually show the range (among other things), or at least sort the data and identify the minimum and maximum items. (The associated symbols may be something like MIN Σ and MAX Σ, or min$X$ and max$X$.) Given these two values, a simple subtraction produces the range.

Table 11

Quiz	Max	Molly
1	28	27
2	22	27
3	21	28
4	26	6
5	18	27
Mean	23	23
Median	22	27
Range	10	22

The following chart shows the squares of the deviations for the data in **Example 2.**

Data value		32	41	47	53	57
Deviation		−14	−5	1	7	11
Square of deviation		**196**	**25**	**1**	**49**	**121**

$(-14) \cdot (-14) = 196$ $11 \cdot 11 = 121$

An average of the squared deviations could now be found by dividing their sum by the number of data values n (5 in this case), which we would do if our data values composed a population. However, since we are considering the data to be a sample, we divide by $n - 1$ instead.*

The average that results is itself a measure of dispersion, called the **variance,** but a more common measure is obtained by taking the square root of the variance. This makes up, in a way, for squaring the deviations earlier, and gives a kind of average of the deviations from the mean, which is called the sample **standard deviation.** It is denoted by the letter s. (The standard deviation of a population is denoted σ, the lowercase Greek letter *sigma*.)

Continuing our calculations from the chart above, we obtain

$$s = \sqrt{\frac{196 + 25 + 1 + 49 + 121}{4}} = \sqrt{\frac{392}{4}} = \sqrt{98} \approx 9.90.$$

Most calculators find square roots, such as $\sqrt{98}$, to as many digits as you need using a key like $\boxed{\sqrt{x}}$. In this book, we normally give from two to four significant figures for such calculations.

---

stdDev({32,41,47,53,57})
                9.899494937
$\sqrt{98}$
                9.899494937

This screen supports the text discussion. Note that the standard deviation reported agrees with the approximation for $\sqrt{98}$.

The algorithm (process) described above for finding the sample standard deviation can be summarized as follows.

Calculation of Standard Deviation

Let a sample of n numbers $x_1, x_2, \ldots, x_n$ have mean $\bar{x}$. Then the **sample standard deviation, s,** of the numbers is calculated as follows.

$$s = \sqrt{\frac{\Sigma(x - \bar{x})^2}{n - 1}}$$

The individual steps involved in this calculation are as follows.

Step 1   Calculate $\bar{x}$, the mean of the numbers.

Step 2   Find the deviations from the mean.

Step 3   Square each deviation.

Step 4   Sum the squared deviations.

Step 5   Divide the sum in Step 4 by $n - 1$.

Step 6   Take the square root of the quotient in Step 5.

The preceding description helps show why standard deviation measures the amount of spread in a data set. For actual calculation purposes, we recommend the use of a scientific calculator, or a statistical calculator, that does all the detailed steps automatically. We illustrate both methods in **Example 3** on the next page.

---

*Although the reasons cannot be explained at this level, dividing by $n - 1$ rather than n produces a sample measure that is more accurate for purposes of inference. In most cases, the results using the two divisors are only slightly different.

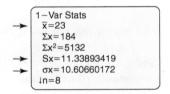

The sample in **Example 3** is stored in a list. (The last entry, 40, is not shown here.)

```
1-Var Stats
→  x̄=23
   Σx=184
   Σx²=5132
→  Sx=11.33893419
→  σx=10.60660172
   ↓n=8
```

The arrows point to the mean and the sample and population standard deviations. See **Example 3**.

EXAMPLE 3 Finding a Sample Standard Deviation

Find the standard deviation of the following sample by using **(a)** the step-by-step process, and **(b)** the statistical functions of a calculator.

$$7, 9, 18, 22, 27, 29, 32, 40$$

SOLUTION

(a) Carry out the six steps summarized above.

Step 1 Find the mean of the values.

$$\frac{7 + 9 + 18 + 22 + 27 + 29 + 32 + 40}{8} = 23$$

Step 2 Find the deviations from the mean.

Data value	7	9	18	22	27	29	32	40
Deviation	−16	−14	−5	−1	4	6	9	17

Step 3 Square each deviation.

Squares of deviations: 256 196 25 1 16 36 81 289

Step 4 Sum the squared deviations.

$$256 + 196 + 25 + 1 + 16 + 36 + 81 + 289 = 900$$

Step 5 Divide by $n - 1 = 8 - 1 = 7$: $\frac{900}{7} \approx 128.57$.

Step 6 Take the square root: $\sqrt{128.57} \approx 11.3$.

(b) Enter the eight data values. (The key for entering data may look something like $\boxed{\Sigma +}$. Find out which key it is on your calculator.) Then press the key for standard deviation. It may look like one of these.

$$\boxed{\text{STDEV}} \quad \text{or} \quad \boxed{\text{SD}} \quad \text{or} \quad \boxed{S_{n-1}} \quad \text{or} \quad \boxed{\sigma_{n-1}}$$

If your calculator also has a key that looks like σ_n, it is probably for *population* standard deviation, which involves dividing by n rather than by $n - 1$, as mentioned earlier.

The result should again be 11.3.

If you mistakenly used the population standard deviation key, the result would be 10.6.

∎∎∎

For data given in the form of a frequency distribution, some calculators allow entry of both values and frequencies, or each value can be entered separately the number of times indicated by its frequency. Then press the standard deviation key.

The following example is included only to strengthen your understanding of frequency distributions and standard deviation, not as a practical algorithm for calculating.

Table 12

Value	Frequency
2	5
3	8
4	10
5	2

EXAMPLE 4 Finding the Standard Deviation of a Frequency Distribution

Find the sample standard deviation for the frequency distribution shown in **Table 12**.

SOLUTION

Complete the calculations as shown in **Table 13** on next page. To find the numbers in the "Deviation" column, first find the mean, and then subtract the mean from the numbers in the "Value" column.

stdDev({2,3,4,5},{5,8,10,2})
.9073771726
√19.76/24
.9073771726

The screen supports the result in **Example 4.**

Table 13

Value	Frequency	Value Times Frequency	Deviation	Squared Deviation	Squared Deviation Times Frequency
2	5	10	−1.36	1.8496	9.2480
3	8	24	−0.36	0.1296	1.0368
4	10	40	0.64	0.4096	4.0960
5	2	10	1.64	2.6896	5.3792
Sums	25	84			19.76

$$\bar{x} = \frac{84}{25} = 3.36 \qquad s = \sqrt{\frac{19.76}{24}} \approx \sqrt{0.8233} \approx 0.91$$ ▮▮▮

Central tendency and dispersion (or "spread tendency") are different and independent aspects of a set of data. Which one is more critical can depend on the specific situation.

For example, suppose tomatoes sell by the basket. Each basket costs the same, and each contains one dozen tomatoes. If you want the most fruit possible per dollar spent, you would look for the basket with the highest average weight per tomato (regardless of the dispersion of the weights). On the other hand, if the tomatoes are to be served on an hors d' oeuvre tray where "presentation" is important, you would look for a basket with uniform-sized tomatoes, that is a basket with the lowest weight dispersion (regardless of the average of the weights). See the illustration at the side.

Another situation involves target shooting (also illustrated at the side). The five hits on the top target are, *on average,* very close to the bulls eye, but the large dispersion (spread) implies that improvement will require much effort. On the other hand, the bottom target exhibits a poorer average, but the smaller dispersion means that improvement will require only a minor adjustment of the gun sights. (In general, consistent errors can be corrected more easily than more dispersed errors.)

Interpreting Measures of Dispersion

A main use of dispersion measures is to compare the amounts of spread in two (or more) data sets as we did with distributions A and B at the beginning of this section. A common technique in inferential statistics is to draw comparisons between populations by analyzing samples that come from those populations.

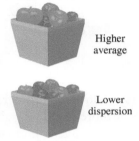

Higher average

Lower dispersion

The more desirable basket depends on your objective.

Good average, poor consistency

Good consistency, poor average

In this case, good consistency (lesser dispersion) is more desirable than a good average (central tendency).

▮▮ **EXAMPLE 5** Comparing Populations Based on Samples

Two companies, *A* and *B*, sell 12-ounce jars of instant coffee. Five jars of each were randomly selected from markets, and the contents were carefully weighed, with the following results.

$$A: \quad 12.02, \quad 12.08, \quad 11.99, \quad 11.96, \quad 11.99$$
$$B: \quad 12.40, \quad 12.21, \quad 12.36, \quad 12.22, \quad 12.27$$

Find **(a)** which company provides more coffee in their jars, and **(b)** which company fills its jars more consistently.

SOLUTION

The mean and standard deviation values for both samples are shown in **Table 14.**

(a) Since $\bar{x}_B$ is greater than $\bar{x}_A$, we *infer* that Company *B* most likely provides more coffee (greater mean) per jar.

(b) Since s_A is less than s_B, we *infer* that Company *A* seems more consistent (smaller standard deviation). ▮▮▮

Table 14

Sample A	Sample B
$\bar{x}_A = 12.008$	$\bar{x}_B = 12.292$
$s_A = 0.0455$	$s_B = 0.0847$

Pafnuty Lvovich Chebyshev (1821–1894) was a Russian mathematician known mainly for his work on the theory of prime numbers. Chebyshev and French mathematician and statistician **Jules Bienaymé** (1796–1878) independently developed an important inequality of probability now known as the Bienaymé–Chebyshev inequality.

The conclusions drawn in **Example 5** are tentative, because the samples were small. We could place more confidence in our inferences if we used larger samples, for then it would be more likely that the samples were accurate representations of their respective populations.

It is clear that a larger dispersion value means more "spread" than a smaller one. But it is difficult to say exactly what a single dispersion value says about a data set. *It is impossible* (though it would be nice) to make a general statement like: "Exactly half of the items of any distribution lie within one standard deviation of the mean of the distribution." Such a statement can be made only of specialized kinds of distributions. (See, for example, **Section 12.5** on the normal distribution.) There is, however, one useful result that does apply to all data sets, no matter what their distributions are like. This result is named for the Russian mathematician Pafnuty Lvovich Chebyshev.

Chebyshev's Theorem

For any set of numbers, regardless of how they are distributed, the fraction of them that lie within k standard deviations of their mean (where $k > 1$) is *at least*

$$1 - \frac{1}{k^2}.$$

Be sure to notice the words *at least* in the theorem. In certain distributions the fraction of items within k standard deviations of the mean may be more than $1 - \frac{1}{k^2}$, but in no case will it ever be less. The theorem is meaningful for any value of k greater than 1 (integer or noninteger).

▌▌ **EXAMPLE 6**   Applying Chebyshev's Theorem

What is the minimum percentage of the items in a data set that lie within 3 standard deviations of the mean?

SOLUTION

With $k = 3$, we calculate as follows.

$3^2 = 3 \cdot 3, \text{not } 3 \cdot 2$ ⟶ $1 - \frac{1}{3^2} = 1 - \frac{1}{9} = \frac{8}{9} \approx 0.889 = 88.9\%$ ← Minimum percentage   ▐▐▐

Coefficient of Variation

Look again at the top target pictured on **page 657.** The dispersion, or spread, among the five bullet holes may not be especially impressive if the shots were fired from 100 yards, but would be much more so at, say, 300 yards. There is another measure, the *coefficient of variation*, which takes this distinction into account. It is not strictly a measure of dispersion, as it combines central tendency and dispersion. It expresses the standard deviation as a percentage of the mean. ***Often this is a more meaningful measure than a straight measure of dispersion, especially when comparing distributions whose means are appreciably different.***

Coefficient of Variation

For any set of data, the **coefficient of variation** is calculated as follows.

$$V = \frac{s}{\bar{x}} \cdot 100 \quad \text{for a sample} \qquad \text{or} \qquad V = \frac{\sigma}{\mu} \cdot 100 \quad \text{for a population}$$

▌▌ EXAMPLE 7 Comparing Samples

Compare the dispersions in the two samples A and B.

$$A:\ 12,\ 13,\ 16,\ 18,\ 18,\ 20 \qquad B:\ 125,\ 131,\ 144,\ 158,\ 168,\ 193$$

Table 15

Sample A	Sample B
$\bar{x}_A = 16.167$	$\bar{x}_B = 153.167$
$s_A = 3.125$	$s_B = 25.294$
$V_A = 19.3$	$V_B = 16.5$

SOLUTION

Using a calculator, we obtain the values shown in **Table 15**. The values of V_A and V_B were found using the formula on the previous page. From the calculated values, we see that sample B has a much larger dispersion (standard deviation) than sample A. But sample A actually has the larger *relative* dispersion (coefficient of variation). The dispersion within sample A is larger as a percentage of the sample mean. ▮▮▮

For Further Thought

Measuring Skewness in a Distribution

Section 12.2 included a discussion of "symmetry in data sets." Here we present a common method of measuring the amount of "skewness," or nonsymmetry, inherent in a distribution.

In a skewed distribution, the mean will be farther out toward the tail than the median, as shown in the sketch.

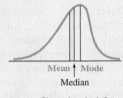

Mean ↑ Mode	Mode ↑ Mean
Median	Median
Skewed to the left	Skewed to the right

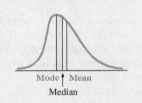

The degree of skewness can be measured by the **skewness coefficient**, which involves both central tendency and dispersion, and is calculated as follows.

$$SK = \frac{3 \cdot (\text{mean} - \text{median})}{\text{standard deviation}}$$

For Group or Individual Investigation

1. Under what conditions would the skewness coefficient be each of the following?

    (a) positive   **(b)** negative

2. Explain why the mean of a skewed distribution is always farther out toward the tail than the median.

3. In a skewed distribution, how many standard deviations apart are the mean and median in each case?

    (a) $SK = \frac{1}{2}$ **(b)** $SK = 1$ **(c)** $SK = 3$

12.3 EXERCISES

1. If your calculator finds both kinds of standard deviation, the sample standard deviation and the population standard deviation, which of the two will be a larger number for a given set of data? (*Hint:* Recall the difference between how the two standard deviations are calculated.)

2. If your calculator finds only one kind of standard deviation, explain how you would determine whether it is sample or population standard deviation (assuming your calculator manual is not available).

*Find **(a)** the range, and **(b)** the standard deviation for each sample in Exercises 3–12. Round answers to the nearest hundredth.*

3. 2, 5, 6, 8, 9, 11, 15

4. 6, 5, 10, 8, 9, 15, 22, 16, 5

5. 27, 34, 22, 41, 30, 25, 31

6. 57, 81, 55, 63, 77, 61, 84, 72, 65

7. 348, 326, 330, 308, 316, 322, 310, 319, 324, 330

8. 4.7, 5.3, 9.4, 6.6, 7.4, 6.2, 7.1, 8.0, 8.8, 7.9, 7.1, 7.4, 7.9, 8.1

9. 84.96, 84.60, 84.58, 84.48, 84.72, 85.62, 85.03, 85.10, 84.53

10. 312.3, 310.4, 309.3, 311.1, 310.8, 313.5, 312.6, 310.5, 311.0, 314.2

11.
Value	Frequency
13	3
10	4
7	7
4	5
1	2

12.
Value	Frequency
14	6
16	12
18	14
20	15
22	10
24	4
26	3

Use Chebyshev's theorem for Exercises 13–28.

Find the least possible fraction of the numbers in a data set lying within the given number of standard deviations of the mean. Give answers as standard fractions reduced to lowest terms.

13. 2   **14.** 4   **15.** $\dfrac{5}{2}$ **16.** $\dfrac{7}{4}$

Find the least possible percentage (to the nearest tenth of a percent) of the items in a distribution lying within the given number of standard deviations of the mean.

17. 3   **18.** 6   **19.** $\dfrac{5}{3}$ **20.** $\dfrac{9}{2}$

In a certain distribution of numbers, the mean is 80 and the standard deviation is 8. At least what fraction of the numbers are between the following pairs of numbers? Give answers as common fractions reduced to lowest terms.

21. 64 and 96   **22.** 56 and 104

23. 48 and 112   **24.** 40 and 120

In the same distribution (mean 80 and standard deviation 8), find the largest fraction of the numbers that could meet the following requirements. Give answers as common fractions reduced to lowest terms.

25. less than 64 or more than 96

26. less than 60 or more than 100

27. less than 52 or more than 108

28. less than 62 or more than 98

Bonus Pay for a Baseball Team *Mairead Jacoby owns a minor league baseball team. Each time the team wins a game, Mairead pays the nine starting players, the manager, and two coaches bonuses, which are certain percentages of their regular salaries. The amounts paid are listed here.*

$80,	$105,	$120,	$175,	$185,	$190,
$205,	$210,	$215,	$300,	$320,	$325

Use this distribution of bonuses for Exercises 29–34.

29. Find the mean of the distribution.

30. Find the standard deviation of the distribution.

31. How many of the bonus amounts are within one standard deviation of the mean?

32. How many of the bonus amounts are within two standard deviations of the mean?

33. What does Chebyshev's theorem say about the number of the amounts that are within two standard deviations of the mean?

34. Explain any discrepancy between your answers for **Exercises 32 and 33.**

In Exercises 35 and 36, two samples are given. In each case, (a) find both sample standard deviations, (b) find both sample coefficients of variation, (c) decide which sample has the higher dispersion, and (d) decide which sample has the higher relative dispersion.

35. *A:* 3, 7, 4, 3, 8   *B:* 10, 8, 10, 6, 7, 3, 5

36. *A:* 68, 72, 69, 65, 71, 72, 68, 71, 67, 67
B: 26, 35, 30, 28, 31, 36, 38, 29, 34, 33

37. **Comparing Battery Lifetimes** Two brands of car batteries, both carrying 6-year warranties, were sampled and tested under controlled conditions. Five of each brand failed after the numbers of months shown here.

> Brand A: 74, 65, 70, 64, 71
>
> Brand B: 69, 70, 62, 72, 60

(a) Calculate both sample means.

(b) Calculate both sample standard deviations.

(c) Which brand apparently lasts longer?

(d) Which brand has the more consistent lifetime?

Lifetimes of Engine Control Modules *Chris Englert manages the service department of a trucking company. Each truck in the fleet utilizes an electronic engine control module. Long-lasting modules are desirable. A preventive replacement program also avoids costly breakdowns. For this purpose it is desirable that the modules be fairly consistent in their lifetimes, so that preventive replacements can be timed efficiently.*

Chris tested a sample of 20 Brand A modules, and they lasted 48,560 highway miles on the average (mean), with a standard deviation of 2116 miles. The listing below shows how long each of another sample of 20 Brand B modules lasted. Use these data for Exercises 38–40.

44,660,	51,300,	45,680,	48,840,	47,510,
61,220,	49,100,	48,660,	47,790,	47,210,
48,050,	49,920,	47,420,	45,880,	50,110,
52,910,	47,930,	45,800,	46,690,	49,240

38. According to the sampling, which brand of module has the longer average life (in highway miles)?

39. Which brand of module apparently has a more consistent (or uniform) length of life (in highway miles)?

40. If Brands A and B are the only modules available, which one should Chris purchase for the maintenance program? Explain your reasoning.

Utilize the following sample for Exercises 41–46.

$$13, 14, 17, 19, 21, 22, 25$$

41. Compute the mean and standard deviation for the sample (each to the nearest hundredth).

42. Now add 5 to each item of the given sample and compute the mean and standard deviation for the new sample.

43. Go back to the original sample. This time subtract 10 from each item, and compute the mean and standard deviation of the new sample.

44. Based on your answers for **Exercises 41–43,** make conjectures about what happens to the mean and standard deviation when all items of the sample have the same constant k added or subtracted.

45. Go back to the original sample again. This time multiply each item by 3, and compute the mean and standard deviation of the new sample.

46. Based on your answers for **Exercises 41 and 45,** make conjectures about what happens to the mean and standard deviation when all items of the sample are multiplied by the same constant k.

47. In **Section 12.2** we showed that the mean, as a measure of central tendency, is highly sensitive to extreme values. Which measure of dispersion, covered in this section, would be more sensitive to extreme values? Illustrate your answer with one or more examples.

A Cereal Marketing Survey *A food distribution company conducted a survey to determine whether a proposed premium to be included in boxes of their cereal was appealing enough to generate new sales. Four cities were used as test markets, where the cereal was distributed with the premium, and four cities as control markets, where the cereal was distributed without the premium. The eight cities were chosen on the basis of their similarity in terms of population, per capita income, and total cereal purchase volume. The results follow.*

		Percent Change in Average Market Share per Month
Test cities	1	+18
	2	+15
	3	+7
	4	+10
Control cities	1	+1
	2	−8
	3	−5
	4	0

48. Find the mean of the percent change in market share for the four test cities.

49. Find the mean of the percent change in market share for the four control cities.

50. Find the standard deviation of the percent change in market share for the test cities.

51. Find the standard deviation of the percent change in market share for the control cities.

52. Find the difference between the means of the test cities and the control cities. This difference represents the estimate of the percent change in sales due to the premium.

53. The two standard deviations from the test cities and the control cities were used to calculate an "error" of ±7.95 for the estimate in **Exercise 52.** With this amount of error, what are the least and greatest estimates of the increase in sales?

(On the basis of the interval estimate of **Exercise 53** the company decided to mass produce the premium and distribute it nationally.)

*For Exercises 54–56, refer to the grouped frequency distribution shown below. (Also refer to **Exercises 59–61** in **Section 12.2.**)*

Class Limits	Frequency f
21–25	5
26–30	3
31–35	8
36–40	12
41–45	21
46–50	38
51–55	35
56–60	20

54. Is it possible to identify any specific data items that occurred in this sample?

55. Is it possible to compute the actual standard deviation for this sample?

56. Describe how you might approximate the standard deviation for this sample. Justify your procedure.

57. Suppose the frequency distribution of **Example 4** involved 50 or 100 (or even more) distinct data values, rather than just four. Explain why the procedure of that example would then be very inefficient.

58. A "J-shaped" distribution can be skewed either to the right or to the left. (When skewed right, it is sometimes called a "reverse J" distribution.)

  (a) In a J-shaped distribution skewed to the right, which data item would be the mode, the greatest or the least item?

  (b) In a J-shaped distribution skewed to the left, which data item would be the mode, the greatest or the least item?

  (c) Explain why the mode is a weak measure of central tendency for a J-shaped distribution.

12.4 MEASURES OF POSITION

The z-Score • Percentiles • Deciles and Quartiles • The Box Plot

The **top ten jobs of 2010** did not vary much from recent earlier rankings despite the treacherous economy of 2008–2010. All ten require considerable education and/or training, and most require a good deal of mathematical ability. The rankings are based on the following five criteria.

(a) stress level
(b) working environment
(c) physical demands
(d) income
(e) hiring outlook

The rankings:

1. Actuary
2. Software Engineer
3. Computer Systems Analyst
4. Biologist
5. Historian
6. Mathematician
7. Paralegal Assistant
8. Statistician
9. Accountant
10. Dental Hygienist

To learn more, go to www.careercast.com

Measures of central tendency and measures of dispersion give us an effective way of characterizing an overall set of data. Central tendency indicates where, along a number scale, the overall data set is centered. Dispersion indicates how much the data set is spread out from the center point. And Chebyshev's theorem, stated in the previous section, tells us in a general sense what portions of the data set may be dispersed different amounts from the center point.

In some cases, we are interested in certain individual items within a data set, rather than in that set as a whole. So we would like to measure how an item fits into the collection, how it compares to other items in the collection, or even how it compares to another item in another collection. There are several common ways of creating such measures. Since they measure an item's position within the data set, they usually are called **measures of position.**

The z-Score

Each individual item in a sample can be assigned a **z-score,** which is defined as follows.

> **The z-score**
>
> If x is a data item in a sample with mean $\bar{x}$ and standard deviation s, then the **z-score** of x is calculated as follows.
>
> $$z = \frac{x - \bar{x}}{s}$$

Because $x - \bar{x}$ gives the amount by which x differs (or deviates) from the mean $\bar{x}$, $\frac{x - \bar{x}}{s}$ gives the number of standard deviations by which x differs from $\bar{x}$. Notice that z will be positive if x is greater than $\bar{x}$ but negative if x is less than $\bar{x}$. Chebyshev's theorem assures us that, in any distribution whatsoever, at least 89% (roughly) of the items will lie within three standard deviations of the mean. That is, at least 89% of the items will have z-scores between -3 and 3. In fact, many common distributions, especially symmetric ones, have considerably more than 89% of their items within three standard deviations of the mean (as we will see in the next section). Hence, a z-score greater than 3 or less than -3 is a rare occurrence.

▐▐ **EXAMPLE 1** Comparing Positions Using z-Scores

Two friends, Ann Kuick and Kay Allen, who take different history classes, had midterm exams on the same day. Ann's score was 86 while Kay's was only 78. Which student did relatively better, given the class data shown here?

	Ann	Kay
Class mean	73	69
Class standard deviation	8	5

SOLUTION

Calculate as follows.

$$\text{Ann: } z = \frac{86 - 73}{8} = 1.625 \qquad \text{Kay: } z = \frac{78 - 69}{5} = 1.8$$

Since Kay's z-score is higher, she was positioned relatively higher within her class than Ann was within her class. ▐▐▐

Percentiles

When you take the Scholastic Aptitude Test (SAT), or any other standardized test taken by large numbers of students, your raw score usually is converted to a **percentile** score, which is defined as follows.

Percentile

If approximately n percent of the items in a distribution are less than the number x, then x is the **nth percentile** of the distribution, denoted P_n.

For example, if you scored at the eighty-third percentile on the SAT, it means that you outscored approximately 83% of all those who took the test. (It does *not* mean that you got 83% of the answers correct.) Since the percentile score gives the position of an item within the data set, it is another "measure of position." The following example approximates percentiles for a fairly small collection of data.

▌▌ EXAMPLE 2 Finding Percentiles

The following are the numbers of dinner customers served by a restaurant on 40 consecutive days. (The numbers have been ranked least to greatest.)

46	51	52	55	56	56	58	59	59	59
61	61	62	62	63	63	64	64	64	65
66	66	66	67	67	67	68	68	69	69
70	70	71	71	72	75	79	79	83	88

For this data set, find **(a)** the thirty-fifth percentile, and **(b)** the eighty-sixth percentile.

SOLUTION

(a) The thirty-fifth percentile can be taken as the item below which 35 percent of the items are ranked. Since 35 percent of 40 is $0.35(40) = 14$, we take the fifteenth item, or 63, as the thirty-fifth percentile.

(b) Since 86 percent of 40 is $0.86(40) = 34.4$, we round *up* and take the eighty-sixth percentile to be the thirty-fifth item, or 72.   ■■■

Technically, percentiles originally were conceived as a set of 99 values $P_1, P_2, P_3,$ $\ldots, P_{99}$ (not necessarily data items) along the scale that would divide the data set into 100 equal-sized parts. They were computed only for very large data sets. With smaller data sets, as in **Example 2,** dividing the data into 100 parts would necessarily leave many of those parts empty. However, the modern techniques of exploratory data analysis seek to apply the percentile concept to even small data sets. Thus, we use approximation techniques as in **Example 2.** Another option is to divide the data into a lesser number of equal-sized (or nearly equal-sized) parts.

Deciles and Quartiles

Deciles are the nine values (denoted $D_1, D_2, \ldots, D_9$) along the scale that divide a data set into ten (approximately) equal-sized parts, and **quartiles** are the three values ($Q_1, Q_2,$ and Q_3) that divide a data set into four (approximately) equal-sized parts. Since deciles and quartiles serve to position particular items within portions of a distribution, they also are "measures of position." We can evaluate deciles by finding their equivalent percentiles.

$$D_1 = P_{10}, \quad D_2 = P_{20}, \quad D_3 = P_{30}, \quad \ldots, \quad D_9 = P_{90}$$

▮▮ **EXAMPLE 3** Finding Deciles

Find the fourth decile for the dinner customer data of **Example 2.**

SOLUTION

Refer to the ranked data table. The fourth decile is the fortieth percentile, and 40% of 40 is $0.40(40) = 16$. We take the fourth decile to be the seventeenth item, or 64. ▮▮▮

   Although the three quartiles also can be related to corresponding percentiles, notice that the second quartile, Q_2, also is equivalent to the median, a measure of central tendency introduced in **Section 12.2.** A common convention for computing quartiles goes back to the way we computed the median.

> **Finding Quartiles**
>
> For any set of data (ranked in order from least to greatest):
>
> The **second quartile, Q_2,** is just the median, the middle item when the number of items is odd, or the mean of the two middle items when the number of items is even.
> The **first quartile, Q_1,** is the median of all items below Q_2.
> The **third quartile, Q_3,** is the median of all items above Q_2.

▮▮ **EXAMPLE 4** Finding Quartiles

Find the three quartiles for the data of **Example 2.**

SOLUTION

Refer to the ranked data. The two middle data items are 65 and 66.

$$Q_2 = \frac{65 + 66}{2} = 65.5$$

The least 20 items (an even number) are all below Q_2, and the two middle items in that set are 59 and 61.

$$Q_1 = \frac{59 + 61}{2} = 60$$

The greatest 20 items are above Q_2.

$$Q_3 = \frac{69 + 70}{2} = 69.5$$ ▮▮▮

The Box Plot

A **box plot,** or **box-and-whisker plot,** involves the median (a measure of central tendency), the range (a measure of dispersion), and the first and third quartiles (measures of position), all incorporated into a simple visual display.

> **Box Plot**
>
> For a given set of data, a **box plot** (or **box-and-whisker plot**) consists of a rectangular box positioned above a numerical scale, extending from Q_1 to Q_3, with the value of Q_2 (the median) indicated within the box, and with "whiskers" (line segments) extending to the left and right from the box out to the minimum and maximum data items.

▐▐ **EXAMPLE 5** Constructing a Box Plot

Construct a box plot for the weekly study times data of **Example 2** in **Section 12.1.**

SOLUTION

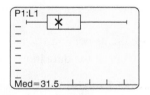

1 – Var Stats
↑n=40
minX=12
Q₁=24
Med=31.5
Q₃=44.5
maxX=72

This screen supports the results of
Example 5.

To determine the quartiles and the minimum and maximum values more easily, we use the stem-and-leaf display (with leaves ranked), given in **Table 9** of **Section 12.2.**

1	2 4 5 6 7 8
2	0 2 3 4 4 5 6 6 9 9 9
3	0 1 1 2 3 6 6 8 9
4	0 1 4 4 5 5 7
5	2 5 5 8
6	0 2
7	2

The median (determined earlier in **Example 6** of **Section 12.2**) is

$$\frac{31 + 32}{2} = 31.5.$$

From the stem-and-leaf display,

$$Q_1 = \frac{24 + 24}{2} = 24 \quad \text{and} \quad Q_3 = \frac{44 + 45}{2} = 44.5.$$

The minimum and maximum items are evident from the stem-and-leaf display. They are 12 and 72. The box plot is shown in **Figure 10**.

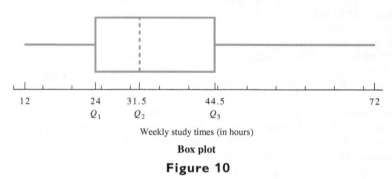

Weekly study times (in hours)

Box plot

Figure 10

▪▪▪

This box plot corresponds to the results of **Example 5.** It indicates the median in the display at the bottom. The TRACE function of the TI-83/84 Plus will locate the minimum, maximum, and quartile values as well.

The box plot in **Figure 10** conveys the following important information:

1. central tendency (the location of the median);
2. the location of the middle half of the data (the extent of the box);
3. dispersion (the range is the extent of the whiskers); and
4. skewness (the nonsymmetry of both the box and the whiskers).

12.4 EXERCISES

Numbers of Restaurant Customers Refer to the dinner customers data of **Example 2.** *Approximate each of the following. (Use the methods illustrated in this section.)*

1. the fifteenth percentile

2. the seventy-fifth percentile

3. the third decile   4. the eighth decile

In Exercises 5–8, make use of z-scores.

5. *Relative Positions on Geometry Quizzes* In a geometry class, Neil Hunnewell scored 5 on a quiz for which the class mean and standard deviation were 4.6 and 2.1, respectively. Janet Hunnius scored 6 on another quiz for which the class mean and standard deviation were 4.9 and 2.3, respectively. Relatively speaking, which student did better?

6. Relative Performances in Track Events In Saturday's track meet, Edgar Espina, a high jumper, jumped 6 feet 3 inches. Conference high jump marks for the past season had a mean of 6 feet even and a standard deviation of 3.5 inches. Kurt Massey, Edgar's teammate, achieved 18 feet 4 inches in the long jump. In that event the conference season average (mean) and standard deviation were 16 feet 6 inches and 1 foot 10 inches, respectively. Relative to this past season in this conference, which athlete had a better performance on Saturday?

7. Relative Lifetimes of Tires The lifetimes of Brand A tires are distributed with mean 45,000 miles and standard deviation 4500 miles, while Brand B tires last for only 38,000 miles on the average (mean) with standard deviation 2080 miles. Nicole Britt's Brand A tires lasted 37,000 miles and Yvette Angel's Brand B tires lasted 35,000 miles. Relatively speaking, within their own brands, which driver got the better wear?

8. Relative Ratings of Fish Caught In a certain lake, the trout average 12 inches in length with a standard deviation of 2.75 inches. The bass average 4 pounds in weight with a standard deviation of 0.8 pound. If Tobi Casper caught an 18-inch trout and Katrina Bass caught a 6-pound bass, then relatively speaking, which catch was the better trophy?

Leading U.S. Trade Partners *Countries in the table are ranked by value of 2008 imports to the United States from the countries. Exports are from the United States to the countries. Use this information for Exercises 9–20.*

Country	Population (millions)	Trade Volume (billion U.S. $)	
		Imports	Exports
Canada	33	339	261
China	1339	338	70
Mexico	110	216	151
Japan	127	139	65
Germany	82	97	55
United Kingdom	61	59	54
Saudi Arabia	28	55	12
Venezuela	26	51	13
South Korea	48	48	35
France	64	44	29

Sources: The World Almanac and Book of Facts 2010, www.google.com

Compute z-scores (accurate to one decimal place) for Exercises 9–12.

9. Japan's population   **10.** imports from China

11. exports to Mexico

12. imports from Venezuela

In each of Exercises 13–16, determine which country occupied the given position.

13. the fifteenth percentile in population

14. the third quartile in exports

15. the fourth decile in imports

16. the first quartile in exports

17. Determine who was relatively higher: China in imports or Canada in exports.

18. Construct box plots for both exports and imports, one above the other in the same drawing.

19. What does your box plot of **Exercise 18** *for exports* indicate about the following characteristics of the exports data?
 (a) the central tendency **(b)** the dispersion
 (c) the location of the middle half of the data items

20. Comparing your two box plots of **Exercise 18,** what can you say about the 2008 trade balance with this group of countries?

21. The text stated that, for *any* distribution of data, at least 89% of the items will be within three standard deviations of the mean. Why couldn't we just move some items farther out from the mean to obtain a new distribution that would violate this condition?

22. Describe the basic difference between a measure of central tendency and a measure of position.

This chapter has introduced three major characteristics, central tendency, dispersion, and position, and has developed various ways of measuring them in numerical data. In each of Exercises 23–26, a new measure is described. Explain in each case which of the three characteristics you think it would measure and why.

23. Midrange $= \dfrac{\text{minimum item} + \text{maximum item}}{2}$

24. Midquartile $= \dfrac{Q_1 + Q_3}{2}$

25. Interquartile range $= Q_3 - Q_1$

26. Semi-interquartile range $= \dfrac{Q_3 - Q_1}{2}$

27. The "skewness coefficient" was defined in **For Further Thought** in the previous section, and it is calculated as follows.

$$SK = \frac{3 \cdot (\bar{x} - Q_2)}{s}$$

Is this a measure of individual data items or of the overall distribution?

28. For the U.S. trade partners data preceding **Exercise 9,** calculate the skewness coefficient for **(a)** exports, and **(b)** imports.

29. From **Exercise 28,** how would you compare the skewness of exports versus imports?

30. In a national standardized test, Kimberly Austin scored at the ninety-second percentile. If 67,500 individuals took the test, about how many scored higher than Kimberly did?

31. Let the three quartiles (from least to greatest) for a large population of scores be denoted Q_1, Q_2, and Q_3.

(a) Is it necessarily true that

$$Q_2 - Q_1 = Q_3 - Q_2?$$

(b) Explain your answer to part (a).

In Exercises 32–35, answer yes or no and explain your answer. (Consult Exercises 23–26 for definitions.)

32. Is the midquartile necessarily the same as the median?

33. Is the midquartile necessarily the same as the midrange?

34. Is the interquartile range necessarily half the range?

35. Is the semi-interquartile range necessarily half the interquartile range?

	Raw Score	z-score
Omer	60	0.69
Alessandro	72	1.67

36. *Relative Positions on a Standardized Chemistry Test* Omer and Alessandro participated in the standardization process for a new statewide chemistry test. Within the large group participating, their raw scores and corresponding z-scores were as shown here.

Find the overall mean and standard deviation of the distribution of scores. (Give answers to two decimal places.)

Rating Passers in the National Football League Since the National Football League began keeping official statistics in 1932, the passing effectiveness of quarterbacks has been rated by several different methods. The current system, adopted in 1973, is based on four performance components: completions, touchdowns, yards gained, and interceptions, as percentages of the number of passes attempted. The computation can be accomplished using the following formula.

$$Rating = \frac{\left(250 \cdot \frac{C}{A}\right) + \left(1000 \cdot \frac{T}{A}\right) + \left(12.5 \cdot \frac{Y}{A}\right) + 6.25 - \left(1250 \cdot \frac{I}{A}\right)}{3},$$

where A = attempted passes,
C = completed passes,
T = touchdown passes,
Y = yards gained passing,
and I = interceptions.

In addition to the weighting factors (coefficients) appearing in the formula, the four category ratios are limited to non-negative values with the following maximums.

$$0.775 \text{ for } \frac{C}{A}, \quad 0.11875 \text{ for } \frac{T}{A}, \quad 12.5 \text{ for } \frac{Y}{A}, \quad 0.095 \text{ for } \frac{I}{A}$$

These limitations are intended to prevent any one component of performance from having an undue effect on the overall rating. They are not often invoked but in special cases can have a significant effect.

The preceding formula rates all passers against the same performance standard and is applied, for example, after a single game, an entire season, or a career. The ratings for the ten leading passers in the league for 2009 regular season play are ranked in the following table.

Rank	NFL Passer	Rating Points
1	Drew Brees, New Orleans	109.6
2	Brett Favre, Minnesota	107.2
3	Philip Rivers, San Diego	104.4
4	Aaron Rodgers, Green Bay	103.2
5	Ben Roethlisberger, Pittsburgh	100.5
6	Peyton Manning, Indianapolis	99.9
7	Matt Schaub, Houston	98.6
8	Tony Romo, Dallas	97.6
9	Tom Brady, New England	96.2
10	Kurt Warner, Arizona	93.2

Source: www.espn.go.com

Find the measures (to one decimal place) in Exercises 37–42.

37. the three quartiles

38. the third decile

39. the sixty-fifth percentile

40. the midrange (See **Exercise 23.**)

41. the midquartile (see **Exercise 24.**)

42. the interquartile range (See **Exercise 25.**)

43. Construct a box plot for the rating points data.

44. The eleventh-ranked passer in the 2009 regular season was Eli Manning of the New York Giants. Eli attempted 509 passes, completed 317, passed for 27 touchdowns, gained 4021 yards passing, and was intercepted 14 times. Compute his rating.

45. If Eli Manning had completed one more pass in 2009, what would his rating have been?

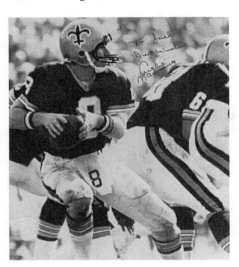

Archie Manning, father of NFL quarterbacks Peyton and Eli, signed this photo for author Hornsby's son, Jack.

46. In the case of **Exercise 45,** how would Eli Manning have ranked for 2009?

47. Steve Young, of the San Francisco 49ers, set a full season rating record of 112.8 in 1994 and held that record until Peyton Manning achieved a rating of 121.1 in 2004. (As of 2010, Manning's all-time record holds.) If, in 2004, Manning had 336 completions, 49 touchdowns, and 4557 yards, for 497 attempts, how many times was he intercepted that year?

48. Refer to the passer rating formula and determine the highest rating possible (considered a "perfect" passer rating).

12.5 THE NORMAL DISTRIBUTION

Discrete and Continuous Random Variables • Definition and Properties of a Normal Curve • A Table of Standard Normal Curve Areas • Interpreting Normal Curve Areas

Discrete and Continuous Random Variables

A random variable that can take on only certain fixed values is called a **discrete random variable.** For example, the number of heads in 5 tosses of a coin is discrete since its only possible values are 0, 1, 2, 3, 4, and 5. A variable whose values are not restricted in this way is a **continuous random variable.** For example, the diameter of camellia blossoms would be a continuous variable, spread over a scale perhaps from 5 to 25 centimeters. The values would not be restricted to whole numbers, or even to tenths, or hundredths, etc. A discrete random variable takes on only a countable number of values, whereas a continuous random variable takes on an uncountable number of values.

Most distributions discussed earlier in this chapter were *empirical* (based on observation). The distributions covered in this section are *theoretical* (based on theoretical probabilities). A knowledge of theoretical distributions enables us to identify when actual observations are inconsistent with stated assumptions, which is the key to inferential statistics.

The theoretical probability distribution for the discrete random variable "number of heads" when 5 fair coins are tossed is shown in **Table 16**. **Figure 11** shows the corresponding histogram. The probability values can be found using the binomial probability formula (**Section 11.4**) or using Pascal's triangle (**Section 10.4**).

The normal curve was first developed by **Abraham De Moivre** (1667–1754), but his work went unnoticed for many years. It was independently redeveloped by Pierre de Laplace (1749–1827) and Carl Friedrich Gauss (1777–1855). Gauss found so many uses for this curve that it is sometimes called the *Gaussian curve*.

Table 16	Probability Distribution
x	*P(x)*
0	0.03125
1	0.15625
2	0.31250
3	0.31250
4	0.15625
5	0.03125
Sum:	1.00000

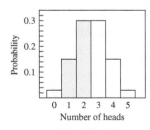

Figure 11

Since each rectangle in **Figure 11** is 1 unit wide, the *area* of the rectangle is also equal to the probability of the corresponding number of heads. The area, and thus the probability, for the event "1 head or 2 heads" is shaded in the figure. The graph consists of 6 distinct rectangles since "number of heads" is a *discrete* variable with 6 possible values. The sum of the 6 rectangular areas is exactly 1 square unit.

In contrast to the discrete "number of heads" distribution in **Table 16**, a probability distribution for camellia blossom diameters cannot be tabulated or graphed in quite the same way, since this variable is *continuous*. The graph would be smeared out into a "continuous" bell-shaped curve (rather than a set of rectangles) as shown in **Figure 12**. The vertical scale on the graph in this case shows what we call "probability density," the probability per unit along the horizontal axis.

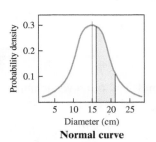

Normal curve

Figure 12

Definition and Properties of a Normal Curve

The camellia blossom curve is highest at a diameter value of 15 cm, its center point, and drops off rapidly and equally toward a zero level in both directions. Such a symmetric, bell-shaped curve is called a **normal curve.** Any random variable whose graph has this characteristic shape is said to have a **normal distribution.**

The area under the curve along a certain interval is numerically equal to the probability that the random variable will have a value in the corresponding interval. The area of the shaded region in **Figure 12** is equal to the probability of a randomly chosen blossom having a diameter in the interval from the left extreme, say 16.4, to the right extreme, say 21.2. Normal curves are very important in the study of statistics because *a great many continuous random variables have normal distributions, and many discrete variables are distributed approximately normally.*

Each point on the horizontal scale of a normal curve lies some number of standard deviations from the mean (positive to the right, negative to the left). This number is the "standard score" for that point. It is the same as the *z*-score defined in **Section 12.4**. By relabeling the horizontal axis, as in **Figure 13**, we obtain the **standard normal curve,** which we can use to analyze *any* normal (or approximately normal) distribution. We relate the random variable value, *x*, to its *z*-score by

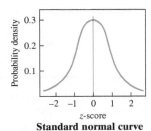

Standard normal curve

Figure 13

$$z = \frac{x - \overline{x}}{s}.$$

Figure 14 shows several of infinitely many possible normal curves. Each is completely characterized by its mean and standard deviation. Only one of these, the one marked *S*, is the *standard* normal curve. That one has mean 0 and standard deviation 1.

Close but Never Touching When a curve approaches closer and closer to a line, without ever actually meeting it (as a normal curve approaches the horizontal axis), the line is called an **asymptote**, and the curve approaches the line **asymptotically**.

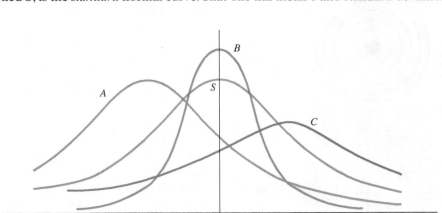

Normal curve *S* is standard, with mean = 0 and standard deviation = 1.
Normal curve *A* has mean < 0 and standard deviation = 1.
Normal curve *B* has mean = 0 and standard deviation < 1.
Normal curve *C* has mean > 0 and standard deviation > 1.

Figure 14

Mean = median = mode

Figure 15

Several properties of normal curves are summarized below and are illustrated in **Figure 15**.

> **Properties of Normal Curves**
>
> The graph of a normal curve is bell-shaped and symmetric about a vertical line through its center.
>
> The mean, median, and mode of a normal curve are all equal and occur at the center of the distribution.
>
> ***Empirical Rule*** About 68% of all data values of a normal curve lie within 1 standard deviation of the mean (in both directions), about 95% within 2 standard deviations, and about 99.7% within 3 standard deviations.

The empirical rule indicates that a very small percentage of the items in a normal distribution will lie more than 3 standard deviations from the mean (approximately 0.3%, divided equally between the upper and lower tails of the distribution). As we move away from the center, the curve *never* actually touches the horizontal axis. No matter how far out we go, there is always a chance of an item occurring even farther out. Theoretically then, the range of a true normal distribution is infinite.

■■ **EXAMPLE 1** Applying the Empirical Rule

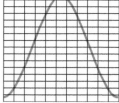

Suppose 300 chemistry students take a midterm exam and that the distribution of their scores can be treated as normal. Find the number of scores falling into each of the following intervals.

(a) Within 1 standard deviation of the mean

(b) Within 2 standard deviations of the mean

SOLUTION

(a) By the empirical rule, 68% of all scores lie within 1 standard deviation of the mean. Since there is a total of 300 scores, the number of scores within 1 standard deviation is as follows.

$$0.68(300) = 204 \quad \text{68\% = 0.68}$$

(b) A total of 95% of all scores lie within 2 standard deviations of the mean.

$$0.95(300) = 285 \quad \text{95\% = 0.95}$$ ■■■

A Table of Standard Normal Curve Areas

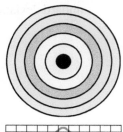

A normal distribution occurs in darts if the player, always aiming at the bull's-eye, tosses a fairly large number of times, and the aim on each toss is affected by independent random errors.

Most questions we need to answer about normal distributions involve regions other than those within 1, 2, or 3 standard deviations of the mean. We might need the percentage of items within $1\frac{1}{2}$ or $2\frac{1}{5}$ standard deviations of the mean, or perhaps the area under the curve from 0.8 to 1.3 standard deviations above the mean.

In such cases, we need more than the empirical rule. The traditional approach is to refer to a table of area values, such as **Table 17**, which appears on **page 671.** Computer software packages designed for statistical uses usually will produce the required values on command and some advanced calculators also have this capability. Those tools are recommended. As an optional approach, we illustrate the use of **Table 17** here.

The column under *A* gives the proportion of the area under the entire curve that is between *z* = 0 and a positive value of *z*.

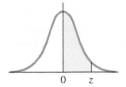

Because the curve is symmetric about the 0-value, the area between *z* = 0 and a *negative* value of *z* can be found by using the corresponding positive value of *z*.

Table 17 Areas Under the Standard Normal Curve

z	A	z	A	z	A	z	A	z	A	z	A
.00	.000	.56	.212	1.12	.369	1.68	.454	2.24	.487	2.80	.497
.01	.004	.57	.216	1.13	.371	1.69	.454	2.25	.488	2.81	.498
.02	.008	.58	.219	1.14	.373	1.70	.455	2.26	.488	2.82	.498
.03	.012	.59	.222	1.15	.375	1.71	.456	2.27	.488	2.83	.498
.04	.016	.60	.226	1.16	.377	1.72	.457	2.28	.489	2.84	.498
.05	.020	.61	.229	1.17	.379	1.73	.458	2.29	.489	2.85	.498
.06	.024	.62	.232	1.18	.381	1.74	.459	2.30	.489	2.86	.498
.07	.028	.63	.236	1.19	.383	1.75	.460	2.31	.490	2.87	.498
.08	.032	.64	.239	1.20	.385	1.76	.461	2.32	.490	2.88	.498
.09	.036	.65	.242	1.21	.387	1.77	.462	2.33	.490	2.89	.498
.10	.040	.66	.245	1.22	.389	1.78	.462	2.34	.490	2.90	.498
.11	.044	.67	.249	1.23	.391	1.79	.463	2.35	.491	2.91	.498
.12	.048	.68	.252	1.24	.393	1.80	.464	2.36	.491	2.92	.498
.13	.052	.69	.255	1.25	.394	1.81	.465	2.37	.491	2.93	.498
.14	.056	.70	.258	1.26	.396	1.82	.466	2.38	.491	2.94	.498
.15	.060	.71	.261	1.27	.398	1.83	.466	2.39	.492	2.95	.498
.16	.064	.72	.264	1.28	.400	1.84	.467	2.40	.492	2.96	.498
.17	.067	.73	.267	1.29	.401	1.85	.468	2.41	.492	2.97	.499
.18	.071	.74	.270	1.30	.403	1.86	.469	2.42	.492	2.98	.499
.19	.075	.75	.273	1.31	.405	1.87	.469	2.43	.492	2.99	.499
.20	.079	.76	.276	1.32	.407	1.88	.470	2.44	.493	3.00	.499
.21	.083	.77	.279	1.33	.408	1.89	.471	2.45	.493	3.01	.499
.22	.087	.78	.282	1.34	.410	1.90	.471	2.46	.493	3.02	.499
.23	.091	.79	.285	1.35	.411	1.91	.472	2.47	.493	3.03	.499
.24	.095	.80	.288	1.36	.413	1.92	.473	2.48	.493	3.04	.499
.25	.099	.81	.291	1.37	.415	1.93	.473	2.49	.494	3.05	.499
.26	.103	.82	.294	1.38	.416	1.94	.474	2.50	.494	3.06	.499
.27	.106	.83	.297	1.39	.418	1.95	.474	2.51	.494	3.07	.499
.28	.110	.84	.300	1.40	.419	1.96	.475	2.52	.494	3.08	.499
.29	.114	.85	.302	1.41	.421	1.97	.476	2.53	.494	3.09	.499
.30	.118	.86	.305	1.42	.422	1.98	.476	2.54	.494	3.10	.499
.31	.122	.87	.308	1.43	.424	1.99	.477	2.55	.495	3.11	.499
.32	.126	.88	.311	1.44	.425	2.00	.477	2.56	.495	3.12	.499
.33	.129	.89	.313	1.45	.426	2.01	.478	2.57	.495	3.13	.499
.34	.133	.90	.316	1.46	.428	2.02	.478	2.58	.495	3.14	.499
.35	.137	.91	.319	1.47	.429	2.03	.479	2.59	.495	3.15	.499
.36	.141	.92	.321	1.48	.431	2.04	.479	2.60	.495	3.16	.499
.37	.144	.93	.324	1.49	.432	2.05	.480	2.61	.495	3.17	.499
.38	.148	.94	.326	1.50	.433	2.06	.480	2.62	.496	3.18	.499
.39	.152	.95	.329	1.51	.434	2.07	.481	2.63	.496	3.19	.499
.40	.155	.96	.331	1.52	.436	2.08	.481	2.64	.496	3.20	.499
.41	.159	.97	.334	1.53	.437	2.09	.482	2.65	.496	3.21	.499
.42	.163	.98	.336	1.54	.438	2.10	.482	2.66	.496	3.22	.499
.43	.166	.99	.339	1.55	.439	2.11	.483	2.67	.496	3.23	.499
.44	.170	1.00	.341	1.56	.441	2.12	.483	2.68	.496	3.24	.499
.45	.174	1.01	.344	1.57	.442	2.13	.483	2.69	.496	3.25	.499
.46	.177	1.02	.346	1.58	.443	2.14	.484	2.70	.497	3.26	.499
.47	.181	1.03	.348	1.59	.444	2.15	.484	2.71	.497	3.27	.499
.48	.184	1.04	.351	1.60	.445	2.16	.485	2.72	.497	3.28	.499
.49	.188	1.05	.353	1.61	.446	2.17	.485	2.73	.497	3.29	.499
.50	.191	1.06	.355	1.62	.447	2.18	.485	2.74	.497	3.30	.500
.51	.195	1.07	.358	1.63	.448	2.19	.486	2.75	.497	3.31	.500
.52	.198	1.08	.360	1.64	.449	2.20	.486	2.76	.497	3.32	.500
.53	.202	1.09	.362	1.65	.451	2.21	.486	2.77	.497	3.33	.500
.54	.205	1.10	.364	1.66	.452	2.22	.487	2.78	.497	3.34	.500
.55	.209	1.11	.367	1.67	.453	2.23	.487	2.79	.497	3.35	.500

Carl Friedrich Gauss (1777–1855) was one of the greatest mathematical thinkers of history. In his *Disquisitiones Arithmeticae*, published in 1798, he pulled together work by predecessors and enriched and blended it with his own into a unified whole. The book is regarded by many as the true beginning of the theory of numbers (**Chapter 5**).

Of his many contributions to science, the statistical method of least squares is the most widely used today in astronomy, biology, geodesy, physics, and the social sciences. Gauss took special pride in his contributions to developing the method. Despite an aversion to teaching, he taught an annual course in the method for the last twenty years of his life.

It has been said that Gauss was the last person to have mastered all of the mathematics known in his day.

The table gives the fraction of all scores in a normal distribution that lie between the mean and z standard deviations from the mean. ***Because of the symmetry of the normal curve, the table can be used for values above the mean or below the mean.*** All of the items in the table can be thought of as corresponding to the area under the curve. The total area is arranged to be 1.000 square unit, with 0.500 square unit on each side of the mean. The table shows that at 3.30 standard deviations from the mean, essentially all of the area is accounted for. Whatever remains beyond is so small that it does not appear in the first three decimal places.

▮▮ **EXAMPLE 2** Applying the Normal Curve Table

Use **Table 17** to find the percent of all scores that lie between the mean and the following values.

(a) One standard deviation above the mean

(b) 2.45 standard deviations below the mean

SOLUTION

(a) Here $z = 1.00$ (the number of standard deviations, written as a decimal to the nearest hundredth). Refer to **Table 17**. Find 1.00 in the z column. The table entry is 0.341, so 34.1% of all values lie between the mean and one standard deviation above the mean.

Another way of looking at this is to say that the area in color in **Figure 16** represents 34.1% of the total area under the normal curve.

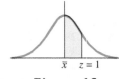

Figure 16

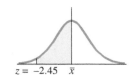

Figure 17

(b) Even though we go *below* the mean here (to the left), **Table 17** still works since the normal curve is symmetrical about its mean. Find 2.45 in the z column. A total of 0.493, or 49.3%, of all values lie between the mean and 2.45 standard deviations below the mean. This region is colored in **Figure 17**. ▮▮▮

▮▮ **EXAMPLE 3** Finding Probabilities of Phone Call Durations

The time lengths of phone calls placed through a certain company are distributed normally with mean 6 minutes and standard deviation 2 minutes. If 1 call is randomly selected from phone company records, what is the probability that it will have lasted more than 10 minutes?

SOLUTION

Here 10 minutes is two standard deviations above the mean. The probability of such a call is equal to the area of the colored region in **Figure 18**.

From **Table 17**, the area between the mean and two standard deviations above is 0.477 ($z = 2.00$). The total area to the right of the mean is 0.500. Find the area from $z = 2.00$ to the right by subtracting.

$$0.500 - 0.477 = 0.023$$

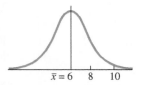

Figure 18

The probability of a call exceeding 10 minutes is 0.023, or 2.3%. ▮▮▮

▌▌ **EXAMPLE 4** Finding Areas Under the Normal Curve

Find the total areas indicated in the regions in color in each of **Figures 19** and **20**.

SOLUTION

For **Figure 19**, find the area from 1.45 standard deviations below the mean to 2.71 standard deviations above the mean. From **Table 17**, $z = 1.45$ leads to an area of 0.426, while $z = 2.71$ leads to 0.497. The total area is the sum of these, or $0.426 + 0.497 = 0.923$.

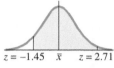

$z = -1.45$ $\bar{x}$ $z = 2.71$

Figure 19

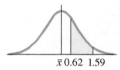

$\bar{x}$ 0.62 1.59

Figure 20

To find the indicated area in **Figure 20**, refer again to **Table 17**. From the table, $z = 0.62$ leads to an area of 0.232, while $z = 1.59$ gives 0.444. To get the area between these two values of z, subtract the areas.

$$0.444 - 0.232 = 0.212$$ ▌▌▌

Interpreting Normal Curve Areas

Examples 2–4 emphasize the *equivalence* of three quantities, as follows.

> **Meaning of Normal Curve Areas**
>
> In the standard normal curve, the following three quantities are equivalent.
>
> 1. **Percentage** (of total items that lie in an interval)
> 2. **Probability** (of a randomly chosen item lying in an interval)
> 3. **Area** (under the normal curve along an interval)

Which quantity we think of depends upon how a particular question is formulated. They are all evaluated by using A-values from **Table 17**.

In general, when we use **Table 17**, z is the z-score of a particular data item x. When one of these values is known and the other is required, as in **Examples 5 and 6,** we use the formula

$$z = \frac{x - \bar{x}}{s}.$$

▌▌ **EXAMPLE 5** Applying the Normal Curve to Driving Distances

In one area, the distribution of monthly miles driven by motorists has mean 1200 miles and standard deviation 150 miles. Assume that the number of miles is closely approximated by a normal curve, and find the percent of all motorists driving the following distances.

(a) Between 1200 and 1600 miles per month

(b) Between 1000 and 1500 miles per month

A Basic Consumer (T)issue It all started when a reporter on consumer issues for a Midwest TV station received a complaint that rolls of Brand X toilet paper manufactured by Company Y did not have the number of sheets claimed on the wrapper. Brand X is supposed to have 375 sheets, but three rolls of it were found by reporters to have 360, 361, and 363.

Shocked Company Y executives said that the **odds against** six rolls having fewer than 375 sheets each are 1 billion to 1. They counted sheets and found that several rolls of Brand X actually had 380 sheets each (machines count the sheets only in 10s). TV reporters made an independent count, and their results agreed with Company Y.

What happened the first time? Well, the reporters hadn't actually counted sheets, but had measured rolls and divided the length of a roll by the length of one sheet. Small variations in length can be expected, which add up over a roll, giving false results.

This true story perhaps points up the distinction in probability and statistics between **discrete values** and **continuous values.**

SOLUTION

(a) Start by finding how many standard deviations 1600 miles is above the mean. Use the formula for z.

$$z = \frac{1600 - 1200}{150} = \frac{400}{150} \approx 2.67$$

From **Table 17**, 0.496, or 49.6%, of all motorists drive between 1200 and 1600 miles per month.

(b) As shown in **Figure 21**, values of z must be found for both 1000 and 1500.

$$\text{For 1000:} \quad z = \frac{1000 - 1200}{150} = \frac{-200}{150} \approx -1.33$$

$$\text{For 1500:} \quad z = \frac{1500 - 1200}{150} = \frac{300}{150} = 2.00$$

From **Table 17**, $z = -1.33$ leads to an area of 0.408, while $z = 2.00$ gives 0.477. This means a total of

$$0.408 + 0.477 = 0.885, \quad \text{or} \quad 88.5\%,$$

of all motorists drive between 1000 and 1500 miles per month. ■■■

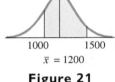

1000   1500
$\bar{x} = 1200$

Figure 21

■■ **EXAMPLE 6** Identifying a Data Value Within a Normal Distribution

A particular normal distribution has mean $\bar{x} = 81.7$ and standard deviation $s = 5.21$. What data value from the distribution would correspond to $z = -1.35$?

SOLUTION

$$\boxed{\text{Solve for x.}} \quad z = \frac{x - \bar{x}}{s} \qquad \text{z-score formula}$$

$$-1.35 = \frac{x - 81.7}{5.21} \qquad \text{Substitute the given values for } z, \bar{x}, \text{and } s.$$

$$-1.35(5.21) = \frac{x - 81.7}{5.21}(5.21) \qquad \text{Multiply each side by 5.21 to clear the fraction.}$$

$$-7.0335 = x - 81.7 \qquad \text{Simplify.}$$

$$74.6665 = x \qquad \text{Add 81.7.}$$

Rounding to the nearest tenth, the required data value is 74.7. ■■■

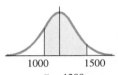

Figure 22

■■ **EXAMPLE 7** Finding z-Values for Given Areas Under the Normal Curve

Assuming a normal distribution, find the z-value meeting each condition.

(a) 30% of the total area is to the right of z.

(b) 80% of the total area is to the left of z.

SOLUTION

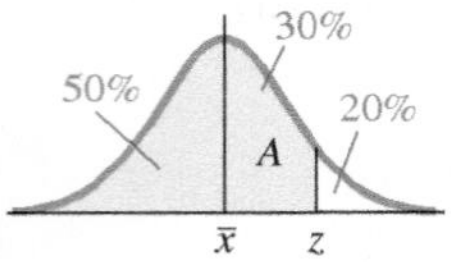

(a) Because 50% of the area lies to the right of the mean, there must be 20% between the mean and z. (See **Figure 22**.) In **Table 17**, $A = 0.200$ corresponds to $z = 0.52$ or 0.53, or we could average the two: $z = 0.525$.

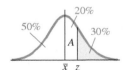

Figure 23

(b) This situation is shown in **Figure 23**. The 50% to the left of the mean plus 30% additional makes up the 80%. From **Table 17**, $A = 0.300$ implies $z = 0.84$. ■■■

12.5 EXERCISES

Note: For problems requiring the calculation of z-scores or A-values, our answers are based on Table 17. By using a calculator or computer package, you will sometimes obtain a slightly more accurate answer.

Identify each variable quantity as discrete *or* continuous.

1. the number of heads in 50 tossed coins

2. the number of babies born in one day at a certain hospital

3. the average weight of babies born in a week

4. the heights of seedling pine trees at six months of age

5. the time as shown on a digital watch

6. the time as shown on a watch with a sweep hand

Measuring the Mass of Ore Samples *Suppose 100 geology students measure the mass of an ore sample. Due to human error and limitations in the reliability of the balance, not all the readings are equal. The results are found to closely approximate a normal curve, with mean 86 g and standard deviation 1 g.*

Use the symmetry of the normal curve and the empirical rule to estimate the number of students reporting readings in the following ranges.

7. more than 86 g

8. more than 85 g

9. between 85 and 87 g

10. between 84 and 87 g

Distribution of IQ Scores *On standard IQ tests, the mean is 100, with a standard deviation of 15. The results come very close to fitting a normal curve. Suppose an IQ test is given to a very large group of people. Find the percent of people whose IQ scores fall into each category.*

11. less than 100

12. greater than 115

13. between 70 and 130

14. more than 145

Find the percent of area under a normal curve between the mean and the given number of standard deviations from the mean. (Note that positive indicates above the mean, while negative indicates below the mean.)

15. 1.50

16. 0.92

17. −1.08

18. −2.25

Find the percent of the total area under a normal curve between the given values of z.

19. $z = 1.41$ and $z = 1.83$

20. $z = -1.74$ and $z = -1.14$

21. $z = -3.11$ and $z = 2.06$

22. $z = -1.98$ and $z = 1.02$

Find a value of z such that each condition is met.

23. 10% of the total area is to the right of z.

24. 4% of the total area is to the left of z.

25. 9% of the total area is to the left of z.

26. 23% of the total area is to the right of z.

Lifetimes of Lightbulbs *The Better lightbulb has an average life of 600 hr, with a standard deviation of 50 hr. The length of life of the bulb can be closely approximated by a normal curve. A warehouse manager buys and installs 10,000 such bulbs. Find the total number that can be expected to last each amount of time.*

27. at least 600 hr

28. between 600 and 675 hr

29. between 675 and 740 hr

30. between 490 and 720 hr

31. less than 740 hr

32. less than 510 hr

Weights of Chickens *The chickens at Benny and Ann Rice's farm have a mean weight of 1850 g with a standard deviation of 150 g. The weights of the chickens are closely approximated by a normal curve. Find the percent of all chickens having each weight.*

33. more than 1700 g

34. less than 1800 g

35. between 1750 and 1900 g

36. between 1600 and 2000 g

Filling Cereal Boxes   *A certain dry cereal is packaged in 24-oz boxes. The machine that fills the boxes is set so that, on the average, a box contains 24.5 oz. The machine-filled boxes have contents weights that can be closely approximated by a normal curve. What percentage of the boxes will be underweight if the standard deviation is as follows?*

37. 0.5 oz

38. 0.4 oz

39. 0.3 oz

40. 0.2 oz

41. *Recommended Daily Vitamin Allowances* In nutrition, the recommended daily allowance of vitamins is a number set by the government to guide an individual's daily vitamin intake. Actually, vitamin needs vary drastically from person to person, but the needs are closely approximated by a normal curve. To calculate the recommended daily allowance, the government first finds the average need for vitamins among people in the population and the standard deviation. The **recommended daily allowance** is then defined as the mean plus 2.5 times the standard deviation. What fraction of the population will receive adequate amounts of vitamins under this plan?

Recommended Daily Vitamin Allowances   *Find the recommended daily allowance for each vitamin if the mean need and standard deviation are as follows. (See **Exercise 41**.)*

42. mean need = 1800 units;
standard deviation = 140 units

43. mean need = 159 units;
standard deviation = 12 units

*Assume the following distributions are all normal, and use the areas under the normal curve given in **Table 17** to find the appropriate areas.*

44. *Filling Cartons with Milk* A machine that fills quart milk cartons is set up to average 32.2 oz per carton, with a standard deviation of 1.2 oz. What is the probability that a filled carton will contain less than 32 oz of milk?

45. *Finding Blood Clotting Times* The mean clotting time of blood is 7.47 sec, with a standard deviation of 3.6 sec. What is the probability that an individual's blood-clotting time will be less than 7 sec or greater than 8 sec?

46. *Sizes of Fish* The average length of the fish caught in Lake Amotan is 12.3 in., with a standard deviation of 4.1 in. Find the probability that a fish caught there will be longer than 18 in.

47. *Size Grading of Eggs* To be graded extra large, an egg must weigh at least 2.2 oz. If the average weight for an egg is 1.5 oz, with a standard deviation of 0.4 oz, how many of five dozen randomly chosen eggs would you expect to be extra large?

Distribution of Student Grades Peter Davis teaches a course in marketing. He uses the following system for assigning grades to his students.

Grade	Score in Class
A	Greater than $\bar{x} + 1.5s$
B	$\bar{x} + 0.5s$ to $\bar{x} + 1.5s$
C	$\bar{x} - 0.5s$ to $\bar{x} + 0.5s$
D	$\bar{x} - 1.5s$ to $\bar{x} - 0.5s$
F	Below $\bar{x} - 1.5s$

From the information in the table, what percent of the students receive the following grades?

48. A   **49.** B   **50.** C

51. Do you think this system would be more likely to be fair in a large freshman class in psychology or in a graduate seminar of five students? Why?

Normal Distribution of Student Grades A teacher gives a test to a large group of students. The results are closely approximated by a normal curve. The mean is 75 with a standard deviation of 5. The teacher wishes to give As to the top 8% of the students and Fs to the bottom 8%. A grade of B is given to the next 15%, with Ds given similarly. All other students get Cs. Find the bottom cutoff (rounded to the nearest whole number) for the following grades. (Hint: Use **Table 17** to find z-scores from known A-values.)

52. A   **53.** B   **54.** C   **55.** D

*A normal distribution has mean 76.8 and standard deviation 9.42. Follow the method of **Example 6** and find data values corresponding to the following values of z. Round to the nearest tenth.*

56. $z = 0.72$ **57.** $z = 1.44$

58. $z = -2.39$ **59.** $z = -3.87$

60. What percentage of the items lie within 1.25 standard deviations of the mean
   (a) in any distribution (using the results of Chebyshev's theorem)?
   (b) in a normal distribution (by **Table 17**)?

61. Explain the difference between the answers to parts (a) and (b) in **Exercise 60**.

EXTENSION Regression and Correlation

Linear Regression • Correlation

Table 18	Age vs. Income	
Resident	**Age**	**Annual Income**
A	19	2150
B	23	2550
C	27	3250
D	31	3150
E	36	4250
F	40	4200
G	44	4350
H	49	5000
I	52	4950
J	54	5650

Linear Regression One very important branch of inferential statistics, called **regression analysis,** is used to compare quantities or variables, to discover relationships that exist between them, and to formulate those relationships in useful ways.

Suppose a sociologist gathers data on a few (say ten) of the residents of a small village in a remote region in order to get an idea of how annual income (in dollars) relates to age in that village. The data are shown in **Table 18**.

The first step in analyzing these data is to graph the results, as shown in the **scatter diagram** of **Figure 24**. (Graphing calculators will plot scatter diagrams.)

Once a scatter diagram has been produced, we can draw a curve that best fits the pattern exhibited by the sample data points. This curve can have any one of many characteristic shapes, depending on how the quantities involved are related. The best-fitting curve for the sample points is called an **estimated regression curve.** If, as in the present discussion, the points in the scatter diagram seem to lie approximately along a straight line, the relation is assumed to be linear, and the line that best fits the data points is called the **estimated regression line.**

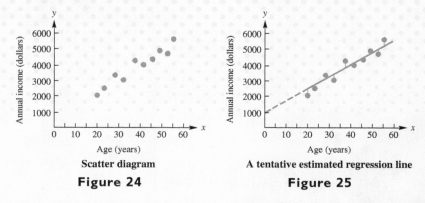

Scatter diagram

Figure 24

A tentative estimated regression line

Figure 25

If we let x denote age and y denote income in the data of **Table 18** and assume that the best-fitting curve is a line, then the equation of that line will take the form

$$y = ax + b,$$

where a is the slope of the line and b is the y-coordinate of the y-intercept (the y-value at which the line, if extended, would intersect the y-axis).

To completely identify the estimated regression line, we must find the values of the **regression coefficients** a and b, which requires some calculation. In **Figure 25**, a *tentative* line has been drawn through the scatter diagram.

For each x-value in the data set, the corresponding y-value usually differs from the value it would have if the data point were exactly on the line. These differences are shown in the figure by vertical segments. Choosing another line would make some of these differences greater and some lesser. The most common procedure is to choose the line where the sum of the squares of all these differences is minimized. This is called the **method of least squares,** and the resulting line is called the **least squares line.**

In the equation of the least squares line, the variable y' can be used to distinguish the *predicted* values (which would give points on the least squares line) from the *observed* values y (those occurring in the data set).

The least squares criterion mentioned above leads to specific values of a and b. We shall not give the details, which involve differential calculus, but the results are given here. (Σ—the Greek letter *sigma*—represents summation just as in earlier sections.)

Regression Coefficient Formulas

The **least squares line** $y' = ax + b$ that provides the best fit to the data points $(x_1, y_1), (x_2, y_2), \ldots, (x_n, y_n)$ has coefficient values as follows.

$$a = \frac{n(\Sigma xy) - (\Sigma x)(\Sigma y)}{n(\Sigma x^2) - (\Sigma x)^2} \qquad b = \frac{\Sigma y - a(\Sigma x)}{n}$$

▮▮ **EXAMPLE 1**   Computing and Graphing a Least Squares Line

Find the equation of the least squares line for the age and income data given in **Table 18**. Graph the line.

SOLUTION

Start with the two columns on the left in **Table 19** (which just repeat the original data). Then find the products $x \cdot y$, and the squares x^2.

Table 19   Age and Income Calculations

x	y	$x \cdot y$	x^2
19	2150	40,850	361
23	2550	58,650	529
27	3250	87,750	729
31	3150	97,650	961
36	4250	153,000	1296
40	4200	168,000	1600
44	4350	191,400	1936
49	5000	245,000	2401
52	4950	257,400	2704
54	5650	305,100	2916
Sums: 375	39,500	1,604,800	15,433

Francis Galton (1822–1911) learned to read at age three, was interested in mathematics and machines, but was an indifferent mathematics student at Trinity College, Cambridge. He became interested in researching methods of predicting weather. It was during this research that Galton developed early intuitive notions of **correlation** and **regression** and posed the problem of multiple regression.

Galton's key statistical work is *Natural Inheritance*. In it, he set forth his ideas on regression and correlation. He discovered the correlation coefficient while pondering Alphonse Bertillon's scheme for classifying criminals by physical characteristics. It was a major contribution to statistical method.

From the table, $\Sigma x = 375$, $\Sigma y = 39,500$, $\Sigma xy = 1,604,800$, and $\Sigma x^2 = 15,433$. There are 10 pairs of values, so $n = 10$. Now find a with the formula given above.

$$a = \frac{10(1,604,800) - 375(39,500)}{10(15,433) - (375)^2} = \frac{1,235,500}{13,705} \approx 90.15$$

Finally, use this value of a to find b.

$$b = \frac{39,500 - 90.15(375)}{10} \approx 569.4$$

The equation of the least squares line can now be written.

$$y' = 90x + 569 \qquad \text{Coefficients are rounded.}$$

Letting $x = 20$ in this equation gives $y' = 2369$, and $x = 50$ implies $y' = 5069$. The two points $(20, 2369)$ and $(50, 5069)$ are used to graph the regression line in **Figure 26** on the next page. Notice that the intercept coordinates $(0, 569)$ also fit the extended line.

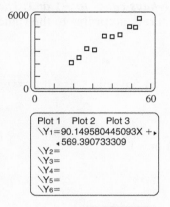

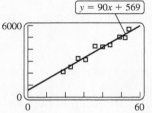

The information in **Figure 26** and the accompanying discussion is supported in these screens.

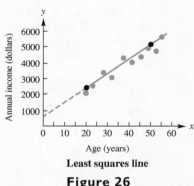

Least squares line

Figure 26

▮▮▮

A computer or a scientific, statistical, or graphing calculator is recommended for finding regression coefficients. (See the margin notes and the statistical options on **pages 630 and 631.**) Tedious calculations, such as in **Example 1,** can be avoided and the regression line produced automatically.

▮▮ **EXAMPLE 2** Predicting from a Least Squares Line

Use the result of **Example 1** to predict the income of a village resident who is 35 years old.

SOLUTION

$$y' = 90x + 569 \qquad \text{Equation from } \textbf{Example 1}$$
$$y' = 90(35) + 569 \qquad \text{Let } x = 35.$$
$$y' = 3719$$

Based on the given data, a 35-year-old will make about $3719 per year. ▮▮▮

Correlation Once an equation for the line of best fit (the least squares line) has been found, it is reasonable to ask, "Just how good is this line for predictive purposes?" If the points already observed fit the line quite closely, then future pairs of scores can be expected to do so. If the points are widely scattered about even the "best-fitting" line, then predictions are not likely to be accurate.

In general, the closer the *sample* data points lie to the least squares line, the more likely it is that the entire *population* of (x, y) points really do form a line, that is, that x and y really are related linearly. Also, the better the fit, the more confidence we can have that our least squares line (based on the sample) is a good estimator of the true population line.

One common measure of the strength of the linear relationship in the sample is called the **sample correlation coefficient,** denoted r. It is calculated from the sample data according to the following formula.

Sample Correlation Coefficient Formula

In linear regression, the strength of the linear relationship is measured by the correlation coefficient r, calculated as follows.

$$r = \frac{n(\Sigma xy) - (\Sigma x)(\Sigma y)}{\sqrt{n(\Sigma x^2) - (\Sigma x)^2} \cdot \sqrt{n(\Sigma y^2) - (\Sigma y)^2}}$$

The value of r is always between −1 and 1, or perhaps equal to −1 or 1. The degree of fit (correlation) can be described in general terms, according to the value of r, as follows.

Degree of Fit of an Estimated Regression Line to Sample Data Points

- Perfect fit: $r = 1$ or $r = -1$
- Strong fit: r close (but not equal) to 1 or −1
- Moderate fit: r not close to 0, and not close to 1 or −1
- Weak fit: r equal, or nearly equal, to 0

The sign (plus or minus) of r determines the type of linear relationship, if any, between the variables x and y.

Direct and Inverse Linear Relationships

- If $r > 0$, the regression line has positive slope. The relationship between x and y is **direct**—as x increases, y also increases.
- If $r < 0$, the regression line has negative slope. The relationship between x and y is **inverse**—as x increases, y decreases.
- If $r = 0$, no linear relationship between x and y is indicated.

▮▮ **EXAMPLE 3** Finding a Correlation Coefficient

Find r for the age and income data of **Table 19** on **page 678.**

SOLUTION

Almost all values needed to find r were computed in **Example 1.**

$$n = 10 \qquad \Sigma x = 375 \qquad \Sigma y = 39{,}500 \qquad \Sigma xy = 1{,}604{,}800 \qquad \Sigma x^2 = 15{,}433$$

The only missing value is Σy^2. Squaring each y in the original data and adding the squares gives

$$\Sigma y^2 = 167{,}660{,}000.$$

Now use the formula to find that $r = 0.98$ (to two decimal places). This value of r, very close to 1, shows that age and income in this village are highly correlated. (The fit of the estimated regression line is strong.) The fact that r is positive indicates that the linear relationship is direct; as age increases, income also increases. ▮▮▮

> LinReg
> y=ax+b
> a=90.14958045
> b=569.3907333
> r²=.9572823948
> r=.9784080922

The slope a and y-intercept b of the regression equation, along with r^2 and r, are given. Compare with **Examples 1 and 3.**

▮▮ **EXAMPLE 4** Analyzing the Aging Trend in the U.S. Population

The World Almanac and Book of Facts 2010 (page 622) reported the following U.S. Census Bureau data concerning the aging U.S. population over the last century.

Year	1910	1920	1930	1940	1950	1960	1970	1980	1990	2000	2010
Percent 65 and over	4.3	4.7	5.4	6.8	8.1	9.2	9.8	11.3	12.5	12.4	13.0

Let x represent time, in decades, from 1910, so $x = 0$ in 1910, $x = 1$ in 1920, $x = 2$ in 1930, and so on. Let y represent percent 65 and over in the population. Based on the data table, carry out the following.

(a) Plot a scatter diagram.

(b) Compute and graph the least squares regression line.

(c) Compute the correlation coefficient.

(d) Use the regression line to predict the percent 65 and over in 2050, and discuss the validity of the prediction.

SOLUTION

(a) The data points are plotted in **Figure 27**.

(b) We entered the x- and y-values into lists L1 and L2, respectively, in a calculator to obtain the equation of the least squares regression line.

$$y' = 0.97x + 4.03 \quad \text{Coefficients are rounded.}$$

This line is shown in **Figure 27** as a dashed line.

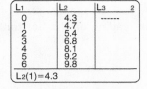
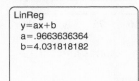
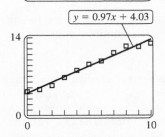

$y = 0.97x + 4.03$

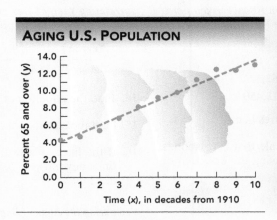

These screens support **Example 4(b)**.

AGING U.S. POPULATION

Figure 27

(c) $\Sigma x = 55, \quad \Sigma x^2 = 385, \quad n = 11, \quad \Sigma y = 97.5,$ All values are from the calculator, using two-variable statistics.
$\Sigma y^2 = 968.97, \quad \Sigma(xy) = 593.8$

$$r = \frac{n(\Sigma xy) - (\Sigma x)(\Sigma y)}{\sqrt{n(\Sigma x^2) - (\Sigma x)^2} \cdot \sqrt{n(\Sigma y^2) - (\Sigma y)^2}} \quad \text{Correlation coefficient formula}$$

$$= \frac{11 \cdot 593.8 - 55 \cdot 97.5}{\sqrt{11 \cdot 385 - 55^2} \cdot \sqrt{11 \cdot 968.97 - 97.5^2}}$$

$$= 0.990211\ldots$$

$$r \approx 0.99$$

(d) $y' = 0.97x + 4.03$ Estimated regression line

      $= 0.97 \cdot 14 + 4.03$ The year 2050 corresponds to $x = 14$.

      $y \approx 17.6$ 17.61 has been rounded here.

Although the correlation was strong ($r \approx 0.99$) for the data points we had, it is risky to extrapolate a regression line too far out. There may be factors (such as declining numbers of baby boomers in the population) that may slow the aging phenomenon. (Incidentally, the Census Bureau projects 20.2% in 2050.) ▮▮▮

EXTENSION EXERCISES

Correlating Fertilizer and Corn Ear Size *In a study to determine the linear relationship between the length (in decimeters) of an ear of corn (y) and the amount (in tons per acre) of fertilizer used (x), the following values were determined.*

$$n = 10 \quad \Sigma xy = 75$$
$$\Sigma x = 30 \quad \Sigma x^2 = 100$$
$$\Sigma y = 24 \quad \Sigma y^2 = 80$$

1. Find an equation for the least squares line.

2. Find the correlation coefficient.

3. If 3 tons per acre of fertilizer are used, what length (in decimeters) would the regression equation predict for an ear of corn?

Correlating Celsius and Fahrenheit Temperatures *In an experiment to determine the linear relationship between temperatures on the Celsius scale (y) and on the Fahrenheit scale (x), a student got the following results.*

$$n = 5 \quad \Sigma xy = 28{,}050$$
$$\Sigma x = 376 \quad \Sigma x^2 = 62{,}522$$
$$\Sigma y = 120 \quad \Sigma y^2 = 13{,}450$$

4. Find an equation for the least squares line.

5. Find the reading on the Celsius scale that corresponds to a reading of 120° Fahrenheit, using the equation of **Exercise 4.**

6. Find the correlation coefficient.

Correlating Heights and Weights of Adult Men *A sample of* 10 *adult men gave the following data on their heights and weights.*

Height (inches) (x)	62	62	63	65	66
Weight (pounds) (y)	120	140	130	150	142

Height (inches) (x)	67	68	68	70	72
Weight (pounds) (y)	130	135	175	149	168

7. Find the equation of the least squares line.

8. Using the results of **Exercise 7,** predict the weight of a man whose height is 60 inches.

9. What would be the predicted weight of a man whose height is 70 inches?

10. Compute the correlation coefficient.

Correlating Reading Ability and IQs *The table below gives reading ability scores and IQs for a group of* 10 *individuals.*

Reading (x)	83	76	75	85	74
IQ (y)	120	104	98	115	87

Reading (x)	90	75	78	95	80
IQ (y)	127	90	110	134	119

11. Plot a scatter diagram with reading on the horizontal axis.

12. Find the equation of a regression line.

13. Use your regression line equation to estimate the IQ of a person with a reading score of 65.

Correlating Yearly Sales of a Company *Sales, in thousands of dollars, of a certain company are shown here.*

Year (x)	0	1	2	3	4	5
Sales (y)	48	59	66	75	80	90

14. Find the equation of the least squares line.

15. Find the correlation coefficient.

16. If the linear trend displayed by this data were to continue beyond year 5, what sales amount would you predict in year 7?

Comparing the Ages of Dogs and Humans *It often is said that a dog's age can be multiplied by* 7 *to obtain the equivalent human age. A more accurate correspondence (through the first* 14 *years) is shown in this table from* The Old Farmer's Almanac, *2000 edition, page 180.*

Dog age (x)	$\frac{1}{2}$	1	2	3	4	5	6	7
Equivalent human age (y)	10	15	24	28	32	36	40	44

Dog age (x)	8	9	10	11	12	13	14
Equivalent human age (y)	48	52	56	60	64	68	70.5

17. Plot a scatter diagram for the given data.

18. Find the equation of the regression line, and graph the line on the scatter diagram of **Exercise 17.**

19. Describe where the data points show the most pronounced departure from the regression line, and explain why this might be so.

20. Compute the correlation coefficient.

Statistics on the Westward Population Movement *The data show the increase in the percentage of U.S. population in the West since about the time of the California Gold Rush.*

Census Year	Time, in Decades from 1850 (x)	Percentage in West (y)
1850	0	0.8%
1870	2	2.6
1890	4	5.0
1910	6	7.7
1930	8	10.0
1950	10	13.3
1970	12	17.1
1990	14	21.2

Source: The World Almanac and Book of Facts 2000.

21. Taking x and y as indicated in the table, find the equation of the regression line.

22. Compute the correlation coefficient.

23. Describe the degree of correlation (for example, as strong, moderate, or weak).

24. Would you expect the linear trend apparent in the table to persist into the mid 21st century? Why or why not?

Comparing State Populations with Governors' Salaries *The table shows the ten most populous states (as of 2008) and the salaries of their governors (as of September 2009).*

Rank	State	Population, in Millions (x)	Governor's Salary, in Thousands of Dollars (y)
1	California	37	174
2	Texas	24	150
3	New York	19	179
4	Florida	18	130
5	Illinois	13	177
6	Pennsylvania	12	175
7	Ohio	11	142
8	Michigan	10	177
9	Georgia	10	139
10	North Carolina	9	140

Source: The World Almanac and Book of Facts 2010.

25. Find the equation of the estimated regression line.

26. Compute the correlation coefficient.

27. Describe the degree of correlation (for example, as strong, moderate, or weak).

28. What governor's salary would this linear model predict for a state with a population of 15 million citizens?

COLLABORATIVE INVESTIGATION

Combining Sets of Data

Divide your class into two separate groups, one consisting of the women and the other consisting of the men. Each group is to select a recorder to write the group's results. As a group, carry out the following tasks. (You may want to devise a way to allow the members of the groups to provide personal data anonymously.)

1. Record the number of members (n) in your group.

2. Collect shoe sizes (x) and heights in inches (y) for all members of the group.

3. Compute the mean, median, and mode(s), if any, for each of the two sets of data.

4. Compute the standard deviation of each of the two sets of data.

5. Construct a box plot for each of the two sets of data.

6. Plot a scatter diagram for the x-y data collected.

7. Find the equation of the least squares regression line

$$y' = ax + b.$$

8. Evaluate the correlation coefficient (*r*).

9. Evaluate the strength of the linear relationship between shoe size and height for your group.

Now re-combine your two groups into one. Discuss and carry out the following tasks.

1. If possible, compute the mean of the heights for the combined group, using only the means for the two individual groups and the number of members in each of the two groups. If this is not possible, explain why and describe how you *could* find the combined mean. Obtain the combined mean.

2. Do the same as in item 1 above for the median of the heights for the combined group.

3. Do the same for the mode of the heights for the combined group.

4. Fill in the table below, pertaining to heights, and discuss any apparent relationships among the computed statistics.

	Number of Members	Mean	Median	Mode
Women				
Men				
Combined				

CHAPTER 12 TEST

Cheaters Never Learn *The table here shows the results of an educational study of university physics students, comparing exam scores with students' rates of copying others' homework. The numbers in the table approximate letter grades on a 4-point scale (4.0 is an A, 3.0 is a B, and so on). Answer the questions in Exercises 1–4 in terms of copy rate.*

Copy Rate	Pretest	Exam 1	Exam 2	Exam 3	Final exam
<10%	2.70	2.75	2.90	2.80	2.95
10% to 30%	2.50	2.45	2.35	2.40	2.30
30% to 50%	2.45	2.43	2.30	2.10	2.00
>50%	2.40	2.05	1.70	1.80	1.60

Source: Table created using data from research reported in Physics Review-Special Topics-Physics Education *by David J. Palazzo, Young-Jin Lee, Rasil Warnakulasooriya, and David E. Pritchard of the Massachusetts Institute of Technology (MIT) physics faculty.*

1. Which students generally improved their exam performance over the course of the semester?

2. Which students did better on exam 3 than or exam 2?

3. Which students had lower scores consistently from one exam to the next throughout the semester?

4. Do you think that copying homework is generally a *cause* of lower exam scores? Explain.

5. *Crude Oil Production* The table in the right column above shows total 2008 production of crude oil (in millions of barrels) by the five top-producing states.

State	Total
Texas	398
Alaska	250
California	215
Louisiana	73
Oklahoma	64

Source: Energy Information Administration.

Use this information to determine each of the following.

(a) the mean production per state

(b) the range

(c) the standard deviation

(d) the coefficient of variation

(e) If 26 additional lesser producing states averaged (mean) 14 million barrels in 2008, what was the mean production for all 31 states?

Champion Trees *The table on the next page lists the 9 largest national champion trees, based on the formula*

$$T = G + H + 0.25C,$$

where T = *total points,*

G = *girth (circumference of trunk 4.5 feet above the ground),*

H = *height,*

and C = *average crown spread.*

Tree Type	G (in.)	H (ft)	C (ft)	T	Location
Giant sequoia	1020	274	107	1321	Sequoia National Park, CA
Coast redwood	950	321	75	1290	Jedediah Smith Redwoods State Park, CA
Coast redwood	895	307	83	1223	Jedediah Smith Redwoods State Park, CA
Coast redwood	867	311	101	1203	Prairie Creek Redwoods State Park, CA
Western red cedar	761	159	45	931	Olympic National Park, WA
Sitka spruce	668	191	96	883	Olympic National Park, WA
Douglas-fir	512	301	65	829	Jedediah Smith Redwoods State Park, CA
Douglas-fir	505	281	71	804	Olympia National Forest, WA
Port-Orford cedar	522	242	35	773	Siskiyou National Forest, OR

Source: The World Almanac and Book of Facts 2010.

Use this information for Exercises 6 and 7.

6. For the nine trees listed, find the following.
   (a) the median height
   (b) the first quartile in girth
   (c) the eighth decile in total points

7. The tenth ranking tree in the country is a Common Bald Cypress on Cat Island, LA, with $G = 647$ inches, $H = 96$ feet, and $C = 74$ feet. For this tree, answer the following questions.
   (a) Find its total points.
   (b) Where would it have ranked based on girth alone?
   (c) How much taller would it have needed to be to displace the ninth ranked tree?
   (d) Assuming roughly a circular cross-section at 4.5 feet above the ground, approximate the diameter of the trunk (to the nearest foot) at that height.

Stimulus Bill *The table shows seven major categories (in alphabetical order) of the 2009 congressional stimulus bill (total $787 billion).*

Expenditure Category	Budgeted Amount ($ billions)
1. Education and Job Training	128.2
2. Energy	70.3
3. Environment	15.6
4. Health	152.0
5. Housing	20.5
6. Infrastructure	32.1
7. Transportation	48.2

Source: Congressional Budget Office.

8. Construct a bar graph for these data.

9. What percentage was assigned to health?

10. If $20 billion was allocated to health care–related information technology, what percentage of the total package went to *other* health categories?

11. What percentage was allocated to the three greatest categories combined?

Client Contacts of a Publisher's Representative *Tami Dreyfus, a publishing company representative, recorded the following numbers of client contacts for twenty-two days in March. Use the given data for Exercises 12–14.*

12	8	15	11	20	18	14	22	13	26	17
19	16	25	19	10	7	18	24	15	30	24

12. Construct grouped frequency and relative frequency distributions. Use five uniform classes of width 5 where the first class has a lower limit of 6. (Round relative frequencies to two decimal places.)

13. From your frequency distribution of **Exercise 12,** construct (a) a histogram and (b) a frequency polygon. Use appropriate scales and labels.

14. For the data above, how many uniform classes would be required if the first class had limits 7–9?

In Exercises 15–18, find the indicated measures for the following frequency distribution.

Value	8	10	12	14	16	18
Frequency	3	8	10	8	5	1

15. the mean   16. the median

17. the mode   18. the range

19. *Exam Scores in a Physics Class* The following data are exam scores achieved by the students in a physics class. Arrange the data into a stem-and-leaf display with leaves ranked.

79	43	65	84	77	70	52	61	80	66
68	48	55	78	71	38	45	64	67	73
77	50	67	91	84	33	49	61	79	72

Use the stem-and-leaf display shown here for Exercises 20–25.

2	3 3 4
2	6 7 8 9 9
3	0 1 1 2 3 3 3 4
3	5 6 7 8 8 9
4	1 2 2 4
4	5 7 9
5	2 4
5	8
6	0

Compute the measures required in Exercises 20–24.

20. the median

21. the mode(s), if any

22. the range

23. the third decile

24. the eighty-fifth percentile

25. Construct a box plot for the given data, showing values for the five important quantities on the numerical scale.

26. *Test Scores in a Training Institute* A certain training institute gives a standardized test to large numbers of applicants nationwide. The resulting scores form a normal distribution with mean 80 and standard deviation 5. Find the percent of all applicants with scores as follows. (Use the empirical rule.)

(a) between 70 and 90

(b) greater than 95 or less than 65

(c) less than 75

(d) between 85 and 90

Heights of Spruce Trees In a certain young forest, the heights of the spruce trees are normally distributed with mean 5.5 meters and standard deviation 2.1 meters. If a single tree is selected randomly, find the probability (to the nearest thousandth) that its height will fall in each of the following intervals.

27. less than 6.5 meters

28. between 6.2 and 9.4 meters

Season Statistics in Major League Baseball *The tables below show the 2009 statistics on games won for all three divisions of both major baseball leagues. In each case,*

n = *number of teams in the division,*

$\bar{x}$ = *average (mean) number of games won,*

and s = *standard deviation of number of games won.*

American League

East Division	Central Division	West Division
$n = 5$	$n = 5$	$n = 4$
$\bar{x} = 84.2$	$\bar{x} = 76.4$	$\bar{x} = 86.0$
$s = 15.5$	$s = 10.9$	$s = 9.0$

National League

East Division	Central Division	West Division
$n = 5$	$n = 6$	$n = 5$
$\bar{x} = 79.0$	$\bar{x} = 78.0$	$\bar{x} = 84.0$
$s = 14.1$	$s = 9.7$	$s = 10.9$

Refer to the preceding tables for Exercises 29–31.

29. Overall, who had the greatest winning average, the East teams, the Central teams, or the West teams?

30. Overall, where were the teams the least "consistent" in number of games won, East, Central, or West?

31. Find (to the nearest tenth) the average number of games won for all West Division teams.

32. The Boston Red Sox, in the East Division of the American League, and the Los Angeles Dodgers, in the West Division of the National League, each won 95 games. Use z-scores to determine which of these two teams did relatively better within its own division of 5 teams.

PERSONAL FINANCIAL MANAGEMENT 13

The second season of *The Andy Griffith Show* provided an episode that beautifully illustrated an application of the mathematics of finance. In "Mayberry Goes Bankrupt," Sheriff Taylor was reluctantly forced to evict kindly old gentleman Frank Myers from his home due to nonpayment of taxes. But Frank then produced a bond purchased for $100 in 1861 and paying 8.5% interest compounded annually. It had been stored away for 100 years. When the town banker told the Mayor he could not pay Frank, Andy explained why this was so.

> *Well, Mayor . . . according to the computation machines down at the bank . . . and they're good machines . . . we . . . owe Frank Myers $349,119.27. (To which Frank responds: I'll take it in cash.)*

By applying the formula for *compound interest* found in **Section 13.1,** you will find that the figure quoted is correct to the penny.

13.1 THE TIME VALUE OF MONEY

Interest • Simple Interest • Future Value and Present Value • Compound Interest
• Effective Annual Yield • Inflation

Interest

To determine the value of money, we consider not only the amount (number of dollars) but also the particular point in time that the value is to be determined. If we borrow an amount of money today, we will repay a larger amount later. This increase in value is known as **interest.** The money *gains value over time.*

The amount of a loan or a deposit is called the **principal.** The interest is usually computed as a percent of the principal. This percent is called the **rate of interest** (or the **interest rate,** or simply the **rate**). The rate of interest is always assumed to be an annual rate unless otherwise stated.

Interest calculated only on principal is called **simple interest.** Interest calculated on principal plus any previously earned interest is called **compound interest.**

Simple Interest

Simple interest is calculated according to the following formula.

> **Simple Interest**
>
> If P = principal, r = annual interest rate, and t = time (in years), then the **simple interest** I is calculated as follows.
>
> $$I = Prt$$

▌▌ **EXAMPLE 1** Finding Simple Interest

Find the simple interest paid to borrow $5350 for 5 months at 6%.

SOLUTION

$$I = Prt \qquad \text{Simple interest formula}$$

$$= \$5350(0.06)\left(\frac{5}{12}\right) \qquad \boxed{\text{5 months is } \tfrac{5}{12} \text{ of a year.}}$$
$$\qquad\qquad\qquad\qquad P = \$5350, r = 6\% = 0.06$$

$$= \$133.75 \qquad \text{Calculate.} \qquad\qquad ▌▌▌$$

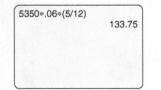
```
5350*.06*(5/12)
                133.75
```

This is the computation required to solve
Example 1.

Future Value and Present Value

In **Example 1,** at the end of 5 months the borrower would have to repay.

Principal   Interest

$5350   + $133.75 = $5483.75.

The total amount repaid is sometimes called the **maturity value** (or simply the **value**) of the loan. We will generally refer to it as the **future value,** or **future amount,** since when a loan is being set up, repayment will be occurring in the future. We use A to denote future amount (or value). The original principal, denoted P, can also be thought of as **present value.**

Future value depends on principal (present value) and interest as follows.

$$A = P + I = P + Prt = P(1 + rt)$$

> **Future Value for Simple Interest**
>
> If a principal P is borrowed at simple interest for t years at an annual interest rate of r, then the **future value** of the loan, denoted A, is calculated as follows.
>
> $$A = P(1 + rt)$$

▋▋ **EXAMPLE 2** Finding Future Value for Simple Interest

James Albertone took out a simple interest loan for $210 to purchase textbooks and school supplies. If the annual interest rate is 6% and he must repay the loan after 8 months, find the future value (the maturity value) of the loan.

SOLUTION

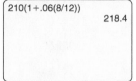

$$
\begin{aligned}
A &= P(1 + rt) &&\text{Future value formula}\\
&= \$210\left[1 + 0.06\left(\frac{8}{12}\right)\right] &&P = \$210, r = 6\% = 0.06, t = \tfrac{8}{12}\\
&= \$218.40 &&\text{Calculate.}
\end{aligned}
$$

This is the computation required to solve **Example 2.**

At the end of 8 months, James will need to repay $218.40.   ▪▪▪

Sometimes the future value is known, and we need to compute the present value. For this purpose, we solve the future value formula for P.

$$A = P(1 + rt) \quad \text{Future value formula for simple interest}$$

$$P = \frac{A}{1 + rt} \quad \text{Solve the formula for } P.$$

▋▋ **EXAMPLE 3** Finding Present Value for Simple Interest

Suppose that James (**Example 2**) is granted an 8-month *deferral* of the $210 payment rather than a loan. That is, instead of incurring interest for 8 months, he will have to pay just the $210 at the end of that period. If he has extra money right now, and if he can earn 2% simple interest on savings, what lump sum must he deposit now so that its value will be $210 after 8 months?

SOLUTION

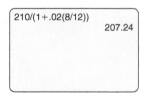

$$P = \frac{A}{1 + rt} \quad \text{Future value formula solved for } P$$

$$P = \frac{\$210}{1 + (0.02)\left(\frac{8}{12}\right)} = \$207.24 \quad \text{Substitute known values and simplify.}$$

This is the computation required to solve **Example 3.**

A deposit of $207.24 now, growing at 2% simple interest, will grow to $210 over an 8-month period.   ▪▪▪

Compound Interest

Interest paid on principal plus interest is called *compound interest*. After a certain period, the interest earned so far is *credited* (added) to the account, and the sum (principal plus interest) then earns interest during the next period.

To borrow from the title of the Clint Eastwood classic *The Good, the Bad, and the Ugly*, the 1994 movie *Blank Check* includes a scene that qualifies as **ugly mathematics.** Twelve-year-old Preston Waters receives a check for $11.00 and uses his computer to determine how long it will take for this amount to grow to $1,000,000 at 3.45% annual interest.

While there is no information on the number of compounding periods, the answer given in the movie is incorrect for any number. The computer determines that it would take 342,506 years. Even with interest compounded just once a year, the time would "only" be 337 years.

▌▌ **EXAMPLE 4**   Comparing Simple and Compound Interest

Compare simple and compound interest for a $1000 deposit at 4% interest for 5 years.

SOLUTION

$$A = P(1 + rt) \qquad \text{Future value formula}$$

$$= \$1000(1 + 0.04 \cdot 5) \qquad P = \$1000, r = 4\% = 0.04, t = 5$$

$$= \$1200 \qquad \text{Calculate.}$$

After 5 years, $1000 grows to $1200 subject to 4% simple interest.

The result of compounding (annually) for 5 years is shown in **Table 1**.

Table 1   **A $1000 Deposit at 4% Interest Compounded Annually**

Year	Beginning Balance	Interest Earned $I = Prt$	Ending Balance
1	$1000.00	$1000.00(0.04)(1) = $40.00	$1040.00
2	$1040.00	$1040.00(0.04)(1) = $41.60	$1081.60
3	$1081.60	$1081.60(0.04)(1) = $43.26	$1124.86
4	$1124.86	$1124.86(0.04)(1) = $44.99	$1169.85
5	$1169.85	$1169.85(0.04)(1) = $46.79	$1216.64

Under annual compounding for 5 years, $1000 grows to $1216.64, which is $16.64 more than under simple interest. ▊▊▊

Based on the compounding pattern of **Example 4,** we now develop a future value formula for compound interest. In practice, earned interest can be credited to an account at time intervals other than 1 year (usually more often). For example, it can be done semiannually, quarterly, monthly, or daily. This time interval is called the **compounding period** (or simply the **period**). Start with the following definitions:

P = original principal deposited, r = annual interest rate,

m = number of periods per year, n = total number of periods.

During each individual compounding period, interest is earned according to the simple interest formula, and as interest is added, the beginning principal increases from one period to the next. During the first period, the interest earned is given by

$$\text{Interest} = P(r)\left(\frac{1}{m}\right) \qquad \begin{array}{l}\text{Interest} = (\text{Principal})(\text{rate})(\text{time}),\\ \text{one period} = \frac{1}{m}\text{ year}\end{array}$$

$$= P\left(\frac{r}{m}\right). \qquad \text{Rewrite } (r)(\frac{1}{m}) \text{ as } (\frac{r}{m}).$$

At the end of the first period, the account then contains

$$\underset{\underset{\text{Beginning amount}}{\downarrow}}{\text{Ending amount} = P} + \underset{\underset{\text{Interest}}{\downarrow}}{P\left(\frac{r}{m}\right)}$$

$$= P\left(1 + \frac{r}{m}\right). \qquad \text{Factor } P \text{ from both terms.}$$

King Hammurabi tried to hold interest rates at 20 percent for both silver and gold, but moneylenders ignored his decrees.

Now during the second period, the interest earned is given by

$$\text{Interest} = \left[P\left(1 + \frac{r}{m}\right)\right](r)\left(\frac{1}{m}\right) \qquad \text{Interest} = [\text{Principal}]\,(\text{rate})\,(\text{time})$$

$$= P\left(1 + \frac{r}{m}\right)\left(\frac{r}{m}\right),$$

so that the account ends the second period containing

$$\overset{\text{Beginning amount}}{\underset{\downarrow}{}} \qquad \overset{\text{Interest}}{\underset{\downarrow}{}}$$

$$\text{Ending amount} = P\left(1 + \frac{r}{m}\right) + P\left(1 + \frac{r}{m}\right)\left(\frac{r}{m}\right)$$

$$= P\left(1 + \frac{r}{m}\right)\left[1 + \frac{r}{m}\right] \qquad \text{Factor } P\left(1 + \frac{r}{m}\right) \text{ from both terms.}$$

$$= P\left(1 + \frac{r}{m}\right)^2. \qquad a \cdot a = a^2$$

Consider one more period, namely, the third. The interest earned is

$$\text{Interest} = \left[P\left(1 + \frac{r}{m}\right)^2\right](r)\left(\frac{1}{m}\right) \qquad \text{Interest} = [\text{Principal}]\,(\text{rate})\,(\text{time})$$

$$= P\left(1 + \frac{r}{m}\right)^2\left(\frac{r}{m}\right),$$

so the account ends the third period containing

$$\overset{\text{Beginning amount}}{\underset{\downarrow}{}} \qquad \overset{\text{Interest}}{\underset{\downarrow}{}}$$

$$\text{Ending amount} = P\left(1 + \frac{r}{m}\right)^2 + P\left(1 + \frac{r}{m}\right)^2\left(\frac{r}{m}\right)$$

$$= P\left(1 + \frac{r}{m}\right)^2\left[1 + \frac{r}{m}\right] \qquad \text{Factor } P\left(1 + \frac{r}{m}\right)^2 \text{ from both terms.}$$

$$= P\left(1 + \frac{r}{m}\right)^3. \qquad a^2 \cdot a = a^3$$

Table 2 summarizes the preceding results.

Table 2	**Compound Amount**		
Period Number	**Beginning Amount**	**Interest Earned During Period**	**Ending Amount**
1	P	$P\left(\frac{r}{m}\right)$	$P\left(1 + \frac{r}{m}\right)$
2	$P\left(1 + \frac{r}{m}\right)$	$P\left(1 + \frac{r}{m}\right)\left(\frac{r}{m}\right)$	$P\left(1 + \frac{r}{m}\right)^2$
3	$P\left(1 + \frac{r}{m}\right)^2$	$P\left(1 + \frac{r}{m}\right)^2\left(\frac{r}{m}\right)$	$P\left(1 + \frac{r}{m}\right)^3$
$\vdots$	$\vdots$	$\vdots$	$\vdots$
n	$P\left(1 + \frac{r}{m}\right)^{n-1}$	$P\left(1 + \frac{r}{m}\right)^{n-1}\left(\frac{r}{m}\right)$	$P\left(1 + \frac{r}{m}\right)^n$

The lower right entry of **Table 2** provides the following formula.

The quantity

$$\left(1 + \frac{r}{m}\right)^n$$

can be evaluated using a key such as $\boxed{y^x}$ on a scientific calculator or $\boxed{\wedge}$ on a graphing calculator.

Future Value for Compound Interest

If P dollars are deposited at an annual interest rate of r, compounded m times per year, and the money is left on deposit for a total of n periods, then the **future value, A** (the final amount on deposit), is calculated as follows.

$$A = P\left(1 + \frac{r}{m}\right)^n$$

▮▮ **EXAMPLE 5** Finding Future Value for Compound Interest

Find the future value (final amount on deposit) and the amount of interest earned for the following deposits.

(a) $12,450 at 3% compounded quarterly for 5 years

(b) $3419 at 4.1% compounded monthly for 30 months

SOLUTION

(a) Here $P = \$12{,}450$, $r = 3\% = 0.03$, and $m = 4$. Over 5 years,

$$n = 5m = (5)(4) = 20.$$

We use the future value formula and a calculator.

$$A = \$12{,}450\left(1 + \frac{0.03}{4}\right)^{20} = \$14{,}456.74$$

Now we subtract to find the interest earned.

Future value   Present value
↓   ↓

$$\text{Interest earned} = \$14{,}456.74 - \$12{,}450$$
$$= \$2006.74$$

```
N=20
I%=3
PV=-12450
PMT=0
→ FV=14456.74257
P/Y=4
C/Y=4
PMT: END  BEGIN
```

The financial functions of the TI-83/84 Plus calculator allow the user to solve for a missing quantity regarding the time value of money. The arrow indicates the display that supports the future value answer in **Example 5(a).**

(b) Here $P = \$3419$, $r = 4.1\% = 0.041$, $m = 12$, and $n = 30$.

$$A = \$3419\left(1 + \frac{0.041}{12}\right)^{30} = \$3787.38$$

Future value   Present value
↓   ↓

$$\text{Interest earned} = \$3787.38 - \$3419$$
$$= \$368.38$$ ▮▮▮

Compound interest problems sometimes require that we solve the formula for P to compute the present value when the future value is known.

$$A = P\left(1 + \frac{r}{m}\right)^n \qquad \text{Future value for compound interest}$$

$$P = \frac{A}{\left(1 + \frac{r}{m}\right)^n} \qquad \text{Solve the formula for } P.$$

The 1957 movie *The Pajama Game* was inspired by the Broadway musical of the same name. It was recently revived on Broadway and starred Harry Connick, Jr. The female lead in the movie, "Babe" Williams, was played by Doris Day. She and her coworkers at the Sleeptite Pajama Factory were attempting to get a $7\frac{1}{2}$ cent per hour raise.

The musical number **"Seven and a Half Cents"** features three computations, determining how much this seemingly small raise will earn in three time periods. Based on pencil and paper calculations, the lyrics state that in 5 years, the raise will amount to $852.74, in 10 years $1705.48, and in 20 years $3411.96. Assuming that the figure for 5 years is correct, is the one for 10 years also correct? Now, how about the one for 20 years? Oops!

EXAMPLE 6   Finding Present Value for Compound Interest

Lisa Ashley will need $27,000 in 5 years to help pay for her college education. What lump sum, deposited today at 4% compounded quarterly, will produce the necessary amount?

SOLUTION

This question requires that we find the present value P based on the following.

Future value:	$A = \$27{,}000$
Annual rate:	$r = 4\% = 0.04$
Periods per year:	$m = 4$
Total number of periods:	$n = (5)(4) = 20$

$$P = \frac{A}{\left(1 + \frac{r}{m}\right)^n} \qquad \text{Future value formula solved for } P$$

$$P = \frac{\$27{,}000}{\left(1 + \frac{0.04}{4}\right)^{20}} \qquad \text{Substitute known values.}$$

$$P = \$22{,}127.70 \qquad \text{Calculate.}$$

Assuming interest of 4% compounded quarterly can be maintained, $27,000 can be attained 5 years in the future by depositing $22,127.70 today.   ███

The next example uses logarithms. See the discussion of logarithms in **Section 8.6** (or your calculator manual).

EXAMPLE 7   Finding the Time Required to Double a Principal Deposit

In a savings account paying 3% interest, compounded daily, when will the amount in the account be twice the original principal?

SOLUTION

The future value must equal two times the present value.

$$2P = P\left(1 + \frac{r}{m}\right)^n \qquad \text{Substitute } 2P \text{ for } A \text{ in the future value formula.}$$

$$2 = \left(1 + \frac{r}{m}\right)^n \qquad \text{Divide both sides by } P.$$

$$2 = \left(1 + \frac{0.03}{365}\right)^n \qquad \text{Substitute values of } r \text{ and } m.$$

$$\log 2 = \log\left(1 + \frac{0.03}{365}\right)^n \qquad \text{Take the logarithm of both sides.}$$

$$\log 2 = n \log\left(1 + \frac{0.03}{365}\right) \qquad \text{Use the power property of logarithms.}$$

$$n = \frac{\log 2}{\log\left(1 + \frac{0.03}{365}\right)} \qquad \text{Solve for } n.$$

$$n = 8434 \qquad \text{Round to the nearest whole number.}$$

Because n denotes the number of periods, which is days in this case, the required amount of time is 8434 days, or 23 years, 39 days (ignoring leap years).   ███

The power of compound interest is being put to use in the town of Union City, Michigan. Eli Hooker, chairman of the local Bicentennial Committee in 1976, saw that there was not enough money to put on a proper celebration that year. So, in order to help his town prepare for the tricentennial, in 2076, he collected twenty-five dollars apiece from 42 patriotic residents and deposited the money in a local bank. Compounded at seven percent, that money would grow to a million dollars by 2076.

Unfortunately, the million dollars won't be worth as much then as we might think. If the community decides to hire people to parade around in historical costumes, it might have paid them $4 per hour in 1976. The going wage in 2076, assuming 7% annual inflation for a hundred years, would be well over $3000 per hour.

Example 8 shows the importance of starting early to maximize the long-term advantage of compounding.

EXAMPLE 8 Comparing Retirement Plans

Compare the results at age 65 for the following two retirement plans. Both plans earn 8% annual interest throughout the account building period.

Plan A: Gina Fox begins saving at age 20, deposits $2000 on every birthday from age 21 to age 30 (10 deposits, or $20,000 total), and thereafter makes no additional contributions.

Plan B: Peter Harris waits until age 30 to start saving, makes deposits of $2000 on every birthday from age 31 to age 65 (35 deposits, or $70,000 total).

SOLUTION

Table 3 shows how both accounts build over the years. $20,000, deposited earlier, produces $83,744 more than $70,000, deposited later.

Table 3		
Age	**Plan A**	**Plan B**
20	0	0
25	11,733	0
30	28,973	0
35	42,571	11,733
40	62,551	28,973
45	91,908	54,304
50	135,042	91,524
55	198,422	146,212
60	291,547	226,566
65	428,378	344,634

In **Example 8,** the *early* deposits of Plan A outperformed the *greater number* of deposits of Plan B because the interest rate was high enough to result in a Plan A balance at age 30 that Plan B could never overtake, despite additional Plan B deposits from then on. If the interest rate had been 6% rather than 8%, Plan B would have overtaken Plan A (at age 57) and at age 65 would have come out ahead by $20,253 (to the nearest dollar).

Effective Annual Yield

Banks, credit unions, and others often advertise two rates: first, the actual annualized interest rate, or **nominal rate** (the "named" or "stated" rate), and second, the equivalent rate that would produce the same final amount, or future value, at the end of 1 year if the interest being paid were simple rather than compound. This is called the "effective rate," or more commonly the **effective annual yield.** (It may be denoted **APY** for **"annual percentage yield."**) Because the interest is normally compounded multiple times per year, the yield will usually be somewhat higher than the nominal rate.

▮▮ **EXAMPLE 9**   Finding Effective Annual Yield

What is the effective annual yield of an account paying a nominal rate of 2.50%, compounded quarterly?

SOLUTION

From the given data, $r = 0.025$ and $m = 4$. Suppose we deposited $P = \$1$ and left it for 1 year $(n = 4)$. Then the compound future value formula gives

$$A = 1 \cdot \left(1 + \frac{0.025}{4}\right)^4 \approx 1.0252.$$

The initial deposit of $1, after 1 year, has grown to $1.0252.

Interest earned $= 1.0252 - 1$ Interest = future value − present value

$$= 0.0252, \quad \text{or} \quad 2.52\%$$

A nominal rate of 2.50% results in an effective annual yield of 2.52%.   ▮▮▮

Generalizing the procedure of **Example 9** gives the following formula.

▶Eff(2.50,4)
                    2.523535309

Financial calculators are programmed to compute effective interest rate. Compare to the result in **Example 9.**

Effective Annual Yield

A nominal interest rate of r, compounded m times per year, is equivalent to the following **effective annual yield.**

$$Y = \left(1 + \frac{r}{m}\right)^m - 1$$

When shopping for loans or savings opportunities, a borrower should seek the least yield available, while a depositor should look for the greatest.

▮▮ **EXAMPLE 10**   Comparing Savings Rates

Christine Ellington wants to deposit $2800 into a savings account and has narrowed her choices to the three institutions represented here. Which is the best choice?

Institution	Rate on Deposits of $1000 to $5000
Friendly Credit Union	2.08% annual rate, compounded monthly
Premier Savings	2.09% annual yield
Neighborhood Bank	2.05% compounded daily

SOLUTION

Compare the effective annual yields for the three institutions.

Friendly: $Y = \left(1 + \dfrac{0.0208}{12}\right)^{12} - 1 = 0.0210 = 2.10\%$

Premier: $Y = 2.09\%$

Neighborhood: $Y = \left(1 + \dfrac{0.0205}{365}\right)^{365} - 1 = 0.0207 = 2.07\%$

The best of the three yields, 2.10%, is offered by Friendly Credit Union.   ▮▮▮

Table 4	Consumer Price Index (CPI-U)*	
Year	**Average CPI-U**	**Percent Change in CPI-U**
1979	72.6	11.3
1980	82.4	13.5
1981	90.9	10.3
1982	96.5	6.2
1983	99.6	3.2
1984	103.9	4.3
1985	107.6	3.6
1986	109.6	1.9
1987	113.6	3.6
1988	118.3	4.1
1989	124.0	4.8
1990	130.7	5.4
1991	136.2	4.2
1992	140.3	3.0
1993	144.5	3.0
1994	148.2	2.6
1995	152.4	2.8
1996	156.9	3.0
1997	160.5	2.3
1998	163.0	1.6
1999	166.6	2.2
2000	172.2	3.4
2001	177.1	2.8
2002	179.9	1.6
2003	184.0	2.3
2004	188.9	2.7
2005	195.3	3.4
2006	201.6	3.2
2007	207.3	2.8
2008	215.3	3.8
2009	214.5	−0.4

Source: Bureau of Labor Statistics.

*The period 1982 to 1984: 100

Inflation

Interest reflects how money *gains value over time* when it is borrowed or lent. On the other hand, in terms of the equivalent number of goods or services that a given amount of money will buy, money normally *loses value over time*. This results in a periodic increase in the cost of living, which is called **price inflation.**

In the United States, the Bureau of Labor Statistics publishes **consumer price index (CPI)** figures, which reflect the prices of certain items purchased by large numbers of people. The items include such things as food, housing, automobiles, fuel, and clothing. Items such as yachts or expensive jewelry are not included.

Current data are published regularly at www.bls.gov/cpi. **Table 4** gives values of the primary index representing "all urban consumers" (the CPI-U). The value shown for a given year is actually the average (arithmetic mean) of the twelve monthly figures for that year. The table shows, for example, that the average CPI-U for 2007 (207.3) was 2.8% greater than the average value for 2006 (201.6).

Deflation is a *decrease* in price levels from one year to the next. A brief period of minor deflation, along with a general economic slowdown, usually is called a **recession.** (For example, in **Table 4**, note the 2009 rate of −0.4.)

Unlike account values under interest compounding, which make sudden jumps at just certain points in time (such as quarterly, monthly, or daily), price levels tend to fluctuate gradually over time. Thus, it is appropriate, for inflationary estimates, to use the formula for continuous compounding (introduced in **Section 8.6.**)

Future Value for Continuous Compounding

If an initial deposit of P dollars earns continuously compounded interest at an annual rate r for a period of t years, then the **future value, A,** is calculated as follows.

$$A = Pe^{rt}$$

▮▮ **EXAMPLE 11** Predicting Inflated Salary Levels

Suppose you earn a salary of $34,000 per year. About what salary would you need 20 years from now to maintain your purchasing power in case the inflation rate were to persist at each of the following levels?

(a) 2% (approximately the 1999 level)

(b) 13% (approximately the 1980 level)

SOLUTION

(a) In this case we can use the continuous compounding future value formula with $P = \$34{,}000$, $r = 0.02$, and $t = 20$, and the $\boxed{e^x}$ key on a calculator.

$$A = Pe^{rt} = (\$34{,}000)e^{(0.02)(20)} = \$50{,}722.04$$

The required salary 20 years from now would be about $51,000.

(b) For this level of inflation, we would have the following.

$$A = Pe^{rt} = (\$34{,}000)e^{(0.13)(20)} = \$457{,}767.09$$

The required salary 20 years from now would be about $458,000. ▮▮▮

To compare equivalent general price levels in any 2 years, we can use the proportion at the top of the next page. (A proportion is a statement that says that two ratios are equal. See **Section 7.3.**)

$34000e^{(.02*20)}$

$\qquad\qquad$ 50722.04

$34000e^{(.13*20)}$

$\qquad\qquad$ 457767.09

These are the computations required to solve the two parts of **Example 11.**

Inflation Proportion

For a given consumer product or service subject to average inflation, prices in two different years are related as follows.

$$\frac{\text{Price in year A}}{\text{Price in year B}} = \frac{\text{CPI in year A}}{\text{CPI in year B}}$$

▌▌ **EXAMPLE 12**   Comparing a Tuition Increase to Average Inflation

Michael Dew's college tuition in 2009 was $9910. His uncle attended the same school in 1990 and paid $4990 in tuition. Compare the school's tuition increase to average inflation over the same period.

SOLUTION

Let x represent what we would expect the tuition to be in 2009 if it had increased at the average rate since 1990.

$$\frac{\text{Price in 2009}}{\text{Price in 1990}} = \frac{\text{CPI in 2009}}{\text{CPI in 1990}} \qquad \text{Inflation proportion}$$

$$\frac{x}{\$4990} = \frac{214.5}{130.7} \qquad \text{Substitute. CPI values are from \textbf{Table 4.}}$$

$$x = \frac{214.5}{130.7} \cdot \$4990 \qquad \text{Solve for } x.$$

$$x \approx \$8189$$

Now compare the actual 2009 tuition, $9910, with the expected figure, $8189.

$$\frac{\$9910}{\$8189} = 1.21 \qquad 1.21 = 100\% + 21\%$$

Over the period from 1990 to 2009, tuition at Michael's college increased approximately 21% more than the average CPI-U rate.   ▌▌▌

When working with quantities, such as inflation, where continual fluctuations and inexactness prevail, we often develop rough "rules of thumb" for obtaining quick estimates. One example is the estimation of the **years to double,** which is the number of years it takes for the general level of prices to double for a given annual rate of inflation. We can derive an estimation rule as follows.

$$A = Pe^{rt} \qquad \text{Future value formula}$$

$$2P = Pe^{rt} \qquad \text{Prices are to double.}$$

$$2 = e^{rt} \qquad \text{Divide both sides by } P.$$

$$\ln 2 = rt \qquad \text{Take the natural logarithm of both sides.}$$

$$t = \frac{\ln 2}{r} \qquad \text{Solve for } t.$$

$$t = \frac{100 \ln 2}{100r} \qquad \text{Multiply numerator and denominator by 100.}$$

$$\textbf{years to double} \approx \frac{\textbf{70}}{\textbf{annual inflation rate}} \qquad 100 \ln 2 \approx 70$$

(Because r is the inflation rate as a *decimal*, $100r$ is the inflation rate as a *percent*.)

The result above usually is called the **rule of 70.** The value it produces, if not a whole number, should be rounded *up* to the next whole number of years.

Monetary inflation devalues the currency just as **price inflation** does, but it does so through a direct increase in the money supply within the economy. An example in the United States was the issuance in 2009 and 2010 of massive government debt and massive government spending on "stimulus" programs. Debate persisted among economists as to whether actions of the government and central bank would accomplish their goals. Would economic recovery continue, or would major deflation occur? Most everyone agreed that the long-term result of monetary inflation would be more and more price inflation. Some deny that any real distinction exists, that due to complex interrelated economic forces, monetary and price inflation are essentially the same thing.

(100*ln(2))/2.3
            30.13683394
70/2.3
            30.43478261

Because 100 ln 2 ≈ 70, the two results shown here are approximately equal. See **Example 13** and the preceding discussion.

▮▮ **EXAMPLE 13** Estimating Years to Double by the Rule of 70

Estimate the years to double for an annual inflation rate of 2.3%.

SOLUTION

$$\text{Years to double} \approx \frac{70}{2.3} \approx 30.43 \quad \text{Rule of 70}$$

With a sustained inflation rate of 2.3%, prices would double in about 31 years. ▮▮▮

13.1 EXERCISES

In the following exercises, assume whenever appropriate that, unless otherwise known, there are 12 months per year, 30 days per month, and 365 days per year.

Find the simple interest owed for each loan.

1. $800 at 6% for 1 year

2. $3000 at 5% for 1 year

3. $920 at 7% for 9 months

4. $5400 at 7% for 4 months

5. $2675 at 7.3% for $2\frac{1}{2}$ years

6. $2620 at 4.82% for 22 months

Find the future value of each deposit if the account pays **(a)** *simple interest, and* **(b)** *interest compounded annually.*

7. $700 at 3% for 6 years

8. $2000 at 4% for 5 years

9. $2500 at 2% for 3 years

10. $3000 at 5% for 4 years

Solve each interest-related problem.

11. **Simple Interest on a Late Property Tax Payment** Andrew Draa was late on his property tax payment to the county. He owed $7500 and paid the tax 4 months late. The county charges a penalty of 5% simple interest. Find the amount of the penalty.

12. **Simple Interest on a Loan for Work Uniforms** Austin Caperton bought a new supply of delivery uniforms. He paid $922 for the uniforms and agreed to pay for them in 5 months at 6% simple interest. Find the amount of interest that he will owe.

13. **Simple Interest on a Small Business Loan** Kelly Kunert opened a security service on March 1. To pay for office furniture and guard dogs, Kelly borrowed $12,800 at the bank and agreed to pay the loan back in 10 months at 7% simple interest. Find the *total amount* required to repay the loan.

14. **Simple Interest on a Tax Overpayment** Paul Lewis is owed $530 by the Internal Revenue Service for overpayment of last year's taxes. The IRS will repay the amount at 4% simple interest. Find the *total amount* Paul will receive if the interest is paid for 8 months.

Find the missing final amount (future value) and/or interest earned.

	Principal	Rate	Compounded	Time	Final Amount	Compound Interest
15.	$ 975	4%	quarterly	4 years	$1143.26	_____
16.	$1150	7%	semiannually	6 years	$1737.73	_____
17.	$ 480	6%	semiannually	9 years	_____	$337.17
18.	$2370	5%	quarterly	5 years	_____	_____
19.	$7500	$3\frac{1}{2}$ %	annually	25 years	_____	_____
20.	$3450	2.4%	semiannually	10 years	_____	_____

For each deposit, find the future value (that is, the final amount on deposit) when compounding occurs (a) annually, (b) semi-annually, and (c) quarterly.

	Principal	Rate	Time
21.	$2000	4%	3 years
22.	$5000	2%	7 years
23.	$18,000	1%	5 years
24.	$10,000	3%	9 years

Occasionally a savings account may actually pay interest compounded continuously. For each deposit, find the interest earned if interest is compounded (a) semiannually, (b) quarterly, (c) monthly, (d) daily, and (e) continuously.

	Principal	Rate	Time
25.	$850	1.6%	4 years
26.	$1550	2.8%	33 months (Assume 1003 days in parts (d) and (e).)

27. Describe the effect of interest being compounded more and more often. In particular, how good is continuous compounding?

Solve each interest-related problem.

28. *Finding the Amount Borrowed in a Simple Interest Loan* Jay Jenkins takes out a 7% simple interest loan today that will be repaid 15 months from now with a payoff amount of $815.63. What amount is Jay borrowing?

29. *Finding the Amount Borrowed in a Simple Interest Loan* What is the maximum amount Ginger Logan can borrow today if it must be repaid in 4 months with simple interest at 8% and she knows that at that time she will be able to repay no more than $1500?

30. In the development of the future value formula for compound interest in the text, at least four specific problem-solving strategies were employed. Identify (name) as many of them as you can and describe their use in this case.

Find the present value for each future amount.

31. $1000 (6% compounded annually for 5 years)

32. $14,000 (4% compounded quarterly for 3 years)

33. $9860 (8% compounded semiannually for 10 years)

34. $15,080 (5% compounded monthly for 4 years)

Finding the Present Value of a Compound Interest Retirement Account *Robyn Martin wants to establish an account that will supplement her retirement income beginning 30 years from now. For each interest rate find the lump sum she must deposit today so that $500,000 will be available at time of retirement.*

35. 5% compounded quarterly

36. 6% compounded quarterly

37. 5% compounded daily

38. 6% compounded daily

Finding the Effective Annual Yield in a Savings Account *Suppose a savings and loan pays a nominal rate of 2% on savings deposits. Find the effective annual yield if interest is compounded as stated in Exercises 39–45. (Give answers to the nearest thousandth of a percent.)*

39. annually

40. semiannually

41. quarterly

42. monthly

43. daily

44. 1000 times per year

45. 10,000 times per year

46. Judging from **Exercises 39–45,** what do you suppose is the effective annual yield if a nominal rate of 2% is compounded continuously? Explain your reasoning.

Comparing Savings Rates and Yields *The table shows the two best savings rates available on a certain online listing on May 25, 2010. Use this information in Exercises 47 and 48.*

	Rate	Yield
Sallie Mae	1.390%	1.400%
Capital One Direct Banking	1.340%	1.349%

47. If you deposit $30,000 with Sallie Mae, how much would you have in 1 year?

48. How often does compounding occur in the Capital One account: daily, monthly, quarterly, or semiannually?

Solve each problem.

49. *Finding Years to Double* How long would it take to double your money in an account paying 4% compounded quarterly? (Answer in years plus days, ignoring leap years.)

50. *Comparing Principal and Interest Amounts* After what time period would the interest earned equal the original principal in an account paying 2% compounded daily? (Answer in years plus days, ignoring leap years.)

51. Solve the effective annual yield formula for *r* to obtain a general formula for nominal rate in terms of yield and the number of compounding periods per year.

52. *Finding the Nominal Rate of a Savings Account* Ridgeway Savings compounds interest monthly, and the effective annual yield is 1.95%. What is the nominal rate?

53. *Comparing Bank Savings Rates* Bank A pays a nominal rate of 3.800% compounded daily on deposits. Bank B produces the same annual yield as the first but compounds interest only quarterly and pays no interest on funds deposited for less than an entire quarter.

(a) What nominal rate does Bank B pay (to the nearest thousandth of a percent)?

(b) Which bank should Nancy Dennis choose if she has $2000 to deposit for 10 months? How much more interest will she earn than in the other bank?

(c) Which bank should Dara Lanier choose for a deposit of $6000 for one year? How much interest will be earned?

Estimating the Years to Double by the Rule of 70 *Use the rule of 70 to estimate the years to double for each annual inflation rate.*

54. 1%   **55.** 2%

56. 8%   **57.** 9%

Estimating the Inflation Rate by the Rule of 70 *Use the rule of 70 to estimate the annual inflation rate (to the nearest tenth of a percent) that would cause the general level of prices to double in each time period.*

58. 5 years   **59.** 7 years

60. 16 years   **61.** 22 years

62. Derive a rule for estimating the "years to triple," that is, the number of years it would take for the general levels of prices to triple for a given annual inflation rate.

Estimating Future Prices for Constant Annual Inflation *The year 2010 prices of several items are given below. Find the estimated future prices required to fill the blanks in the chart. (Give a number of significant figures consistent with the 2010 price figures provided.)*

Item	2010 Price	2015 Price 2% Inflation	2025 Price 2% Inflation	2015 Price 10% Inflation	2025 Price 10% Inflation
63. Fast food meal	$ 5.89	_____	_____	_____	_____
64. House	$265,000	_____	_____	_____	_____
65. Small car	$ 18,500	_____	_____	_____	_____
66. Gallon of gasoline	$ 2.65	_____	_____	_____	_____

Estimating Future Prices for Variable Annual Inflation *As seen in* **Table 4**, *inflation rates do not often stay constant over a period of years. Assume that prices for the items below increased at the average annual rates shown in* **Table 4**. *Use the inflation proportion to find the missing prices in the last column of the chart. Round to the nearest dollar.*

Item	Price	Year Purchased	Price in 2009
67. Evening dress	$ 175	2000	_____
68. Desk	$ 450	2002	_____
69. Lawn tractor	$1099	1996	_____
70. Designer puppy	$ 250	1998	_____

Solve each interest-related problem.

71. *Finding the Present Value of a Future Equipment Purchase* Human gene sequencing is a major research area of biotechnology. PE Biosystems leased 300 of its sequencing machines to a sibling company, Celera. If Celera was able to earn 7% compounded quarterly on invested money, what lump sum did they need to invest in order to purchase those machines 18 months later at a price of $300,000 each? (*Source: Forbes,* February 21, 2000, p. 102.)

72. *Finding the Present Value of a Future Real Estate Purchase* A California couple are selling their small dairy farm to a developer, but they wish to defer receipt of the money until 2 years from now, when they will be in a lower tax bracket. Find the lump sum that the developer can deposit today, at 5% compounded quarterly, so that enough will be available to pay the couple $1,450,000 in 2 years.

13.2 CONSUMER CREDIT

Types of Consumer Credit • Installment Loans • Revolving Loans

Types of Consumer Credit

Consumer credit refers to borrowing money to finance purchases of cars, furniture, appliances, jewelry, electronics, and many other things. Technically, **real estate mortgages,** loans to finance home purchases, are also consumer credit, but they usually involve much larger amounts and longer repayment periods.

In this section we discuss two common types of consumer credit. The first type, **installment loans,** or **closed-end** credit, involves borrowing a set amount up front and paying a series of equal installments (payments) until the loan is paid off. Furniture, appliances, and cars commonly are financed through closed-end credit.

With the second type of consumer credit, **revolving loans,** or **open-end** credit, there is no fixed number of installments—the consumer continues paying until no balance is owed. With revolving loans, additional credit often is extended before the initial amount is paid off. Examples of open-end credit include most department store charge accounts and bank charge cards such as MasterCard and VISA.

Installment Loans

Installment loans, set up under closed-end credit, often are based on **add-on interest.** This means that interest is calculated by the simple interest formula $I = Prt$, and we simply "add on" this amount of interest to the principal borrowed to arrive at the total debt (or amount to be repaid).

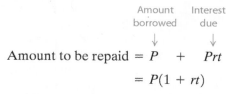

$$\text{Amount to be repaid} = P + Prt$$

$$= P(1 + rt)$$

The total debt is then equally divided among the payments (usually monthly) to be made over the t years.

Credit card debt among students has raised increasing concern in recent years among lawmakers, college officials, and consumer advocacy groups. As a result, hundreds of colleges have banned card marketers from campus, and new federal law brought significant new regulations effective in 2010.

A 2010 study by Sallie Mae (a college financing company) pegged average undergraduate credit card debt at $3,173. The National Center for Education Statistics reported that average total debt among graduating seniors (including credit cards and private and federal loans) was $27,803. (*Source:* www.thelantern.com, Ohio State University student newspaper)

‖ EXAMPLE 1 Repaying an Add-On Loan

Mary Kaye Leonard buys $5400 worth of furniture and appliances for her first apartment. She pays $1100 down and agrees to pay the balance at a 7% add-on rate for 2 years. Find

(a) the total amount to be repaid,

(b) the monthly payment, and

(c) the total cost of the purchases, including finance charges.

SOLUTION

(a) Amount to be financed = $5400 − $1100

$\qquad\qquad\qquad\qquad = \$4300$

Amount to be repaid $= P(1 + rt)$ Future value formula

$\qquad\qquad\qquad = \$4300(1 + 0.07 \cdot 2)$ Substitute known values.

$\qquad\qquad\qquad = \$4902$ Calculate.

(b) Monthly payment $= \dfrac{\$4902}{24}$ ⟵ Amount to be repaid

⟵ Number of payments

$= \$204.25$

Down payment   Loan repayment

(c) Total cost of purchases $= \$1100 \ + \ \$4902$

$= \$6002$

Mary Kaye will end up paying $6002, which is 11.1% more than the price tag total. ▮▮▮

Notice that the repayment amount in **Example 1,** $P(1 + rt)$, was the same as the final amount A in a savings account paying a simple interest rate r for t years. (See **Section 13.1.**) But in the case of savings, the bank keeps all of your money for the entire time period. In **Example 1,** Mary Kaye did not keep the full principal amount for the full time period. She repaid it in 24 monthly installments. The 7% add-on rate turns out to be equivalent to a much higher "true annual interest" rate.

Revolving Loans

With a typical department store account, or bank card, a credit limit is established initially and the consumer can make many purchases during a month (up to the credit limit). The required monthly payment can vary from a set minimum (which may depend on the account balance) up to the full balance.

For purchases made in a store or other retail location, the customer may authorize adding the purchase price to his or her charge account by signing on a paper "charge slip," or perhaps on an electronic signature pad. Authorization also can be given by telephone or over the Internet for mail orders and other expenditures.

At the end of each billing period (normally once a month), the customer receives an **itemized billing,** a statement listing purchases and cash advances, the total balance owed, the minimum payment required, and perhaps other account information. Any charges beyond cash advanced and cash prices of items purchased are called **finance charges.** Finance charges may include interest, an annual fee, credit insurance coverage, a time payment differential, or carrying charges.

Most revolving credit plans calculate finance charges by the **average daily balance method.** The average daily balance is the *weighted mean* (see **Section 12.2**) of the various amounts of credit utilized for different parts of the billing period, with the weighting factors being the number of days that each credit amount applied.

| **EXAMPLE 2** | Using the Average Daily Balance Method for Credit Card Charges |

The activity in Jessica Lasda's MasterCard account for one billing period is shown below. If the previous balance (on March 3) was $209.46, and the bank charges 1.3% per month on the average daily balance, find

(a) the average daily balance for the next billing (April 3),

(b) the finance charge to appear on the April 3 billing, and

(c) the account balance on April 3.

March 3	Billing date	
March 12	Payment	$50.00
March 17	Clothes	$28.46
March 20	Mail order	$31.22
April 1	Auto parts	$59.10

SEPTEMBER

30

Learning the following rhyme will help you in problems like the one found in **Example 2.**

Thirty days hath September, April, June, and November. All the rest have thirty-one, Save February which has twenty-eight days clear, And twenty-nine in each leap year.

SOLUTION

(a) First make a table that shows the beginning date of the billing period and the dates of all transactions in the billing period. Along with each of these, compute the running balance on that date.

Date	Running Balance
March 3	$209.46
March 12	$209.46 − $50 = $159.46
March 17	$159.46 + $28.46 = $187.92
March 20	$187.92 + $31.22 = $219.14
April 1	$219.14 + $59.10 = $278.24

Next, tabulate the running balance figures, along with the number of days until the balance changed. Multiply each balance amount by the number of days. The sum of these products gives the "sum of the daily balances."

Date	Running Balance	Number of Days Until Balance Changed	$\left(\begin{array}{c}\text{Running}\\\text{Balance}\end{array}\right) \cdot \left(\begin{array}{c}\text{Number}\\\text{of Days}\end{array}\right)$
March 3	$209.46	9	$1885.14
March 12	$159.46	5	$ 797.30
March 17	$187.92	3	$ 563.76
March 20	$219.14	12	$2629.68
April 1	$278.24	2	$ 556.48
		Totals: 31	$6432.36

$$\text{Average daily balance} = \frac{\text{Sum of daily balances}}{\text{Days in billing period}} = \frac{\$6432.36}{31} = \$207.50$$

Jessica will pay a finance charge based on the average daily balance of $207.50.

(b) The finance charge for the April 3 billing will be

$$1.3\% \text{ of } \$207.50 = 0.013 \cdot \$207.50 \quad {\scriptstyle 1.3\% = 1.3 \times 0.01 = 0.013}$$
$$= \$2.70.$$

(c) The account balance on the April 3 billing will be the latest running balance plus the finance charge.

$$\$278.24 + \$2.70 = \$280.94 \qquad ▮▮▮$$

Credit cards and other revolving loans are relatively expensive credit. The monthly rate of 1.3% in **Example 2** is typical and is equivalent to an annual rate of 15.6%. A single card (like VISA or MasterCard), however, can be a great convenience, as most all merchants accept it and it eliminates the need to carry cash or write checks.

A wise practice, if at all possible, is *not* to carry a balance from month to month, but to pay the entire new balance by the due date each month. Since purchases made during the month are not billed until the next billing date, and the payment due date may be 20 days or more after the billing date, items can often be charged on a card without actually paying for them for nearly two months. To obtain this form of "free credit," resist the temptation to buy more than can be paid for by the next payment date.

Other features of revolving accounts can be at least as important as interest. For example:

1. Is an annual fee charged? If so, how much is it?
2. Is a special "introductory" rate offered? If so, how long will it last?
3. Are there other incentives, such as rebates, credits toward certain purchases, "free" airline miles, or return of interest charges for long-time use?

13.2 EXERCISES

Round all monetary answers to the nearest cent unless directed otherwise. Assume that unless otherwise known, there are 12 months per year, 30 days per month, and 365 days per year

Financing an Appliance Purchase *Krishna Gil bought appliances costing $3450 at a store charging 8% add-on interest. She made a $500 down payment and agreed to monthly payments over two years.*

1. Find the total amount to be financed.

2. Find the total interest to be paid.

3. Find the total amount to be repaid.

4. Find the monthly payment.

5. Find the total cost, for appliances plus interest.

Financing a New Car Purchase *Suppose you want to buy a new car that costs $16,500. You have no cash—only your old car, which is worth $3000 as a trade-in.*

6. How much do you need to finance to buy the new car?

7. The dealer says the interest rate is 9% add-on for 3 years. Find the total interest.

8. Find the total amount to be repaid.

9. Find the monthly payment.

10. Find your total cost, for the new car plus interest.

In Exercises 11–16, use the add-on method of calculating interest to find the total interest and the monthly payment.

	Amount of Loan	Length of Loan	Interest Rate
11.	$4500	3 years	9%
12.	$2700	2 years	8%
13.	$ 750	18 months	7.4%
14.	$2450	30 months	9.2%
15.	$ 535	16 months	11.1%
16.	$ 798	29 months	10.3%

Work each problem.

17. **Finding the Monthly Payment for an Add-On Interest Furniture Loan** The Giordanos buy $8500 worth of furniture for their new home. They pay $3000 down. The store charges 10% add-on interest. The Giordanos will pay off the furniture in 30 monthly payments ($2\frac{1}{2}$ years). Find the monthly payment.

18. **Finding the Monthly Payment for an Add-On Interest Auto Loan** Find the monthly payment required to pay off an auto loan of $9780 over 3 years if the add-on interest rate is 9.3%.

19. **Finding the Monthly Payment for an Add-On Interest Home Electronics Loan** The total purchase price of a new home entertainment system is $14,240. If the down payment is $2900 and the balance is to be financed over 48 months at 10% add-on interest, what is the monthly payment?

20. **Finding the Monthly Payment for an Add-On Interest Loan** What are the monthly payments Donna De Simone pays on a loan of $1680 for a period of 10 months if 9% add-on interest is charged?

21. **Finding the Amount Borrowed in an Add-On Interest Car Loan** Joshua Eurich has misplaced the sales contract for his car and cannot remember the amount he originally financed. He does know that the add-on interest rate was 9.8% and the loan required a total of 48 monthly payments of $314.65 each. How much did Joshua borrow (to the nearest dollar)?

22. **Finding an Add-On Interest Rate** Susan Dratch is making monthly payments of $207.31 to pay off a $3\frac{1}{2}$ year loan for $6400. What is her add-on interest rate (to the nearest tenth of a percent)?

23. **Finding the Term of an Add-On Interest Loan** How long (in years) will it take Michael Garbin to pay off an $8000 loan with monthly payments of $172.44 if the add-on interest rate is 9.2%?

24. **Finding the Number of Payments of an Add-On Interest Loan** How many monthly payments must Jawann make on a $10,000 loan if he pays $417.92 a month and the add-on interest rate is 10.15%?

Finding Finance Charges *Find the finance charge for each charge account. Assume interest is calculated on the average daily balance of the account.*

	Average Daily Balance	Monthly Interest Rate
25.	$ 249.94	1.4%
26.	$ 350.75	1.5%
27.	$ 419.95	1.38%
28.	$ 450.21	1.26%
29.	$1073.40	1.425%
30.	$1320.42	1.375%

Finding Finance Charges and Account Balances Using the Average Daily Balance Method *For each credit card account, assume one month between billing dates (with the appropriate number of days) and interest of 1.3% per month on the average daily balance. Find* **(a)** *the average daily balance,* **(b)** *the monthly finance charge, and* **(c)** *the account balance for the next billing.*

31. Previous balance: $728.36

May 9	Billing date	
May 17	Payment	$200
May 30	Dinner	$ 46.11
June 3	Theater tickets	$ 64.50

32. Previous balance: $514.79

January 27	Billing date	
February 9	Candy	$11.08
February 13	Returns	$26.54
February 20	Payment	$59
February 25	Repairs	$71.19

33. Previous balance: $462.42

June 11	Billing date	
June 15	Returns	$106.45
June 20	Jewelry	$115.73
June 24	Car rental	$ 74.19
July 3	Payment	$115
July 6	Flowers	$ 68.49

34. Previous balance: $983.25

August 17	Billing date	
August 21	Mail order	$ 14.92
August 23	Returns	$ 25.41
August 27	Beverages	$ 31.82
August 31	Payment	$108
September 9	Returns	$ 71.14
September 11	Concert tickets	$110
September 14	Cash advance	$100

Finding Finance Charges *Assume no purchases or returns are made in Exercises 35 and 36.*

35. At the beginning of a 31-day billing period, Sandra Lazzaro has an unpaid balance of $720 on her credit card. Three days before the end of the billing period, she pays $600. Find her finance charge at 1.4% per month using the average daily balance method.

36. Anthony Marsella's VISA bill dated April 14 shows an unpaid balance of $1070. Five days before May 14, the end of the billing period, Anthony makes a payment of $900. Find his finance charge at 1.32% per month using the average daily balance method.

Analyzing a "90 Days Same as Cash" Offer *One version of the "90 Days Same as Cash" promotion was offered by a "major purchase card," which established an account charging 1.3167% interest per month on the account balance. Interest charges are added to the balance each month, becoming part of the balance on which interest is computed the next month.*

If you pay off the original purchase charge within 3 months, all interest charges are cancelled. Otherwise you are liable for all the interest. Suppose you purchase $2900 worth of carpeting under this plan.

37. Find the interest charge added to the account balance at the end of

  (a) the first month,

  (b) the second month,

  (c) the third month.

38. Suppose you pay off the account 1 day late (3 months plus 1 day). What total interest amount must you pay? (Do not include interest for the one extra day.)

39. Treating the 3 months as $\frac{1}{4}$ year, find the equivalent simple interest rate for this purchase (to the nearest tenth of a percent).

Various Charges of a Bank Card Account *Beth Johnson's bank card account charges 1.1% per month on the average daily balance as well as the following special fees:*

Cash advance fee:	2% (not less than $2 nor more than $10)
Late payment fee:	$15
Over-the-credit-limit fee:	$5

In the month of June, Beth's average daily balance was $1846. She was on vacation during the month and did not get her account payment in on time, which resulted in a late payment and resulted in charges accumulating to a sum above her credit limit. She also used her card for six $100 cash advances while on vacation. Find the following based on account transactions in that month.

40. interest charges to the account

41. special fees charged to the account

Write out your response to each of the following.

42. Is it possible to use a bank credit card for your purchases without paying anything for credit? If so, explain how.

43. Obtain applications or descriptive brochures for several different bank card programs, compare their features (including those in fine print), and explain which deal would be best for you, and why.

44. Research and explain the difference, if any, between a "credit" card and a "debit" card.

45. Many charge card offers include the option of purchasing credit insurance coverage, which would make your monthly payments if you became disabled and could not work and/or would pay off the account balance if you died. Find out the details on at least one such offer, and discuss why you would or would not accept it.

46. Make a list of "special incentives" offered by bank cards you are familiar with, and briefly describe the pros and cons of each one.

47. One bank offered a card with a "low introductory rate" of 5.9%, good through the end of the year. And furthermore, you could receive back a percentage (up to 100%!) of all interest you pay, as shown in the table.

Use your card for:	2 years	5 years	10 years	15 years	20 years
Get back:	10%	25%	50%	75%	100%

(As soon as you take a refund, the time clock starts over.) Because you can eventually claim all your interest payments back, is this card a good deal? Explain.

48. Recall a car-buying experience you have had, or visit a new-car dealer and interview a salesperson. Describe the procedure involved in purchasing a car on credit.

Comparing Bank Card Accounts *Dorothy Laymon is considering two bank card offers that are the same in all respects except for the following:*

> *Bank A charges no annual fee and charges monthly interest of 1.18% on the unpaid balance.*

> *Bank B charges a $30 annual fee and monthly interest of 1.01% on the unpaid balance.*

From her records, Dorothy has found that the unpaid balance she tends to carry from month to month is quite consistent and averages $900.

49. Estimate her total yearly cost to use the card if she chooses the card from

  (a) Bank A

  (b) Bank B.

50. Which card is her better choice?

13.3 TRUTH IN LENDING

Annual Percentage Rate (APR) • Unearned Interest

Annual Percentage Rate (APR)

The Consumer Credit Protection Act, which was passed in 1968, has commonly been known as the **Truth in Lending Act.** In this section we discuss two major issues addressed in the law:

1. How can we tell the true annual interest rate a lender is charging?

2. How much of the finance charge are we entitled to save if we decide to pay off a loan sooner than originally scheduled?

Question 1 above arose because lenders were computing and describing the interest they charged in several different ways. For example, how does 1.5% per month at Sears compare to 9% per year add-on interest at a furniture store? Truth in Lending standardized the so-called true annual interest rate, or **annual percentage rate,** commonly denoted **APR.** All sellers (car dealers, stores, banks, insurance agents, credit card companies, and the like) must disclose the APR when asked, and the written contract must state the APR in all cases. This enables a borrower to more easily compare the true costs of different loans.

Theoretically, a borrower should not need to calculate APR, but it is possible to verify the value stated by the lender. Since the formulas for finding APR are quite involved, it is easiest to use a table provided by the Federal Reserve Bank. We show an abbreviated version in **Table 5** on the next page. It identifies APR values to the nearest half percent from 8.0% to 14.0%, for loans requiring *monthly* payments and extending over the most common lengths for consumer loans from 6 to 60 months.

Table 5 relates the following three quantities.

APR = true annual interest rate (shown across the top)

  n = total number of scheduled monthly payments (shown down the left side)

  h = finance charge per $100 of amount financed (shown in the body of the table)

Table 5 Annual Percentage Rate (APR) for Monthly Payment Loans

Number of Monthly Payments (*n*)	Annual Percentage Rate (APR)												
	8.0%	8.5%	9.0%	9.5%	10.0%	10.5%	11.0%	11.5%	12.0%	12.5%	13.0%	13.5%	14.0%
	(Finance charge per $100 of amount financed) (*h*)												
6	$2.35	$2.49	$2.64	$2.79	$2.94	$3.08	$3.23	$3.38	$3.53	$3.68	$3.83	$3.97	$4.12
12	4.39	4.66	4.94	5.22	5.50	5.78	6.06	6.34	6.62	6.90	7.18	7.46	7.74
18	6.45	6.86	7.28	7.69	8.10	8.52	8.93	9.35	9.77	10.19	10.61	11.03	11.45
24	8.55	9.09	9.64	10.19	10.75	11.30	11.86	12.42	12.98	13.54	14.10	14.66	15.23
30	10.66	11.35	12.04	12.74	13.43	14.13	14.83	15.54	16.24	16.95	17.66	18.38	19.10
36	12.81	13.64	14.48	15.32	16.16	17.01	17.86	18.71	19.57	20.43	21.30	22.17	23.04
48	17.18	18.31	19.45	20.59	21.74	22.90	24.06	25.23	26.40	27.58	28.77	29.97	31.17
60	21.66	23.10	24.55	26.01	27.48	28.96	30.45	31.96	33.47	34.99	36.52	38.06	39.61

▮▮ EXAMPLE 1 Finding the APR for an Add-On Loan

Recall that Mary Kaye (in **Example 1** of **Section 13.2**) paid $1100 down on a $5400 purchase and agreed to pay the balance at a 7% add-on rate for 2 years. Find the APR for her loan.

SOLUTION

As shown previously, the total amount financed was

$$\underset{\substack{\uparrow \\ \text{Purchase price}}}{\$5400} - \underset{\substack{\uparrow \\ \text{Down payment}}}{\$1100} = \$4300.$$

The finance charge (interest) was

$$I = Prt = \$4300 \cdot 0.07 \cdot 2 = \$602.$$

Next find the finance charge per $100 of the amount financed. To do this, divide the finance charge by the amount financed, then multiply by $100.

$$\left(\begin{matrix}\text{Finance charge per} \\ \$100 \text{ financed}\end{matrix}\right) = \frac{\text{Finance charge}}{\text{Amount financed}} \cdot \$100$$

$$= \frac{\$602}{\$4300} \cdot \$100, \quad \text{or} \quad \$14$$

This amount, $14, represents *h*, the finance charge per $100 of the amount financed. Because the loan was to be paid over 24 months, look down to the "24 monthly payments" row of **Table 5** (*n* = 24). Then look across the table for the *h*-value closest to $14.00, which is $14.10. From that point, read up the column to find the APR, 13.0% (to the nearest half percent). In this case, a 7% add-on rate is equivalent to an APR of 13.0%. ▮▮▮

5400−1100	
	4300
4300*.07*2	
	602
(602/4300)*100	
	14

These are the computations required in the solution of **Example 1**.

▐▐   **EXAMPLE 2**   Finding the APR for a Car Loan

After a down payment on her new car, Yvette Freeman still owed $7454. She agreed to repay the balance in 48 monthly payments of $185 each. What is the APR on her loan?

SOLUTION

First find the finance charge.

Total payments · Amount financed

$$\text{Finance charge} = 48 \cdot \$185 - \$7454$$
$$= \$1426$$

> Multiply first. Then subtract.

Now find the finance charge per $100 financed as in **Example 1.**

$$\left(\begin{array}{c} \text{Finance charge per} \\ \$100 \text{ financed} \end{array} \right) = \frac{\text{Finance charge}}{\text{Amount financed}} \cdot \$100$$

$$= \frac{\$1426}{\$7454} \cdot \$100, \quad \text{or} \quad \$19.13$$

```
48*185−7454
              1426.00
(1426/7454)*100
                19.13
```

These are the computations required in the solution of **Example 2.**

Find the "48 payments" row of **Table 5**, read across to find the number closest to 19.13, which is 19.45. From there read up to find the APR, which is 9.0%.   ▓▓▓

Unearned Interest

Question 2 at the beginning of the section arises when a borrower decides to pay off an installment loan earlier than originally scheduled. In such a case, it turns out that the lender has not loaned as much money for as long as planned and so he has not really "earned" the full finance charge originally disclosed.

If a loan is paid off early, the amount by which the original finance charge is reduced is called the **unearned interest.** We will discuss two common methods of calculating unearned interest, the **actuarial method** and the **rule of 78.** The Truth in Lending Act requires that the method for calculating this refund (or reduction) of finance charge be disclosed at the time the loan is initiated. Whichever method is used, the borrower may not, in fact, save all the unearned interest, since the lender is entitled to impose an **early payment penalty** to recover certain costs. A lender's intention to impose such a penalty in case of early payment also must be disclosed at initiation of the loan.

Rights and responsibilities apply to all credit accounts, and the consumer should read all disclosures provided by the lender. *The Fair Credit Billing Act* and *The Fair Credit Reporting Act* regulate, among other things, procedures for billing and for disputing bills, and for providing and disputing personal information on consumers.

If you have ever applied for a charge account, a personal loan, insurance, or a job, then information about where you work and live, how you pay your bills, and whether you've been sued, arrested, or have filed for bankruptcy appears in the files of Consumer Reporting Agencies (CRAs), which sell that information to creditors, employers, insurers, and other businesses.

For more detailed information on these and many other consumer issues, you may want to consult the Web site www.consumeraction.gov.

> **Unearned Interest—Actuarial Method**
>
> For an installment loan requiring *monthly* payments, which is paid off earlier than originally scheduled, let
>
> R = regular monthly payment,
>
> k = remaining number of scheduled payments (*after* current payment), and
>
> h = finance charge per $100, corresponding to a loan with the same APR and k monthly payments.
>
> Then the **unearned interest, u,** is calculated as follows.
>
> $$u = kR \left(\frac{h}{\$100 + h} \right)$$

Once the unearned interest u is calculated (by any method), the amount required to pay off the loan early is easily found. It consists of the present regular payment due, plus k additional future payments, minus the unearned interest.

Payoff Amount

An installment loan requiring regular monthly payments R can be paid off early, along with the current payment. If the original loan had k additional payments scheduled (after the current payment), and the unearned interest is u, then, disregarding any possible prepayment penalty, the **payoff amount** is calculated as follows.

$$\text{Payoff amount} = (k + 1)R - u$$

▮▮ EXAMPLE 3   Finding the Early Payoff Amount by the Actuarial Method

Yvette Freeman got an unexpected pay raise and wanted to pay off her car loan of **Example 2** at the end of 3 years rather than paying for 4 years as originally agreed.

(a) Find the unearned interest (the amount she will save by retiring the loan early).

(b) Find the "payoff amount" (the amount required to pay off the loan at the end of 3 years).

SOLUTION

(a) From **Example 2,** recall that $R = \$185$ and APR $= 9.0\%$. The current payment is payment number 36, so $k = 48 - 36 = 12$. Use **Table 5**, with 12 payments and APR 9.0%, to obtain $h = \$4.94$. Then use the actuarial method formula.

$$u = 12 \cdot \$185\left(\frac{\$4.94}{\$100 + \$4.94}\right) = \$104.51$$

By this method, Yvette will save $104.51 in interest by retiring the loan early.

(b) The payoff amount is found by using the appropriate formula.

$$\text{Payoff amount} = (12 + 1)\$185 - \$104.51 = \$2300.49$$

The required payoff amount at the end of 3 years is $2300.49.   ▮▮▮

The actuarial method, because it is based on the APR value, probably is the better method. However, some lenders still use the second method, the **rule of 78.**

```
12*185(4.94/(100+4.94))
                  104.51
(12+1)*185−104.51
                 2300.49
```

These are the computations required in the solution of **Example 3.**

Unearned Interest—Rule of 78

For a closed-end loan requiring *monthly* payments, which is paid off earlier than originally scheduled, let

$F =$ original finance charge,
$n =$ number of payments originally scheduled, and
$k =$ remaining number of scheduled payments (*after* current payment).

Then the **unearned interest, u,** is calculated as follows.

$$u = \frac{k(k + 1)}{n(n + 1)} \cdot F$$

▮▮ **EXAMPLE 4** Finding the Early Payoff Amount by the Rule of 78

Again assume that the loan in **Example 2** is paid off at the time of the thirty-sixth monthly payment. This time however, instead of the actuarial method, use the rule of 78 to find

(a) the unearned interest, and **(b)** the payoff amount.

SOLUTION

(a) From **Example 2,** the original finance charge is $F = \$1426$. Also, $n = 48$ and $k = 12$.

$$u = \frac{12(12 + 1)}{48(48 + 1)} \cdot \$1426 = \$94.58 \quad \text{Rule of 78}$$

By the rule of 78, Yvette will save $94.58 in interest, which is $9.93 *less* than her savings by the actuarial method.

(b) Payoff amount $= (12 + 1)\$185 - \$94.58 = \$2310.42$

The payoff amount is $2310.42, which is $9.93 *more* than the payoff amount calculated by the actuarial method in **Example 3.** ▮▮▮

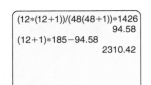

These are the computations required in the solution of **Example 4.**

When the rule of 78 was first introduced into financial law (by the Indiana legislature in 1935), loans were ordinarily written for 1 year or less, interest rates were relatively low, and loan amounts were less than they tend to be today. For these reasons the rule of 78 was acceptably accurate then. Today, however, with very accurate tables and/or calculators readily available, the rule of 78 is used much less often than previously.

Suppose we want to compute unearned interest accurately (so we don't trust the rule of 78), but the APR value, or the number of scheduled payments, or the number of remaining payments (or at least one of the three) is not included in **Table 5.** Then what? Actually, in the actuarial method, we can evaluate h (the finance charge per $100 financed) using the same formula that was used to generate **Table 5.**

Finance Charge per $100 Financed

If an installment loan requires n equal monthly payments and APR denotes the true annual interest rate for the loan (as a decimal), then h, the **finance charge per $100 financed,** is calculated as follows.

$$h = \frac{n \cdot \frac{\text{APR}}{12} \cdot \$100}{1 - \left(1 + \frac{\text{APR}}{12}\right)^{-n}} - \$100$$

▮▮ **EXAMPLE 5** Finding Unearned Interest and Early Payoff Amount

Mark Foss borrowed $4000 to pay for music equipment for his band. His loan contract states an APR of 9.8% and stipulates 28 monthly payments of $160.39 each. Mark decides to pay the loan in full at the time of his nineteenth scheduled payment. Find

(a) the unearned interest, and **(b)** the payoff amount.

SOLUTION

(a) First find h from the finance charge formula just given.

> **Remember to use the remaining number of payments, $28 - 19 = 9$, as the value of n.**

$$h = \frac{9\left(\frac{0.098}{12}\right)(\$100)}{1 - \left(1 + \frac{0.098}{12}\right)^{-9}} - \$100 = \$4.13$$

Next use the actuarial formula for unearned interest.

Regular monthly payment:	$R = \$160.39$
Remaining number of payments:	$k = 28 - 19 = 9$
Finance charge per 100:	$h = \$4.13$

$$u = 9 \cdot \$160.39 \cdot \frac{\$4.13}{\$100 + \$4.13} = \$57.25$$

The amount of interest Mark will save is $57.25.

(b)   Payoff amount $= (9 + 1)(\$160.39) - \$57.25 = \$1546.65.$

To pay off the loan at the time of his nineteenth scheduled payment, Mark must pay $1546.65.   ▮▮▮

(9*(.098/12)*100)/(1−(1+◂
◂.098/12)⁻⁹)−100
                 4.13
9*160.39*4.13/(100+4.13)
                 57.25

These are the computations required in the solution of **Example 5(a)**.

13.3 EXERCISES

Round all monetary answers to the nearest cent unless otherwise directed.

Finding True Annual Interest Rate *Find the APR (true annual interest rate), to the nearest half percent, for each loan.*

	Amount Financed	Finance Charge	Number of Monthly Payments
1.	$1000	$75	12
2.	$1700	$202	24
3.	$6600	$750	30
4.	$5900	$1150	48

Finding the Monthly Payment *Find the monthly payment for each loan.*

	Purchase Price	Down Payment	Finance Charge	Number of Monthly Payments
5.	$3000	$500	$250	24
6.	$4280	$450	$700	36
7.	$3950	$300	$800	48
8.	$8400	$2500	$1300	60

Finding True Annual Interest Rate *Find the APR (true annual interest rate), to the nearest half percent, for each loan.*

	Purchase Price	Down Payment	Add-on Interest Rate	Number of Payments
9.	$4190	$390	6%	12
10.	$3250	$750	7%	36
11.	$7480	$2200	5%	18
12.	$12,800	$4500	6%	48

Unearned Interest by the Actuarial Method *Each loan was paid in full before its due date.* **(a)** *Obtain the value of h from* **Table 5**. *Then* **(b)** *use the actuarial method to find the amount of unearned interest, and* **(c)** *find the payoff amount.*

	Regular Monthly Payment	APR	Remaining Number of Scheduled Payments After Payoff
13.	$346.70	11.0%	18
14.	$783.50	8.5%	12
15.	$595.80	9.5%	6
16.	$314.50	10.0%	24

Finding Finance Charge and True Annual Interest Rate   *For each loan, find* **(a)** *the finance charge, and* **(b)** *the APR.*

17. John Lanza financed a $1990 computer with 24 monthly payments of $91.50 each.

18. Jessica Luther bought a horse trailer for $5090. She paid $1240 down and paid the remainder at $152.70 per month for $2\frac{1}{2}$ years.

19. Brandon Hight still owed $2000 on his new garden tractor after the down payment. He agreed to pay monthly payments for 18 months at 6% add-on interest.

20. Alfred Juarez paid off a $15,000 car loan over 3 years with monthly payments of $487.54 each.

Comparing the Actuarial Method and the Rule of 78 for Unearned Interest *Each loan was paid off early. Find the unearned interest by* **(a)** *the actuarial method, and* **(b)** *the rule of 78.*

	Amount Financed	Regular Monthly Payments	Total Number of Payments Scheduled	Remaining Number of Scheduled Payments After Payoff
21.	$3310	$201.85	18	6
22.	$10,230	$277.00	48	12
23.	$29,850	$641.58	60	12
24.	$16,730	$539.82	36	18

Unearned Interest by the Actuarial Method   *Each loan was paid in full before its due date.* **(a)** *Obtain the value of h from the appropriate formula. Then* **(b)** *use the actuarial method to find the amount of unearned interest, and* **(c)** *find the payoff amount.*

	Regular Monthly Payment	APR	Remaining Number of Scheduled Payments After Payoff
25.	$212	8.6%	4
26.	$575	9.33%	8

Comparing Loan Choices *Laura Kennedy needs to borrow $5000 to pay for NBA season tickets for her family. She can borrow the amount from a finance company (at 6.5% add-on interest for 3 years) or from the credit union (36 monthly payments of $164.50 each). Use this information for Exercises 27–30.*

27. Find the APR (to the nearest half percent) for each loan and decide which one is Laura's better choice.

28. Laura takes the credit union loan. At the time of her thirtieth payment she pays it off. If the credit union uses the rule of 78 for computing unearned interest, how much will she save by paying in full now?

29. What would Laura save in interest if she paid in full at the time of the thirtieth payment and the credit union used the actuarial method for computing unearned interest?

30. Under the conditions of **Exercise 29,** what amount must Laura come up with to pay off her loan?

31. Describe why, in **Example 1,** the APR and the add-on rate differ. Which one is more legitimate? Why?

Approximating the APR of an Add-On Rate *To convert an add-on interest rate to its corresponding APR, some people recommend using the formula*

$$APR = \frac{2n}{n+1} \cdot r,$$

where r is add-on rate and n is total number of payments.

32. Apply the given formula to calculate the APR (to the nearest half percent) for the loan of **Example 1** ($r = 0.07, n = 24$).

33. Compare your APR value in **Exercise 32** to the value in **Example 1.** What do you conclude?

The Rule of 78 with Prepayment Penalty *A certain retailer's credit contract designates the rule of 78 for computing unearned interest and imposes a "prepayment penalty." In case of any payoff earlier than the due date, they will charge an additional 10% of the original finance charge. Find the least value of k (remaining payments after payoff) that would result in any net savings in each case.*

34. 24 payments originally scheduled

35. 36 payments originally scheduled

36. 48 payments originally scheduled

The actuarial method of computing unearned interest assumes that, throughout the life of the loan, the borrower is paying interest at the rate given by APR for money actually being used by the borrower. When contemplating complete payoff along with the current payment, think of k future payments as applying to a separate loan with the same APR and h being the finance charge per $100 of that loan. Refer to the following formula.

$$u = kR\left(\frac{h}{\$100 + h}\right)$$

37. Describe in words the quantity represented by

$$\frac{h}{\$100 + h}.$$

38. Describe in words the quantity represented by kR.

39. Explain why the product of the two quantities above represents unearned interest.

✎ *Write out your response to each exercise.*

40. Why might a lender be justified in imposing a prepayment penalty?

41. Discuss reasons that a borrower may want to pay off a loan early.

42. Find out what federal agency you can contact if you have questions about compliance with the Truth in Lending Act. (Any bank, or retailer's credit department, should be able to help you with this, or you could try a Web search.)

43. Study the table at the right, which pertains to a 12-month loan. The column-3 entries are designed so that they are in the same ratios as the column-2 entries but will add up to 1 because their denominators are all equal to

$$1 + 2 + 3 + 4 + 5 + \ldots + 12 = \frac{12 \cdot 13}{2} = 78.$$

(This is the origin of the term "rule of 78.")

Month	Fraction of Loan Principal Used by Borrower	Fraction of Finance Charge Owed
1	12/12	12/78
2	11/12	11/78
3	10/12	10/78
4	9/12	9/78
5	8/12	8/78
6	7/12	7/78
7	6/12	6/78
8	5/12	5/78
9	4/12	4/78
10	3/12	3/78
11	2/12	2/78
12	1/12	1/78
		78/78 = 1

Suppose the loan is paid in full after eight months. Use the table to determine the unearned fraction of the total finance charge.

44. Find the fraction of unearned interest of **Exercise 43** by using the rule of 78 formula.

13.4 THE COSTS AND ADVANTAGES OF HOME OWNERSHIP

Fixed-Rate Mortgages • Adjustable-Rate Mortgages • Closing Costs • Taxes, Insurance, and Maintenance

Fixed-Rate Mortgages

Heating a house is another cost that may get you involved with banks and interest rates after you finally get a roof over your head. The roof you see above does more than keep off the rain. It holds solar panels, part of the solar heating system in the building.

For many decades, home ownership has been considered a centerpiece of the "American dream." For most people, a home represents the largest purchase of their lifetime, and it is certainly worth careful consideration.

A loan for a substantial amount, extending over a lengthy time interval (typically up to 30 years), for the purpose of buying a home or other property or real estate, and for which the property is pledged as security for the loan, is called a **mortgage.** (In some areas, a mortgage may also be called a **deed of trust** or a **security deed.**) The time until final payoff is called the **term** of the mortgage. The portion of the purchase price of the home that the buyer pays initially is called the **down payment.** The **principal amount of the mortgage** (the amount borrowed) is found by subtracting the down payment from the purchase price.

With a **fixed-rate mortgage,** the interest rate will remain constant throughout the term, and the initial principal balance, together with interest due on the loan, is repaid to the lender through regular (constant) periodic (we assume monthly) payments. This is called **amortizing** the loan. The regular monthly payment needed to amortize a loan depends on the amount financed, the term of the loan, and the interest rate, according to the formula on the next page.

Regular Monthly Payment

The **regular monthly payment** required to repay a loan of P dollars, together with interest at an annual rate r, over a term of t years, is calculated as follows.

$$R = \frac{P\left(\frac{r}{12}\right)}{1 - \left(\frac{12}{12 + r}\right)^{12t}}$$

▌▌ **EXAMPLE 1** Using a Formula to Find a Monthly Mortgage Payment

Find the monthly payment necessary to amortize a $75,000 mortgage at 5.5% annual interest for 15 years.

SOLUTION

$$R = \frac{\$75{,}000\left(\frac{0.055}{12}\right)}{1 - \left(\frac{12}{12 + 0.055}\right)^{(12)(15)}} = \$612.81$$

▌▌▌

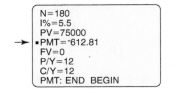

N=180
I%=5.5
PV=75000
→ ▪PMT=‑612.81
FV=0
P/Y=12
C/Y=12
PMT: END BEGIN

The arrow indicates a payment of $612.81, supporting the result of **Example 1**.

With a programmable or financial calculator, you can store the formula above and minimize the work. Another option is to use a tool such as **Table 6**, which gives payment values (per $1000 principal) for typical ranges of mortgage terms and interest rates. The entries in the table are given to five decimal places so that accuracy to the nearest cent can be obtained for most normal mortgage amounts.

Table 6 **Monthly Payments to Repay Principal and Interest on a $1000 Mortgage**

Annual rate (r)	Term of Mortgage (Years) (t)					
	5	10	15	20	25	30
4.0%	$18.41652	$10.12451	$7.39688	$6.05980	$5.27837	$4.77415
4.5%	18.64302	10.36384	7.64993	6.32649	5.55832	5.06685
5.0%	18.87123	10.60655	7.90794	6.59956	5.84590	5.36822
5.5%	19.10116	10.85263	8.17083	6.87887	6.14087	5.67789
6.0%	19.33280	11.10205	8.43857	7.16431	6.44301	5.99551
6.5%	19.56615	11.35480	8.71107	7.45573	6.75207	6.32068
7.0%	19.80120	11.61085	8.98828	7.75299	7.06779	6.65302
7.5%	20.03795	11.87018	9.27012	8.05593	7.38991	6.99215
8.0%	20.27639	12.13276	9.55652	8.36440	7.71816	7.33765
8.5%	20.51653	12.39857	9.84740	8.67823	8.05227	7.68913
9.0%	20.75836	12.66758	10.14267	8.99726	8.39196	8.04623
9.5%	21.00186	12.93976	10.44225	9.32131	8.73697	8.40854
10.0%	21.24704	13.21507	10.74605	9.65022	9.08701	8.77572
10.5%	21.49390	13.49350	11.05399	9.98380	9.44182	9.14739
11.0%	21.74242	13.77500	11.36597	10.32188	9.80113	9.52323
11.5%	21.99261	14.05954	11.68190	10.66430	10.16469	9.90291
12.0%	22.24445	14.34709	12.00168	11.01086	10.53224	10.28613

N=300.00
I%=6.50
PV=98000.00
→ ▪PMT=⁻661.70
FV=0.00
P/Y=12.00
C/Y=12.00
PMT: END BEGIN

Under the conditions of **Example 2,** the monthly payment is $661.70. Compare with the table method.

▌▌ **EXAMPLE 2** Using a Table to Find a Monthly Mortgage Payment

Find the monthly payment necessary to amortize a $98,000 at 6.5% for 25 years.

SOLUTION

In **Table 6,** read down to the 6.5% row and across to the column for 25 years, to find the entry 6.75207. As this is the monthly payment amount needed to amortize a loan of $1000, and our loan is for $98,000, our required monthly payment is

$$98 \cdot \$6.75207 = \$661.70.$$ ▰▰▰

So that the borrower pays interest only on the money actually owed in a month, interest on real-estate loans is computed on the decreasing balance of the loan. Each equal monthly payment is first applied toward interest for the previous month. The remainder of the payment is then applied toward reduction of the principal amount owed.

Payments in the early years of a real-estate loan are mostly interest (typically 80% or more); only a small amount goes toward reducing the principal. The amount of interest decreases each month, so that larger and larger amounts of the payment will apply to the principal. During the last years of the loan, most of the monthly payment is applied toward the principal. (See **Table 8** on **page 716.**)

Once the regular monthly payment has been determined, as in **Examples 1 and 2,** an **amortization schedule** (or **repayment schedule**) can be generated. It will show the allotment of payments for interest and principal, and the principal balance, for one or more months during the life of the loan. Tables showing these breakdowns are available from lenders or can be produced on a computer spreadsheet. The following steps demonstrate how the computations work.

Step 1 Interest for the month $= \left(\dfrac{\text{Old balance}}{\text{of principal}}\right)\left(\dfrac{\text{Annual}}{\text{interest rate}}\right)\left(\dfrac{1}{12}\,\text{year}\right)$

Step 2 Payment on principal $= \left(\dfrac{\text{Monthly}}{\text{payment}}\right) - \left(\dfrac{\text{Interest for}}{\text{the month}}\right)$

Step 3 New balance of principal $= \left(\dfrac{\text{Old balance}}{\text{of principal}}\right) - \left(\dfrac{\text{Payment on}}{\text{principal}}\right)$

This sequence of steps is done for the end of each month. The new balance obtained in Step 3 becomes the Step 1 old balance for the next month.

▌▌ **EXAMPLE 3** Preparing an Amortization Schedule

The Petersons have a $60,000 mortgage with a term of 30 years and a 4.5% interest rate. Prepare an amortization schedule for the first 2 months of their mortgage.

SOLUTION

First get the monthly payment. We use **Table 6.** (You could also use the formula.)

Mortgage amount in $1000s   Intersection of 4.5% row with 30-year column in **Table 6**
↓   ↓
$$R = 60 \quad \cdot \quad \$5.06685 = \$304.01$$

Now apply Steps 1–3.

Step 1 Interest for the month $= \$60,000(0.045)\left(\tfrac{1}{12}\right) = \$225$

Step 2 Payment on principal $= \$304.01 - \$225 = \$79.01$

Step 3 New balance of principal $= \$60,000 - \$79.01 = \$59,920.99$

The book, *You Can Do the Math,* by Ron Lipsman of the University of Maryland, is a practical resource for most aspects of **personal financial management.** The associated Web site, www.math.umd.edu/~rll/cgi-bin/finance.html, provides "calculators," with which you can easily input your own values to get the results of many different financial computations.

Starting with an old balance of $59,920.99, repeat the steps for the second month.

Step 1 Interest for the month $= \$59,920.99(0.045)\left(\frac{1}{12}\right) = \$224.70$

Step 2 Payment on principal $= \$304.01 - \$224.70 = \$79.31$

Step 3 New balance of principal $= \$59,920.99 - \$79.31 = \$59,841.68$

These calculations are summarized in **Table 7**.

Table 7 Amortization Schedule

Payment Number	Interest Payment	Principal Payment	Balance of Principal
			$60,000.00
1	$225.00	$79.01	$59,920.99
2	$224.70	$79.31	$59,841.68

▪▪▪

Prevailing mortgage interest rates have varied considerably over the years. **Table 8** shows portions of the amortization schedule for the Petersons' loan of **Example 3** and shows what the corresponding values would have been had their interest rate been 14.5%. (Rates that high have not been seen for many years.) Notice how much interest is involved in this home mortgage. At the (low) 4.5% rate, $49,444.03 in interest was paid along with the $60,000 principal. At a rate of 14.5%, the interest alone would total the huge sum of $204,504.88, which is about 3.4 times greater than the mortgage principal.

Table 8 Amortization Schedules for a $60,000, 30-Year Mortgage

	4.5% Interest Monthly Payment: $304.01				14.5% Interest Monthly Payment: $734.73		
Payment Number	Interest Payment	Principal Payment	Balance of Principal	Payment Number	Interest Payment	Principal Payment	Balance of Principal
Initially →			60,000.00	Initially →			60,000.00
1	225.00	79.01	59,920.99	1	725.00	9.73	59,990.27
2	224.70	79.31	59,841.68	2	724.88	9.85	59,980.42
3	224.41	79.60	59,762.08	3	724.76	9.97	59,970.45
12	221.68	82.33	59,032.06	12	723.63	11.11	59,875.11
60	205.47	98.54	54,694.75	60	714.96	19.77	59,149.53
175	152.47	151.54	40,506.65	175	656.05	78.69	54,214.82
176	151.90	152.11	40,354.54	176	655.10	79.64	54,135.18
236	113.60	190.41	30,102.65	236	571.02	163.72	47,092.76
237	112.88	191.13	29,911.52	237	569.04	165.70	46,927.07
240	110.73	193.28	29,333.83	240	562.96	171.78	46,417.87
303	59.33	244.68	15,575.66	303	368.65	366.09	30,142.47
304	58.41	245.60	15,330.05	304	364.22	370.51	29,771.96
359	2.27	301.74	302.88	359	17.44	717.29	725.96
360	1.14	302.88	0.00	360	8.77	725.96	0.00
Totals:	49,444.03	60,000.00		**Totals:**	204,504.88	60,000.00	

Adjustable-Rate Mortgages

The lending industry uses many variations on the basic fixed-rate mortgage. An **adjustable-rate mortgage (ARM),** also known as a **variable-rate mortgage (VRM),** generally starts out with a lower rate than similar fixed-rate loans, but the rate changes periodically, reflecting changes in prevailing rates.

Quantities Governing Adjustable-rate Mortgages (ARMS)

- **Adjustment period**—Time interval between rate adjustments (typically 1, 3, or 5 years)
- **Index**—Standard fluctuating average that is the basis for the new, adjusted rate (typically the 1-, 3-, or 5-year U.S. Treasury security rate, or a national or regional "cost of funds" index)
- **Margin**—Additional amount added to the index by the lender (typically a few percentage points)
- **Discount**—Amount by which the *initial* rate may be less than the sum of the index and the margin (typically arranged between the seller and the lender)
- **Interest rate cap**—Limits on (interest) rate increases
- **Periodic cap**—Limit on rate increase per adjustment period (typically about 1% per 6 months or 2% per year)
- **Overall cap**—Limit on rate increases over the life of the loan (typically about 5% total)
- **Payment cap**—Limit on how much the payment can increase at each adjustment
- **Negative amortization**—An increasing loan principal (perhaps caused by a payment cap preventing the payment from covering a higher interest rate)
- **Convertibility feature**—A contractual ability to convert to a fixed-rate mortgage (usually at certain designated points in time)
- **Prepayment penalty**—Charges imposed by the lender if payments are made early

---

EXAMPLE 4   Comparing ARM Payments Before and After a Rate Adjustment

---

We pay $20,000 down on a $180,000 house and take out a 1-year ARM for a 30-year term. The lender uses the 1-year Treasury index (at 4%) and a 2% margin.

(a) Find the monthly payment for the first year.

(b) Suppose that after a year the 1-year Treasury index has increased to 5.1%. Find the monthly payment for the second year.

SOLUTION

(a)

$$\text{Mortgage amount} = \underset{\uparrow}{\$180,000} - \underset{\uparrow}{\$20,000} = \$160,000$$
$$\quad\quad\quad\quad\quad\quad\quad\text{Cost of house}\quad\text{Down payment}$$

The first-year interest rate will be

$$\text{ARM interest rate} = \text{Index rate} + \text{Margin} = 4\% + 2\% = 6\%.$$

Now from **Table 6** (using 6% over 30 years) we obtain 5.99551.

$$\text{First-year monthly payment} = 160 \cdot \$5.99551 = \$959.28$$

(b) During the first year, a small amount of the mortgage principal has been paid, so in effect we will now have a new "mortgage amount." (Also, the term will now be 1 year less than the original term.) The amortization schedule for the first year (not shown here) yields a loan balance, after the twelfth monthly payment, of $158,035.19.

For the second year,

ARM interest rate = Index rate + Margin = 5.1% + 2% = 7.1%.

Because 7.1% is not included in **Table 6**, we use the regular monthly payment formula with the new mortgage balance and 29 years for the remaining term.

$$\text{Second-year monthly payment} = \frac{P\left(\frac{r}{12}\right)}{1 - \left(\frac{12}{12+r}\right)^{12t}} \qquad \text{Regular payment formula}$$

$$= \frac{\$158,035.19\left(\frac{0.071}{12}\right)}{1 - \left(\frac{12}{12+0.071}\right)^{(12)(29)}} \qquad \text{Substitute known values.}$$

$$= \$1072.74$$

The first ARM interest rate adjustment has caused the second-year monthly payment to rise to $1072.74, which is an increase of $113.46 over the initial monthly payment. ▐▐▐

A "seller buydown" occurs when the seller (a new-home builder, for example) pays the lender an amount in order to discount the buyer's loan. This reduces the initial rate and monthly payments, but it may be combined with higher initial fees or even an increase in the price of the house.

▐▐ **EXAMPLE 5** Discounting a Mortgage Rate

In **Example 4,** suppose that a seller buydown discounts our initial (first-year) rate by 1.5%. Find the first-year and second-year monthly payments.

SOLUTION

The 4% index rate is discounted to 2.5%. Adding the 2% margin yields a net first-year rate of 4.5% (rather than the 6% of **Example 4**), so the **Table 6** entry is 5.06685.

First-year monthly payment = 160($5.06685) = $810.70

The amortization schedule shows a balance at the end of the first year of $157,418.79. The discount now expires, and the index has increased to 5.1%, so for the second year,

ARM interest rate = Index rate + Margin = 5.1% + 2% = 7.1%.

(This is just as in **Example 4.**) Using the monthly payment formula, with $r = 7.1\%$ and $t = 29$,

$$\text{Second-year monthly payment} = \frac{\$157,418.79\left(\frac{0.071}{12}\right)}{1 - \left(\frac{12}{12+0.071}\right)^{(12)(29)}} \qquad \text{Substitute values in the monthly payment formula.}$$

$$= \$1068.55.$$

The initial monthly payment of $810.70 looks considerably better than the $959.28 of **Example 4,** but at the start of year two, monthly payments jump by $257.85. ▐▐▐

Making sure an ARM has adequate rate and payment caps will help avoid "payment shock." It is also wise to have convertibility and no prepayment penalty.

Closing Costs

Apart from principal and interest payments, buying a home involves a variety of one-time expenses called **closing costs,** or **settlement charges,** which are imposed when the loan is finalized (at "closing"). A buyer is entitled to a "good faith estimate" of these costs from the lender and, if desired, may shop for alternative providers of settlement services. Typical closing costs are illustrated in the following example.

EXAMPLE 6   Computing Total Closing Costs

For a $58,000 mortgage, the borrower was charged the following closing costs.

Loan origination fee (1% of mortgage amount)	$____
Broker loan fee	1455
Lender document and underwriting fees	375
Lender tax and wire fees	205
Fee to title company	200
Title insurance fee	302
Title reconveyance fee	65
Document recording fees	35

Compute the total closing costs for this mortgage.

SOLUTION

"Loan origination fees" are commonly referred to as **points**. Each "point" amounts to 1% of the mortgage amount. By imposing points, the lender can effectively raise the interest rate without raising monthly payments (because points are normally paid at closing rather than over the life of the loan). In this case, "one point" translates to $580. Adding this to the other amounts listed gives total closing costs of $3217.   ■■■

As there is considerable potential for abuse in the area of closing costs, Truth in Lending regulations require the lender to provide clarifying information, including the APR for the loan. The APR, the cost of the loan as a yearly rate, will probably be higher than the stated interest rate since it must reflect all points and other fees paid directly for credit as well as the actual interest.

Taxes, Insurance, and Maintenance

The primary financial considerations for most new homeowners are the following.

1. Accumulating the down payment
2. Having sufficient cash and income to qualify for the loan
3. Making the mortgage payments

Three additional ongoing expenses are

taxes, insurance, and maintenance,

all of which should be anticipated realistically. They can be significant.

Property taxes are collected by a county or other local government. Depending on location and the home value, they can range up to several thousand dollars annually. An advantage is that property taxes and mortgage interest are income tax deductible. Therefore, money expended for those items will decrease income taxes. This is one way that the government, through the tax code, encourages home ownership.

∎∎ **EXAMPLE 7** Taking Taxes into Account in Home Ownership

Darryl Graves is in a 30% combined state and federal income tax bracket. He has calculated that he can afford a net average monthly expenditure of $1400 for a home. Can he afford the home of his dreams, which would require a 20-year, $205,000 fixed-rate mortgage at 6% plus $1920 in annual property taxes?

SOLUTION

Let's "do the math."

$$\begin{array}{cc} \text{Mortgage amount} & \text{Value from} \\ \text{in \$1000s} & \textbf{Table 6} \\ \downarrow & \downarrow \end{array}$$

$$\text{Regular monthly mortgage payment} = 205 \quad \cdot \quad \$7.16431$$
$$\approx \$1469$$

$$\text{Monthly property taxes} = \frac{\$1920}{12} \begin{array}{l} \leftarrow \text{Annual taxes} \\ \leftarrow \text{Months per year} \end{array}$$
$$= \$160$$

$$\begin{array}{cc} \text{Mortgage payment} & \text{Property taxes} \\ \downarrow & \downarrow \end{array}$$
$$\text{Total monthly expense} = \$1469 \quad + \quad \$160$$
$$= \$1629$$

Because $1629 > $1400, it seems that Darryl cannot afford this home. But wait—remember that mortgage interest and property taxes are both income tax deductible. Let's consider further.

$$\text{Monthly interest} = \$205{,}000\,(0.06)\left(\frac{1}{12}\right) \quad \text{Interest} = Prt$$
$$= \$1025$$

Of the $1469 mortgage payment, $1025 would be interest (initially).

$$\begin{array}{cc} \text{Mortgage interest} & \text{Property tax} \\ \downarrow & \downarrow \end{array}$$
$$\text{Monthly deductible expenses} = \$1025 \quad + \quad \$160$$
$$= \$1185$$

$$\begin{array}{cc} \text{Deductible expense} & \text{Tax bracket} \\ \downarrow & \downarrow \end{array}$$
$$\text{Monthly income tax savings} = \$1185 \quad \cdot \quad 30\%$$
$$\approx \$356$$

$$\begin{array}{cc} \text{Gross cost} & \text{Tax savings} \\ \downarrow & \downarrow \end{array}$$
$$\text{Net monthly cost of home} = \$1629 \quad - \quad \$356$$
$$= \$1273$$

By considering the effect of taxes, we see that the net monthly cost, $1273, is indeed within Darryl's $1400 affordability limit. ∎∎∎

Homeowner's insurance usually covers losses due to fire, storm damage, and other casualties. Some types, such as earthquake or hurricane coverage, could be unavailable or very expensive, depending on location. Also, all homes require **maintenance,** but these costs can vary greatly, depending mainly on the size, construction type, age, and condition of the home. These expenses are necessary in order to protect the home investment. They are not generally tax deductible.

Government-backed mortgages, including FHA (Federal Housing Administration) and VA (Veterans Administration) loans, carry a government guarantee to protect the lender in case the borrower fails to repay the loan. Those who do not qualify for these loans, and obtain a conventional loan instead, usually are required to buy private mortgage insurance (PMI) as part of the loan package.

This feature can be a surprise to first-time home purchasers. It was introduced to protect lenders but indirectly protects the buyers, who may lose a bundle if some catastrophe makes it impossible to make the payments.

Over the second half of the twentieth century the amount of credit life insurance in force (for the purpose of covering consumer debt) increased by over 500 times, while group life insurance increased by only about 200 times, ordinary life insurance increased by about 60 times, and industrial life insurance actually decreased. (*Source:* American Council of Life Insurance.)

EXAMPLE 8 Including Insurance and Maintenance in Home Costs

In moving ahead with his home purchase, Darryl (**Example 7**) estimates that homeowner's insurance will be about $550 per year, and that maintenance will be about $650 per year. Will these additional expenses mean that he cannot afford the home?

SOLUTION

These items carry no tax advantage (they are not deductible), so the added monthly expense is simply

$$\text{Monthly insurance and maintenance expense} = \frac{\$550 + \$650}{12} = \$100.$$

With insurance and maintenance included, we obtain

$$\text{Adjusted monthly expense} = \$1273 + \$100 = \$1373,$$

which is still less than $1400. Darryl can still afford the purchase. ▮▮▮

Payments for property taxes and homeowner's insurance are commonly made from a **reserve account** (also called an **escrow,** or **impound, account**) maintained by the mortgage lender. The borrower must pay enough each month, along with amortization costs, so that the reserve account will be sufficient to make the payments when they come due. (In some cases, the homeowner pays taxes directly to the taxing authority and insurance premiums directly to an insurance company, totally separate from mortgage payments to the lender.)

Examples 7 and 8 raise some reasonable questions.

1. Is it wise to buy a house close to your spending limit, in light of future uncertainties?

2. What about the fact that the interest portion of mortgage payments, and therefore the tax savings, will decrease over time?

3. Won't taxes, insurance, and maintenance costs likely increase over time, making it more difficult to keep up the payments?

Some possible responses follow.

1. Darryl may have built in sufficient leeway when he decided on his $1400 per month allowance.

2. **(a)** Look again at **Table 8** to see how slowly the interest portion drops.
   (b) Most people find that their income over time increases faster than expenses for a home that carries a fixed-rate mortgage. (A variable-rate mortgage is more risky and should have its initial rate locked in for as long as possible.)
   (c) Prevailing interest rates rise and fall over time. While rising rates will not affect a fixed-rate mortgage, falling rates may offer the opportunity to reduce mortgage expenses by refinancing. (See the margin note on refinancing for guidelines.)

3. Here again, increases in income will probably keep pace. While most things, including personal income, tend to follow inflation, the fixed-rate mortgage insures that mortgage amortization, a major item, will stay constant.

Round all monetary answers to the nearest cent unless directed otherwise.

Monthly Payment on a Fixed-Rate Mortgage *Find the monthly payment needed to amortize principal and interest for each fixed-rate mortgage. You can use either the regular monthly payment formula or* **Table 6**, *as appropriate.*

	Loan Amount	Interest Rate	Term			Loan Amount	Interest Rate	Term
1.	$70,000	10.0%	20 years	**5.**		$227,750	12.5%	25 years
2.	$50,000	11.0%	15 years	**6.**		$95,450	15.5%	5 years
3.	$57,300	8.7%	25 years	**7.**		$132,500	7.6%	22 years
4.	$85,000	7.9%	30 years	**8.**		$205,000	5.5%	10 years

Amortization of a Fixed-Rate Mortgage *Complete the first one or two months (as required) of each amortization schedule for a fixed-rate mortgage.*

9. Mortgage: $58,500
Interest rate: 10.0%
Term of loan: 30 years

Amortization Schedule

Payment Number	Total Payment	Interest Payment	Principal Payment	Balance of Principal
1	**(a)** _____	**(b)** _____	**(c)** _____	**(d)** _____

10. Mortgage: $87,000
Interest rate: 8.5%
Term of loan: 20 years

Amortization Schedule

Payment Number	Total Payment	Interest Payment	Principal Payment	Balance of Principal
1	**(a)** _____	**(b)** _____	**(c)** _____	**(d)** _____

11. Mortgage: $143,200
Interest rate: 6.5%
Term of loan: 15 years

Amortization Schedule

Payment Number	Total Payment	Interest Payment	Principal Payment	Balance of Principal
1	**(a)** _____	**(b)** _____	**(c)** _____	**(d)** _____
2	**(e)** _____	**(f)** _____	**(g)** _____	**(h)** _____

12. Mortgage: $124,750
Interest rate: 9%
Term of loan: 25 years

Amortization Schedule

Payment Number	Total Payment	Interest Payment	Principal Payment	Balance of Principal
1	**(a)** _____	**(b)** _____	**(c)** _____	**(d)** _____
2	**(e)** _____	**(f)** _____	**(g)** _____	**(h)** _____

13. Mortgage: $113,650
Interest rate: 8.2%
Term of loan: 10 years

Amortization Schedule

Payment Number	Total Payment	Interest Payment	Principal Payment	Balance of Principal
1	**(a)** _____	**(b)** _____	**(c)** _____	**(d)** _____
2	**(e)** _____	**(f)** _____	**(g)** _____	**(h)** _____

14. Mortgage: $150,000
Interest rate: 6.25%
Term of loan: 16 years

Amortization Schedule

Payment Number	Total Payment	Interest Payment	Principal Payment	Balance of Principal
1	(a) _____	(b) _____	(c) _____	(d) _____
2	(e) _____	(f) _____	(g) _____	(h) _____

Finding Monthly Mortgage Payments *Find the total monthly payment, including taxes and insurance.*

	Mortgage	Interest Rate	Term of Loan	Annual Taxes	Annual Insurance
15.	$ 62,300	7%	20 years	$610	$220
16.	$ 51,800	10%	25 years	$570	$145
17.	$ 89,560	6.5%	10 years	$915	$409
18.	$ 72,890	5.5%	15 years	$1850	$545
19.	$115,400	8.8%	20 years	$1295.16	$444.22
20.	$128,100	11.3%	30 years	$1476.53	$565.77

Comparing Total Principal and Interest on a Mortgage *Suppose $140,000 is owed on a house. The monthly payment for principal and interest at 8.5% for 30 years is* $140 \cdot \$7.68913 = \$1076.48$.

21. How many monthly payments will be made over the 30-year period?

22. What is the total amount that will be paid for principal and interest?

23. The total interest charged is the total amount paid minus the amount financed. What is the total interest?

24. Which is more—the amount financed or the total interest paid? By how much?

Long-Term Effect of Interest Rates *You may remember seeing home mortgage interest rates fluctuate widely in a period of not too many years. The following exercises show the effect of changing rates. Refer to* **Table 8**, *which compared the amortization of a $60,000, 30-year mortgage for rates of 4.5% and 14.5%. Give values of each of the following for* **(a)** *a 4.5% rate, and* **(b)** *a 14.5% rate.*

25. monthly payments

26. percentage of first monthly payment that is principal

27. balance of principal after 1 year

28. balance of principal after 20 years

29. the first monthly payment that includes more toward principal than toward interest

30. amount of interest included in final monthly payment of mortgage

The Effect of the Term on Total Amount Paid *Suppose a $60,000 mortgage is to be amortized at 7.5% interest. Find the total amount of interest that would be paid for each term.*

31. 10 years   **32.** 20 years   **33.** 30 years   **34.** 40 years

The Effect of Adjustable Rates on the Monthly Payment *For each adjustable-rate mortgage, find* **(a)** *the initial monthly payment,* **(b)** *the monthly payment for the second adjustment period, and* **(c)** *the change in monthly payment at the first adjustment.*

	Beginning Balance	Term	Initial Index Rate	Margin	Adjustment Period	Adjusted Index Rate	Adjusted Balance	
35.	$75,000	20 years	6.5%	2.5%	1 year	8.0%	$73,595.52	*(The "adjusted balance" is the principal balance at the time of the first rate adjustment. Assume no caps apply.)*
36.	$44,500	30 years	7.2%	2.75%	3 years	6.6%	$43,669.14	

The Effect of Rate Caps on Adjustable-Rate Mortgages *James Kinchen has a 1-year ARM for $50,000 over a 20-year term. The margin is 2% and the index rate starts out at 7.5% and increases to 10.0% at the first adjustment. The balance of principal at the end of the first year is $49,119.48. The ARM includes a periodic rate cap of 2% per adjustment period. (Use this information for Exercises 37–40.)*

37. Find **(a)** the interest owed and **(b)** the monthly payment due for the first month of the first year.

38. Find **(a)** the interest owed and **(b)** the monthly payment due for the first month of the second year.

39. What is the monthly payment adjustment at the end of the first year?

40. If the index rate has dropped slightly at the end of the second year, will the third-year monthly payments necessarily drop? Why or why not?

Closing Costs of a Mortgage *For Exercises 41–44, refer to the following list of closing costs for the purchase of a $175,000 house requiring a 20% down payment, and find each requested amount.*

Title insurance premium	$240
Document recording fee	30
Loan fee (two points)	___
Appraisal fee	225
Prorated property taxes	685
Prorated fire insurance premium	295

41. the mortgage amount

42. the loan fee

43. the total closing costs

44. the total amount of cash required of the buyer at closing (including down payment)

Consider the scenario of **Example 7.** *Recalling that mortgage interest is income tax deductible, find (to the nearest dollar) the additional initial net monthly savings resulting from each strategy. (In each case, only the designated item changes. All other features remain the same.)*

45. Change the mortgage term from 20 years to 30 years.

46. Change the mortgage from fixed at 6% to an ARM with an initial rate of 5%.

For each of Exercises 47–50, find all of the following quantities for a $200,000 fixed-rate mortgage. (Give answers to the nearest dollar.)

(a) *Monthly mortgage payment (principal and interest)*

(b) *Monthly house payment (including property taxes and insurance)*

(c) *Initial monthly interest*

(d) *Income tax deductible portion of initial house payment*

(e) *Net initial monthly cost for the home (considering tax savings)*

Term of Mortgage	Interest Rate	Annual Property Tax	Annual Insurance	Owner's Income Tax Bracket
47. 15 years	5.5%	$960	$480	20%
48. 20 years	6.0%	$840	$420	25%
49. 10 years	6.5%	$1092	$540	30%
50. 30 years	7.5%	$1260	$600	40%

On the basis of material in this section, or your own research, give brief written responses to each problem.

51. Give other ways Darryl (**Examples 7 and 8**) could possibly decrease the initial net monthly payments for his home.

52. Suppose your ARM allows conversion to a fixed-rate loan at each of the first five adjustment dates. Describe circumstances under which you would want to convert.

53. Describe each type of mortgage.

Graduated payment

Balloon payment

Interest-only

Option ARM ("neg-am")

54. Should a home buyer always pay the smallest down payment that will be accepted? Explain.

55. Should a borrower always choose the shortest term available in order to minimize the total interest expense? Explain.

56. Under what conditions would an ARM probably be a better choice than a fixed-rate mortgage?

57. Why are second-year monthly payments (slightly) less in **Example 5** than in **Example 4** even though the term, 29 years, and the interest rate, 7.1%, are the same in both cases?

58. Do you think that the discount in **Example 5** actually makes the overall cost of the mortgage less? Explain.

59. Discuss the term "payment shock" mentioned at the end of **Example 5.**

60. Find out what is meant by each term and describe some of the features of each.

FHA-backed mortgage

VA-backed mortgage

Conventional mortgage

EXTENSION Ponzi Schemes and Other Investment Frauds*

Geometric Sequences • Pyramid Schemes • Ponzi Schemes

Geometric Sequences In a **geometric sequence** (first seen in **Chapter 1**), each term after the first is generated by multiplying the previous term by the **common ratio,** a number remaining constant throughout the sequence. For example, a geometric sequence with first term 3 and common ratio 2 starts out as follows:

$$3, 6, 12, 24, 48, 96, \ldots .$$

Sources: www.usatoday.com, www.moneymorning.com, www.nytimes.com, www.wikipedia.org

In general, if the first term is denoted a, the common ratio is denoted r, and there are n terms altogether, then the complete sequence is

$$a, ar, ar^2, ar^3, \ldots, ar^{n-1}.$$

(Verify by inductive reasoning that the nth term really is ar^{n-1}.)

The sum of all n terms of the geometric sequence above can be written

$$S = a + ar + ar^2 + \cdots + ar^{n-2} + ar^{n-1}.$$

Multiply both sides of this equation by r:

$$Sr = ar + ar^2 + ar^3 + \cdots + ar^{n-1} + ar^n.$$

Now position these two equations, one below the other, and subtract as follows.

$$
\begin{array}{llllll}
S = a & + ar & + ar^2 & + \cdots + ar^{n-2} & + ar^{n-1} \\
Sr = ar & + ar^2 & + ar^3 & + \cdots + ar^{n-1} & + ar^n \\
\hline
S - Sr = (a - ar) + (ar - ar^2) + (ar^2 - ar^3) + \cdots + (ar^{n-2} - ar^{n-1}) + (ar^{n-1} - ar^n)
\end{array}
$$

Now we can rearrange and regroup the terms on the right to obtain the following.

$$S - Sr = a + (ar - ar) + (ar^2 - ar^2) + \cdots + (ar^{n-1} - ar^{n-1}) - ar^n$$
$$= a + 0 + 0 + \cdots + 0 - ar^n$$

Notice that all terms on the right, except a and $-ar^n$, were arranged in pairs to cancel out. So we get the following.

$$S - Sr = a - ar^n$$
$$S(1 - r) = a(1 - r^n) \quad \text{Factor both sides.}$$
$$S = \frac{a(1 - r^n)}{1 - r} \quad \text{Solve for the sum } S.$$

The Sum of a Geometric Sequence

If a geometric sequence has first term a and common ratio r, and has n terms altogether, then the sum of all n terms is calculated as follows.

$$S = \frac{a(1 - r^n)}{1 - r}$$

The ability to recognize a geometric sequence and to sum its terms is very helpful in many applications, including detecting investment fraud.

Pyramid Schemes Most everyone has been invited, through email or otherwise, to pass on some message to two (or more) other people. Sometimes it is an innocent "chain letter." But if it involves sending money to someone, it is likely a **pyramid scheme.**

▐▐ **EXAMPLE 1** Analyzing Payoffs in a Pyramid Scheme

You receive a letter with a list of three names, along with the following instructions.

1. Send $1 to the top name on the list.

2. Remove that name and move the other two names up on the list.

3. Add your own name at the bottom of the list.

4. Send the same letter, with the new list, to two other people.

Suppose you decide to participate (become a member), both of your two recruits also participate, all of their four recruits participate, and all of their eight recruits participate. We call this the "each one recruits two" model. (It is also known, classically, as the 8-ball model.) You and the next three levels of participation are illustrated in **Figure 1**.

Level	Participation Chart	Number of Members
1	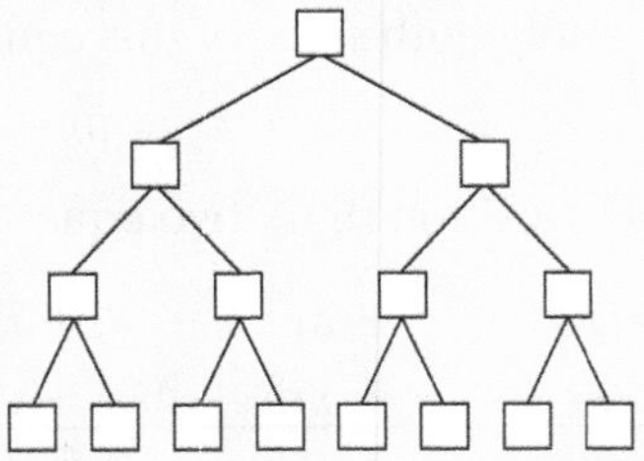	1
2		2
3		4
4		8

Participation chart for an 8-ball pyramid scheme

Figure 1

(a) With you and all your downstream recruits, how many members are there?

(b) How much money will you receive?

(c) What is your profit?

SOLUTION

(a) $1 + 2 + 4 + 8 = 15$

(b) You receive \$1 from each level-4 member, for a total of \$8.

Income Cost
↓   ↓

(c) Profit = \$8 − \$1 = \$7 (minus two envelopes and two postage stamps)   ■■■

Observe, from **Figure 1** of **Example 1,** that, beginning with one member at level 1, the number of members in a given level is double the number of members in the previous level.

■■ **EXAMPLE 2**   Finding the Number of Members in a Pyramid Scheme

For each of the following numbers of levels, find the total number of members, from level 1 up to and including the given level. Use inductive reasoning in part (c).

(a) 4   **(b)** 7   **(c)** N

SOLUTION

(a) $1 + 2 + 4 + 8 = 15$ (or, $2^4 - 1$)

(b) $1 + 2 + 4 + 8 + 16 + 32 + 64 = 127$ (or, $2^7 - 1$)

(c) Assuming the pattern observed in parts (a) and (b) holds, the total number of members from level 1 through level N, inclusive, would be

$$2^N - 1.$$ ■■■

The expression, $2^N - 1$, of **Example 2(c)** was derived inductively, but can also be deduced using the formula for the sum of a geometric sequence given earlier.

| **EXAMPLE 3** | Deducing the Number of Members in a Pyramid Scheme |

Use deductive reasoning to *prove* that $2^N - 1$ is the total number of members in an "each one recruits two" pyramid with N levels.

SOLUTION

The number of members in the N levels are 1, 2, 4, 8, . . . , and 2^{N-1}. Their sum is the sum of a geometric sequence with

first term $a = 1$, common ratio $r = 2$, number of terms $n = N$.

So the sum is found as follows.

$$S = \frac{a(1 - r^n)}{1 - r} \qquad \text{Sum formula}$$

$$= \frac{1(1 - 2^N)}{1 - 2} \qquad \text{Substitute } a = 1, r = 2, n = N.$$

$$= \frac{2^N - 1}{2 - 1} \qquad \text{Multiply numerator and denominator by } -1.$$

$$= 2^N - 1 \qquad \text{Simplify.} \qquad\qquad ▪▪▪$$

Table 11 summarizes the various values involved as the pyramid builds downward.

Table 11	The Numbers in an "Each One Recruits Two" Pyramid Scheme	
Level Number n	**Number of Members in Level** n	**Total Number of Members in all Levels Up To and Including Level** n
1	$1 = 2^{1-1}$	$1 = 2^1 - 1$
2	$2 = 2^{2-1}$	$1 + 2 = 3 = 2^2 - 1$
3	$4 = 2^{3-1}$	$1 + 2 + 4 = 7 = 2^3 - 1$
4	$8 = 2^{4-1}$	$1 + 2 + 4 + 8 = 15 = 2^4 - 1$
5	$16 = 2^{5-1}$	$1 + 2 + 4 + 8 + 16 = 31 = 2^5 - 1$
.	.	.
.	.	.
.	.	.
N	2^{N-1}	$1 + 2 + 4 + 8 + 16 + \ldots + 2^{N-1} = 2^N - 1$

The pyramid must keep building downward indefinitely if all the members are to receive their profit. But a pyramid with, say, 20 levels requires

$$2^{20} - 1 = 1{,}048{,}575 \text{ members.}$$

And just 33 levels would involve

$$2^{33} - 1 = 8{,}589{,}934{,}591 \text{ members,}$$

which exceeds the population of the world. Therefore, every pyramid scheme must eventually fail, and most likely long before achieving 33 levels. And when it fails, the members in the last three levels will not get paid. This means that if failure occurs after N levels, then the number of members who lose their money is

$$2^{N-1} + 2^{N-2} + 2^{N-3}.$$

The fact that a **pyramid scheme** profits relatively few at the expense of many, most of whom don't really understand how it works, is part of why these schemes are illegal in the United States (and many other countries). If participants are provided goods or services comparable in value to their "entry fee," then the combination of promotion (recruiting) and selling (goods or services) can become (technically) a legal multi-level marketing (MLM) plan. But there is a fine line between legitimate business and fraud. The legal distinction rests on whether the recruitment exists to promote the product or the product exists to promote the recruitment.

We can now express the fraction of all participants who will lose money as follows.

$$\text{Fraction who lose} = \frac{2^{N-1} + 2^{N-2} + 2^{N-3}}{2^N - 1} \quad \begin{array}{l} \longleftarrow \text{Number who lose} \\ \longleftarrow \text{Number who participate} \end{array}$$

$$= \frac{2^{N-3}(2^2 + 2 + 1)}{2^N - 1} \qquad \text{Factor } 2^{N-3} \text{ from numerator.}$$

$$= \frac{2^{N-3}(7)}{2^N - 1} \qquad \text{Add.}$$

Now deleting the −1 from the denominator makes the denominator (slightly) greater, hence the overall fraction lesser. So we can state the following.

$$\text{Fraction who lose} > \frac{2^{N-3}(7)}{2^N}$$

$$= \frac{7}{2^{N-(N-3)}} \qquad \text{Apply rule of exponents.}$$

$$= \frac{7}{2^3} \qquad \text{Simplify exponent.}$$

$$= \frac{7}{8} \qquad \text{Simplify.}$$

No matter how many levels succeed, everyone in the last three levels loses, and these are more than $\frac{7}{8}$ of all participants.

Ponzi Schemes Pyramid schemes are relatively straightforward, though promoters tend to avoid the use of terms like "pyramid" and "scheme." **Ponzi schemes,** on the other hand, come in many varieties and usually involve financial instruments (like "derivatives") and terms (like "alternative asset classes") that can confuse even experienced investors. These scams always pretend to offer real investment returns of one kind or another, but in fact an investor's "returns" come only from his own money or from the deposits of later investors.

The name comes from the years following World War I, when an Italian immigrant, Charles Ponzi, realized that non-uniform international currency exchange rates and other factors made it possible, theoretically, to profit by buying postal reply coupons in Italy and exchanging them for U.S. stamps. There was a money-making potential in this, but over time, Ponzi solicited and received far more deposits ("investments") than could be placed in that market. His operation, mostly in the New England area, drew in more and more participants as he returned profits to early investors out of the deposits of later investors.

Charles Ponzi, like many other scheme operators who followed him, possessed personal attributes, including charm and salesmanship, that allowed him to accummulate much more than what was required just to pay out the profits demanded. As he seemed to be making good on his promises, most investors left both principal and profit to increase in the plan. On some days, he had thousands of zealous investors lined up to give him their money.

It is important, for the success of a Ponzi scheme, that the illusion of successful investment returns be maintained early on to build confidence and attract an ever-growing number of investors. And it helps if the true details of the operation are obscure and difficult or impossible to actually verify.

▌▌ **EXAMPLE 4** Finding the Minimum Number of Investors Needed to Support a Ponzi Scheme

Ponzi promised investors a 50% profit within 45 days or a 100% profit within 90 days. Assuming that he started the year with one investor, who put in $1000, and that all investors always withdrew their 90-day profit and left their principal with Ponzi, how many investors would he need within a year?

SOLUTION

Consider the absolute minimum number of investors required at the end of each quarter (although this certainly was not Ponzi's objective).

- After one quarter (90 days) the single investor's $1000 could be paid back to him as his quarterly profit. So at that point no new investors are necessary.

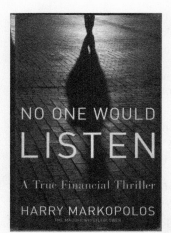

The 2010 book *No One Would Listen,* by Harry Markopolos, describes the longest running and largest Ponzi scheme ever revealed, as well as the futile efforts made by Markopolos, over a decade, to convince governmental regulators to take action against its operator, Bernard Madoff. (See **Exercises 23–25.**) Extensive resources, for the general reader and for classroom use, are available at www.noonewouldlisten.com.

- At the end of the second quarter, the investor wants another $1000 profit, and no money is available without an additional investor. So one investor must be added. His deposit can be used to pay the original investor.

- At the end of the third quarter, there are two investors, and no money. Two additional investors must be recruited to pay profits to the two previous investors.

- At the end of the fourth quarter (one year), four investors expect quarterly profit, so four new investors must be recruited.

Just to pay out profits, Ponzi would need to double his number of investors at the end of each quarter starting with the second. By the end of the year, 1 has doubled to 2, 2 to 4, and 4 to 8. He must end the year with 8 investors. Nothing is left for Ponzi. And if anyone wanted their principal back, he would be in trouble. ▮▮▮

▮▮ EXAMPLE 5 Analyzing Cash Flow in a Ponzi Scheme

Suppose that investors are promised 100% profit per quarter. At the beginning of each quarter (90 days), 1000 investors contribute $1000 each, and all monies stay in until the end of the year. There are then four categories of investors.

1. those who have been in for 4 quarters

2. those who have been in for 3 quarters

3. those who have been in for 2 quarters

4. those who have been in for 1 quarter

At the end of the year, 10% of those in each category take out their profits, but leave their principal. What amount does that leave with the operator?

SOLUTION

The amount taken in during the year is $4000 \cdot \$1000 = \$4,000,000$. At the end of the year, the supposed profits would be: $4000 for each category 1 investor, $3000 for each category 2 investor, $2000 for each category 3 investor, and $1000 for each category 4 investor. Ten percent of each category take out their profits, and 10% of 1000 is 100, so the payout would then be

Category 1 Category 2 Category 3 Category 4

$$100 \cdot \$4000 + 100 \cdot \$3000 + 100 \cdot \$2000 + 100 \cdot \$1000 = \$1,000,000.$$

The amount the operator retains is

$$\$4,000,000 - \$1,000,000 = \$3,000,000. \qquad ▮▮▮$$

EXTENSION EXERCISES

Analyzing an "Each One Recruits Three" Pyramid Scheme For Exercises 1–11, consider a pyramid scheme just like in **Example 1,** *except that "each one recruits three," rather than two. (Work these all, in order.)*

1. Draw a chart like in **Example 1** showing the first four levels.

2. How many members are in each of the following levels?
   (a) 1   (b) 2   (c) 3   (d) 4

3. If the chart is extended, in general how many members are in level N?

4. If you are the top person in the chart, and each person's entry fee is $1, how much money will you receive?

5. What will your profit be?

6. What is the total number of members, from level 1 through each of the following levels, inclusive?
   (a) 1   (b) 2
   (c) 3   (d) 4
   (e) 5   (f) 6

7. Fill in the blanks in the following statements. The total number of members in levels 1 through N, inclusive, is $1 + 3 + 9 + \ldots +$ _____. This is the sum of a _____ sequence with $a =$ ____, $r =$ ____, and $n =$ ____. So the total number of members is _____.

8. If the pyramid fails after level N, how many members will lose?

9. Suppose the scheme runs through level 6 and then fails. How many members lose?

10. Under the conditions of **Exercise 9,** what fraction of the members lose?

11. In an "each one recruits two" pyramid scheme, it was shown that more than $\frac{7}{8}$ of all members will lose. Use a similar analysis to characterize the fraction who will lose in an "each one recruits three" scheme.

12. Suppose you enter an "each one recruits two" pyramid scheme (at level 1), paying your $1 entry fee. If x denotes the number of level-4 recruits that eventually send you $1, then x is a random variable that can take on any of the values 0, 1, 2, 3, 4, 5, 6, 7, or 8. If the probability that any given person invited to join actually will join is $\frac{1}{2}$, then, using binomial probabilities gives the following probability distribution for x.

x	$P(x)$
0	0.34361
1	0.39270
2	0.19635
3	0.05610
4	0.01002
5	0.00114
6	0.00008
7	0.00000
8	0.00000

Find each of the following.

(a) the sum of these probability values

(b) your expected income

13. In **Exercise 12,** what is your expected profit?

14. If you were initiating a pyramid scheme, what would be the advantages and disadvantages of "each one recruits three" rather than two?

15. In a pyramid scheme, even if you and your three levels of recruits are embedded in a much larger chart, with multiple levels above you and many more below you, it is still only your four levels that affect your cost and income. Explain why this is so.

16. In an "each one recruits two" pyramid scheme, more than $\frac{7}{8}$ of all members will lose. What is the *greatest* fraction that could lose, and how could it happen?

17. Discuss places you have encountered "chain letters" or pyramid schemes with promises of money rewards for entering.

18. A number of other types of frauds have surfaced over the years. (Someone always has a new angle.) Research and write a report on "matrix schemes."

Finding the Required Number of Investors in a Ponzi Scheme *Refer to* **Example 4** *for Exercises 19 and 20.*

19. How many investors would be required by the end of two years with the same promised return of 100% per 90 days?

20. If the year began with 1000 investors, how many would be required at the end of each time period?

(a) one year   **(b)** two years   **(c)** three years

Exploring Cash Flow in a Ponzi Scheme *Refer to* **Example 5** *for Exercises 21 and 22.*

21. Suppose that at the end of the year, those 10% of investors actually invest another $1000 rather than taking out profit. Now what amount stays with the operator going into the second year?

22. Explain what factors may have convinced investors to put in more money and not take out profit.

Bernie Made Off with Billions. *As of mid 2010, the largest Ponzi scheme in history was operated by Bernard Madoff, a New York financier and former chairman of the NASDAQ Stock Market. When he was arrested in December of 2008, Mr. Madoff had swindled investors, including charities, foundations, large hedge funds, and funds of funds, as well as individuals, out of some $21 billion. He claimed to be trading in Standard & Poor's 500 Index options, but no one could tell what his fund actually held because he sold out of each option before reporting became mandatory.*

23. Assume that Charles Ponzi bilked his investors out of $4 million in 1920. If inflation averaged 3% from 1920 to 2008, compare the magnitudes of the Ponzi and Madoff scams in comparable dollars.

24. Speculate as to whether Bernard Madoff set out to swindle his investors in the beginning.

25. Considering the serious economic downturn in 2008, why do you think the Madoff scheme, and many others also, were discovered around the same time.

26. Research online or elsewhere to find out about other notable Ponzi schemes over the years. Can you identify any common traits among the operators?

COLLABORATIVE INVESTIGATION

To Buy or to Rent?

Divide your class into groups of at least four students each. Every group is to first read the following.

Ian and Tami, a young couple with a child, live in a rented apartment. After taxes, Ian earns $38,180 per year and Tami's part-time job brings in $7000 per year. In the foreseeable future, their earnings probably will just keep pace with inflation. They are presently operating on the following monthly budget.

Rent	$1050
Food	600
Day care	525
Clothing	420
Utilities	120
Entertainment	300
Savings	450
Other	300

They have accumulated $36,000 in savings.

Having found a house they would like to buy, which is priced at $162,500, they have consulted several lenders and have discovered that, at best, purchasing the house would involve costs as shown here.

Down payment required (20%)	_____
Closing costs (required at closing):	
Loan fee (1 point)	_____
Appraisal fee	300
Title insurance premium	375
Document and recording fees	70
Prorated property taxes	650
Prorated fire insurance premium	270
Other	230
Total immediate costs:	_____

Ongoing monthly ownership costs would be as follows.

Fixed-rate 30-year mortgage at 7.5%	_____
Taxes ($1350 annually)	_____
Fire insurance ($540 annually)	_____

In order to own their own home, Ian and Tami are willing to cut their clothing and entertainment expenditures by 30% each and could decrease their savings allotments by 20%. (Some savings still will be necessary to provide for additional furnishings they would need and for expenses of an expanding family in the future.) They also figure that the new house and yard would require $130 monthly for maintenance and that utilities will be twice what they have been in the apartment. Other than that, their present budget allotments would remain the same.

Now divide your group into two "subgroups." The first subgroup is to answer these questions:

1. What amount would the home purchase cost Ian and Tami in immediate expenditures?

2. Do they have enough cash on hand?

The second subgroup is to answer these questions:

3. What amount would the house cost Ian and Tami on an ongoing monthly basis?

4. What amount will their monthly budget allow toward this cost?

5. Can they meet the monthly expenses of owning the house?

Within your group, decide whether Ian and Tami can afford to purchase the house. Select a representative to report your findings to the class.

Compare the evaluations of the various groups, and try to resolve any discrepancies.

CHAPTER 13 TEST

Find all monetary answers to the nearest cent. Use tables and formulas from the chapter as necessary.

Finding the Future Value of a Deposit *Find the future value of each deposit.*

1. $100 for 5 years at 6% simple interest

2. $50 for 2 years at 8% compounded quarterly

Solve each problem.

3. *Effective Annual Yield of an Account* Find the effective annual yield to the nearest hundredth of a percent for an account paying 3% compounded monthly.

4. *Years to Double by the Rule of 70* Use the rule of 70 to estimate the years to double at an inflation rate of 5%.

5. *Finding the Present Value of a Deposit* What amount deposited today in an account paying 4% compounded semiannually would grow to $100,000 in 10 years?

6. *Finding Bank Card Interest by the Average Daily Balance Method* Caroline DiJullio's MasterCard statement shows an average daily balance of $680. Find the interest due if the rate is 1.6% per month.

Analyzing a Consumer Loan *Jason Hoffa buys a turquoise necklace for his wife on their anniversary. He pays $4000 for the necklace with $1000 down. The dealer charges add-on interest of 7.5% per year. Jason agrees to make payments for 24 months. Use this information for Exercises 7–10.*

7. Find the total amount of interest he will pay.

8. Find the monthly payment.

9. Find the APR value (to the nearest half percent).

10. Find the unearned interest if he repays the loan in full with six payments remaining. Use the most accurate method available.

11. *True Annual Interest Rate in Consumer Financing* Newark Hardware wants to include financing terms in their advertising. If the price of a floor waxer is $150 and the finance charge with no down payment is $5 over a 6-month period (six equal monthly payments), find the true annual interest rate (APR).

12. Explain what a mutual fund is and discuss several of its advantages and disadvantages.

Finding the Monthly Payment on a Home Mortgage *Find the monthly payment required for each home loan.*

13. The mortgage is for $150,000 at a fixed rate of 7% for 20 years. Amortize principal and interest only, disregarding taxes, insurance, and other costs.

14. The purchase price of the home is $218,000. The down payment is 20%. Interest is at 8.5% fixed for a term of 30 years. Annual taxes are $1500 and annual insurance is $750.

Solve each problem.

15. *Cost of Points in a Home Loan* If the lender in **Exercise 14** charges two *points,* how much does that add to the cost of the loan?

16. Explain in general what *closing costs* are. Are they different from *settlement charges*?

17. *Adjusting the Rate in an Adjustable-Rate Mortgage* To buy your home you obtain a 1-year ARM with 2.25% margin and a 2% periodic rate cap. The index starts at 7.85% but has increased to 10.05% by the first adjustment date. What interest rate will you pay during the second year?

18. *Reading Stock Charts* According to the stock table (**Table 9** on **page 726**), how many shares of Sara Lee were traded on June 4, 2010?

Finding the Return on a Stock Investment *Laurie Campbell bought 1000 shares of stock at $12.75 per share. She received a dividend of $1.38 per share shortly after the purchase and another dividend of $1.02 per share one year later. Eighteen months after buying the stock she sold the 1000 shares for $10.36 per share.*

19. Find Laurie's total return on this stock.

20. Find her percentage return. Is this the *annual rate of return* on this stock transaction? Why or why not?

21. *The Final Value of a Retirement Account* $1800 is deposited at the end of each year in a tax-deferred retirement account. The account earns a 6% annual return, the account owner's marginal tax rate is 25%, and taxes are paid at the end of 30 years. Find the final value of the account.

22. What is meant by saying that a retirement account is "adjusted for inflation"?

APPENDIX:
THE METRIC SYSTEM

Joseph Louis Lagrange (1736–1813) was born in Turin, Italy, and became a professor at age 19. In 1776 he came to Berlin at the request of Frederick the Great to take the position Euler left. A decade later Lagrange settled permanently in Paris. Napoleon was among many who admired and honored him.

Lagrange's greatest work was in the theory and application of **calculus.** He carried forward Euler's work of putting calculus on firm algebraic ground in his theory of functions. His *Analytic Mechanics* (1788) applied calculus to the motion of objects.

Lagrange's contributions to algebra had great influence on Galois and, hence, the theory of groups. He also wrote on number theory, proving that every integer is the sum of at most four squares.

The metric system was developed by a committee of the French Academy just after the French Revolution of 1789. The president of the committee was the mathematician Joseph Louis Lagrange. The advantages of the metric system can be seen when compared to our English system. In the English system, one inch is one-twelfth of a foot, while one foot is one-third of a yard. One mile is equivalent to 5280 feet, or 1760 yards. Obviously, there is no consistency in subdivisions.

In the metric system, prefixes are used to indicate multiplications or divisions by powers of ten. For example, the basic unit of length in the metric system is the *meter* (which is a little longer than one yard). To indicate one thousand meters, attach the prefix **"kilo-"** to get **kilo**meter. To indicate one one-hundredth of a meter, use the prefix **"centi-"** to obtain **centi**meter. A complete list of the prefixes of the metric system is shown in **Table 1**, with the most commonly used prefixes appearing in bold type.

Table 1 Metric Prefixes

Prefix	Multiple	Prefix	Multiple
exa	1,000,000,000,000,000,000	deci	0.1
peta	1,000,000,000,000,000	**centi**	0.01
tera	1,000,000,000,000	**milli**	0.001
giga	1,000,000,000	micro	0.000001
mega	1,000,000	nano	0.000000001
kilo	1000	pico	0.000000000001
hecto	100	femto	0.000000000000001
deka	10	atto	0.000000000000000001

Length and Area

Lagrange urged the committee devising the metric system to find some natural measure for length from which weight and volume measures could be derived. It was decided that one **meter (m)** would be the basic unit of length, with a meter being defined as one ten-millionth of the distance from the equator to the North Pole.

To obtain measures longer than one meter, Greek prefixes were added. For measures smaller than a meter, Latin prefixes were used. A meter is a little longer than a yard (about 39.37 inches). A **centimeter (cm)** is one one-hundredth of a meter and is about $\frac{2}{5}$ of an inch. See **Figure 1**.

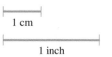

1 cm

1 inch

Figure 1

A Comparison of Distances

Length in Meters	Approximate Related Distances
10^{19}	Distance to the North Star
10^{12}	Distance of Saturn from the sun
10^{11}	Distance of Venus from the sun
10^{9}	Diameter of the sun
10^{8}	Diameter of Jupiter
10^{7}	Diameter of Earth; distance from Washington, D.C. to Tokyo
10^{6}	Distance from Chicago to Wichita, Kansas
10^{5}	Average distance across Lake Michigan
10^{4}	Average width of the Grand Canyon
10^{3}	Length of the Golden Gate Bridge
10^{2}	Length of a football field
10^{1}	Average height of a two-story house
10^{0}	Width of a door
10^{-1}	Width of your hand
10^{-2}	Diameter of a piece of chalk
10^{-3}	Thickness of a dime
10^{-4}	Thickness of a piece of paper
10^{-5}	Diameter of a red blood cell
10^{-7}	Thickness of a soap bubble
10^{-8}	Average distance between molecules of air in a room
10^{-9}	Diameter of a molecule of oil
10^{-14}	Diameter of an atomic nucleus
10^{-15}	Diameter of a proton

Because the metric system is based on decimals and powers of ten, conversions within the system involve multiplying and dividing by powers of ten. For example, to convert 2.5 m to centimeters, multiply 2.5 by 100 (since 100 cm = 1 m) to obtain 250 cm. On the other hand, to convert 18.6 cm to meters, divide by 100 to obtain 0.186 m. Other conversions are made in the same manner, using the meanings of the prefixes. Why is 42 m equal to 42,000 millimeters (mm)?

Long distances usually are measured in kilometers. A **kilometer (km)** is 1000 meters. (According to a popular dictionary, the word *kilometer* may be pronounced with the accent on either the first or the second syllable. Scientists usually stress the second syllable.) A kilometer is equal to about 0.6 mile. **Figure 2** shows the ratio of 1 kilometer to 1 mile.

Conversions from meters to kilometers, and vice versa, are made by multiplying or dividing by 1000 as necessary. For example, 37 kilometers equals 37,000 meters, while 583 meters equals 0.583 km.

The area of a figure can be measured in square metric units. **Figure 3** shows a square that is 1 cm on each side. Thus, it is a **square centimeter (cm^2).** One square meter (m^2) is the area of a square with sides one meter long. How many cm^2 are in one m^2?

According to Paul G. Hewitt, in *Conceptual Physics,* 7th edition (HarperCollins):

The distance from the equator to the North Pole was thought at the time to be close to 10,000 kilometers. One ten-millionth of this, the meter, was carefully determined and marked off by means of scratches on a bar of platinum-iridium alloy. This bar is kept at the International Bureau of Weights and Measures in France. The standard meter in France has since been calibrated in terms of the wavelength of light—it is 1,650,763.73 times the wavelength of orange light emitted by the atoms of the gas krypton-86. The meter is now defined as being the length of the path traveled by light in a vacuum during a time interval of 1/299,792,458 of a second.

1 kilometer

1 mile

Observe the ratio.

Figure 2

1 cm

1 cm

Area is 1 cm^2.

Figure 3

Volume, Mass, and Weight

The volume of a three-dimensional figure is measured in cubic units. If, for example, the dimensions are given in centimeters, the volume may be determined by the appropriate formula from geometry, and it will be in **cubic centimeters (cm³).** See **Figure 4** for a sketch of a box whose volume is one cm³.

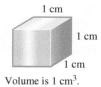

Volume is 1 cm³.

Figure 4

In September 1999, the **Mars *Climate Orbiter*** was lost due to "a failure to use metric units in the coding of a ground software file. . . ." According to Edward Weiler, associate administrator for NASA's Office of Space Science, the metric conversion error that led to the loss "should have been caught five ways to Sunday," but it wasn't. (*Source:* "NASA's Mars Losses Spark Anger and Opportunity" by Leonard David, Washington Contributing Editor to www.space.com.)

In the metric system, one **liter (L)** is the quantity assigned to the volume of a box that is 10 cm on a side. (See **Figure 5**.) A liter is a little more than a quart as seen in **Figure 6**. Notice the advantage of this definition over the equivalent one in the English system—using a ruler marked in centimeters, a volume of 1 liter (symbolized 1 L) can be constructed. On the other hand, given a ruler marked in inches, it would be difficult to construct a volume of 1 quart.

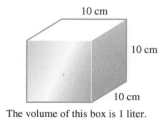

The volume of this box is 1 liter.

Figure 5

1 liter   1 quart

Figure 6

The prefixes mentioned earlier are used throughout the metric system, so one **milliliter (ml)** is one one-thousandth of a liter, one **centiliter (cl)** is one one-hundredth of a liter, one **kiloliter (kl)** is 1000 liters, and so on. Milliliters are used extensively in science and medicine. Many beverages now are sold by milliliters and by liters. For example, 750 ml is a common size for wine bottles, and many soft drinks now are sold in 1- and 2-liter bottles.

Because of the way a liter is defined as the volume of a box 10 cm on a side,

$$1\text{ L} = 10\text{ cm} \times 10\text{ cm} \times 10\text{ cm} = 1000\text{ cm}^3 \quad \text{or} \quad \frac{1}{1000}\text{ L} = 1\text{ cm}^3.$$

Since $\frac{1}{1000}$ L = 1 ml, we have the following relationship.

$$\textbf{1 ml} = \textbf{1 cm}^3$$

For example, the volume of a box which is 8 cm by 6 cm by 5 cm may be given as 240 cm³ or as 240 ml.

The box in **Figure 4** is 1 cm by 1 cm by 1 cm. The volume of this box is

$$1\text{ cm}^3, \quad \text{or} \quad 1\text{ ml}.$$

The original scale of **Anders Celsius** had the freezing point of water at 100° and the boiling point at 0°, but biologist Carl von Linne inverted the scale, giving us the familiar Celsius scale of today.

By definition, the mass of the water that fills such a box is **1 gram (g).** A nickel five-cent piece has a mass close to 5 grams, or 5 g. The volume of water used to define a gram is very small, so a gram is a very small mass. For everyday use, a **kilogram (kg),** or one thousand grams, is more practical. A kilogram weighs about 2.2 pounds. A common abbreviation for kilogram is the word **kilo.**

This photo shows that 13 feet, 6 inches is equal to 4.1 meters. Use this information and a proportion to show that one yard is equal to 0.91 meter.

Extremely small masses can be measured with **milligrams (mg)** and **centigrams (cg).** These measures are so small that they, like centiliters and milliliters, are used mainly in science and medicine.

Temperature

In the metric system temperature is measured in **degrees Celsius.** On the Celsius temperature scale, water freezes at 0° and boils at 100°. These two numbers are easier to remember than the corresponding numbers on the Fahrenheit scale, 32° and 212°. The thermometer in **Figure 7** shows some typical temperatures in both Fahrenheit and Celsius.

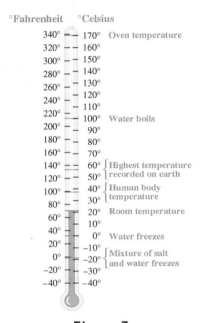

Figure 7

The formulas given below can be used to convert between Celsius and Fahrenheit temperatures.

Celsius-Fahrenheit Conversion Formulas

To convert a reading from Fahrenheit to Celsius, use $C = \frac{5}{9}(F - 32)$.

To convert from Celsius to Fahrenheit, use $F = \frac{9}{5}C + 32$.

Metric Conversions

Due to legislation enacted by Congress, the metric system is used in the United States, and an ultimate goal is for the two systems to be in use, side-by-side, with public acceptance of both systems. Industries that export a great many goods are using the metric system, since this is compatible with most of the countries with which they trade.

Some scientific calculators are programmed to do conversions between the English and metric systems. Approximate conversions can be made with the aid of **Tables 2 and 3** on the next page.

Table 2	Metric to English	
To Convert from	**To**	**Multiply by**
meters	yards	1.0936
meters	feet	3.2808
meters	inches	39.37
kilometers	miles	0.6214
grams	pounds	0.0022
kilograms	pounds	2.20
liters	quarts	1.0567
liters	gallons	0.2642

Table 3	English to Metric	
To Convert from	**To**	**Multiply by**
yards	meters	0.9144
feet	meters	0.3048
inches	meters	0.0254
miles	kilometers	1.609
pounds	grams	454
pounds	kilograms	0.454
quarts	liters	0.9464
gallons	liters	3.785

APPENDIX EXERCISES

Perform each conversion by multiplying or dividing by the appropriate power of 10.

1. 8 m to millimeters

2. 14.76 m to centimeters

3. 8500 cm to meters

4. 250 mm to meters

5. 68.9 cm to millimeters

6. 3.25 cm to millimeters

7. 59.8 mm to centimeters

8. 3.542 mm to centimeters

9. 5.3 km to meters

10. 9.24 km to meters

11. 27,500 m to kilometers

12. 14,592 m to kilometers

Use a metric ruler to perform each measurement, first in centimeters, then in millimeters.

13. ├────────────┤

14. ├──────────────────┤

15. ├────────────────────────────┤

16. Based on your measurement of the line segment in **Exercise 13,** one inch is about how many centimeters? How many millimeters?

Perform each conversion by multiplying or dividing by the appropriate power of 10.

17. 6 L to centiliters

18. 4.1 L to milliliters

19. 8.7 L to milliliters

20. 12.5 L to centiliters

21. 925 cl to liters

22. 412 ml to liters

23. 8974 ml to liters

24. 5639 cl to liters

25. 8000 g to kilograms

26. 25,000 g to kilograms

27. 5.2 kg to grams

28. 12.42 kg to grams

29. 4.2 g to milligrams

30. 3.89 g to centigrams

31. 598 mg to grams

32. 7634 cg to grams

Use the formulas given in the text to perform each conversion. Round to the nearest degree.

33. 86°F to Celsius

34. 536°F to Celsius

35. −114°F to Celsius

36. −40°F to Celsius

37. 10°C to Fahrenheit

38. 25°C to Fahrenheit

39. −40°C to Fahrenheit

40. −15°C to Fahrenheit

Solve each problem. Refer to geometry formulas as necessary.

41. Weight of Nickels   One nickel weighs 5 g. How many nickels are in 1 kg of nickels?

42. Salt in Sea Water   Sea water contains about 3.5 g salt per 1000 ml of water. How many grams of salt would be in one liter of sea water?

43. Weight of Helium   Helium weighs about 0.0002 g per milliliter. How much would one liter of helium weigh?

44. Sugar Solution   About 1500 g sugar can be dissolved in a liter of warm water. How much sugar could be dissolved in one milliliter of warm water?

45. Cost of Metal   Northside Foundry needed seven metal strips, each 67 cm long. Find the total cost of the strips, if they sell for $8.74 per meter.

46. Cost of Lace   Uptown Dressmakers bought fifteen pieces of lace, each 384 mm long. The lace sold for $54.20 per meter. Find the cost of the fifteen pieces.

47. Cost of Marble   Imported marble for desktops costs $174.20 per square meter. Find the cost of a piece of marble 128 cm by 174 cm.

48. Cost of Paper   A special photographic paper sells for $63.79 per square meter. Find the cost to buy 80 pieces of the paper, each 9 cm by 14 cm.

49. Volume of a Box   An importer received some special coffee beans in a box measuring 82 cm by 1.1 m by 1.2 m. Give the volume of the box, both in cubic centimeters and cubic meters.

50. Volume of a Crate   A fabric center receives bolts of woolen cloth in crates measuring 1.5 m by 74 cm by 97 cm. Find the volume of a crate, both in cubic centimeters and cubic meters.

51. Medicine Bottles   A medicine is sold in small bottles holding 800 ml each. How many of these bottles can be filled from a vat holding 160 L of the medicine?

52. Bottles of Soda Pop   How many 2-liter bottles of soda pop would be needed for a wedding reception if 80 people are expected, and each drinks 400 ml of soda?

Perform each conversion. Use a calculator and/or the table in the text as necessary.

53. 982 yd to meters

54. 12.2 km to miles

55. 125 mi to kilometers

56. 1000 mi to kilometers

57. 1816 g to pounds

58. 1.42 lb to grams

59. 47.2 lb to grams

60. 7.68 kg to pounds

61. 28.6 L to quarts

62. 59.4 L to quarts

63. 28.2 gal to liters

64. 16 qt to liters

Metric measures are very common in medicine. Since we convert among metric measures by moving the decimal point, errors in locating the decimal point in medical doses are not unknown. Decide whether each dose of medicine seems reasonable *or* unreasonable.

65. Take 2 kg of aspirin three times a day.

66. Take 4 L of liquid Mylanta every evening just before bedtime.

67. Take 25 ml of cough syrup daily.

68. Soak your feet in 6 L of hot water.

69. Inject $\frac{1}{2}$ L of insulin every morning.

70. Apply 40 g of salve to a cut on your finger.

Select the most reasonable choice for each of the following.

71. length of an adult cow
  A. 1 m   **B.** 3 m   **C.** 5 m

72. length of a Lexus
  A. 1 m   **B.** 3 m   **C.** 5 m

73. distance from Seattle to Miami
  A. 500 km   **B.** 5000 km   **C.** 50,000 km

74. length across an average nose
   A. 3 cm   **B.** 30 cm   **C.** 300 cm

75. distance across a page of a book
   A. 1.93 mm   **B.** 19.3 mm   **C.** 193 mm

76. weight of a book
   A. 1 kg   **B.** 10 kg   **C.** 1000 kg

77. weight of a large automobile
   A. 1300 kg   **B.** 130 kg   **C.** 13 kg

78. volume of a 12-ounce bottle of beverage
   A. 35 ml   **B.** 355 ml   **C.** 3550 ml

79. height of a person
   A. 180 cm   **B.** 1800 cm   **C.** 18 cm

80. diameter of the earth
   A. 130 km   **B.** 1300 km   **C.** 13,000 km

81. length of a long freight train
   A. 8 m   **B.** 80 m   **C.** 800 m

82. volume of a grapefruit
   A. 1 L   **B.** 4 L   **C.** 8 L

83. the length of a pair of Levi jeans
   A. 70 cm   **B.** 700 cm   **C.** 7 cm

84. a person's weight
   A. 700 kg   **B.** 7 kg   **C.** 70 kg

85. diagonal measure of a small TV monitor
   A. 5 cm   **B.** 50 cm   **C.** 500 cm

86. width of a standard bedroom door
   A. 1 m   **B.** 3 m   **C.** 5 m

87. thickness of a marking pen
   A. 0.9 mm   **B.** 9 mm   **C.** 90 mm

88. length around the rim of a coffee mug
   A. 300 mm   **B.** 30 mm   **C.** 3000 mm

89. the temperature at the surface of a frozen lake
   A. 0°C   **B.** 10°C   **C.** 32°C

90. the temperature in the middle of Death Valley on a July afternoon
   A. 25°C   **B.** 40°C   **C.** 65°C

91. surface temperature of desert sand on a hot summer day
   A. 30°C   **B.** 60°C   **C.** 90°C

92. temperature of boiling water
   A. 100°C   **B.** 120°C   **C.** 150°C

93. air temperature on a day when you need a sweater
   A. 30°C   **B.** 20°C   **C.** 10°C

94. air temperature on a day when you go swimming
   A. 30°C   **B.** 15°C   **C.** 10°C

95. temperature when baking a cake
   A. 120°C   **B.** 170°C   **C.** 300°C

96. temperature of bath water
   A. 35°C   **B.** 50°C   **C.** 65°C

ANSWERS TO SELECTED EXERCISES

CHAPTER 1 THE ART OF PROBLEM SOLVING

1.1 Exercises *(pages 6–8)*

1. deductive **3.** inductive **5.** deductive **7.** deductive
9. inductive **11.** inductive **13.** Answers will vary.
15. 21 **17.** 3072 **19.** 63 **21.** $\frac{11}{12}$ **23.** 216 **25.** 52
27. 5 **29.** One such list is 10, 20, 30, 40, 50, ...
31. $(98{,}765 \times 9) + 3 = 888{,}888$
33. $3367 \times 15 = 50{,}505$
35. $33{,}334 \times 33{,}334 = 1{,}111{,}155{,}556$
37. $3 + 6 + 9 + 12 + 15 = \frac{15(6)}{2}$
39. $5(6) + 5(36) + 5(216) + 5(1296) + 5(7776) = 6(7776 - 1)$
41. $\frac{1}{2} + \frac{1}{4} + \frac{1}{8} + \frac{1}{16} + \frac{1}{32} = 1 - \frac{1}{32}$
43. 20,100 **45.** 320,400 **47.** 15,400 **49.** 2550
51. 1 (These are the numbers of chimes a clock rings, starting with 12 o'clock, if it rings the number of hours on the hour, and 1 chime on the half-hour.)
53. (a) The middle digit is always 9, and the sum of the first and third digits is always 9 (considering 0 as the first digit if the difference has only two digits). **(b)** Answers will vary. **55.** 142,857; 285,714; 428,571; 571,428; 714,285; 857,142. Each result consists of the same six digits, but in a different order. $142{,}857 \times 7 = 999{,}999$

1.2 Exercises *(pages 15–18)*

1. arithmetic; 56 **3.** geometric; 1215 **5.** neither
7. geometric; 8 **9.** neither **11.** arithmetic; 22
13. 79 **15.** 450 **17.** 4032 **19.** 32,758 **21.** 57; 99
23. $(4321 \times 9) - 1 = 38{,}888$
25. $999{,}999 \times 4 = 3{,}999{,}996$
27. $21^2 - 15^2 = 6^3$ **29.** $5^2 - 4^2 = 5 + 4$
31. $1 + 5 + 9 + 13 = 4 \times 7$ **33.** 45,150 **35.** 228,150
37. 2601 **39.** 250,000 **41.** $S = n(n + 1)$
43. Answers will vary. **45.** *row 1*: 28, 36; *row 2*: 36, 49, 64; *row 3*: 35, 51, 70, 92; *row 4*: 28, 45, 66, 91, 120; *row 5*: 18, 34, 55, 81, 112, 148; *row 6*: 8, 21, 40, 65, 96, 133, 176
47. $8(1) + 1 = 9 = 3^2; 8(3) + 1 = 25 = 5^2; 8(6) + 1 = 49 = 7^2; 8(10) + 1 = 81 = 9^2$
49. The pattern is 1, 0, 1, 0, 1, 0, ...
51.

53. 256 **55.** 117 **57.** 235 **59.** $N_n = \frac{n(7n - 5)}{2}$
61. a square number **63.** a perfect cube **65.** 42
67. 419 **69.** $\frac{101}{2}$ **71.** 2048 **73.** $\frac{1}{2048}$ **75.** $\frac{5}{2048}$

CHAPTER 2 THE BASIC CONCEPTS OF SET THEORY

2.1 Exercises *(pages 47–49)*

1. F **3.** E **5.** B **7.** H **9.** $\{1, 2, 3, 4, 5, 6\}$
11. $\{0, 1, 2, 3, 4\}$ **13.** $\{6, 7, 8, 9, 10, 11, 12, 13, 14\}$
15. $\{-15, -13, -11, -9, -7, -5, -3, -1\}$
17. $\{2, 4, 8, 16, 32, 64, 128, 256\}$ **19.** $\{0, 2, 4, 6, 8, 10\}$
21. $\{21, 22, 23, \ldots\}$ **23.** {Lake Erie, Lake Huron, Lake Michigan, Lake Ontario, Lake Superior}
25. $\{5, 10, 15, 20, 25, \ldots\}$ **27.** $\left\{1, \frac{1}{2}, \frac{1}{3}, \frac{1}{4}, \frac{1}{5}, \ldots\right\}$
In Exercises 29 and 31, there are other ways to describe the sets. **29.** $\{x \,|\, x$ is a rational number$\}$ **31.** $\{x \,|\, x$ is an odd natural number less than 76$\}$ **33.** the set of single-digit integers **35.** the set of states of the United States
37. finite **39.** infinite **41.** infinite **43.** infinite
45. 8 **47.** 500 **49.** 26 **51.** 39 **53.** 28
55. Answers will vary. **57.** well defined
59. not well defined **61.** $\in$ **63.** $\notin$ **65.** $\notin$ **67.** $\in$
69. false **71.** true **73.** true **75.** true **77.** false
79. true **81.** true **83.** true **85.** false **87.** true
89. Answers will vary.
91. $\{2\}$ and $\{3, 4\}$ (Other examples are possible.)
93. $\{a, b\}$ and $\{a, c\}$ (Other examples are possible.)
95. (a) {Drew Barrymore, Leonardo DiCaprio, Samuel L. Jackson, Jim Carrey} **(b)** {Will Ferrell, Ewan McGregor}

2.2 Exercises *(pages 54–55)*

1. D **3.** B **5.** $\not\subset$ **7.** $\subseteq$ **9.** $\subseteq$ **11.** $\not\subseteq$ **13.** both
15. $\subseteq$ **17.** both **19.** neither **21.** true **23.** false
25. true **27.** false **29.** true **31.** true **33.** false
35. true **37.** true **39.** false **41. (a)** 64 **(b)** 63
43. (a) 32 **(b)** 31 **45.** $\{5, 7, 9, 10\}$ **47.** $\{2\}$ **49.** $\emptyset$
51. {Higher cost, Lower cost, Educational, More time to see the sights in California, Less time to see the sights in California, Cannot visit relatives along the way, Can visit relatives along the way} **53.** {Higher cost, More time to see the sights in California, Cannot visit relatives along the way}

55. ∅ **57.** {A, B, C, D, E} (All are present.)
59. {A, B, C}, {A, B, D}, {A, B, E}, {A, C, D}, {A, C, E}, {A, D, E}, {B, C, D}, {B, C, E}, {B, D, E}, {C, D, E}
61. {A}, {B}, {C}, {D}, {E} **63.** 32
65. $2^{25} - 1 = 33,554,431$ **67. (a)** 15 **(b)** 16; It is now possible to select *no* bills. **69. (a)** s **(b)** s **(c)** $2s$
(d) Adding one more element will always double the number of subsets, so the expression 2^n is true in general.

2.3 Exercises *(pages 65–68)*
1. B **3.** A **5.** E **7.** {a, c} **9.** {a, b, c, d, e, f}
11. {a, b, c, d, e, f, g} **13.** {b, d, f} **15.** {d, f}
17. {a, b, c, e, g} **19.** {a, c, e, g} **21.** {a} **23.** {e, g}
25. {e, g} **27.** {d, f} **29.** {e, b, g}
In Exercises 31–35, there may be other acceptable descriptions.
31. the set of all elements that either are in *A*, or are not in *B* and not in *C* **33.** the set of all elements that are in *C* but not in *B*, or are in *A* **35.** the set of all elements that are in *A* but not in *C*, or in *B* but not in *C*
37. {e, h, c, l, b} **39.** {l, b} **41.** {e, h, c, l, b} **43.** the set of all tax returns showing business income or filed in 2009
45. the set of all tax returns filed in 2009 without itemized deductions **47.** the set of all tax returns with itemized deductions or showing business income, but not selected for audit **49.** always true **51.** always true
53. not always true **55. (a)** {1, 3, 5, 2} **(b)** {1, 2, 3, 5}
(c) For any sets *X* and *Y*, $X \cup Y = Y \cup X$.
57. (a) {1, 3, 5, 2, 4} **(b)** {1, 3, 5, 2, 4} **(c)** For any sets *X*, *Y*, and *Z*, $X \cup (Y \cup Z) = (X \cup Y) \cup Z$.
59. (a) {4} **(b)** {4} **(c)** For any sets *X* and *Y*, $(X \cup Y)' = X' \cap Y'$. **61.** $X \cup \emptyset = X$; For any set *X*, $X \cup \emptyset = X$. **63.** true **65.** false **67.** true **69.** true
71. $A \times B = \{(2, 4), (2, 9), (8, 4), (8, 9), (12, 4), (12, 9)\}$; $B \times A = \{(4, 2), (4, 8), (4, 12), (9, 2), (9, 8), (9, 12)\}$
73. $A \times B = \{(d, p), (d, i), (d, g), (o, p), (o, i),$ $(o, g), (g, p), (g, i), (g, g)\}; B \times A = \{(p, d), (p, o),$ $(p, g), (i, d), (i, o), (i, g), (g, d), (g, o), (g, g)\}$
75. $n(A \times B) = 6; n(B \times A) = 6$
77. $n(A \times B) = 210; n(B \times A) = 210$ **79.** 6
81.
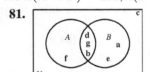
83.
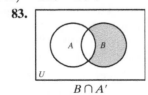
$B \cap A'$

85.
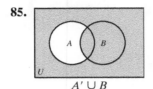
$A' \cup B$

87.
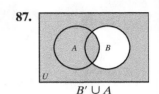
$B' \cup A$

89.
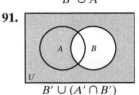
$B' \cap B = \emptyset$

91.
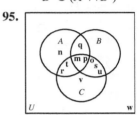
$B' \cup (A' \cap B')$

93.
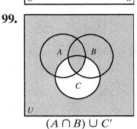
$U' = \emptyset$

95.
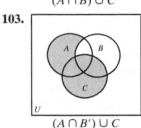

97.
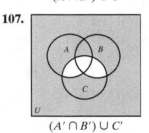
$(A \cap B) \cap C$

99.
$(A \cap B) \cup C'$

101.
$(A' \cap B') \cap C$

103.
$(A \cap B') \cup C$

105.
$(A \cap B') \cap C'$

107.
$(A' \cap B') \cup C'$

109. $A' \cap B'$, or $(A \cup B)'$
111. $(A \cup B) \cap (A \cap B)'$, or $(A \cup B) - (A \cap B)$, or $(A - B) \cup (B - A)$
113. $(A \cap B) \cup (A \cap C)$, or $A \cap (B \cup C)$
115. $(A \cap B) \cap C'$, or $(A \cap B) - C$

117. $A \cap B = \emptyset$ **119.** This statement is true for any set A.
121. $A = \emptyset$ **123.** $A = \emptyset$ **125.** $A = \emptyset$ **127.** $B \subseteq A$
129. always true **131.** always true
133. not always true **135.** always true
137. (a) $\{x \mid x \text{ is a real number}\}$ **(b)** $\emptyset$

2.4 Exercises (pages 71–74)

1. (a) 5 **(b)** 7 **(c)** 0 **(d)** 2 **(e)** 8 **3. (a)** 1 **(b)** 3
(c) 4 **(d)** 0 **(e)** 2 **(f)** 8 **(g)** 2 **(h)** 6 **5.** 21
7. 7 **9.** 35

11. 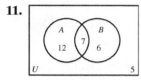 **13.**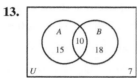

15. 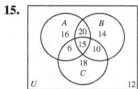 **17.**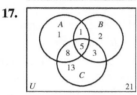

19. (a) 2 **(b)** 4 **21. (a)** 25 **(b)** 20 **(c)** 12 **(d)** 10
(e) 19 **23. (a)** 37 **(b)** 38 **25. (a)** 500 **(b)** 91
27. (a) 31 **(b)** 24 **(c)** 11 **(d)** 45 **29. (a)** 1
(b) 1, 2, 3, 4, 5, 6, 7, 8, 9, 10, 11, 12, 13, 14, 15
(c) 1, 2, 3, 4, 5, 9, 11 **(d)** 5, 8, 13 **31. (a)** 9 **(b)** 9
(c) 20 **(d)** 20 **(e)** 27 **(f)** 15 **33.** Answers will vary.

Extension Exercises (pages 79–80)

1. B; 1 **3.** A; $\aleph_0$ **5.** F; 0
7. (Other correspondences are possible.)

$$\{\text{I}, \quad \text{II}, \quad \text{III}\}$$
$$\updownarrow \quad \updownarrow \quad \updownarrow$$
$$\{\text{x}, \quad \text{y}, \quad \text{z}\}$$

9. (Other correspondences are possible.)

$$\{\text{a}, \quad \text{d}, \quad \text{i}, \quad \text{t}, \quad \text{o}, \quad \text{n}\}$$
$$\updownarrow \quad \updownarrow \quad \updownarrow \quad \updownarrow \quad \updownarrow \quad \updownarrow$$
$$\{\text{a}, \quad \text{n}, \quad \text{s}, \quad \text{w}, \quad \text{e}, \quad \text{r}\}$$

11. 11 **13.** 0 **15.** $\aleph_0$ **17.** $\aleph_0$ **19.** $\aleph_0$ **21.** 12
23. $\aleph_0$ **25.** both **27.** equivalent **29.** equivalent

31. $\{2, \quad 4, \quad 6, \quad 8, \quad \ldots, \quad 2n, \quad \ldots\}$
$\quad\; \updownarrow \quad \updownarrow \quad \updownarrow \quad \updownarrow \qquad\quad \updownarrow$
$\{1, \quad 2, \quad 3, \quad 4, \quad \ldots, \quad n, \quad \ldots\}$

33. $\{1{,}000{,}000, \quad 2{,}000{,}000, \quad 3{,}000{,}000, \quad \ldots, \quad 1{,}000{,}000n, \quad \ldots\}$
$\qquad\quad \updownarrow \qquad\qquad \updownarrow \qquad\qquad \updownarrow \qquad\qquad\qquad \updownarrow$
$\{ \quad\; 1, \qquad\quad 2, \qquad\quad 3, \qquad \ldots, \qquad n, \qquad \ldots\}$

35. $\{2, \quad 4, \quad 8, \quad 16, \quad 32, \quad \ldots, \quad 2^n, \quad \ldots\}$
$\quad\; \updownarrow \quad \updownarrow \quad \updownarrow \quad \updownarrow \quad \updownarrow \qquad\qquad \updownarrow$
$\{1, \quad 2, \quad 3, \quad 4, \quad 5, \quad \ldots, \quad n, \quad \ldots\}$

37. This statement is not always true. For example, let $A =$ the set of counting numbers, $B =$ the set of real numbers.

39. This statement is not always true. For example, A could be the set of all subsets of the set of reals. Then $n(A)$ would be an infinite number *greater* than c.

41. (a) Rays emanating from point P will establish a geometric pairing of the points on the semicircle with the points on the line.

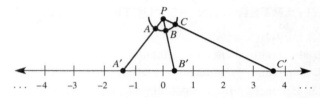

(b) The set of real numbers is infinite, having been placed in a one-to-one correspondence with a proper subset of itself.

43. $\{3, \quad 6, \quad 9, \quad 12, \quad \ldots, \quad 3n, \quad \ldots\}$
$\quad\; \updownarrow \quad \updownarrow \quad \updownarrow \quad \updownarrow \qquad\qquad \updownarrow$
$\{6, \quad 9, \quad 12, \quad 15, \quad \ldots, \quad 3n + 3, \quad \ldots\}$

45. $\left\{\dfrac{3}{4}, \quad \dfrac{3}{8}, \quad \dfrac{3}{12}, \quad \dfrac{3}{16}, \quad \ldots, \quad \dfrac{3}{4n}, \quad \ldots\right\}$
$\qquad \updownarrow \quad \updownarrow \quad \updownarrow \quad \updownarrow \qquad\qquad \updownarrow$
$\left\{\dfrac{3}{8}, \quad \dfrac{3}{12}, \quad \dfrac{3}{16}, \quad \dfrac{3}{20}, \quad \ldots, \quad \dfrac{3}{4n + 4}, \quad \ldots\right\}$

47. $\left\{\dfrac{1}{9}, \quad \dfrac{1}{18}, \quad \dfrac{1}{27}, \quad \ldots, \quad \dfrac{1}{9n}, \quad \ldots\right\}$
$\qquad \updownarrow \quad \updownarrow \quad \updownarrow \qquad\qquad \updownarrow$
$\left\{\dfrac{1}{18}, \quad \dfrac{1}{27}, \quad \dfrac{1}{36}, \quad \ldots, \quad \dfrac{1}{9n + 9}, \quad \ldots\right\}$

49. Answers will vary. **51.** Answers will vary.

Chapter 2 Test (pages 81–82)

1. $\{a, b, c, d, e\}$ **2.** $\{a, b, d\}$ **3.** $\{c, f, g, h\}$ **4.** $\{a, c\}$
5. true **6.** false **7.** true **8.** true **9.** false **10.** true
11. true **12.** true **13.** 8 **14.** 15
Answers may vary in Exercises 15.–18. **15.** the set of odd integers between -4 and 10 **16.** the set of months of the year **17.** $\{x \mid x \text{ is a negative integer}\}$ **18.** $\{x \mid x$ is a multiple of 8 between 20 and 90$\}$ **19.** $\subseteq$ **20.** neither
21. 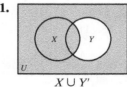 **22.**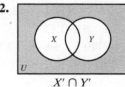

$X \cup Y'$ $X' \cap Y'$

23.

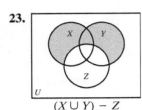

$(X \cup Y) - Z$

24.

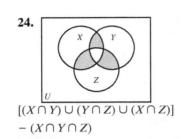

$[(X \cap Y) \cup (Y \cap Z) \cup (X \cap Z)]$
$- (X \cap Y \cap Z)$

25. {Electric razor} **26.** {Adding machine, Barometer, Pendulum clock, Thermometer} **27.** {Electric razor} **28.** Answers will vary. **29. (a)** 22 **(b)** 12 **(c)** 28
30. (a) 16 **(b)** 32 **(c)** 33 **(d)** 45 **(e)** 14 **(f)** 26

CHAPTER 3 INTRODUCTION TO LOGIC

3.1 Exercises *(pages 88–90)*

1. statement **3.** not a statement **5.** statement
7. statement **9.** statement **11.** not a statement
13. statement **15.** compound **17.** not compound
19. not compound **21.** compound **23.** Her aunt's
name is not Hermione. **25.** At least one dog does not
have its day. **27.** No book is longer than this book.
29. At least one computer repairman can play blackjack.
31. Someone does not love somebody sometime.
33. $x \le 12$ **35.** $x < 5$ **37.** Answers will vary.
39. She does not have green eyes. **41.** She has green
eyes and he is 60 years old. **43.** She does not have green
eyes or he is 60 years old. **45.** She does not have green
eyes or he is not 60 years old. **47.** It is not the case that
she does not have green eyes and he is 60 years old.
49. $p \wedge \sim q$ **51.** $\sim p \vee q$ **53.** $\sim(p \vee q)$ or,
equivalently, $\sim p \wedge \sim q$ **55.** Answers will vary.
57. C **59.** A, B **61.** A, C **63.** B **65.** true
67. true **69.** true **71.** true **73.** false **75.** Answers
will vary. **77.** Every person here has done that at one
time or another.

3.2 Exercises *(pages 99–100)*

1. false **3.** true **5.** They must both be false. **7.** T
9. T **11.** F **13.** T **15.** T **17.** T **19.** It is a
disjunction, because it means "6 > 2 or 6 = 2." **21.** T
23. F **25.** T **27.** T **29.** F **31.** F **33.** T **35.** T
37. T **39.** 4 **41.** 16 **43.** 128 **45.** seven **47.** FFTF
49. FTTT **51.** TTTT **53.** FFFT **55.** TFFF
57. FFFFTFFF **59.** FTFTTTTT
61. TTTTTTTTTTTTFTTT **63.** You can't pay me now
and you can't pay me later. **65.** It is not summer or
there is snow. **67.** I did not say yes or she did not say
no. **69.** $6 - 1 \ne 5$ or $9 + 13 = 7$ **71.** Neither Prancer
nor Vixen will lead Santa's reindeer sleigh next Christmas.

73. T **75.** F **77.**

p	q	$p \underline{\vee} q$
T	T	F
T	F	T
F	T	T
F	F	F

79. F **81.** T **83.** The lady is behind Door 2. *Reasoning:*
Suppose that the sign on Door 1 is true. Then the sign on
Door 2 would also be true, but this is impossible. So the
sign on Door 2 must be true, and the sign on Door 1 must
be false. Because the sign on Door 1 says the lady is in
Room 1, and this is false, the lady must be behind Door 2.

3.3 Exercises *(pages 107–109)*

1. If you see it on the Internet, then you can believe it.
3. If an integer is divisible by 10, then it is divisible by 5.
5. If the soldier is a marine, then the soldier loves boot
camp. **7.** If it is a panda, then it does not live in Idaho.
9. If it is an opium-eater, then it has no self-command.
11. true **13.** true **15.** false **17.** true **19.** Answers
will vary. **21.** F **23.** T **25.** T **27.** If they do not raise
alpacas, then he trains dogs. **29.** If she has a bird for a
pet, then they raise alpacas and he trains dogs. **31.** If he
does not train dogs, then they do not raise alpacas or she
has a bird for a pet. **33.** $b \rightarrow p$ **35.** $p \rightarrow \sim s$
37. $p \wedge (s \rightarrow \sim b)$ **39.** $p \rightarrow s$ **41.** T **43.** F
45. T **47.** F **49.** T **51.** T **53.** Answers will vary.
55. TTTF **57.** TTFT **59.** TTTT; tautology **61.** TFTF
63. TTTTTTFT **65.** TTTFTTTTTTTTTTTT
67. one **69.** That is an authentic Rolex watch and I am
not surprised. **71.** The English measures are not
converted to metric measures and the spacecraft does not
crash on the surface of Saturn. **73.** You want to be
happy for the rest of your life and you make a pretty
woman your wife. **75.** You do not give your plants
tender, loving care or they flourish. **77.** She does or he
will. **79.** The person is not a resident of Pensacola or is
a resident of Florida. **81.** equivalent **83.** equivalent
85. not equivalent **87.** equivalent **89.** equivalent
91. $(p \wedge q) \vee (p \wedge \sim q)$; The statement simplifies to p.
93. $p \vee (\sim q \wedge r)$ **95.** $\sim p \vee (p \vee q)$; The statement
simplifies to T.
97. The statement
simplifies to $p \wedge q$.

99. The statement
simplifies to F.

101. The statement simplifies to $(r \wedge \sim p) \wedge q$.

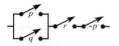

103. The statement simplifies to $p \vee q$.

105. $525.60

3.4 Exercises (pages 114–115)

1. (a) If you were an hour, then beauty would be a minute. **(b)** If beauty were not a minute, then you would not be an hour. **(c)** If you were not an hour, then beauty would not be a minute. **3. (a)** If you don't fix it, then it ain't broke. **(b)** If it's broke, then fix it. **(c)** If you fix it, then it's broke. **5. (a)** If it is dangerous to your health, then you walk in front of a moving car. **(b)** If you do not walk in front of a moving car, then it is not dangerous to your health. **(c)** If it is not dangerous to your health, then you do not walk in front of a moving car. **7. (a)** If they flock together, then they are birds of a feather. **(b)** If they are not birds of a feather, then they do not flock together. **(c)** If they do not flock together, then they are not birds of a feather. **9. (a)** If he comes, then you built it. **(b)** If you don't build it, then he won't come. **(c)** If he doesn't come, then you didn't build it. **11. (a)** $\sim q \rightarrow p$ **(b)** $\sim p \rightarrow q$ **(c)** $q \rightarrow \sim p$ **13. (a)** $\sim q \rightarrow \sim p$ **(b)** $p \rightarrow q$ **(c)** $q \rightarrow p$ **15. (a)** $(q \vee r) \rightarrow p$ **(b)** $\sim p \rightarrow (\sim q \wedge \sim r)$ **(c)** $(\sim q \wedge \sim r) \rightarrow \sim p$ **17.** Answers will vary. **19.** If it is muddy, then I'll wear my galoshes. **21.** If 19 is positive, then $19 + 1$ is positive. **23.** If a number is an integer, then it is a rational number. **25.** If I do logic puzzles, then I am driven crazy. **27.** If Jeff Marsalis is to shave, then he must have a day's growth of beard. **29.** If I go from Boardwalk to Baltic Avenue, then I pass GO. **31.** If a number is a whole number, then it is an integer. **33.** If their pitching improves, then the Nationals will win the pennant. **35.** If the figure is a rectangle, then it is a parallelogram with a right angle. **37.** If a triangle has two perpendicular sides, then it is a right triangle. **39.** If a two-digit number whose units digit is 5 is squared, then the square will end in 25. **41.** D **43.** Answers will vary. **45.** true **47.** false **49.** false **51.** contrary **53.** consistent **55.** contrary **57.** consistent **59.** Answers will vary. One example is: That man is Otis Taylor. That man sells books.

3.5 Exercises (pages 119–120)

1. valid **3.** invalid **5.** valid **7.** invalid **9.** invalid **11.** invalid **13.** yes

15. All people with blue eyes have blond hair.
Natalie Graham does not have blond hair.
Natalie Graham does not have blue eyes.

17. invalid **19.** valid **21.** invalid **23.** valid **25.** invalid **27.** invalid **29.** valid

Extension Exercises (pages 122–124)

1. Drew, spanakopita, Fresh Air, spearmint; Ilse, buffalo-chicken sandwich, Deltoids, cinnamon; Nash, French onion soup, Liplickers, vanilla; Uma, tuna-salad sandwich, TKO, wintergreen; Xerxes, garlic shrimp, Inti-mints, orange **3.** 1st, Earl, Ox, fire; 2nd, Philip, Rooster, metal; 3rd, Toni, Cow, water; 4th, Lucy, Dragon, earth; 5th, Ivana, Horse, wood

5.

7	4	2	1	6	8	9	3	5
3	1	9	4	5	7	6	2	8
8	6	5	9	3	2	7	1	4
6	2	4	7	8	9	1	5	3
1	3	8	5	4	6	2	9	7
5	9	7	2	1	3	8	4	6
2	5	3	8	7	1	4	6	9
9	7	6	3	2	4	5	8	1
4	8	1	6	9	5	3	7	2

7.

8	3	9	6	5	7	2	4	1
7	1	2	9	4	3	8	5	6
4	5	6	2	1	8	3	7	9
2	6	7	1	9	4	5	3	8
3	9	1	8	2	5	4	6	7
5	4	8	7	3	6	1	9	2
1	2	3	5	6	9	7	8	4
9	8	4	3	7	2	6	1	5
6	7	5	4	8	1	9	2	3

9.

6	1	7	9	2	3	5	8	4
4	5	9	8	6	1	2	7	3
3	2	8	4	5	7	9	6	1
8	3	5	6	4	9	1	2	7
7	6	1	5	3	2	8	4	9
2	9	4	7	1	8	3	5	6
5	7	2	3	9	6	4	1	8
1	8	3	2	7	4	6	9	5
9	4	6	1	8	5	7	3	2

3.6 Exercises (pages 130–133)

1. valid by reasoning by transitivity **3.** valid by modus ponens **5.** fallacy by fallacy of the converse **7.** valid by modus tollens **9.** fallacy by fallacy of the inverse **11.** valid by disjunctive syllogism **13.** invalid **15.** valid **17.** invalid **19.** valid **21.** invalid **23.** invalid **25.** invalid

27. Every time something squeaks, I use WD-40.
Every time I use WD-40, I go to the hardware store.
Every time something squeaks, I go to the hardware store.

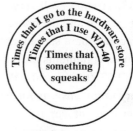

29. valid **31.** invalid **33.** invalid **35.** valid **37.** valid **39.** If I tell you the time, then my life will be miserable. **41.** If it is my poultry, then it is a duck.

43. If it is a guinea pig, then it is hopelessly ignorant of music.   **45.** If it is a teachable kitten, then it does not have green eyes.   **47.** If I can read it, then I have not filed it.   **49. (a)** $p \rightarrow \sim s$ **(b)** $r \rightarrow s$ **(c)** $q \rightarrow p$
(d) None of my poultry are officers.   **51. (a)** $r \rightarrow \sim s$
(b) $u \rightarrow t$ **(c)** $\sim r \rightarrow p$ **(d)** $\sim u \rightarrow \sim q$ **(e)** $t \rightarrow s$
(f) All pawnbrokers are honest.   **53. (a)** $r \rightarrow w$
(b) $\sim u \rightarrow \sim t$ **(c)** $v \rightarrow \sim s$ **(d)** $x \rightarrow r$ **(e)** $\sim q \rightarrow t$
(f) $y \rightarrow p$ **(g)** $w \rightarrow s$ **(h)** $\sim x \rightarrow \sim q$ **(i)** $p \rightarrow \sim u$
(j) I can't read any of Brown's letters.

Collaborative Investigation *(pages 134–135)*
1. Jan. 1, Vandyke Facility, *Penchant*, repair satellite; Feb. 5, San Simeon Launch Center, *Falconer*, investigate radiation; Mar. 3, Cape Carnival, *Liberty*, land on moon; Apr. 4, Willard Island, *Twilight*, test propulsion; May 2, Eddings Air Force Base, *Bravura*, measure magnetic fields

2.

⑤	10	11	4	1	6	14	2	16	7	12	8	15	9	13	③
12	⑮	7	3	8	4	9	13	2	11	5	1	16	10	⑭	6
13	8	⑥	14	11	16	10	7	9	15	3	4	5	①	12	2
9	1	2	⑯	5	3	12	15	6	14	10	13	⑪	4	7	8
11	13	9	10	②	14	16	3	1	12	8	⑥	7	15	4	5
7	6	16	2	12	⑩	15	4	13	5	⑨	11	1	3	8	14
1	4	15	12	6	8	⑪	5	3	⑯	7	14	9	2	10	13
3	14	8	5	13	9	7	①	④	2	15	10	12	6	16	11
4	7	5	11	14	12	3	⑩	⑧	6	2	15	13	16	1	9
15	16	1	9	7	5	②	11	10	③	13	12	14	8	6	4
2	12	10	6	9	⑬	4	8	11	1	⑭	16	3	5	15	7
14	3	13	8	⑮	1	6	16	5	9	4	⑦	2	12	11	10
10	9	14	⑦	16	2	8	12	15	13	6	3	④	11	5	1
6	2	⑫	15	4	11	5	14	7	8	1	9	10	⑬	3	16
16	⑤	4	13	3	7	1	6	12	10	11	2	8	14	⑨	15
⑧	11	3	1	10	15	13	9	14	4	16	5	6	7	2	⑫

Chapter 3 Test *(pages 135–136)*
1. $6 - 3 \neq 3$ **2.** Some men are not created equal.
3. No members of the class went on the field trip.
4. That's the way you feel and I won't accept it.
5. She did not apply or did not get a student loan.
6. $\sim p \rightarrow q$ **7.** $p \rightarrow q$ **8.** $\sim q \leftrightarrow \sim p$ **9.** You won't love me and I will love me.   **10.** It is not the case that you will love me or I will not love you. (Equivalently: You won't love me and I will love you.)   **11.** T   **12.** T
13. T   **14.** F   **15.** Answers will vary.   **16. (a)** The antecedent must be true and the consequent must be false.   **(b)** Both component statements must be true.
(c) Both component statements must be false.
17. TFFF   **18.** TTTT (tautology)   **19.** false   **20.** true
Wording may vary in the answers for Exercises 21–25.
21. If the number is an integer, then it is a rational number.   **22.** If a polygon is a rhombus, then it is a quadrilateral.   **23.** If a number is divisible by 4, then it is divisible by 2.   **24.** If she digs dinosaur bones, then she is a paleontologist.   **25. (a)** If the graph helps me

understand it, then a picture paints a thousand words.
(b) If a picture doesn't paint a thousand words, then the graph won't help me understand it.   **(c)** If the graph doesn't help me understand it, then a picture doesn't paint a thousand words.   **26. (a)** $(q \wedge r) \rightarrow \sim p$
(b) $p \rightarrow (\sim q \vee \sim r)$ **(c)** $(\sim q \vee \sim r) \rightarrow p$ **27.** valid
28. (a) A   **(b)** F   **(c)** C   **(d)** D   **29.** valid   **30.** invalid

CHAPTER 6 THE REAL NUMBERS AND THEIR REPRESENTATIONS

6.5 Exercises *(pages 272–276)*
1. true   **3.** false   **5.** true   **7.** true   **9.** false   **11.** 11.315
13. −4.215   **15.** 0.8224   **17.** 47.5   **19.** 31.6
21. $525 billion   **23.** three (and you would have 0.01¢ left over)   **25.** $0.06, or 6¢   **27.** 1000   **29. (a)** 0.031
(b) 0.035   **31.** 297   **33. (a)** 78.4   **(b)** 78.41
35. (a) 0.1   **(b)** 0.08   **37. (a)** 12.7   **(b)** 12.69   **39.** 42%
41. 36.5%   **43.** 0.8%   **45.** 210%   **47.** 20%   **49.** 1%
51. $37\frac{1}{2}$%   **53.** 150%   **55.** Answers will vary.   **57. (a)** 5
(b) 24   **(c)** 8   **(d)** 0.5, or $\frac{1}{2}$ **(e)** 600   **59.** No, the price is $57.60.   **61. (a)** .586   **(b)** .519   **(c)** .463   **(d)** .395
63. 124.8   **65.** 2.94   **67.** 150%   **69.** 600   **71.** 1.4%
73. 8%   **75.** 3.8%   **77.** 47.5%   **79.** A   **81.** C
83. about 139%   **85. (a)** $14.7 - 40 \cdot 0.13$ **(b)** 9.5
(c) 8.075; walking (5 mph)   **87.** 892%   **89.** $4.50
91. $0.75   **93.** $12.00   **95.** $36.00   **97.** Answers will vary.

CHAPTER 7 THE BASIC CONCEPTS OF ALGEBRA

7.1 Exercises *(pages 290–293)*
1. A and C   **3.** Both sides are evaluated as 48, so 12 is a solution.   **5.** solution set   **7.** B   **9.** $\{-1\}$ **11.** $\{3\}$
13. $\{-7\}$ **15.** $\{0\}$ **17.** $\{-\frac{5}{3}\}$ **19.** $\{-\frac{1}{2}\}$ **21.** $\{2\}$
23. $\{-2\}$ **25.** $\{7\}$ **27.** $\{2\}$ **29.** $\{\frac{3}{2}\}$ **31.** $\{-5\}$
33. $\{3\}$ **35.** 2 (that is, 10^2, or 100)   **37.** $\{4\}$ **39.** $\{0\}$
41. $\{0\}$ **43.** $\{2000\}$ **45.** $\{25\}$ **47.** $\{40\}$
49. identity, contradiction   **51.** contradiction; $\emptyset$
53. conditional; $\{-8\}$ **55.** conditional; $\{0\}$
57. identity; {all real numbers}   **59.** D   **61.** $t = \frac{d}{r}$
63. $b = \frac{A}{h}$ **65.** $a = P - b - c$ **67.** $b = \frac{2A}{h}$
69. $h = \frac{S - 2\pi r^2}{2\pi r}$, or $h = \frac{S}{2\pi r} - r$ **71.** $F = \frac{9}{5}C + 32$
73. $h = \frac{3V}{\pi r^2}$ **75. (a)** $5460   **(b)** 2013
77. (a) 0.0352   **(b)** approximately 0.015, or 1.5%
(c) approximately 1 case

7.2 Exercises *(pages 301–305)*

1. expression **3.** equation **5.** expression **7.** yes
9. $x - 12$ **11.** $(x - 6)(x + 4)$ **13.** $\frac{25}{x}\,(x \neq 0)$
15. Answers will vary. **17.** 3 **19.** 6 **21.** −3
23. Bon Jovi: $210.7 million; Bruce Springsteen:
$204.6 million **25.** wins: 62; losses: 20
27. Democrats: 58; Republicans: 40 **29.** shortest piece:
15 inches; middle piece: 20 inches; longest piece: 24 inches
31. gold: 51; silver: 21; bronze: 28 **33.** 70 milliliters
35. $250 **37.** $24.85 **39.** 4 liters **41.** 5 liters
43. 1 gallon **45.** $4000 at 3%; $8000 at 4%
47. $10,000 at 4.5%; $19,000 at 3% **49.** $58,000
51. 17 pennies, 17 dimes, 10 quarters **53.** 305 students,
105 nonstudents **55.** 54 seats on Row 1; 51 seats on Row 2
57. 44-cent stamps: 30; 17-cent stamps: 25
59. 328 miles **61.** No, it is not correct. The distance is
$55\left(\frac{1}{2}\right) = 27.5$ miles. **63.** $1\frac{3}{4}$ hours **65.** 11:00 A.M.
67. 8 hours **69.** 18 miles **71.** 3.326 hours
73. 1.715 hours **75.** 7.97 meters per second
77. 8.47 meters per second

7.3 Exercises *(pages 313–318)*

1. $\frac{5}{8}$ **3.** $\frac{1}{4}$ **5.** $\frac{2}{1}$ **7.** $\frac{3}{1}$ **9.** D **11.** Answers will vary.
13. true **15.** false **17.** true **19.** {35} **21.** {−1}
23. $\left\{-\frac{27}{4}\right\}$ **25.** $30.00 **27.** $8.75 **29.** $67.50
31. $44.55 **33.** 4 feet **35.** 2.7 inches **37.** 2.0 inches
39. $2\frac{5}{8}$ cups **41.** $428.82 **43.** 12,500 fish
45. 10-lb size; $0.429 **47.** 32-oz size; $0.093
49. 128-oz size; $0.051 **51.** 36-oz size; $0.049
53. $x = 4$ **55.** $x = 1$; $y = 4$
57. (a) **(b)** 54 feet

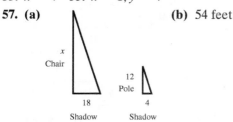

59. $237 **61.** $272 **63.** 9 **65.** 125 **67.** $\frac{4}{9}$ **69.** $40.32
71. 20 miles per hour **73.** about 302 pounds
75. 100 pounds per square inch **77.** 20 pounds per
square foot **79.** 144 feet **81.** 1.105 liters
83. $\frac{8}{9}$ metric ton **85.** 6.2 pounds

7.5 Exercises *(pages 337–339)*

1. A **3.** A **5.** D **7.** 625 **9.** −32 **11.** −8 **13.** −81
15. $\frac{1}{49}$ **17.** $-\frac{1}{49}$ **19.** −128 **21.** $\frac{16}{5}$ **23.** 125 **25.** $\frac{25}{16}$
27. $\frac{9}{20}$ **29.** 1 **31.** 1 **33.** 0 **35.** reciprocal; additive
inverse **37.** D **39.** x^{16} **41.** 5 **43.** $\frac{1}{27}$ **45.** $\frac{1}{81}$ **47.** $\frac{1}{t^7}$

49. $9x^2$ **51.** $\frac{1}{a^5}$ **53.** x^{11} **55.** r^6 **57.** $-\frac{56}{k^2}$ **59.** $\frac{1}{z^4}$
61. $-\frac{3}{r^7}$ **63.** $\frac{27}{a^{18}}$ **65.** $\frac{x^5}{y^2}$ **67.** D **69.** 2.3×10^2
71. 2×10^{-2} **73.** 6500 **75.** 0.0152 **77.** 6×10^5
79. 2×10^5 **81.** 2×10^5 **83.** 1×10^9; 1×10^{12};
3.1×10^{12}; 2.10385×10^5 **85.** 1.869×10^{10}
87. 1×10^{10} **89.** 2,000,000,000 **91. (a)** 3.041×10^8
(b) 1×10^{12} **(c)** $3288 **93.** approximately
9.474×10^{-7} parsec **95.** 300 seconds
97. approximately 5.87×10^{12} miles **99.** 20,000 hours

CHAPTER 10 COUNTING METHODS

10.1 Exercises *(pages 531–533)*
1. *AB, AC, AD, AE, BA, BC, BD, BE, CA, CB, CD,
CE, DA, DB, DC, DE, EA, EB, EC, ED*; 20 ways
3. *AB, AD, BA, BD, CE, DA, DB, EC*; 8 ways
5. *ACE, AEC, BCE, BEC, DCE, DEC*; 6 ways
7. *ABC, ABD, ABE, ACD, ACE, ADE, BCD, BCE,
BDE, CDE*; 10 ways **9.** 1 **11.** 3 **13.** 5 **15.** 5
17. 3 **19.** 1 **21.** 18 **23.** 15
25.

	2	3	5	7
2	22	23	25	27
3	32	33	35	37
5	52	53	55	57
7	72	73	75	77

27. 22, 33, 55, 77 **29.** 23, 37, 53, 73 **31. (a)** tttt
(b) hhhh, hhht, hhth, hhtt, hthh, htht, htth, thhh, thht,
thth, tthh **(c)** httt, thtt, ttht, ttth, tttt
(d) hhhh, hhht, hhth, hhtt, hthh, htht, htth, httt, thhh,
thht, thth, thtt, tthh, thtt, ttth

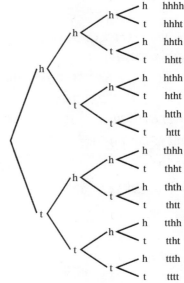

33. 16   **35.** 36   **37.** 17   **39.** 72   **41.** 12   **43.** 10
45. 6   **47.** 3   **49.** 9   **51.** 49   **53.** 21   **55.** 15
57. 16   **59.** 13   **61.** 4   **63.** 637   **65.** 3
67. (a) Find the number of ways to select an ordered pair of letters from the letters $A, B, C, D,$ and E if repetition of letters is not allowed.   (b) Find the number of ways to select an ordered pair of letters from the letters $A, B, C, D,$ and E if the selection is done without replacement.

10.2 Exercises (pages 541–543)

1. Answers will vary.   **3.** (a) no   (b) Answers will vary.   **5.** (a) no   (b) Answers will vary.   **7.** 24
9. 72   **11.** 20   **13.** 28   **15.** 840   **17.** 3,628,800
19. 3,991,680   **21.** 184,756   **23.** 980,179,200   **25.** 60
27. $2^3 = 8$ **29.** Answers will vary.   **31.** $6^3 = 216$
33. $2^{10} = 1024$ **35.** $5! = 120$ **37.** $3 \cdot 2 = 6$
39. $3 \cdot 3 = 9$ **41.** $3 \cdot 2 \cdot 1 = 6$ **43.** $5 \cdot 2 \cdot 4 = 40$
45. $2^6 = 64$ **47.** $2 \cdot 3 \cdot 4 \cdot 5 = 120$
49. $2 \cdot 3 \cdot 4 \cdot 3 = 72$ **51.** $2 \cdot 3 \cdot 1 \cdot 3 = 18$
53. $2 \cdot 4 \cdot 6 = 48$ **55.** $5! = 120$ **57.** 800   **59.** (a) 5
(b) 2   (c) 4   (d) 3   (e) 2   (f) 1; 240   **61.** (a) 6
(b) 3   (c) 2   (d) 2   (e) 1   (f) 1; 72   **63.** Answers will vary.   **65.** 516,243   **67.** 6

10.3 Exercises (pages 553–556)

1. 504   **3.** 330   **5.** 116,280   **7.** 126
9. $1.805037696 \times 10^{11}$ **11.** Answers will vary.
13. Answers will vary.
15. (a) permutation   (b) permutation
(c) combination   (d) combination   (e) permutation
(f) combination   (g) permutation   (h) permutation
17. $_8P_5 = 6720$ **19.** $_{12}P_2 = 132$
21. $_{25}P_5 = 6,375,600$ **23.** (a) $_4P_4 = 24$
(b) $_4P_4 = 24$ **25.** $_{18}C_5 = 8568$
27. (a) $_{13}C_5 = 1287$ (b) $_{26}C_5 = 65,780$
(c) 0 (impossible)   **29.** (a) $_6C_3 = 20$
(b) $_6C_2 = 15$ **31.** $_9C_3 = 84$ **33.** (a) 5   (b) 9
35. $_{26}P_3 \cdot _{10}P_3 \cdot _{26}P_3 = 175,219,200,000$
37. $2 \cdot _{25}P_3 = 27,600$ **39.** $7 \cdot _{12}P_8 = 139,708,800$
41. (a) $7^7 = 823,543$ (b) $7! = 5040$
43. $_{15}C_1 \cdot _{14}C_2 \cdot _{12}C_3 \cdot _9C_4 \cdot _5C_5 = 37,837,800$
45. $\dfrac{_8C_3 \cdot _5C_3 \cdot _2C_2}{2!} = 280$ **47.** $_{20}C_3 = 1140$

49. (a) $_7P_2 = 42$ (b) $3 \cdot 6 = 18$ (c) $_7P_2 \cdot 5 = 210$
51. $_8P_3 = 336$ **53.** $_9C_3 \cdot _6C_3 \cdot _3C_3 \cdot 3^3 = 7560$
55. (a) $6! = 720$ (b) 745,896
57. (a) $6! = 720$ (b) $2 \cdot 4! = 48$ (c) $4! = 24$
59. (a) $2 \cdot 4! = 48$ (b) $3 \cdot 4! = 72$
61. Each equals 220.

10.4 Exercises (pages 560–562)

1. 6   **3.** 20   **5.** 56   **7.** 36   **9.** $_7C_1 \cdot _3C_3 = 7$
11. $_7C_3 \cdot _3C_1 = 105$ **13.** $_8C_3 = 56$ **15.** $_8C_5 = 56$
17. $_9C_4 = 126$ **19.** $1 \cdot _8C_3 = 56$ **21.** 1   **23.** 10
25. 5   **27.** 32   **29.** the even-numbered rows
31. (a) All are multiples of the row number.
(b) The same pattern holds.   (c) The same pattern holds.
33. . . . 8, 13, 21, 34, . . . ; A number in this sequence is the sum of the two preceding terms. This is the Fibonacci sequence.   **35.** row 8   **37.** The sum of the squares of the entries across the top row equals the entry at the bottom vertex.   **39.** Answers will vary.
Wording may vary for Exercises 41 and 43.
41. sum $= N$; Any entry in the array equals the sum of the two entries immediately above it and immediately to its left.   **43.** sum $= N$; Any entry in the array equals the sum of the row of entries from the cell immediately above it to the left boundary of the array.

Extension Exercises (pages 564–567)

1.

2	7	6
9	5	1
4	3	8

3.

11	10	4	23	17
18	12	6	5	24
25	19	13	7	1
2	21	20	14	8
9	3	22	16	15

5.

15	16	22	3	9
8	14	20	21	2
1	7	13	19	25
24	5	6	12	18
17	23	4	10	11

7.

24	9	12
3	15	27
18	21	6

Magic sum is 45.

9.

$\frac{17}{2}$	12	$\frac{1}{2}$	4	$\frac{15}{2}$
$\frac{23}{2}$	$\frac{5}{2}$	$\frac{7}{2}$	7	8
2	3	$\frac{13}{2}$	10	11
5	6	$\frac{19}{2}$	$\frac{21}{2}$	$\frac{3}{2}$
$\frac{11}{2}$	9	$\frac{25}{2}$	1	$\frac{9}{2}$

Magic sum is $32\frac{1}{2}$.

11. 479 **13.** 467 **15.** 269
17. (a) 73 **(b)** 70 **(c)** 74
(d) 69 **19. (a)** 7 **(b)** 22
(c) 5 **(d)** 4 **(e)** 15
(f) 19 **(g)** 6 **(h)** 23

21.

30	39	48	1	10	19	28
38	47	7	9	18	27	29
46	6	8	17	26	35	37
5	14	16	25	34	36	45
13	15	24	33	42	44	4
21	23	32	41	43	3	12
22	31	40	49	2	11	20

23. Each sum is equal to 34.
25. Each sum is equal to 68.
27. Each sum is equal to 9248.
29. Each sum is equal to 748.

31.

16	2	3	13
5	11	10	8
9	7	6	12
4	14	15	1

33.

18	20	10
8	16	24
22	12	14

The second and third columns are interchanged.

35.

39	48	57	10	19	28	37
47	56	16	18	27	36	38
55	15	17	26	35	44	46
14	23	25	34	43	45	54
22	24	33	42	51	53	13
30	32	41	50	52	12	21
31	40	49	58	11	20	29

Magic sum is 238.
37. 260
39. $52 + 45 + 16 + 17 + 54 + 43 + 10 + 23 = 260$

41.

5	13	21	9	17
6	19	2	15	23
12	25	8	16	4
18	1	14	22	10
24	7	20	3	11

43.

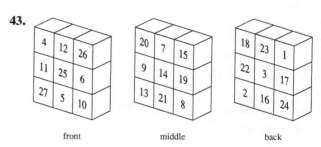

front   middle   back

10.5 Exercises *(pages 572–574)*
1. $2^4 - 1 = 15$ **3.** $2^7 - 1 = 127$ **5.** 120
7. $36 - 6 = 30$ **9.** $6 + 6 - 1 = 11$ **11.** 51
13. $90 - 9 = 81$ **15. (a)** $_{10}C_3 = 120$ **(b)** $_9C_3 = 84$
(c) $120 - 84 = 36$ **17.** $_7C_3 - _5C_3 = 25$
19. $_8P_4 - _5P_4 = 1560$ **21.** $_{10}P_3 - _7P_3 = 510$
23. $2 \cdot 26^2 + 2 \cdot 26^3 = 36{,}504$ **25.** $_{12}C_4 - _8C_4 = 425$
27. $13 + 4 - 1 = 16$ **29.** $25 + 22 - 18 = 29$
31. $2{,}598{,}960 - _{13}C_5 = 2{,}597{,}673$
33. $2{,}598{,}960 - _{40}C_5 = 1{,}940{,}952$
35. 56 **37.** $_{10}C_0 + _{10}C_1 + _{10}C_2 = 56$
39. $2^{10} - 56 = 968$
41. $26^2 \cdot 10^3 - _{26}P_2 \cdot _{10}P_3 = 208{,}000$
43. Answers will vary. **45.** $_4C_3 + _3C_3 + _5C_3 = 15$
47. $_{12}C_3 - _4C_1 \cdot _3C_1 \cdot _5C_1 = 160$ **49.** Answers will vary.
51. Answers will vary. **53.** Answers will vary.

Chapter 10 Test *(pages 575–576)*
1. $6 \cdot 7 \cdot 7 = 294$ **2.** $6 \cdot 7 \cdot 3 = 126$
3. $6 \cdot 6 \cdot 5 = 180$ **4.** $6 \cdot 5 \cdot 1 = 30$ end in 0;
$5 \cdot 5 \cdot 1 = 25$ end in 5; $30 + 25 = 55$ **5.** 13
6.

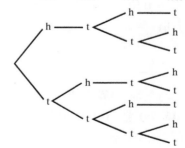

7. $4! = 24$ **8.** $3 \cdot 4! = 72$ **9.** 720
10. 56 **11.** 1320 **12.** 56 **13.** $_{26}P_5 = 7{,}893{,}600$
14. $32^5 = 33{,}554{,}432$ **15.** $_7P_2 = 42$ **16.** $5! = 120$
17. $\frac{6!}{2! \cdot 3!} = 60$ **18.** $_{10}C_4 = 210$ **19.** $\frac{_{10}C_2 \cdot _8C_2}{2!} = 630$
20. $\frac{_{10}C_5 \cdot _5C_5}{2!} = 126$ **21.** $\frac{_{10}C_4 \cdot _6C_4}{2!} = 1575$
22. $2^{10} - (_{10}C_0 + _{10}C_1 + _{10}C_2) = 968$ **23.** $2^5 = 32$

24. $2^3 = 8$ **25.** $2 \cdot 2^3 = 16$ **26.** 13   **27.** 2
28. $32 - (1 + 5) = 26$ **29.** $_6C_2 = 15$ **30.** $_5C_1 = 5$
31. $2 \cdot {}_5C_2 = 20$ **32.** $_5C_1 = 5$
33. $_5C_3 + {}_5C_2 \cdot {}_2C_1 = 30$ **34.** $_9C_4 = 126$
35. Answers will vary.   **36.** $495 + 220 = 715$
37. the counting numbers   **38.** Answers will vary.

33.

x	$P(x)$
3	0.1
4	0.1
5	0.2
6	0.2
7	0.2
8	0.1
9	0.1

35. $n(A') = s - a$
37. $P(A) + P(A') = 1$
39. 180   **41.** $\frac{2}{3}$ **43.** 1

CHAPTER 11 PROBABILITY

11.1 Exercises (pages 585–588)

1. (a) $\frac{1}{3}$ (b) $\frac{1}{3}$ (c) $\frac{1}{3}$ **3.** (a) $\frac{1}{2}$ (b) $\frac{1}{3}$ (c) $\frac{1}{6}$
5. (a) $\{1, 2, 3\}$ (b) 2 (c) 1 (d) 3 (e) $\frac{2}{3}$ (f) 2 to 1
7. (a) $\{11, 12, 13, 21, 22, 23, 31, 32, 33\}$ (b) $\frac{2}{3}$ (c) $\frac{1}{3}$
(d) $\frac{1}{3}$ (e) $\frac{4}{9}$ **9.** (a) 7 to 4 (b) 6 to 5 (c) 9 to 2
11. (a) $\frac{1}{50}$ (b) $\frac{2}{50} = \frac{1}{25}$ (c) $\frac{3}{50}$ (d) $\frac{4}{50} = \frac{2}{25}$
(e) $\frac{5}{50} = \frac{1}{10}$ **13.** (a) $\frac{1}{36}$ (b) $\frac{2}{36} = \frac{1}{18}$ (c) $\frac{3}{36} = \frac{1}{12}$
(d) $\frac{4}{36} = \frac{1}{9}$ (e) $\frac{5}{36}$ (f) $\frac{6}{36} = \frac{1}{6}$ (g) $\frac{5}{36}$ (h) $\frac{4}{36} = \frac{1}{9}$
(i) $\frac{3}{36} = \frac{1}{12}$ (j) $\frac{2}{36} = \frac{1}{18}$ (k) $\frac{1}{36}$ **15.** 0.329 **17.** $\frac{1}{9}$
19. $\frac{1}{4}$ **21.** $\frac{1}{4}$ **23.** (a) $\frac{3}{4}$ (b) $\frac{1}{4}$
25. $\frac{1}{250,000} = 0.000004$ **27.** $\frac{1}{4}$ **29.** $\frac{1}{4}$ **31.** $\frac{2}{4} = \frac{1}{2}$
33. $\frac{1}{500} = 0.002$ **35.** about 160 **37.** $\frac{2}{4} = \frac{1}{2}$ **39.** (a) 0
(b) no (c) yes **41.** Answers will vary. **43.** $\frac{12}{31}$
45. $\frac{36}{2,598,960} \approx 0.00001385$ **47.** $\frac{624}{2,598,960} \approx 0.00024010$
49. $\frac{1}{4} \cdot \frac{5108}{2,598,960} \approx 0.00049135$ **51.** (a) $\frac{5}{9}$ (b) $\frac{49}{144}$
(c) $\frac{5}{48}$ **53.** $3 \cdot 1 \cdot 2 \cdot 1 \cdot 1 \cdot 1 = 6; \frac{6}{720} = \frac{1}{120} \approx 0.0083$
55. $4 \cdot 3! \cdot 3! \doteq 144; \frac{144}{720} = \frac{1}{5} = 0.2$
57. $\frac{2}{_7C_2} = \frac{2}{21} \approx 0.095$ **59.** $\frac{_5C_3}{_{12}C_3} = \frac{1}{22} \approx 0.045$
61. $\frac{1}{_{26}P_3} \approx 0.000064$ **63.** $\frac{3}{28} \approx 0.107$
65. (a) $\frac{8}{9^2} = \frac{8}{81} \approx 0.099$ (b) $\frac{4}{_9C_2} = \frac{1}{9} \approx 0.111$ **67.** 1
69. $\frac{9}{9 \cdot 10} = \frac{1}{10}$ **71.** $\frac{1}{15}$

11.2 Exercises (pages 594–596)

1. yes **3.** Answers will vary. **5.** $\frac{1}{2}$ **7.** $\frac{5}{6}$ **9.** $\frac{2}{3}$
11. (a) $\frac{2}{13}$ (b) 2 to 11 **13.** (a) $\frac{11}{26}$ (b) 11 to 15
15. (a) $\frac{9}{13}$ (b) 9 to 4 **17.** $\frac{2}{3}$ **19.** $\frac{7}{36}$
21. $P(A) + P(B) + P(C) + P(D) = 1$ **23.** 0.005365
25. 0.971285 **27.** 0.76 **29.** 0.92 **31.** 6 to 19

11.3 Exercises (pages 603–606)

1. independent **3.** not independent **5.** independent
7. $\frac{52}{100} = \frac{13}{25}$ **9.** $\frac{69}{100}$ **11.** $\frac{14}{31}$ **13.** $\frac{4}{7} \cdot \frac{4}{7} = \frac{16}{49}$
15. $\frac{2}{7} \cdot \frac{1}{7} = \frac{2}{49}$ **17.** $\frac{4}{7} \cdot \frac{3}{6} = \frac{2}{7}$ **19.** $\frac{1}{6}$ **21.** 0
23. $\frac{12}{51} = \frac{4}{17}$ **25.** $\frac{12}{52} \cdot \frac{11}{51} = \frac{11}{221}$ **27.** $\frac{4}{52} \cdot \frac{11}{51} = \frac{11}{663}$
29. $\frac{1}{3}$ **31.** 1 **33.** $\frac{3}{10}$ (the same)
35. $\frac{1}{2} \cdot \frac{1}{2} \cdot \frac{1}{2} \cdot \frac{1}{2} \cdot \frac{1}{2} \cdot \frac{1}{2} = \frac{1}{64}$ **37.** 0.490 **39.** 0.027
41. 0.95 **43.** 0.23 **45.** $\frac{1}{20}$ **47.** $\frac{1}{5}$ **49.** $\frac{1}{5}$ **51.** (a) $\frac{3}{4}$
(b) $\frac{1}{2}$ (c) $\frac{5}{16}$ **53.** 0.2704 **55.** 0.2496
57. Answers will vary. **59.** $\frac{1}{64} \approx 0.0156$ **61.** 10
63. 0.400 **65.** 0.080 **67.** $(0.90)^4 = 0.6561$
69. $_4C_2 \cdot (0.10) \cdot (0.20) \cdot (0.70)^2 = 0.0588$ **71.** 0.30
73. 0.49 **75.** Answers will vary.

11.4 Exercises (pages 610–612)

1. $\frac{1}{8}$ **3.** $\frac{3}{8}$ **5.** $\frac{3}{4}$ **7.** $\frac{1}{2}$ **9.** $\frac{3}{8}$ **11.** $x; n; n$ **13.** $\frac{7}{128}$
15. $\frac{35}{128}$ **17.** $\frac{21}{128}$ **19.** $\frac{1}{128}$ **21.** $\frac{25}{72}$ **23.** $\frac{1}{216}$ **25.** 0.041
27. 0.268 **29.** Answers will vary. **31.** Answers will vary.
33. 0.016 **35.** 0.020 **37.** 0.137 **39.** 0.572 **41.** 0.669
43. 0.975 **45.** 0.883 **47.** $6p^2(1 - p)^2$
49. $\frac{1}{1024} \approx 0.001$ **51.** $\frac{45}{1024} \approx 0.044$
53. $\frac{210}{1024} = \frac{105}{512} \approx 0.205$ **55.** $\frac{772}{1024} \approx 0.754$

11.5 Exercises (pages 619–622)

1. Answers will vary. **3.** $\frac{5}{2}$ **5.** \$1 **7.** \$0.50
9. no $\left(\text{expected net winnings: } -\frac{3}{4}¢\right)$ **11.** 1.69
13. (a) $-\$60$ (b) \$36,000 (c) \$72,000 **15.** \$0.46
17. \$2700 **19.** 2.7 **21.** a decrease of 50 **23.** Answers
will vary. **25.** Project C **27.** \$2200 **29.** \$81,000
31. Do not purchase the insurance (because
$\$86,000 > \$81,000$). **33.** \$1500; \$3000; \$17,500; \$27,000
35. \$56,000 **37.** 48.7%

Extension Exercises *(page 625)*

1. Answers will vary. **3.** no **5.** $\frac{18}{50} = 0.36$ (This is quite close to 0.375, the theoretical value.) **7.** $\frac{6}{50} = 0.12$
9. Answers will vary. **11.** Answers will vary.

Chapter 11 Test *(page 627)*

1. Answers will vary. **2.** Answers will vary. **3.** 3 to 1
4. 25 to 1 **5.** 11 to 2 **6.** row 1: CC; row 2: cC, cc

7. $\frac{1}{2}$ **8.** 1 to 3 **9.** $\frac{7}{7} \cdot \frac{6}{7} \cdot \frac{5}{7} = \frac{30}{49}$ **10.** $\frac{7}{19}$

11. $1 - \left(\frac{30}{49} + \frac{1}{49}\right) = \frac{18}{49}$ **12.** $\frac{{}_2C_2}{{}_5C_2} = \frac{1}{10}$

13. $\frac{{}_3C_2}{{}_5C_2} = \frac{3}{10}$ **14.** $\frac{6}{10} = \frac{3}{5}$ **15.** $\frac{3}{10}$

16. $\frac{3}{10}; \frac{6}{10}; \frac{1}{10}$ **17.** $\frac{9}{10}$ **18.** $\frac{18}{10} = \frac{9}{5}$ **19.** $\frac{6}{36} = \frac{1}{6}$

20. 35 to 1 **21.** 7 to 2 **22.** $\frac{4}{36} = \frac{1}{9}$ **23.** $(0.78)^3 \approx 0.475$

24. ${}_3C_2 \cdot (0.78)^2 \cdot (0.22) \approx 0.402$

25. $1 - (0.22)^3 \approx 0.989$

26. $(0.78) \cdot (0.22) \cdot (0.78) \approx 0.134$ **27.** $\frac{25}{102}$ **28.** $\frac{25}{51}$

29. $\frac{4}{51}$ **30.** $\frac{3}{26}$

CHAPTER 12 STATISTICS

12.1 Exercises *(pages 636–640)*

1. (a)

x	f	$\frac{f}{n}$
0	10	$\frac{10}{30} \approx 33\%$
1	7	$\frac{7}{30} \approx 23\%$
2	6	$\frac{6}{30} = 20\%$
3	4	$\frac{4}{30} \approx 13\%$
4	2	$\frac{2}{30} \approx 7\%$
5	1	$\frac{1}{30} \approx 3\%$

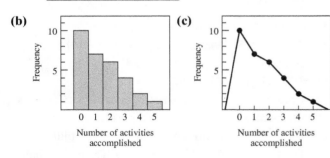

3. (a)

Class Limits	Tally	Frequency f	Relative Frequency $\frac{f}{n}$
45–49	|||	3	$\frac{3}{54} \approx 5.6\%$
50–54	ⵜⵜ ⵜⵜ ||||	14	$\frac{14}{54} \approx 25.9\%$
55–59	ⵜⵜ ⵜⵜ ⵜⵜ		16	$\frac{16}{54} \approx 29.6\%$
60–64	ⵜⵜ ⵜⵜ ⵜⵜ ||	17	$\frac{17}{54} \approx 31.5\%$
65–69	||||	4	$\frac{4}{54} \approx 7.4\%$

Total: $n = 54$

(b) 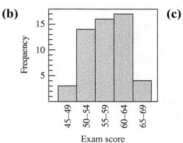 **(c)**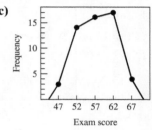

5. (a)

Class Limits	Tally	Frequency f	Relative Frequency $\frac{f}{n}$
70–74	||	2	$\frac{2}{30} \approx 6.7\%$
75–79			1	$\frac{1}{30} \approx 3.3\%$
80–84	|||	3	$\frac{3}{30} = 10.0\%$
85–89	||	2	$\frac{2}{30} \approx 6.7\%$
90–94	ⵜⵜ	5	$\frac{5}{30} \approx 16.7\%$
95–99	ⵜⵜ	5	$\frac{5}{30} \approx 16.7\%$
100–104	ⵜⵜ		6	$\frac{6}{30} = 20.0\%$
105–109	||||	4	$\frac{4}{30} \approx 13.3\%$
110–114	||	2	$\frac{2}{30} \approx 6.7\%$

Total: $n = 30$

(b) 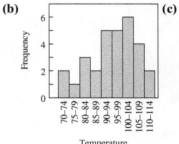 **(c)**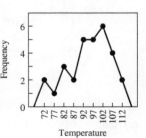

7.
```
0 | 7 9 8
1 | 1 1 2 8 9 4 3 1 0 5 0 5 5
2 | 7 0 9 6 6 2 2 5 2 3 4 4
3 | 8 1
```

9.
```
0 | 8 5 4 9 6 9 4 8
1 | 6 0 1 8 8 2 4 0 2 8 6 3
2 | 6 1 2 5 1 3
3 | 0 4 6
4 | 4
```

11. 2001   **13.** 2005, 2006, 2007, and 2011

15.

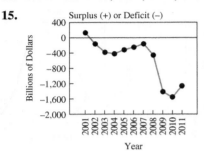

17. 3.8% in 2008   **19.** Answers will vary.

21. Medicare & Medicaid; 83°

23.

25. about 79 years   **27. (a)** about 6 years   **(b)** Answers will vary.   **29.** Answers will vary.   **31.** Answers will vary.   **33.** Answers will vary.

35. (a)

Letter	Probability
A	0.208
E	0.338
I	0.169
O	0.208
U	0.078

(b)

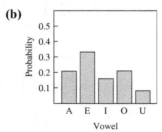

37. Answers will vary.   **39. (a)** 0.225   **(b)** 0.275   **(c)** 0.425   **(d)** 0.175

41. (a)

Sport	Probability
Sailing	0.225
Hang gliding	0.125
Snowboarding	0.175
Bicycling	0.075
Canoeing	0.300
Rafting	0.100

(b) empirical   **(c)** Answers will vary.

12.2 Exercises (pages 650–653)

1. (a) 15.2   **(b)** 12   **(c)** none   **3. (a)** 216.2   **(b)** 221   **(c)** 196   **5. (a)** 5.2   **(b)** 5.35   **(c)** 4.5 and 6.2   **7. (a)** 0.8   **(b)** 0.795   **(c)** none   **9. (a)** 129   **(b)** 128   **(c)** 125 and 128   **11. (a)** 10.7 million   **(b)** 10.65 million   **(c)** 10.6 million   **13. (a)** 73.9   **(b)** 17.5   **(c)** 0   **15.** mean = 47.4; median and mode remain the same   **17.** $59.7 billion   **19.** 5.27 seconds   **21.** 2.42 seconds   **23.** the mean   **25.** mean = 77; median = 80; mode = 79   **27.** 92   **29. (a)** 597.4   **(b)** 600   **(c)** 615   **31.** 2.41   **33.** 648 million   **35.** China: 372; India: 1008; United States: 87; Indonesia: 324; Brazil: 61   **37.** 328.2 million   **39. (a)** 8.25   **(b)** 8   **41. (a)** 66.25   **(b)** 64.5   **43.** 6   **45. (a)** 19.4   **(b)** 15.5   **(c)** 11   **47. (a)** 74.8   **(b)** 77.5   **(c)** 78   **49.** Answers will vary.   **51. (a)** mean = 13.7; median = 16; mode = 18   **(b)** median   **53. (a)** 4   **(b)** 4.25   **55. (a)** 6   **(b)** 9.33   **57.** 80   **59.** no   **61.** Answers will vary.

12.3 Exercises (pages 659–661)

1. the sample standard deviation   **3. (a)** 13   **(b)** 4.24   **5. (a)** 19   **(b)** 6.27   **7. (a)** 40   **(b)** 11.51   **9. (a)** 1.14   **(b)** 0.37   **11. (a)** 12   **(b)** 3.61   **13.** $\frac{3}{4}$ **15.** $\frac{21}{25}$ **17.** 88.9%   **19.** 64.0%   **21.** $\frac{3}{4}$ **23.** $\frac{15}{16}$ **25.** $\frac{1}{4}$ **27.** $\frac{4}{49}$ **29.** $202.50   **31.** six   **33.** There are at least nine.   **35. (a)** $s_A = 2.35$; $s_B = 2.58$ **(b)** $V_A = 46.9$; $V_B = 36.9$ **(c)** sample B   **(d)** sample A   **37. (a)** $\bar{x}_A = 68.8$; $\bar{x}_B = 66.6$ **(b)** $s_A = 4.21$; $s_B = 5.27$ **(c)** brand A, since $\bar{x}_A > \bar{x}_B$ **(d)** brand A, since $s_A < s_B$ **39.** Brand A ($s_B = 3539 > 2116$)   **41.** 18.71; 4.35   **43.** 8.71; 4.35   **45.** 56.14; 13.04   **47.** Answers will vary.   **49.** −3.0   **51.** 4.2   **53.** 7.55 and 23.45   **55.** no   **57.** Answers will vary.

12.4 Exercises (pages 665–668)

1. 58   **3.** 62   **5.** Janet (since $z = 0.48 > 0.19$)   **7.** Yvette (since $z = -1.44 > -1.78$)   **9.** −0.2   **11.** 1.0   **13.** Saudi Arabia   **15.** United Kingdom   **17.** Canada in exports (Canada's exports z-score was 2.4, China's imports z-score was 1.7, and 2.4 > 1.7.)   **19. (a)** The median is $54.5 billion.   **(b)** The range is 261 − 12 = 249.   **(c)** The middle half of the items extend from $29 billion to $70 billion.   **21.** Answers will vary.   **23.** Answers will vary.   **25.** Answers will vary.   **27.** the overall distribution   **29.** Both are skewed to the right, imports about twice as much as exports.   **31. (a)** no   **(b)** Answers will vary.   **33.** Answers will vary.   **35.** Answers will vary.   **37.** $Q_1 = 97.6$, $Q_2 = 100.2$, $Q_3 = 104.4$

39. $P_{65} = 103.2$ **41.** 101.0

43.

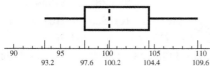

45. 93.3 **47.** 10

12.5 Exercises *(pages 675–676)*

1. discrete **3.** continuous **5.** discrete **7.** 50
9. 68 **11.** 50% **13.** 95% **15.** 43.3% **17.** 36.0%
19. 4.5% **21.** 97.9% **23.** 1.28 **25.** −1.34
27. 5000 **29.** 640 **31.** 9970 **33.** 84.1% **35.** 37.8%
37. 15.9% **39.** 4.7% **41.** 0.994, or 99.4%
43. 189 units **45.** 0.888 **47.** about 2 eggs **49.** 24.2%
51. Answers will vary. **53.** 79 **55.** 68 **57.** 90.4
59. 40.3 **61.** Answers will vary.

Extension Exercises *(pages 682–683)*

1. $y' = 0.3x + 1.5$ **3.** 2.4 decimeters **5.** 48.9°
7. $y' = 3.35x − 78.4$ **9.** 156 lb

11.

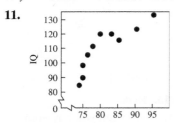

13. 79 **15.** $r = 0.996$

17.

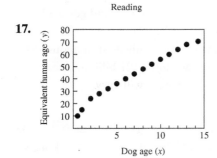

19. Answers will vary. **21.** $y' = 1.44x − 0.39$
23. The linear correlation is strong.
25. $y' = 0.5219x + 149.8$
27. The linear correlation is weak to moderate.

Chapter 12 Test *(pages 684–686)*

1. those who copied less than 10% **2.** those with copy rates from 10% to 30% or greater than 50%
3. those with copy rate from 30% to 50%
4. Answers will vary. **5. (a)** 200 million barrels
(b) 334 million barrels **(c)** 138 million barrels
(d) 69 **(e)** 44 million barrels
6. (a) 281 feet **(b)** 517 inches **(c)** 1290
7. (a) 762 **(b)** 7th **(c)** 12 feet **(d)** 17 feet

8.

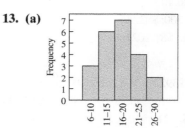

9. 19.3% **10.** 16.8% **11.** 44.5%

12.

Class Limits	Frequency f	Relative Frequency $\frac{f}{n}$
6–10	3	$\frac{3}{22} \approx 0.14$
11–15	6	$\frac{6}{22} \approx 0.27$
16–20	7	$\frac{7}{22} \approx 0.32$
21–25	4	$\frac{4}{22} \approx 0.18$
26–30	2	$\frac{2}{22} \approx 0.09$

13. (a)

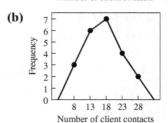

(b)

14. 8 **15.** 12.4 **16.** 12 **17.** 12 **18.** 10

19.

```
3 | 3 8
4 | 3 5 8 9
5 | 0 2 5
6 | 1 1 4 5 6 7 7 8
7 | 0 1 2 3 7 7 8 9 9
8 | 0 4 4
9 | 1
```

20. 35 **21.** 33 **22.** 37 **23.** 31 **24.** 49

25.

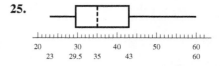

26. (a) about 95% **(b)** about 0.3% **(c)** about 16%
(d) about 13.5% **27.** 0.684 **28.** 0.340 **29.** West
30. East **31.** 84.9 **32.** Dodgers (since $z = 1.01 > 0.70$)

CHAPTER 13 PERSONAL FINANCIAL MANAGEMENT

13.1 Exercises *(pages 698–701)*

1. $48   **3.** $48.30   **5.** $488.19   **7. (a)** $826   **(b)** $835.84

9. (a) $2650   **(b)** $2653.02   **11.** $125   **13.** $13,546.67

15. $168.26   **17.** $817.17   **19.** $17,724.34; $10,224.34

21. (a) $2249.73   **(b)** $2252.32   **(c)** $2253.65

23. (a) $18,918.18   **(b)** $18,920.52   **(c)** $18,921.70

25. (a) $55.95   **(b)** $56.06   **(c)** $56.14   **(d)** $56.18

(e) $56.18   **27.** Answers will vary.   **29.** $1461.04

31. $747.26   **33.** $4499.98   **35.** $112,607.20

37. $111,576.54   **39.** 2.000%   **41.** 2.015%   **43.** 2.020%

45. 2.020%   **47.** $30,420   **49.** 17 years, 152 days

51. $r = m[(Y + 1)^{1/m} - 1]$ **53. (a)** 3.818%

(b) Bank A; $5.63   **(c)** no difference; $232.38

55. 35 years   **57.** 8 years   **59.** 10.0%   **61.** 3.2%

63. $6.51; $7.95; $9.71; $26.40

65. $20,400; $25,000; $30,500; $82,900

67. $218   **69.** $1502   **71.** $81,102,828.75

13.2 Exercises *(pages 704–706)*

1. $2950   **3.** $3422   **5.** $3922   **7.** $3645   **9.** $476.25

11. $1215; $158.75   **13.** $83.25; $46.29   **15.** $79.18; $38.39

17. $229.17   **19.** $330.75   **21.** $10,850   **23.** 6 years

25. $3.50   **27.** $5.80   **29.** $15.30   **31. (a)** $607.33

(b) $7.90   **(c)** $646.87   **33. (a)** $473.96   **(b)** $6.16

(c) $505.54   **35.** $9.27   **37. (a)** $38.18   **(b)** $38.69

(c) $39.20   **39.** 16.0%   **41.** $32.00

43–47. Answers will vary.   **49. (a)** $127.44   **(b)** $139.08

13.3 Exercises *(pages 711–713)*

1. 13.5%   **3.** 8.5%   **5.** $114.58   **7.** $92.71   **9.** 11.0%

11. 9.5%   **13. (a)** $8.93   **(b)** $511.60   **(c)** $6075.70

15. (a) $2.79   **(b)** $97.03   **(c)** $4073.57

17. (a) $206   **(b)** 9.5%   **19. (a)** $180   **(b)** 11.0%

21. (a) $41.29   **(b)** $39.70   **23. (a)** $420.68

(b) $368.47   **25. (a)** $1.80   **(b)** $14.99   **(c)** $1045.01

27. finance company APR: 12.0%; credit union APR: 11.5%; choose credit union   **29.** $32.27

31. Answers will vary.   **33.** Answers will vary.

35. 12   **37.–41.** Answers will vary.   **43.** $\frac{5}{39}$

13.4 Exercises *(pages 722–724)*

1. $675.52   **3.** $469.14   **5.** $2483.28   **7.** $1034.56

9. (a) $513.38   **(b)** $487.50   **(c)** $25.88   **(d)** $58,474.12

11. (a) $1247.43   **(b)** $775.67   **(c)** $471.76

(d) $142,728.24   **(e)** $1247.43   **(f)** $773.11   **(g)** $474.32

(h) $142,253.92   **13. (a)** $1390.93   **(b)** $776.61

(c) $614.32   **(d)** $113,035.68   **(e)** $1390.93   **(f)** $772.41

(g) $618.52   **(h)** $112,417.16   **15.** $552.18   **17.** $1127.27

19. $1168.44   **21.** 360   **23.** $247,532.80   **25. (a)** $304.01

(b) $734.73   **27. (a)** $59,032.06   **(b)** $59,875.11

29. (a) payment 176   **(b)** payment 304   **31.** $25,465.20

33. $91,030.80   **35. (a)** $674.79   **(b)** $746.36

(c) an increase of $71.57   **37. (a)** $395.83   **(b)** $466.07

39. $65.02   **41.** $140,000   **43.** $4275   **45.** $240

47. (a) $1634   **(b)** $1754   **(c)** $917   **(d)** $997

(e) $1555   **49. (a)** $2271   **(b)** $2407   **(c)** $1083

(d) $1174   **(e)** $2055   **51.–59.** Answers will vary.

Extension Exercises *(pages 745–746)*

1.

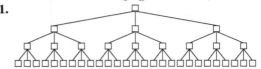

3. 3^{N-1} **5.** $26   **7.** 3^{N-1}; geometric; 1; 3; N; $\frac{3^N - 1}{2}$

9. 351   **11.** more than $\frac{26}{27}$ **13.** $0.00

15. You are in the chart only from when you pay your entry fee until you move up three levels and get paid.

17. Answers will vary.   **19.** 128   **21.** $4,400,000

23. Ponzi's $4 million would be equivalent to about $54 million in today's dollars. Madoff's $21 billion is nearly 400 times as much.   **25.** Answers will vary.

Chapter 13 Test *(page 748)*

1. $130   **2.** $58.58   **3.** 3.04%   **4.** 14 years   **5.** $67,297.13

6. $10.88   **7.** $450   **8.** $143.75   **9.** 14.0%   **10.** $34.13

11. 11.5%   **12.** Answers will vary.   **13.** $1162.95

14. $1528.48   **15.** $3488   **16.** Answers will vary.

17. 12.1%   **18.** 15,235,100 shares   **19.** $10.00

20. 0.078%; no; The given return was not for a 1-year period.   **21.** $106,728.55   **22.** Answers will vary.

CREDITS

10th ed., p. 430. Copyright © 2009 Pearson Education. All Rights Reserved.   **418** "Say Cheese!" graph. From Lial/Hornsby/McGinnis, *Intermediate Algebra*, 9th ed., p. 268. Copyright © 2010 Pearson Education. All Rights Reserved.   **423** Figure 50 (a–g). From Lial/Hornsby/McGinnis, *Intermediate Algebra*, 9th ed. (paperback), p. 283. Copyright © 2010 Pearson Education. All Rights Reserved.   **425** Exercises 1–4, 9–12. From Lial/Hornsby/McGinnis, *Intermediate Algebra*, 9th ed. (paperback), p. 277. Copyright © 2010 Pearson Education. All Rights Reserved.   **431** Example 5. From Lial/Hornsby,/McGinnis, *Intermediate Algebra*, 9th ed. (paperback), p. 299. Copyright © 2010 Pearson Education. All Rights Reserved.   **502** For Further Thought. The authors would like to thank The Math Forum at Drexel and Suzanne Alejandre for permission to reprint this article.   **503** Copyright © Coolmath.com. All Rights Reserved.   **519–520** Exercises 1–25. Pages 1–4 from the National Council of Teachers of Mathematics *Student Math Notes*, November 1991. Reprinted by permission of the National Council of Teachers of Mathematics.   **639** "Retirement Savings Net Worth" graph. From *TSA Guide to Retirement Planning for California Educators*.   **806** Exercise 58 poem. John Keats   **813** Sand tracing. Copyright © 2010 Mathematical Association of America. All Rights Reserved.   **826** "Records for Traveling Salesman" problem solution. From *What's Happening in Mathematical Sciences, Vol. 2*, 1994, p. 46, American Mathematical Society. Reprinted by permission of William Cook, Georgia Institute of Technology.

Photo Credits

1–2 20th Century Fox Film Corp./Everett Collection **4** ABC/Everett Collection   **6** Beth Anderson/Pearson   **7** David Livingston/Getty Images   **13** Disney Enterprises, Inc.   **18** AP Images   **19** Granger Collection   **20** Texas Instruments images used with permission/CBS/Paramount/National Council of Teachers of Mathematics   **21** Courtesy of the London Mathematical Society   **21** Arteki/Shutterstock   **22** Krista Mackey/iStockphoto   **24** Webphotographer/iStockphoto   **24** Digital Vision/Thinkstock   **27** Photos.com/Thinkstock   **27** Andrii Muzyka/Shutterstock   **29** Karl Pawlewicz/Sharp Electronics **30** Jon Le-bon/Shutterstock   **30** Beth Anderson/Pearson **32** Johner Images/Getty Images   **33** Stockbyte/Getty Images **34** iStockphoto/Thinkstock   **35** Photos.com/Thinkstock **36** Kobal Collection   **38** Disney Enterprises, Inc.   **43** Picture Desk/Kobal Collection   **44** Bettmann/Corbis   **46** Beth Anderson/Pearson   **55** Beth Anderson/Pearson   **61** Michael Kempf/Shutterstock   **65** Internal Revenue Service **68** Walt Disney Co./Everett Collection   **71** Everett Collection **73** Everett Collection   **74** Brand X Pictures/Thinkstock **75** Library of Congress Prints and Photographs Division (LC-USZ62-7923)   **77** Koo Eng Yow/Shutterstock   **78** Getty Images/Digital Vision   **79** Joy Brown/Shutterstock **83** Dreamworks SKG/Everett Collection   **84** Bilwissedition Ltd. & Co. KG/Alamy   **86** Erich Lessing/Art Resource, New York **89** Warner Bros./Everett Collection   **93** Library of Congress Prints and Photographs Division (LC-USZ62-61664)   **94** Reprinted with permission of Simon & Schuster, Inc.   **95** Mary Evans Picture Library/Alamy   **100** Stockbyte/Thinkstock   **101** Courtesy of John Hornsby   **104** Disney Enterprises, Inc.   **107** iStockphoto/

Thinkstock   **107** BananaStock/Thinkstock   **108** Strelnikova Tetiana/Shutterstock   **109** Michael Ochs Archives/Getty Images **110** Interfoto/Alamy   **111** Pictorial Press Ltd./Alamy   **113** Library of Congress Prints and Photographs Division (LC-USZ62-10191) **115** Library of Congress Prints and Photographs Division (LC-USZ62-48329)   **118** Steve Liss/Time & Life Images/Getty Images   **120–121** Dell Magazines/Penny Publications **125** Notro Films/Bocaboca Producciones/The Kobal Collection   **128** Mary Evans/Python Pictures/Ronald Grant/Everett Collection **130** Wonderstock/Alamy   **131** Shutterstock   **132** Shutterstock **137** Photofest   **138** PhotoDisc/Getty Images   **138–139** Dorling Kindersley   **140** Thumb/Shutterstock   **141** Mario Savoia/Shutterstock   **144** Granger Collection   **152** The Art Gallery Collection/Alamy   **153** Trinity College. Reprinted by permission of the Master and Fellows of Trinity College, Cambridge **154** Amenhotepov/Shutterstock   **154** Payless Images/Shutterstock   **155** Science Source/Photo Researchers   **155** Mary Evans Picture Library/Alamy   **160** Photosani/Shutterstock **161** Photos.com/Thinkstock   **163** Casio   **165** Courtesy of John Hornsby   **168** Dorling Kindersley   **170** Nhtg/Shutterstock **179** Warner Bros./Southside Amusement Co./The Kobal Collection   **182** Hugh C. Williams, University of Manitoba **187** Urbana IL USPS   **187** Photo Researchers   **193** Prentice Hall College Library   **193** TriStar Pictures/courtesy Everett Collection   **194** The Art Gallery Collection/Alamy   **194** 20th Century Fox Film Corp./Everett Collection   **200** Photos/Thinkstock   **203** Courtesy of John Hornsby   **205** Dreamworks/Universal/Eli Reed/The Kobal Collection   **214** Photodisc/Getty Images   **214** Bloom images/Getty Images   **215** Baloncici/Shutterstock   **215** Scala/Art Resource, New York   **215** PhotoDisc **215** Disney Enterprises, Inc.   **221** 20th Century Fox Film Corp./Everett Collection   **222** Penguin Putnam, Inc.   **232** Imagebroker/Alamy   **237** Comstock/Thinkstock   **242** Pearson Education Management Group EMG Network   **242** Robophobic/Shutterstock   **245** US Mint   **248** Pat Behnke/Alamy   **250** Jubal Harshaw/Shutterstock   **251** US Mint   **252** Edgaras Kurauskas/Shutterstock   **253** Valentyn Volkov/Shutterstock   **255** Courtesy of authors   **256** Universal TV/Everett Collection   **257** New Line Cinema/Kobal Collection   **258** Paramount/Everett Collection **259** Reprinted by permission of St. Martin's Press   **260** Jacket cover from *The Golden Ratio: The Story of Phi, the World's Most Astonishing Number,* by Mario Livio. Used by permission of Broadway Books, a division of Random House, Inc. **261** Reproduced with permission from Princeton University Press   **263** Chad Palmer/Shutterstock   **267** Wolper/Warner Bros./The Kobal Collection   **269** Courtesy of Terry McGinnis **271** Courtesy of John Hornsby   **272** Courtesy of John Hornsby   **272** Fruit Berries, Raspberries Stamp © 1999 USPS. All Rights Reserved.   **275** Courtesy of John Hornsby **275** Goodshoot/Thinkstock   **275** US Mint   **276** Interfoto/Alamy **277** Reproduced with permission from Princeton University Press **283** Paramount/Kobal Collection   **284** Courtesy of John Hornsby **285** Darryl Brooks/Shutterstock   **287** Photo Researchers, Inc. **288** Alamy Images   **289** Elena Elisseeva/Shutterstock **292** Andresr/Shutterstock   **294** Kathy Willens/AP Photo **296** The Everett Collection   **297** 20th Century Fox Film Corp./Everett Collection   **299** Daiju Kitamura/Aflo Foto Agency/Alamy   **302** Lopatinsky Vladislav/Shutterstock

▌▌▌▌▌▌▌ INDEX OF APPLICATIONS